THE **OFFICIAL** GUIDE TO THE DIPLOMA IN

Hair and beauty studies

At Higher Level

THE **OFFICIAL** GUIDE TO THE DIPLOMA IN

Hair and beauty studies

At Higher Level

Jane Goldsbro and Elaine White

Australia • Brazil • Japan • Korea • Mexico • Singapore • Spain • United Kingdom • United States

The Official Guide to the Diploma in Hair and Beauty Studies at Higher Level
Jane Goldsbro and Elaine White

Publisher: Melody Dawes
Development Editor: Lucy Mills
Editorial Assistant: Rebecca Hussey
Content Project Editor: Leonora Dawson-Bowling
Manufacturing Manager: Helen Mason
Senior Production Controller: Maeve Healy
Marketing Manager: Rachel Doyle
Typesetter: ICC Macmillan Inc.
Cover design: HCT Creative
Text design: Design Deluxe, Bath, UK
Illustrators: Oxford Designers and Illustrators unless otherwise stated

Printed by Seng Lee Press, Singapore
1 2 3 4 5 6 7 8 9 10 – 11 10 09

British Library Cataloguing-in-Publication Data

A catalogue record for this book is available from the British Library.

ISBN: 978-1-4080-1761-6

Cengage Learning EMEA
Cheriton House, North Way, Andover, Hampshire,
SP10 5BE, United Kingdom

Cengage Learning products are represented in Canada by Nelson Education Ltd.

For your lifelong learning solutions, visit **www.cengage.co.uk**

Purchase your next print book, e-book or e-chapter at **www.ichapters.co.uk**

Jane Goldsbro

To Alan for all his support during the writing of this book

Elaine White

For Leo, a new joy in my life, with love

Contents

CHAPTER 1 The history of hair and beauty in society

CHAPTER 2 The world of hair and beauty

79

CHAPTER 4 The science of hair and beauty

113

CHAPTER 5 Safe working practices

CHAPTER 6 Communication and client care

CHAPTER 7 Skin care and makeup

CHAPTER 8 Hair care and styling

CHAPTER 9 Hand care and nail art

CHAPTER 10 Selling skills

Foreword

I am delighted that two people whom I have known and worked with for a long time have again joined forces to write this fantastic book.

Jane Goldsbro and Elaine White are also co authors of *The Cutting Book: The Official Guide to Cutting for S/NVQ Levels 2 and 3* and *The Official Guide to the Diploma in Hair and Beauty Studies at Foundation Level*. They are authorities in their field and their input into the hairdressing industry is immense. Through their work with Habia they push forward the standards for hair and beauty education worldwide.

Elaine has over 32 years experience within the industry, including over 16 years as a hairdressing lecturer and course team leader. Her current role as Senior Development Manager for Habia has been pivotal to many developments by Habia, including the new Young Apprenticeship and Foundation Degrees. Elaine is a true professional whose exacting standards and dedication to her work have enabled her to focus on the end product with outstanding results.

Jane has over 27 years experience within the hairdressing industry, including salon management, educator and for the last ten years as Director of Standards and Qualifications at Habia. The commitment she has to her work is phenomenal. From writing standards, managing people and relationships with partners to international development, her wide vision means that she has an impressive ability to see the steps needed to achieve an end result. Jane's contribution to the hair and beauty curriculum has impacted throughout the world; as a developer of structured education she is very much in demand across all continents where her views are consistently sought.

Jane and Elaine were delighted that Joan Scott author of The Official Guide to Spa fame was able to contribute to this new book. I've known Joan for quite a few years, as an educator and a Habia forum member so was pleased to see Joan's specialist contribution.

The launch of Diplomas marks an important step forward in education. The Diploma in Hair and Beauty Studies has been developed with the help of employers, schools and universities and the combination of classroom learning with practical hands-on experience prepares young people for work and university. As well as broadening the options available to young people, the Diploma also brings a range of benefits to employers by preparing new recruits for the world of work and further training, giving them and the people who recruit them a head start on the road to success.

Alan Goldsbro
Chief Executive Officer
Habia

Acknowledgements

The authors and publishers would like to thank the following:

For providing photos for the front cover:

Main image: CREAM Artistic Team, photography by Andrew O'Toole. Courtesy of Gorgeous PR.

Thumbnail images in order top to bottom:

- Hair: Michelle Thompson, Photography: Ernest Collins, Makeup: Louise Shipton, Styling: MTJ Styling.
- I-stock/Izabela Habur
- Habia. Photography: Joachim Norvik
- Habia. Photography: Joachim Norvik
- Hair: Fellowship for British Hairdressing F.A.M.E team 2008, Photography by Andrew O'Toole
- Habia. Photography: Andrew Whitton

For their help with the photoshoot:

Doncaster College

Habia. Photography: Richard Keenan

For providing pictures for the book:

Title page from left to right: Hair: Michelle Thompson, Photography: Ernest Collins, Makeup: Louise Shipton, Styling: MTJ Styling; I-stock/Izabela Habur; Habia (two images). Photography: Joachim Norvik; Hair: CREAM Artistic Team, Photography by Andrew O'Toole; Habia. Photography: Andrew Whitton

Alamy

The Advertising Archives

Beauty Express

Dr M H Beck

British Museum Images

Denman

Gary Russell @ The Chapel, Tunbridge Wells.
Photography by John Rawson @ TRP

Getty

Goldwell UK

Dr John Gray

Guinot

Habia

Habia, the Hair and Beauty Industry Association (PLTS icons)

Hair by Chris Foster for Foss Academy, Photography Andy Kruczek

Hair by Reds Hair and Beauty, Sunderland. Photography
by John Rawson @ TRP

i-stock photography

L'Oréal Professionnel

Marcus King, Hooker and Young. Products: Matrix

Dr P Marazzi/science photo library

Kay McIntyre, McIntyre's Salons

Mediscan

Michelle Thompson for Francesco group

the Penn Museum

Redken

REM

Saks UK, **www.saks.com**

Sémhur

Sanrizz: Arena: Hair: Leonardo Rizzo at Sanrizz, Photograph: Andres Reynaga,
Makeup: Kasia Dziadel, Styling: Eliza Heinezen

Shortcuts Salon

shutterstock photography

Simon Houston hairdressing. Location: Ballymena, Co. Antrim.
Photographer: David Goldman

Sorisa

Spectrum: Hair: Sanrizz artistic team Photography: Stephen Kearney,
Photographer's Assistant: Gavin Douglas, Makeup: Karen Glasgow Bowen
Styling: Lindsay Campbell, Model: Tottie at the Model Team

Viva: Hair: Sharon Cox at Sanrizz, Photography: Andres Reynaga, Makeup:
Kasia Dziadel, Styling: Eliza Heinezen

Wellcome images

Wikipedia Commons

www.style-flash.com

Dr A.L. Wright

Every effort has been made to trace the copyright holders, but if any have been inadvertently overlooked the publisher will be pleased to make the necessary arrangements at the first opportunity. Please contact the publisher directly.

The Diploma in Hair and Beauty studies

Qualification information

The diploma in Hair and Beauty Studies is a new qualification that will give young people at school the opportunity to mix their school studies with work related learning and experience in the workplace.

It will offer the learner a real alternative to the traditional learning routes, offering a blend of both academic and vocational learning.

Mixing general education, job specific theory, background knowledge and selected practical experience related to hair and beauty. It will give the learner the opportunity to explore a range of related careers and opportunities.

The progression route throughout the Diploma remains open, so that learners can progress on to academic study, take a higher level of the Diploma, move into employment, take up an apprenticeship or work related training or carry on to university.

There are three levels of diplomas that a learner can take:

- Foundation Diploma
- Higher level Diploma
- Advanced Diploma

The diagram shows the progression routes within the Diploma – a preparation for work qualification and how a learner can transfer onto job-ready type qualifications, such as a apprenticeship.

Progression routes within the Hair and Beauty Sector

There are two distinctly different routes available for learners within the Hair and Beauty Sector

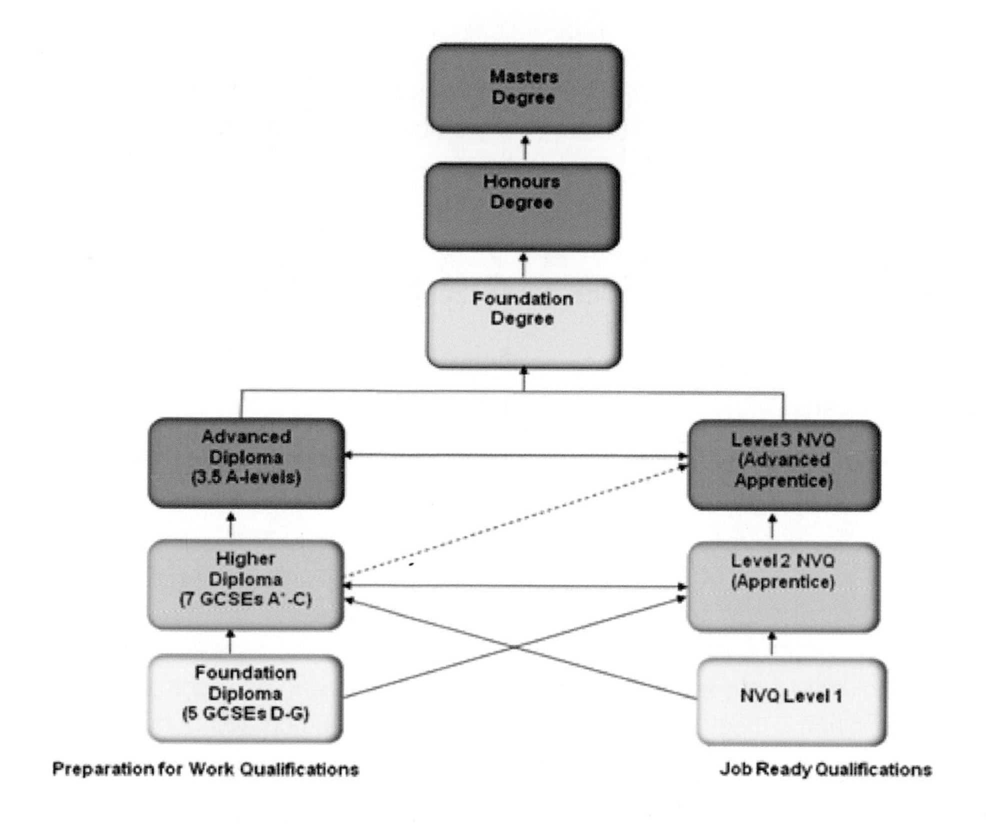

All Diplomas will include:

Principle learning – this allows the learner to look at the breadth of opportunities that are available in the hair and beauty sector as well as learning selected hair and beauty skills in a realistic learning environment across the six industries of hair and beauty Sector.

The six industries are:

- **Hairdressing**
- **Beauty therapy**
- **Nail services**
- **Spa therapy**
- **Barbering**
- **African-type hair**

Throughout the principle learning, learners will develop **Personal Learning and Thinking skills**:

Independent Enquirer

Team Worker

Creative Thinker

Self Manager

Reflective Learner

Effective Participator

The Personal Learning and Thinking skills include the ten employability skills that have been identified by hair and beauty employers as the key skills that businesses need new recruits to have. These employability skills are:

- **Willingness to work**
- **Teamwork**
- **Personal and professional ethics**
- **Flexible working**
- **Customer care**
- **Positive attitude**
- **Self managers**
- **Creativity**
- **Communication skills**
- **Leadership**

This book is based on the Principle learning for the Diploma in Hair and Beauty Studies and within each chapter there are activities that will help learners to achieve both the employability skills and the Personal Learning and Thinking skills. Without these skills it will be difficult for a person to succeed in the Hair and Beauty Sector. And in an increasingly image-conscious world, the opportunities within the hair and beauty sector are endless. Successful people in their chosen field can take their pick from many top jobs – preparing models, working on magazines and photo shoots, in the theatre and film or even tending to the rich and famous.

The UK Hair and Beauty Sector is regarded as the best in the world, giving plenty of opportunities for travelling and working internationally. To get to the top requires hard work and dedication. There are clear progression routes from trainee to manager or owner. The hours can be long and unsociable, but the rewards can more than makeup for it. After all, how many jobs give a person the opportunity to be creative and try out new things every day? How many professions give you the chance to set up and run your own business well before your 30th birthday?

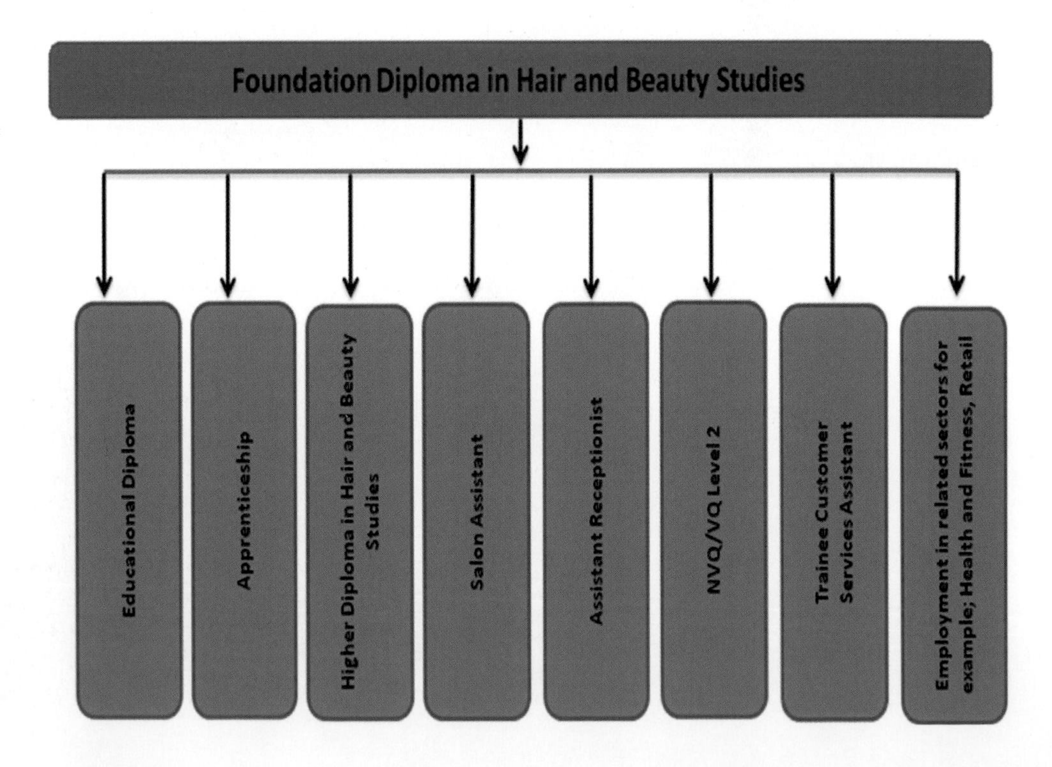

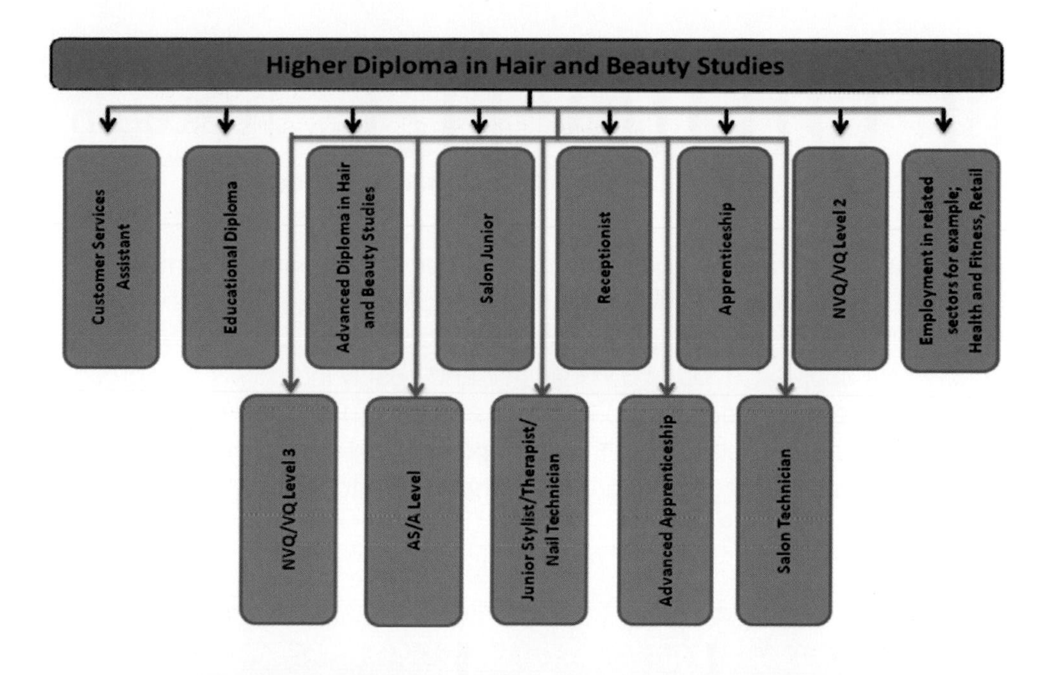

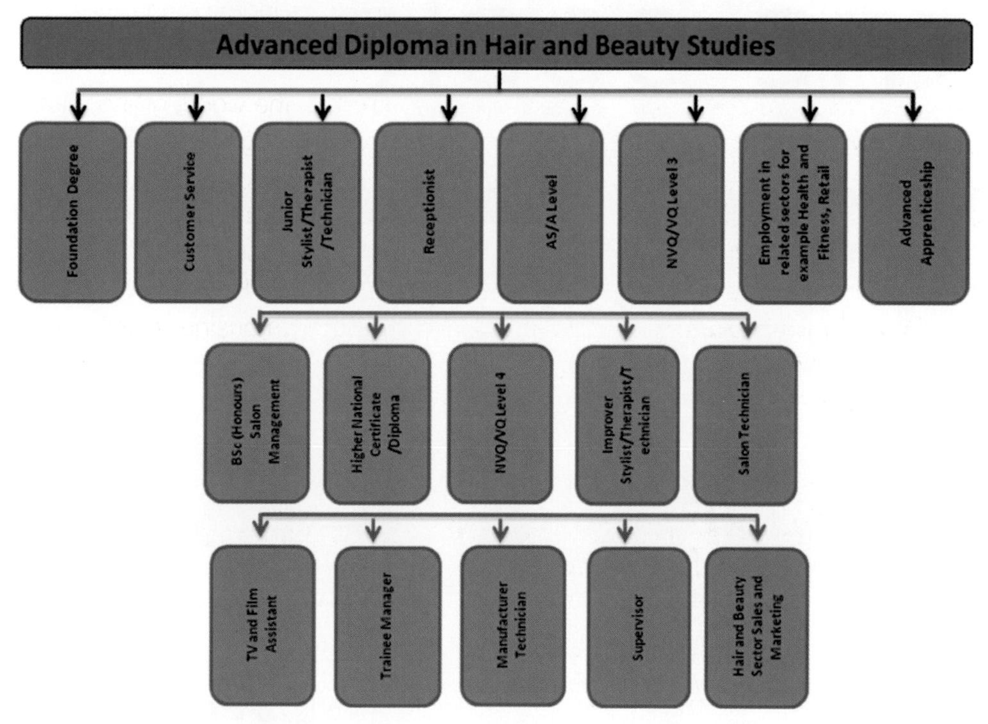

Additional or specialist learning – will allow the learner to choose options that will tailor their programme according to their interests and aspirations. This may include more hairdressing units such as hair colouring or beauty therapy or nail units or a learner can look at complementary areas that would enhance their career options that are outside the Hair and Beauty Sector, or take GCSEs or A Levels.

Generic learning – Encourages the learner to develop the boarder skills and knowledge needed for learning, employment and personal development. This will include Maths, English and ICT. It will develop personal thinking and ensure that learners have a wide base of knowledge. These generic skills are often embedded in other aspects of the Diploma.

U2learn diploma

Also available from Cengage Learning and Habia: U2Learn Diploma
U2learn Diploma provides anytime anywhere access to a wealth of interactive activities to enliven and engage students at school, college or in the workplace. Theory as it applies to today's dynamic hair and beauty industry is truly brought to life, transporting students beyond the classroom into a variety of realistic and hair and beauty settings. Visit **http://diploma.u2learn.co.uk** or email **emea.fesales@cengage.com** or **sales@habia.org** to find out more now!

About the book

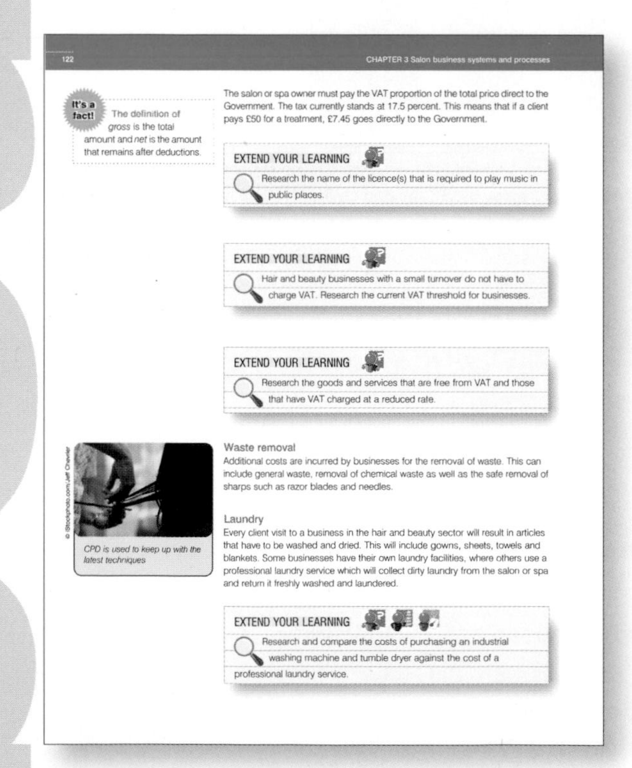

122 CHAPTER 3 Salon business systems and processes

It's a fact! The definition of *gross* is the total amount and *net* is the amount that remains after deductions.

The salon or spa owner must pay the VAT proportion of the total price direct to the Government. The tax currently stands at 17.5 percent. This means that if a client pays £50 for a treatment, £7.45 goes directly to the Government.

EXTEND YOUR LEARNING

Research the name of the licence(s) that is required to play music in public places.

EXTEND YOUR LEARNING

Hair and beauty businesses with a small turnover do not have to charge VAT. Research the current VAT threshold for businesses.

EXTEND YOUR LEARNING

Research the goods and services that are free from VAT and those that have VAT charged at a reduced rate.

© iStockphoto.com/Jeff Chevrier

CPD is used to keep up with the latest techniques

Waste removal

Additional costs are incurred by businesses for the removal of waste. This can include general waste, removal of chemical waste as well as the safe removal of sharps such as razor blades and needles.

Laundry

Every client visit to a business in the hair and beauty sector will result in articles that have to be washed and dried. This will include gowns, sheets, towels and blankets. Some businesses have their own laundry facilities, where others use a professional laundry service which will collect dirty laundry from the salon or spa and return it freshly washed and laundered.

EXTEND YOUR LEARNING

Research and compare the costs of purchasing an industrial washing machine and tumble dryer against the cost of a professional laundry service.

Extend your learning – Practical activities and projects will help you put your learning into practice and encourage further study.

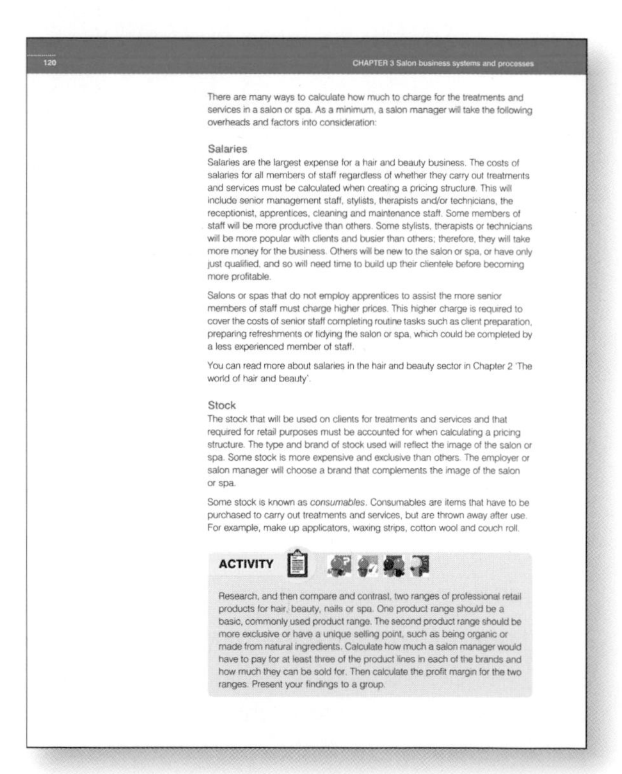

120 CHAPTER 3 Salon business systems and processes

There are many ways to calculate how much to charge for the treatments and services in a salon or spa. As a minimum, a salon manager will take the following overheads and factors into consideration:

Salaries

Salaries are the largest expense for a hair and beauty business. The costs of salaries for all members of staff regardless of whether they carry out treatments and services must be calculated when creating a pricing structure. This will include senior management staff, stylists, therapists and/or technicians, the receptionist, apprentices, cleaning and maintenance staff. Some members of staff will be more productive than others. Some stylists, therapists or technicians will be more popular with clients and busier than others; therefore, they will take more money for the business. Others will be new to the salon or spa, or have only just qualified, and so will need time to build up their clientele before becoming more profitable.

Salons or spas that do not employ apprentices to assist the more senior members of staff must charge higher prices. This higher charge is required to cover the costs of senior staff completing routine tasks such as client preparation, preparing refreshments or tidying the salon or spa, which could be completed by a less experienced member of staff.

You can read more about salaries in the hair and beauty sector in Chapter 2 'The world of hair and beauty'.

Stock

The stock that will be used on clients for treatments and services and that required for retail purposes must be accounted for when calculating a pricing structure. The type and brand of stock used will reflect the image of the salon or spa. Some stock is more expensive and exclusive than others. The employer or salon manager will choose a brand that complements the image of the salon or spa.

Some stock is known as *consumables*. Consumables are items that have to be purchased to carry out treatments and services, but are thrown away after use. For example, make up applicators, waxing strips, cotton wool and couch roll.

ACTIVITY

Research, and then compare and contrast, two ranges of professional retail products for hair, beauty, nails or spa. One product range should be a basic, commonly used product range. The second product range should be more exclusive or have a unique selling point, such as being organic or made from natural ingredients. Calculate how much a salon manager would have to pay for at least three of the product lines in each of the brands and how much they can be sold for. Then calculate the profit margin for the two ranges. Present your findings to a group.

Activity boxes suggest exciting tasks that you can do with your classmates or on your own.

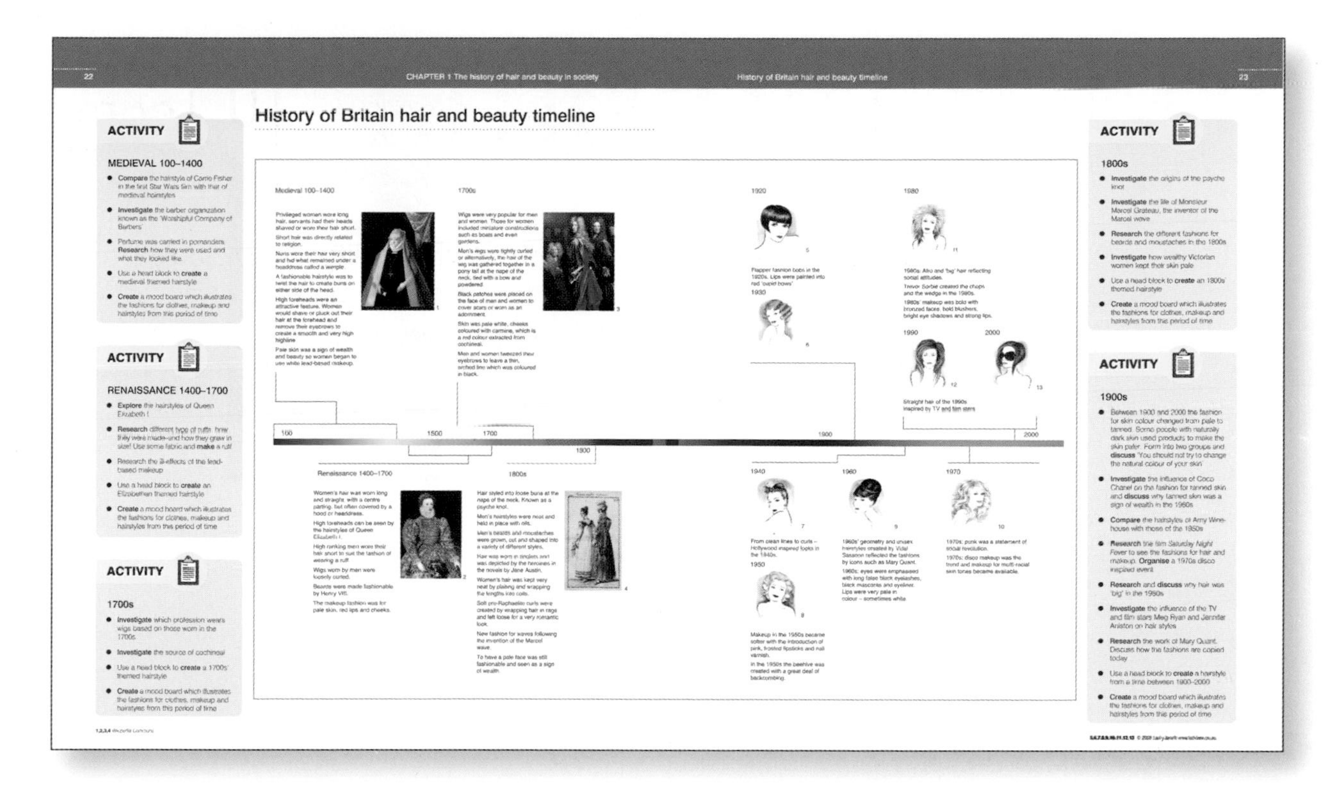

22 CHAPTER 1 The history of hair and beauty in society

History of Britain hair and beauty timeline 23

History of Britain hair and beauty timeline

ACTIVITY

MEDIEVAL 100–1400

ACTIVITY

RENAISSANCE 1400–1700

ACTIVITY

1700s

ACTIVITY

1800s

ACTIVITY

1900s

Timelines in **Chapter 1** are a great visual tool for comparing the history of hair and beauty across different cultures and throughout history.

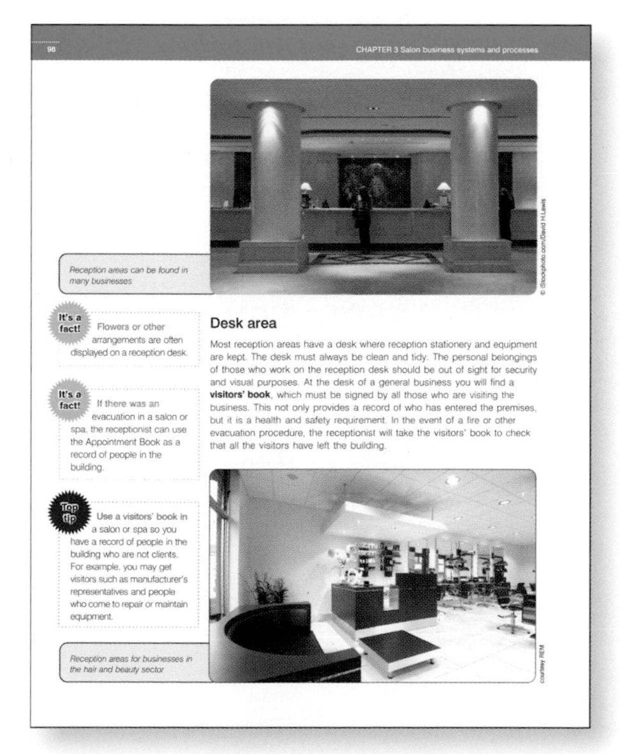

98 CHAPTER 3 Salon business systems and processes

Reception areas can be found in many businesses

It's a fact! Flowers or other arrangements are often displayed on a reception desk.

It's a fact! If there was an evacuation in a salon or spa, the receptionist can use the Appointment Book as a record of people in the building.

Top tip Use a visitors' book in a salon or spa so you have a record of people in the building who are not clients. For example, you may get visitors such as manufacturer's representatives and people who come to repair or maintain equipment.

Desk area

Most reception areas have a desk where reception stationery and equipment are kept. The desk must always be clean and tidy. The personal belongings of those who work on the reception desk should be out of sight for security and visual purposes. At the desk of a general business you will find a **visitors' book**, which must be signed by all those who are visiting the business. This not only provides a record of who has entered the premises, but it is a health and safety requirement. In the event of a fire or other evacuation procedure, the receptionist will take the visitors' book to check that all the visitors have left the building.

Reception areas for businesses in the hair and beauty sector

Top Tip! and **It's a fact!** boxes make information easy to digest and remember.

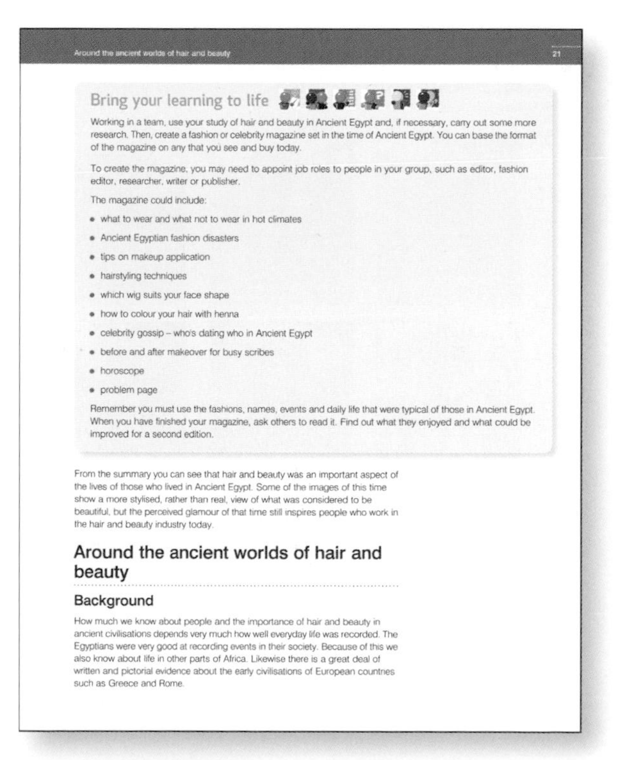

Around the ancient worlds of hair and beauty 21

Bring your learning to life

Working in a team, use your study of hair and beauty in Ancient Egypt and, if necessary, carry out some more research. Then, create a fashion or celebrity magazine set in the time of Ancient Egypt. You can base the format of the magazine on any that you see and buy today.

To create the magazine, you may need to appoint job roles to people in your group, such as editor, fashion editor, researcher, writer or publisher.

The magazine could include:

- what to wear and what not to wear in hot climates
- Ancient Egyptian fashion disasters
- tips on makeup application
- hairstyling techniques
- which wig suits your face shape
- how to colour your hair with henna
- celebrity gossip – who's dating who in Ancient Egypt
- before and after makeover for busy scribes
- horoscope
- problem page

Remember you must use the fashions, names, events and daily life that were typical of those in Ancient Egypt. When you have finished your magazine, ask others to read it. Find out what they enjoyed and what could be improved for a second edition.

From the summary you can see that hair and beauty was an important aspect of the lives of those who lived in Ancient Egypt. Some of the images of this time show a more stylised, rather than real, view of what was considered to be beautiful, but the perceived glamour of that time still inspires people who work in the hair and beauty industry today.

Around the ancient worlds of hair and beauty

Background

How much we know about people and the importance of hair and beauty in ancient civilisations depends very much how well everyday life was recorded. The Egyptians were very good at recording events in their society. Because of this we also know about life in other parts of Africa. Likewise there is a great deal of written and pictorial evidence about the early civilisations of European countries such as Greece and Rome.

Bring your learning to life! is a feature that encourages you to use your skills in the workplace or in everyday life.

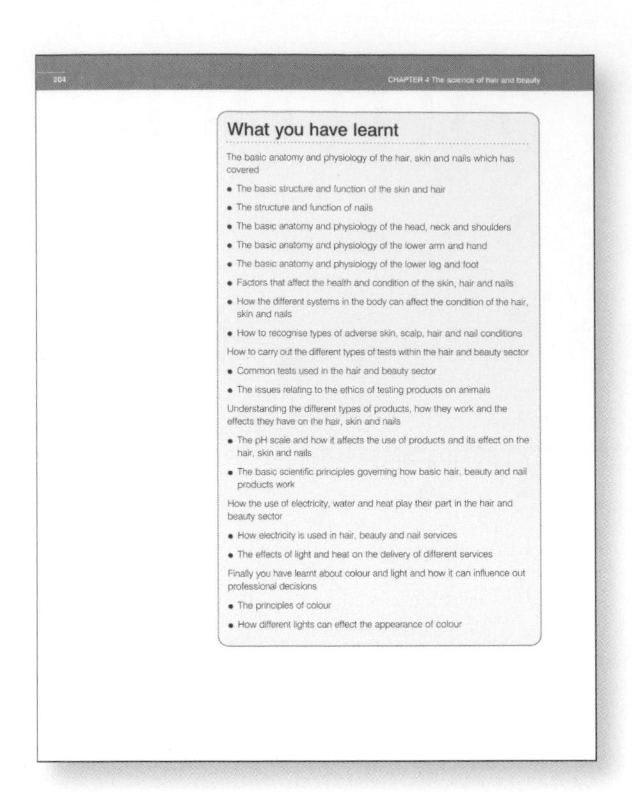
204 CHAPTER 4 The science of hair and beauty

What you have learnt

The basic anatomy and physiology of the hair, skin and nails which has covered

- The basic structure and function of the skin and hair
- The structure and function of nails
- The basic anatomy and physiology of the head, neck and shoulders
- The basic anatomy and physiology of the lower arm and hand
- The basic anatomy and physiology of the lower leg and foot
- Factors that affect the health and condition of the skin, hair and nails
- How the different systems in the body can affect the condition of the hair, skin and nails
- How to recognise types of adverse skin, scalp, hair and nail conditions

How to carry out the different types of tests within the hair and beauty sector

- Common tests used in the hair and beauty sector
- The issues relating to the ethics of testing products on animals

Understanding the different types of products, how they work and the effects they have on the hair, skin and nails

- The pH scale and how it affects the use of products and its effect on the hair, skin and nails
- The basic scientific principles governing how basic hair, beauty and nail products work

How the use of electricity, water and heat play their part in the hair and beauty sector

- How electricity is used in hair, beauty and nail services
- The effects of light and heat on the delivery of different services

Finally you have learnt about colour and light and how it can influence out professional decisions

- The principles of colour
- How different lights can effect the appearance of colour

End of chapter assessments contain short answer questions so you can test yourself on the chapter subject and see how much you have learnt.

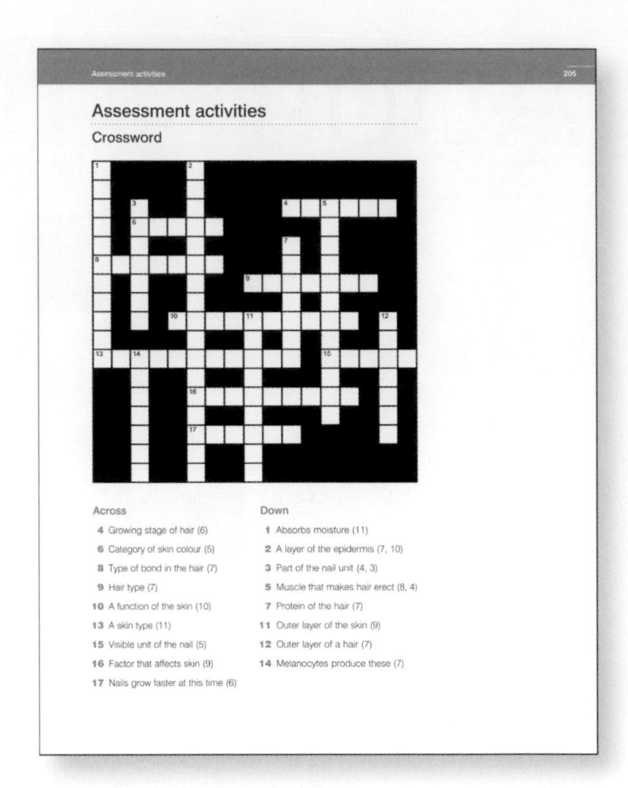
Assessment activities 205

Assessment activities

Crossword

Across

4 Growing stage of hair (6)
6 Category of skin colour (5)
8 Type of bond in the hair (7)
9 Hair type (7)
10 A function of the skin (10)
13 A skin type (11)
15 Visible unit of the nail (5)
16 Factor that affects skin (9)
17 Nails grow faster at this time (6)

Down

1 Absorbs moisture (11)
2 A layer of the epidermis (7, 10)
3 Part of the nail unit (4, 3)
5 Muscle that makes hair erect (8, 4)
7 Protein of the hair (7)
11 Outer layer of the skin (9)
12 Outer layer of a hair (7)
14 Melanocytes produce these (7)

Crosswords and **Wordsearches** test your knowledge of the topics and are fun and interactive revision tools.

Facial treatment procedure 287

Step 2: Facial Scrub

Application of scrub:

1 Place the clean towel on the pillow, and wrap the towel carefully over the head, protecting the hairline.

2 Choose the appropriate scrub for the skin type. Always read and follow carefully the manufacturer's instructions. Place a small amount of scrub on the back of your hand.

3 Apply the scrub to the face with a mask brush. Explain to the client the sensation they will feel.

4 Make sure the scrub is applied evenly all over the neck, chin, cheeks, nose and forehead.

5 With small circular motions, lightly massage the entire face and neck in an upwards direction. Be careful on delicate areas such as the cheeks and avoid the eye area and lips. If the scrub dries out too much, and starts to drag, add water by dampening hands.

6 The scrub is left on the skin for the recommended time, according to the manufacturer's instructions. Use warm damp sponges to remove the scrub, start at the neck, make sure you check the hairline and around the nostrils. Do not have the sponges too wet or it will be uncomfortable for the client.

7 Blot the face with a tissue

© Habia and Cengage Learning 2008/9

Step-by-step photos take you through the basic skills and enable learners to visualise the processes involved.

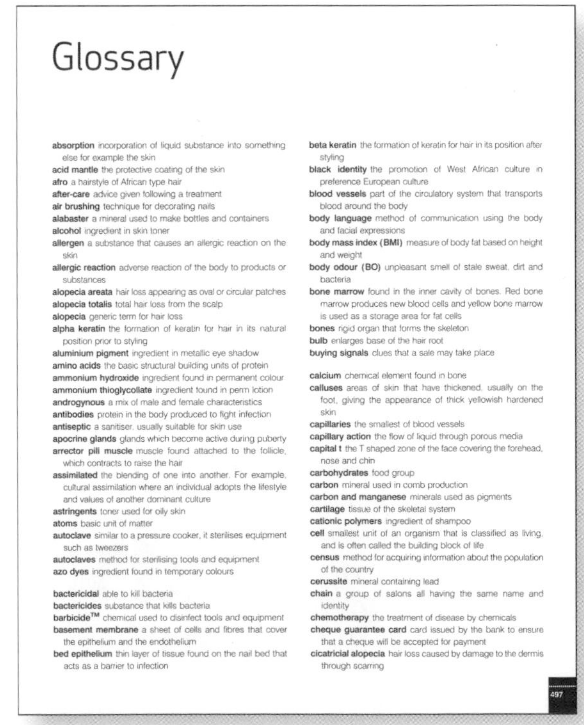
Glossary

absorption incorporation of liquid substance into something else for example the skin
acid mantle the protective coating of the skin
afro a hairstyle of African type hair
after-care advice given following a treatment
air brushing technique for decorating nails
alabaster a mineral used to make bottles and containers
alcohol ingredient in skin toner
allergen a substance that causes an allergic reaction on the skin
allergic reaction adverse reaction of the body to products or substances
alopecia areata hair loss appearing as oval or circular patches
alopecia totalis total hair loss from the scalp
alopecia generic term for hair loss
alpha keratin the formation of keratin for hair in its natural position prior to styling
aluminium pigment ingredient in metallic eye shadow
amino acids the basic structural building units of protein
ammonium hydroxide ingredient found in permanent colour
ammonium thioglycollate ingredient found in perm lotion
androgynous a mix of male and female characteristics
antibodies protein in the body produced to fight infection
antiseptic a sanitiser, usually suitable for skin use
apocrine glands glands which become active during puberty
arrector pili muscle muscle found attached to the follicle, which contracts to raise the hair
assimilated the blending of one into another. For example, cultural assimilation where an individual adopts the lifestyle and values of another dominant culture
astringents toner used for oily skin
atoms basic unit of matter
autoclave similar to a pressure cooker, it sterilises equipment such as tweezers
autoclaves method for sterilising tools and equipment
azo dyes ingredient found in temporary colours

bactericidal able to kill bacteria
bactericides substance that kills bacteria
barbicide™ chemical used to disinfect tools and equipment
basement membrane a sheet of cells and fibres that cover the epithelium and the endothelium
bed epithelium thin layer of tissue found on the nail bed that acts as a barrier to infection
beta keratin the formation of keratin for hair in its position after styling
black identity the promotion of West African culture in preference European culture
blood vessels part of the circulatory system that transports blood around the body
body language method of communication using the body and facial expressions
body mass index (BMI) measure of body fat based on height and weight
body odour (BO) unpleasant smell of stale sweat, dirt and bacteria
bone marrow found in the inner cavity of bones. Red bone marrow produces new blood cells and yellow bone marrow is used as a storage area for fat cells
bones rigid organ that forms the skeleton
bulb enlarges base of the hair root
buying signals clues that a sale may take place

calcium chemical element found in bone
calluses areas of skin that have thickened, usually on the foot, giving the appearance of thick yellowish hardened skin
capillaries the smallest of blood vessels
capillary action the flow of liquid through porous media
capital t the T shaped zone of the face covering the forehead, nose and chin
carbohydrates food group
carbon mineral used in comb production
carbon and manganese minerals used as pigments
cartilage tissue of the skeletal system
cationic polymers ingredient of shampoo
cell smallest unit of an organism that is classified as living, and is often called the building block of life
census method for acquiring information about the population of the country
cerussite mineral containing lead
chain a group of salons all having the same name and identity
chemotherapy the treatment of disease by chemicals
cheque guarantee card card issued by the bank to ensure that a cheque will be accepted for payment
cicatricial alopecia hair loss caused by damage to the dermis through scarring

497

Glossary terms are **highlighted** in the text and you can find all the definitions at the back of the book.

About the authors

Jane Goldsbro

Jane Goldsbro

A qualified hairdresser since 1982, Jane is one of the most influential educators in hair and beauty today. Her skills in developing the structure of UK hair and beauty education are renowned throughout the world.

Jane's early career as a hairdresser took her through a formative path where she ran salons and worked for some of the best companies and key influencers in the field of education such as Alan International and at Redken worked as one of their top technicians.

At an early stage of her career, Jane was a regional winner of the L'Oréal Colour Trophy at the tender age of 17; this led her to start a teaching career at her local college. However, the deep rooted commitment to continued learning saw Jane taking on her biggest challenge when she went to work at Habia.

1992 saw Jane start at Habia as Development Manager for Hairdressing and within four years Jane had risen to Director of Standards and Qualifications. This role saw her take on bigger challenges each and every year. Not only did Jane enhance the development of hairdressing education, she began to expand Habia's remit into Beauty Therapy. Since those heady days of endless development meetings, running standards workshops and training international educators in Habia techniques, Jane still found time to develop her skills.

An established writer of technical material for Habia, Jane is also the author of two hairdressing study guides for Cengage Learning, the leading publisher in hair and beauty. As part of Jane's role, she is responsible for the content in the new Diploma in Hair and Beauty Studies. Her expertise in training and assessing has been picked up by well-known awarding bodies such as City & Guilds and at the inception of a new regulatory regime by the UK government in training, Jane became one of the first inspectors for the Adult Learning Inspectorate.

Her role at Habia as Director of Standards and Qualifications now covers all six sectors of Habia's portfolio in hair, beauty, nails, spa, barbering and African-type hair. She is responsible for setting the standard for hair and beauty education from school leavers to university graduates.

Truly, one of the most knowledgeable hair and beauty educators in the world.

Elaine White

Elaine White

With a driving passion, Elaine White has expanded on her 30 years' experience in the hairdressing Industry by implementing some of the most Influential programmes within work-based learning.

Throughout her career, Elaine has been directly involved in researching processes and developing systems that have raised standards within the hair and beauty industry. Elaine has contributed massively to the development of structures in UK and international hair and beauty education, which are renowned throughout the world. Throughout her career her passion for learning and development, not only for herself but for others, took her into the challenging world of further and higher education. Here she spent more than 16 years as an educator in both Lincolnshire and Nottinghamshire, before joining Habia in 2001 as Senior Development Manager.

Her role as Senior Development Manager allows her to work with a diverse range of stakeholders, encompassing employers, schools, colleges of further education, private training providers and universities. This has allowed Elaine to lead the development of innovative programmes including the Young Apprenticeships, Apprenticeships and Foundation Degrees, setting the standard for hair and beauty education from school pupils to university graduates. One of the most rewarding projects was to research the incidence of dyslexia in the hairdressing industry that culminated in presenting to an invited group at the House of Lords, the home of the upper chamber of the UK Parliament.

This invaluable experience has enabled Elaine to develop and update education over all six sectors of Habia's portfolio in hair, beauty, nails, spa, barbering and African-type hair. Her knowledge and experience has been further recognised through her appointment as the standard setting representative for the Apprenticeship Approval Group for England and Wales.

If this wasn't enough, Elaine is also an associate inspector for Ofsted.
Her passion for quality is paramount and clearly evident through her work.

1

the history of hair and beauty in society

Tracey Devine @ Angels, Aberdeen

"Forget not the past for in the future it may help you grow.

J M BARRIE 1860–1937, NOVELIST

Introduction

For as long as there have been civilisations, people have wanted to change how they look. The history of hair and beauty goes back for hundreds and thousands of years – right back to the most ancient civilisations of the world, from Africa to Asia and from Europe to the British Isles. People all over the world created images about themselves to reflect their society, and their social place within it.

While countries and cultures will be different, image and fashion are still linked together and looks are always changing. When a hair style or makeup trend is worn by a celebrity, promoted on television or shown in the latest magazines, it would be easy to think that something new has been created. But the hair and

What you are going to learn

This chapter will include:

- ★ The influence of civilisations and culture on hair and beauty
- ★ The historical influences of hair and beauty
- ★ The social factors that affect the way individuals look
- ★ How identity is created and what influences it
- ★ Iconic leaders of the hair and beauty sector
- ★ The technological developments of hair and beauty

beauty images you see today are not just born; they have evolved over many years and can be traced back to another time, place, culture or civilisation.

The hair and beauty sector is made up of industries that create images. But you don't have to work in any of the hair and beauty industries to be involved in creating your own image. You can do it all by yourself. Image is important – it states who you are and forms your identity.

Through this chapter you will be able to explore the history and foundations of the latest hair and beauty trends – and check out your own image and find out where it came from.

It's a fact! Human evolution is defined by a number of important changes to man over many thousands of years. These changes include the development of the brain, alterations in the length and strength of the limbs and the development of speech, social skills and emotions.

The influence of civilisations and culture on hair and beauty

A new beginning

When do you think the earliest humans inhabited the world? There is much debate amongst those who study *evolution.*

There is evidence that early humans, who had the ability to walk upright, inhabited the world over 4 million years ago. However, humans that were able to make tools and had a developed language are much more recent.

ACTIVITY

Try to find out when man first started to make tools. What were the tools and what were they used for?

EXTEND YOUR LEARNING

There are people who study the science of *palaeontology*. Palaeontology is the study of life and fossils in prehistoric time. Investigate this science and learn about the stories that fossils can tell us about life and the people who lived on earth before we did.

Being able to make and use tools is important in the development of humans. The flint tools were sharp and could be used for, amongst other things, butchering large animals. Evidence of needles made between 40,000 and 25,000 years ago have been found, so we think that the skins of the animals were sewn into clothes.

ACTIVITY

The wearing of animal skins in prehistoric times would have been necessary to keep warm when the weather was cold. What do you think about fashion designers that use fur and other animal skin to make clothes today?

Split into teams and debate either: 'Only animals should wear their skins' or 'There is no difference to wearing the skin of an animal than eating the meat'.

An early tool used by Stone Age man

iStockphoto.com/Luca Manieri

Wearing clothing meant that very early man could keep warm, was able to travel around and explore his surroundings. The clothes were also important as it is one aspect that led to the beginning of cultural identity and social status, and even the rise of fashion.

And it wasn't just clothing that gave identity, we also know that early man made combs out of boxwood, deer antler and bone – so we know that grooming took place in the form of combing of hair. But what is not clear is why hair was combed – was it for styling or, more likely, was it to get rid of head lice?

It's a fact!

In the Middle Ages, between 1066 and 1485, a new occupation evolved – that of a comb maker.

Top tip

Use a search engine to find information about the fur debate. One useful site is **http:/www.independent.co.uk/news/uk/this-britain/fur–the-fake-debate-534303.html**

EXTEND YOUR LEARNING

The history of comb development is very interesting. Not only in terms of when and how they were made, but also in the folklore that surrounds combs. For example, did you know that there is a superstition which says that if you drop your comb while you are combing your hair that this is a sign of a coming disappointment? When you have discovered some examples of folklore, discuss your findings with others.

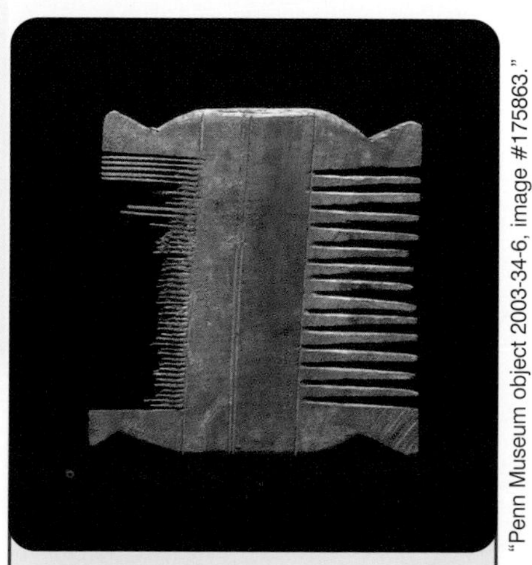

Early combs

"Penn Museum object 2003-34-6, image #175863."

Since our ancient ancestors developed a form of social order, there has never been a civilisation in the world that has not had the desire or need to present a personal image. So, perhaps it was our early Stone Age ancestors who started the hair and beauty industry of today.

Ancient civilisation

You may take the technology you have today for granted. But the world we live in was built on the knowledge and achievements of those who lived tens of thousands of years ago. Evidence has been found to show that people who lived in ancient times were skilled builders, engineers, doctors and farmers.

Some people in ancient times were considered to be more important than others. The position people held could be identified by, amongst other things, the clothes they wore, the length of their hair, the style they wore the hair and, sometimes, their makeup.

Ancient Egypt

When you think of Egypt, what are your first thoughts? Perhaps you think about the pyramids at Giza, which are one of the seven wonders of the ancient world, or maybe you think about the magnificent temples or the enormous Sphinx. You may ask questions like:

- How did they build the pyramids?
- Why are they there?
- Why were the dead mummified?

Or, in relation to hair and beauty, you may also ask:

- Why did men wear makeup?
- Why were cosmetics and even perfume buried with dead kings?
- Why do the images painted on tombs have black hair?

To answer these questions you have to look at the country, culture and social order that was present at the time.

Egyptian pyramids

Egypt, the country

Egypt is one of the most heavily populated countries in Africa and the Middle East, with most people living now, as they did in the past, near the banks of the River Nile.

Egyptian social order

The civilisation in Ancient Egypt was based on religion and all people held the belief that their life on earth was less important than their life after death.

Ancient Egypt was an organised society with a very rigid class structure. At the top was the pharaoh or king who was thought to be a divine god. Then there were Egyptian noblemen and governors. There were also educated people such as scribes or writers and there were doctors and accountants. Lower down the Egyptian social scale were the craftsmen and builders who constructed the pyramids and temples. Then, right at the bottom, according to Ancient Egyptian society, would be found the farmers and slaves.

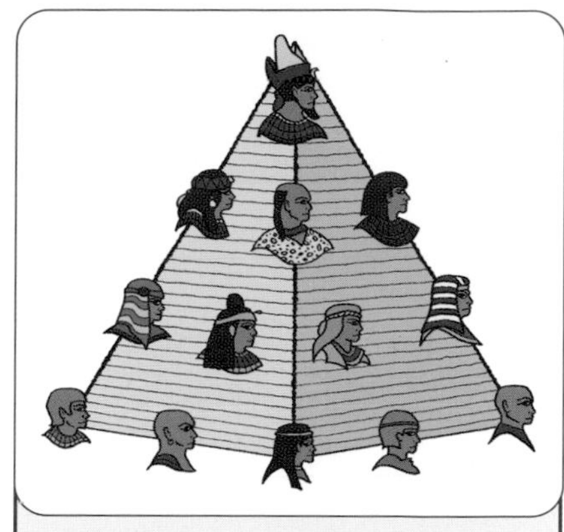

Social order in Ancient Egypt

ACTIVITY  

To investigate the occupations that existed in ancient Egypt, visit the BBC website and see what it would have been like to have been a builder. Play a game to build a pyramid **http:/www.bbc.co.uk/history/ancient/egyptians/launch_gms_pyramid_builder.shtml**

It's a fact!

Bodies were preserved with a special salt like substance to dry out the skin. Oils and perfumes were also used. The Ancient Egyptians also mummified animals. Even crocodiles!

The history of hair and beauty in Ancient Egypt

Personal appearance was an important aspect of daily life in Ancient Egypt. How a person looked would indicate their social and even political status.

We can tell a great deal about the appearance of some people who lived in Ancient Egypt from the remains of mummies.

EXTEND YOUR LEARNING  

The mummification of bodies is one clue to the life that some people led in Ancient Egypt. Research how mummification was carried out and the rituals that lay behind it. Use the BBC website **http:/www.bbc.co.uk/history/ancient/**

If you can, visit the British Museum in London and see the mummies of Ancient Egypt. Alternatively, see them on the British Museum website **http:/www.britishmuseum.org/explore/world_cultures/africa/ancient_egypt.aspx**

You can also play a game about mummification **http:/www.bbc.co.uk/history/ancient/egyptians/launch_gms_mummy_maker.shtml**

Death mask of Tutankhamen

We have a fascination about the stunning appearance of those who lived at this time. However, the raven black hair and the beautiful makeup depicted on masks

It's a fact! You could identify the social status of a person who lived in Ancient Egypt by the clothing that was worn. For example, many men wore an item of clothing that resembled a kilt. It was made from linen, which would be cool in the heat, but the quality of the linen would separate rich from poor people. Wealthy men also wore a long, transparent layer over the top of the linen kilt. Pharaohs would wear the transparent layer as well, and, in addition, clothes that were elaborately decorated and gold jewellery. Slaves wore simple loin cloths. Children often wore no clothes at all until they reached puberty.

of mummies were created as a stylised image of a dead person, and not what they really looked like in life. You may be aware of the famous, beautiful image of the young King Tutankhamen. Recent research has shown that he was not so good looking as his mask, as in reality he had a receding chin and protruding teeth.

Makeup was used not only for decoration and to make people look more attractive, but for healing purposes as well. Scientists who have examined the remnants of makeup found in Egyptian tombs have found the powders and oils used to make cosmetics, which could also be mixed and used as eye drops that would provide protection and ease the irritation of eye infections. Soothing oils were also used to protect the skin against hot, dry winds. This shows that the Egyptians not only wanted to improve their appearance, but wanted to take care of themselves as well.

EXTEND YOUR LEARNING  

Form a discussion group and discuss the importance of clothing today – is clothing still linked to social status? Do you like to look like your friends – or do you have your own particular style? Perhaps you like wearing a uniform which shows that you belong to a particular school or college – or maybe you find this a way of restricting your own self expression. What happens on non-uniform days – do you and your friends still wear similar clothes?

The hair and beauty of Ancient Egypt

The hair and beauty sector today is made up of several separate industries. They are hairdressing, barbering, beauty therapy, nail services, spa therapy. It is interesting to see that many of the skills required for these modern industries existed in Ancient Egypt.

Hairdressing in Ancient Egypt

Hairdressing and wig making was a respected profession in ancient Egypt and was depicted in art, on tombs and in *hieroglyphs.* Because clothing was generally very simple – usually made from undyed linen, there was a chance for people to show their individuality by styling their hair.

Hairstyles in Ancient Egypt

Healthy, glossy hair was associated with youth and sexuality and so images were made of people with shiny, raven black hair, often cut into a bob like shape. You

Ancient Egyptian hairstyles

Hieroglyphs

EXTEND YOUR LEARNING

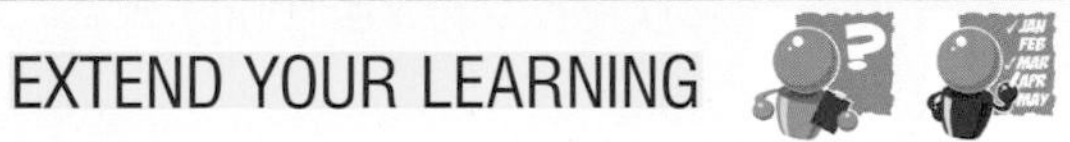

One reason why Egypt was such a well developed country was because some people could read and write. These educated people were able to record information, make calculations or write documents, which is why we know so much about the country. The writing was done in the form of **hieroglyphs**, which were symbols that represented words and individual sounds.

Investigate how hieroglyphs were formed and what the symbols mean. You could even learn to write your own name in hieroglyphs, or write a message to your friends.

It's a fact!

Hieroglyphics can be read from left to right as we read or from right to left, from bottom to top or from top to bottom. The writer would determine the way they should be read by the direction of the symbols used.

might think that people wore their hair like this all the time, but the chances are that the images provided a *symbolic* glimpse into what was considered to be beautiful in Ancient Egypt. In reality the hair depicted on tombs and in hieroglyphics was more likely to be a wig than natural hair.

It was fashionable to wear the hair short during the period of time known as the **Old Kingdom**, but longer in the **New Kingdom** when hair was also worn in plaits. In the New Kingdom, wigs of wealthy women were also decorated with beads, flowers or ribbons. Poor women would also decorate their hair and wigs with flowers or berries.

It's a fact!

The terms Old Kingdom, Middle Kingdom and New Kingdom are used to describe a period of time that spanned from 3100 to 1070 BC. Pyramids were first built in the time of the Old Kingdom.

The children of Ancient Egypt wore a very unique hairstyle which they would keep until puberty. The head was shaved, or cut very, very short, but a tuft of hair was left on the side of the head. The tuft of hair was known as the **side lock of youth**. The lock was formed into a thick plait. The shaved head would have helped to

Wikipedia Commons

Side lock of youth

It's a fact! **The terms BC and AD are used to describe periods of time in** history. BC stands for *Before Christ* and AD stands for *Anno Domini*, which translates to 'the year of the Lord' when it is believed that Jesus Christ was born. In recent times other abbreviations have been used. For example BCE, which replaces BC and stands for *Before the Common Era*. And AD is replaced by *Common Era*. This means that 2010 CE means the same as 2010 AD. The term Common Era has been adopted by non-Christian cultures.

keep the children cool and free from head lice, and the longer tuft of hair acted as a symbol to others that the individual was yet to reach puberty. After puberty young boys shaved their heads completely, while girls grew their hair to wear in pony tails or plaits.

While it is not know how frequently hair was washed in Ancient Egypt, there is evidence that the hair was combed. Single and double sided combs have been found. On one side of the comb there are narrow teeth and the other, wide teeth. The combs were made from wood, bone or elaborately carved ivory. It is thought that the elaborate combs were intended as burial objects, rather than for everyday use.

Wigs in ancient Egypt

Wigs were worn for several reasons. The weather was, and still is, very hot. To overcome the heat many people – men and women, rich and poor, would shave their heads. However they did not like to look bald, therefore, they wore wigs. Greying hair was considered to be ageing and so, by wearing a wig a younger appearance could be achieved. Shaving the head also meant that head lice were kept away.

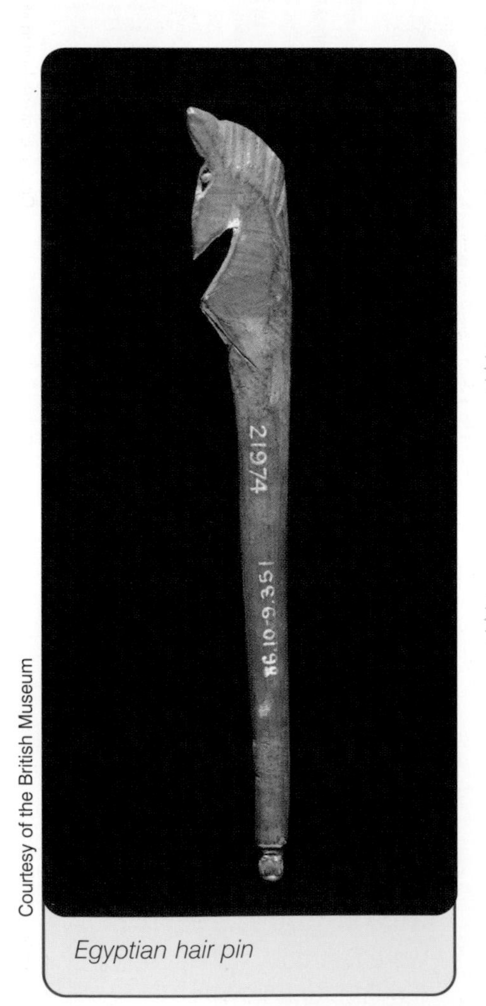

Courtesy of the British Museum

Egyptian hair pin

It's a fact! **Head lice are parasites that feed off blood from the scalp. They** lay eggs called *nits*. Once hatched, the white egg cases remain glued to the hair. The lice are spread by direct head to head contact and much prefer clean hair to dirty hair.

It's a fact! **Dr Joann Fletcher, a British expert in Egyptology and an expert** in analysis of Ancient Egyptian hair found evidence of head lice that were at least 3000 years old. So, Dr Fletcher had discovered one reason why ancient Egyptians shaved off their hair and wore wigs. In addition, she found evidence of the potions that were used to prevent 'that which moves about on the head'. One recipe recommended that 'fruit of the castor-oil plant, ox fat and moringa oil: combine to a paste and apply every day'. Dr Fletcher also found evidence of head lice in the fine teeth of combs.

Joann Fletcher, *The Search for Nefertiti*, William Morrow, New York, 2004.

EXTEND YOUR LEARNING

The life of parasites such as head lice is very interesting. Head lice are totally dependent upon their host to feed and to lay eggs. They never leave their host unless they can transfer to another host, are dying – or already dead.

Investigate the life cycle of the head louse and the ways that it can be destroyed.

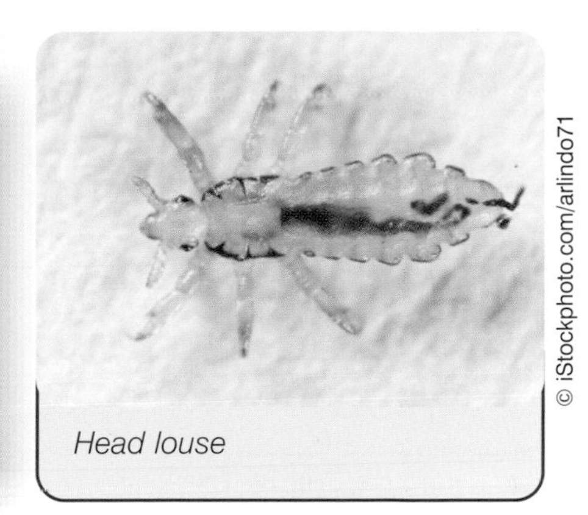

Head louse

The most expensive wigs were made from human hair, but poorer people wore wigs made from sheep wool or vegetable fibres. Elaborate wigs would have been worn for special occasions and it was not uncommon for them to be scented, elaborately decorated or braided. Hair extensions were also popular with women who like to wear their hair longer than men. The hair extensions were attached to natural hair or wigs with beeswax.

It's a fact!

A wig that is at least 3,000 years old was found in the Temple of Isis at Thebes. The wig can be seen in the British Museum. It is unusual as the hair style is in two parts. The top is made from naturally curly human hair and beneath hang several hundred tiny plaits. The colour of the hair is lighter than is normally depicted in Egyptian paintings.

Wig found at Temple of Isis at Thebes, now in the British Museum

It's a fact!

The shaving of heads also had a religious significance. As it was thought that excessive hair was a sign of being unclean, priests shaved their heads and bodies daily. This is why you see images of priests without eyebrows – or even eyelashes.

It's a fact!

When Priests in Ancient Egypt were on duty, they had to wash before entering the temple to remove the dust and dirt of the street and then had to bathe several times each day to remain cleansed and pure.

Priest of Ancient Egypt without hair

Hair colour in Ancient Egypt

Almost every image depicted in paintings of Ancient Egyptian times is of raven black hair. If other hair colours are depicted it is to illustrate a foreigner to the land. However with ageing, hair would lose its natural colour and in time the hair would become white.

Henna plant Lawsonia inermis

One way of disguising the greying hair was to wear a wig. However some people also liked to colour their hair.

The vegetable colour, **henna** was used to give the naturally dark hair of ancient Egyptians a warm, red glow. To use the henna, the dry, ground leaves were mixed with an acidic liquid such as the juice of citrus fruits or wine and the thick paste was applied to the hair. The paste was left for several hours and then rinsed. The henna would not only colour the hair, but leave the hair in very good condition.

However, if henna is applied to white hair, a rather bright orange colour will occur. This is because henna can only produce shades of red. So, to achieve the raven black hair to which the ancient Egyptians aspired, it is likely that another dye would have been used. Shades of black and blue black could be achieved if the dye from the indigo plant was applied with henna or following a henna treatment.

It's a fact! Barbering is the term used today for services relating to the cutting and styling of hair and facial hair on male clients.

It's a fact! The plant from which indigo is made is called *indiofera* – a flowering shrub that grows in tropical and subtropical areas.

Ancient Egyptian men's hairstyle

Barbering in Ancient Egypt

Because barbers were able to help others with their personal appearance and cleanliness, they worked in a respected and prosperous occupation. Barbers worked outside on commoners, and in the homes of the wealthy, to cut and shave hair.

Hair styles for men

You may think that only women ever styled and arranged their hair – but the men did too! Men in Ancient Egypt generally kept their hair short. One male hairstyle that is depicted in Ancient Egyptian art is curly hair. It is likely that this styling was the result of artificially curling the hair. To curl the hair it was first covered in mud, which acted as a setting aid, and then wound around wooden sticks.

But men, like women, also shaved their heads, again for coolness and to avoid head lice. At the same time, shaving the head meant that thinning hair – perhaps as a result of male pattern baldness – could not be seen. Male pattern baldness is associated with ageing and only men of lower classes were depicted with naturally thinning hair. To cover their bald heads, wigs were frequently worn by men. Some were very elaborate – especially for men of wealth.

Beards and facial hair

Only foreigners and enemies of Egypt were ever depicted with overgrown and very full beards. Excessive amounts of facial hair were seen as a sign of being unclean. Any facial hair worn prior to, and up to, the Old Kingdom was short and neat or restricted to a very small moustache.

It's a fact! Razors made from gold have been found in the tombs of pharaohs.

In the Middle and New Kingdom it was very rare to see facial hair at all and shaving became the fashion. During this time the shaving was done with copper and bronze razors, which blunted very quickly and must have been very uncomfortable to use. Later, iron razors were used that were much sharper.

Wealthy men occasionally wore 'goatee' beards and there are many images of pharaohs with false beards that were either pointed or cut square at the end. False beards were held onto the face by the use of straps and can be seen in carvings and paintings. Therefore, this type of beard became a symbol of a divine god.

contemporary goatee beard

It's a fact!

A goatee beard is so called because it resembles the tufts of hair on the chin of a goat and this style of beard has been made even more popular by men in the public eye, such as David Beckham.

Ancient Egyptian statue with beard

Beauty in Ancient Egypt

One thing you may have noticed about the people of ancient Egypt is the very distinct and striking makeup – especially around the eyes.

Even in death Egyptians were concerned with how they looked. Cosmetics were left in tombs and care was taken to ensure that dead people kept to the rules for dress and makeup. This was done to make the right impression to gods during the ritual known as the *Judgement of the Dead.* The people of Ancient Egypt believed that all who died underwent the Judgement of the Dead. By passing through this ritual, the life that would be lived after death would be determined. This life would be based on the conduct of that person during their life time.

Archaeologists have found containers in tombs that were still filled with powders that confirm the colours used included black, white, green and grey. The people of Ancient Egypt were very skilled in their cosmetic chemistry work and were able to mix many ingredients to produce a range of makeup. **Carbon** and **manganese** oxides were used to make black makeup, along with **malachite** and other copper-based minerals to make green. To give colour to the lips and cheeks, ground up red **ochre**, which is made from red clay, was mixed with water. Oil was the base of most cosmetics products. The oils came from nuts and fruit and were finely ground up.

It's a fact!

Makeup was used in Ancient Egypt by people from all walks of life, not only by women, but by men and children as well.

Eye makeup

Unlike other forms of makeup, such as colour for the lips or for the cheeks, eye makeup was used daily by men and women, rich and poor. Rich people had applicators made of carved ivory and jewelled containers for storage, while poor people would simply use a stick to apply theirs.

It's a fact!

Most people would apply makeup to themselves, but some that could afford it would use a professional face painter.

The makeup was applied to the upper and lower lids of the eyes which were underlined and lengthened using a substance known as **kohl**. There were two commonly used colours – green and black kohl. Green, which was also known as **udju** was made by grinding green malachite, and black, known as

© shutterstock.com/Tamara Kulikova
Egyptian eye makcup

mesdemet, made from galena, a grey lead ore. **Cerussite**, a white carbonate of lead (which we now know is poisonous) was used to lighten the black kohl and small amounts of lead compounds **laurionite** and **phosgenite** were also used. The ground ingredients were mixed with vegetable oil or animal fat.

EXTEND YOUR LEARNING

Investigate the chemistry and properties of malachite, galena, cerussite, laurionite and phosgenite which were ingredients used to formulate ancient Egyptian makeup.

Courtesy of the British Museum
Cosmetic container found in an Egyptian tomb

It's a fact! **As with fashions today, there were various changes in the** fashions for the application of kohl. In the period of time known as the Old Kingdom, green kohl was applied from the eyebrow to the base of the nose. In the Middle Kingdom, the use of green kohl was continued on the eyebrow, and stopped at the corners of the eyes. However, by the New Kingdom, the fashion was for black kohl. At other times, the heavy line of kohl was reduced to a very fine line.

Habia
Different types of kohl application

The application to kohl to the upper and lower lids was multi-functional. While it was used to enhance the attractive almond shape of the eye, it was also used as a salve for eye infections and in-growing eyelashes. In addition, having black around the eyes helped to shield the eyes from the very bright sun – a very early form of sunglasses. It was also thought it would fight off the evil spirits of the 'evil eye', this is a superstition that the way certain people look at you can bring bad luck.

EXTEND YOUR LEARNING

The fashion designer Alexander McQueen had an Egyptian theme for his runway fashion show in autumn 2007. The makeup that was used on the models was created by the cosmetic company MAC. The look was inspired by that worn by the actress Elizabeth Taylor, who played the title role in the 1963 film *Cleopatra*.

Research the Alexander McQueen collection and MAC makeup range. Find out if other fashion designers may have been inspired by the same era.

EXTEND YOUR LEARNING

L'Oréal and chemists from the Louvre Museum have conducted major research into the cosmetics that were used by Ancient Egyptians 2000–1200 years before our era. Investigate their findings, which can be found on the L'Oréal website at **www.loreal.co.uk**

Bettman/Corbis
Francois Guillot/Getty

Elizabeth Taylor in the title role in the film Cleopatra, *the inspiration for Alexander McQueen's autumn 2007 collection*

ACTIVITY

Look through fashion magazines and on the Internet. Find a range of clothes that have an Egyptian theme. Work in a team and create a collage with the images. Present the collage to others in your group or perhaps have an art exhibition.

Top tip

You can use fabrics, jewel stones, beads and ribbons to create a 3D aspect to the collage.

Skin care

The average lifespan of those who lived in Ancient Egypt was expected to be 40 years – only half the lifespan we would expect today in the UK. Yet, the Egyptians were still concerned with the premature ageing of their skin. Evidence

EXTEND YOUR LEARNING

The art of Egyptian perfume making was far in advance of any other ancient civilisation at that time – and many of the methods are similar to the methods that are used today. Investigate how the perfumes were made and compare that to how they are made today.

ACTIVITY

The perfume made by ancient Egyptians was stored in beautiful bottles. Some were richly decorated as being functional.

Design a perfume bottle that would be functional and attractive.

has been found of creams that would have been used to combat wrinkles and protect the skin from the sun and hot, dry winds.

Perfume

The Egyptians were experts at perfume making. Egyptian perfume was famous throughout the Mediterranean. The perfumes were made from plants, flowers, roots and spices. The ingredients were cooked or mixed with oils to make liquids, or mixed with animal fats to make a solid perfume. Sometimes people wore little cones in their hair which were blocks of solid perfume. The perfumes would gradually melt in the heat releasing perfumed oils onto the face and neck.

Perfumes were important in Ancient Egypt and were not only used to provide fragrance for the skin and body. Because oils and fats were utilised to make the perfume, some mixtures were also used for healing purposes, as they had properties which soothed and cooled the skin. Perfume was also significant in the burial process. It was thought that if bodies were perfumed during mummification, then the good smell would keep evil spirits away.

The oils used in perfumes included olive, sesame and almond. The Ancient Egyptians also imported perfume ingredients such **frankincense** and **myrrh** from East Africa, although such expensive fragrances would only be used by the very rich.

Perfumes were stored in a variety of stone and glass containers, the most beautiful were made from **alabaster** and the containers were decorated with jewels.

Hair removal

It was not uncommon for the people of Ancient Egypt to remove their body hair. This was done using a method that is similar to the wax hair removal methods of today. To create the wax a mixture of crushed bird bones, oil and sycamore juice and gum were heated, applied to the skin, allowed to harden and then pulled off – removing the hair. Tweezers were also used to remove hair.

Ancient Egyptian tweezers

Courtesy of the Pitt Rivers Museum, Oxford

Nails in Ancient Egypt

The status of a person in Ancient Egypt could be indicated by the condition of their hands, feet and nails. Farmers and slaves who carried out manual and physical labour would not have nails, feet and hands in good condition. However, wealthy people, kings, queens and high ranking officials had the time and opportunity to care for and enhance the appearance of their hands, feet and nails.

Henna was used to dye the finger and toenails in colours of terracotta, orange and yellow. The colours worn would provide an indication of their status. Only queens were allowed to wear very dark colours. The henna would be mixed to a thick paste with an acidic liquid and carefully applied to the finger and toenails. The henna would not only colour the nails, but condition them as well. One advantage of hennaed nails is that the colour does not chip off – it has to grow out.

Henna was also used to provide temporary tattoos. This practice was carried out in ancient Egypt with evidence found on the preserved skin on the arms and thighs of mummies

Cleopatra

© shutterstock.com/Bill McKelvie

Spas in Ancient Egypt

Have you ever visited a spa? A spa treatment today is a relaxing, water-based treatment that is used to enhance a feeling of health and well-being. The word spa comes from the latin *sanitas per aquas*, which means healing by water. The question is – were spas or spa treatments used in Ancient Egypt?

Although we don't know for sure, there is a legend that says that Cleopatra, who was considered to be one of the most beautiful women in Egypt, believed in the healing powers of the Dead Sea. Today we know that sea water is beneficial for a range of skin conditions that includes psoriasis.

It's a fact!

The symptom of psoriasis is excessive scaling on the surface of the skin. Normally, skin cells take around 3–4 weeks from being produced to reaching the top most layers. However psoriasis occurs when the skin cells are produced more quickly. In this case, the cells reach the topmost layers within only two weeks, which then results in excessive cells on the skin's surface.

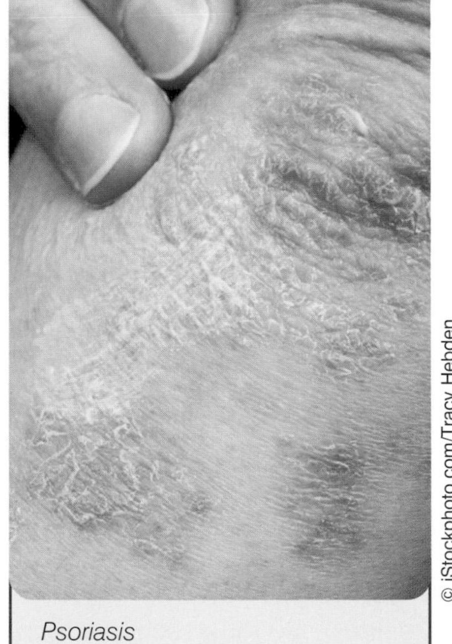

Psoriasis

© iStockphoto.com/Tracy Hebden

So, while we do not know if spa treatments were used, we do know that the people of Ancient Egypt liked to be clean and enjoyed bathing. We also know that priests were probably the cleanest as they had to bathe at least three times each day while in the temple. There is evidence that wealthy people had bathrooms in

It's a fact!

The people of Ancient Egypt used soap. This was made from a scented clay or ash paste which could be lathered and was used for treating skin diseases as well as for cleansing.

Hairstyle by Simon Houston, Salon: Simon Houston hairdressing. Location: Ballymena, Co. Antrim. Photographer: David Golcman

Contemporary hairstyle influenced by the look of Ancient Egypt

their houses that would consist of a shallow stone tub in which they would stand or sit while slaves poured water over them.

However, poor people had to bathe in canals or rivers, such as the Nile. The Nile was not a clean river. It was used to wash clothes and even had sewage poured into it. Therefore, while the poor people bathed, they probably also caught infectious diseases.

African type hair in Ancient Egypt

There is much debate about the presence of people in Ancient Egypt with African type hair. This type of hair is generally very tightly curled, often frizzy and normally dark.

Egypt is an African country, so you might expect that the citizens of Ancient Egypt would have had very tightly curled or frizzy hair. In 1977 a study was

Bring your learning to life      

Working in a team, use your study of hair and beauty in Ancient Egypt and, if necessary, carry out some more research. Then, create a fashion or celebrity magazine set in the time of Ancient Egypt. You can base the format of the magazine on any that you see and buy today.

To create the magazine, you may need to appoint job roles to people in your group, such as editor, fashion editor, researcher, writer or publisher.

The magazine could include:

- what to wear and what not to wear in hot climates
- Ancient Egyptian fashion disasters
- tips on makeup application
- hairstyling techniques
- which wig suits your face shape
- how to colour your hair with henna
- celebrity gossip – who's dating who in Ancient Egypt
- before and after makeover for busy scribes
- horoscope
- problem page

Remember you must use the fashions, names, events and daily life that were typical of those in Ancient Egypt. When you have finished your magazine, ask others to read it. Find out what they enjoyed and what could be improved for a second edition.

carried out by Titlbachova and Titlbach who looked at the hair of mummies kept in Czechoslovakian collections. The hair samples they found matched hair types that would be found today in modern Europe, that is, hair that was naturally straight, wavy or gently curled. It is interesting to note that the researchers found only a minority of hair had the structural characteristics of African type hair.

Contemporary hairstyle influenced by the look of Ancient Egypt

Around the ancient worlds of hair and beauty

Background

How much we know about people and the importance of hair and beauty in ancient civilisations depends very much how well everyday life was recorded. The Egyptians were very good at recording events in their society. Because of this we also know about life in other parts of Africa. Likewise there is a great deal of written and pictorial evidence about the early civilisations of European countries such as Greece and Rome.

Other early Asian civilisations, for example in India, also have writings and other evidence of everyday life. However the recorded history of Japan did not start until around the seventh century as a written language did not appear until the fifth or sixth century.

Bring your learning to life

This project and be carried out in small groups and involve your whole class. Each group should choose one of the ancient civilisations from the 'Hair and beauty in the ancient world' timeline.

Carry out some more research for the ancient civilisation of your choice. Once your group has finished the research, complete the tasks outlined below.

You may want to divide the tasks. If you do this then you will need to determine roles and responsibilities for the people in your group.

- Create a mood board with images of the civilisation of your choice
- Use head blocks and design and create at least two hairstyles worn in any of the periods of time within the timeline
- Use makeup on the face of the head blocks in the way that it was worn at that time
- Produce a hair and beauty careers booklet for someone who would like to work in the ancient civilisation you have chosen. Each member of the group should write a short, descriptive report about working in the ancient world as a hairdresser, barber, therapist or nail technician. Describe the job role and the tasks and skills that would be carried out. Combine the reports into one booklet.

When all the mood boards, head blocks and careers leaflets are completed, arrange a display where other people can see your work.

Hair and beauty fashions in the ancient worlds

ACTIVITY

ANCIENT GREECE

- Plays that were written and performed, in Ancient Greece were known as comedy, tragedy and satoe. **Research** the definitions of these three areas and the subjects that would be written about and performed.
- The plays were performed in huge amphitheatres built to hold tens of thousands of people. Mathematics played a great role in the construction of these theatres. **Research** the designs of the amphitheatres and investigate how sound would be carried in the open spaces
- **Create** a hairstyle inspired by those of Ancient Greece

ACTIVITY

ANCIENT ROME

- **Design** and **make** a wreath that could be worn in a roman inspired hairstyle
- The emperor Hadrian was responsible for the building of a very large wall in Britain. **Investigate** why Hadrian built the wall
- Men in Ancient Rome loved the atmosphere of the barbershop and spent many hours being shaved, groomed, manicured and massaged. **Research** the barber Ticinius Mena who came to Rome from Sicily in 296BC and introduced shaving
- **Look at www.romanbaths.co.uk** to see what a Roman spa looked like
- **Visit** the Roman Baths in the centre of Bath in Somerset
- **Create** a hairstyle inspired by those of Ancient Rome

ANCIENT GREECE

Men wore their hair short or even shaved their heads. And, unless they were soldiers they grew beards.

1

Between 323BC and 146BC, during the Hellenistic period, the fashion for beards disappeared when Alexander the Great, introduced the fashion of being clean shaven.

2

Female slaves wore their hair short, but free women wore long hair that was curled and braided before being tied back or made into a bun.

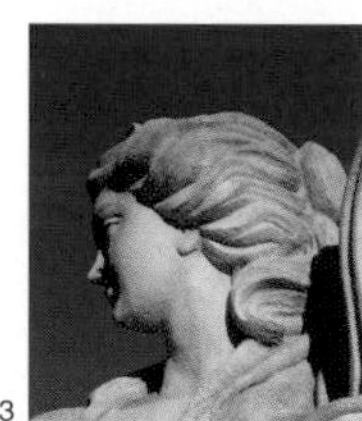

3

Hair was decorated with ribbons, head bands and wreaths made from laurel or bay leaves, flowers or precious stones.

12

13

Pale skin was a sign of beauty, so those who could afford to stayed out of the sun to prevent their skin darkening. White lead based powder, which was poisonous, would be used by some to create a pale looking skin. Others used chalk.

The eyebrows were covered with dark paint so that they appeared to be joined together to create '*unibrows*'

ANCIENT ROME

Young single girls wore simple hairstyles, such as a bun on the top of the head.

4

Fashionable ladies would have hair piled very high with ringlets or tendrils surrounding their face.

5

When Julius Caesar came to power in 49BC men liked to be clean shaven. This fashion lasted until Hadrian became emperor in 117AD when it became fashionable for men to wear a beard

During the Flavian period from 69AD, a style known as a *tutulus* was fashionable.

14

Spas were first used by Roman soldiers from 27BC–19AD.

15

Women created pale skin by applying white lead based powders. Lips were coloured red with red plant dye or red ochre. A yellow eye colour was made from saffron, which is an expensive spice.

16

NCIENT INDIA

During the Kushan Period, 30BC to 185AD, women usually wore their hair long in one or two plaits, or the hair was rolled with fabric and pinned up.

6

Another Kushan hairstyle was to coil braided hair over the front of the head.

7

uring the Gupta Era, 320–550, hair was left ong and curly, or elaborately styled, curled nto ringlets or worn in a bun at the nape of he neck, on the top of the head or the side of he head. The bun could be very simple or olded into a figure of eight.

8

17

The wearing of a bindi on the forehead was used in ancient India.

he art of mehndi began around the 12th century. This is the pplication of henna to the hands, feet and nails to stain the hands, eet and nails, leaving beautiful, intricate designs.

18

ANCIENT JAPAN

During the Kofun period, 250–538, almost everyone wore their hair up in a bun.

9

During the Heian period, 794–1185, hair was left loose and grown very long.

From 1568 to 1603, the Momoyama period, the fashion was to tie the hair up using a long, thin hair pin to wrap the long hair around.

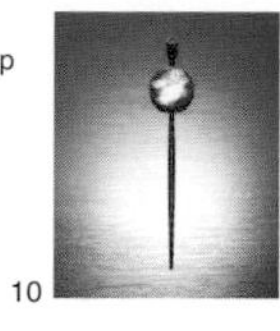

10

11

During the Edo period of 1600–1868, hairstyles and hair ornamentation became the most spectacular.

From the twelfth to the nineteenth century, military noblemen known as Samurai shaved their hair at the top of the head and then gathered the hair remaining at the back and the sides into a plait (or *queue*)

19

20

Geishas wore hairstyles known as *taka shimada, tsubushi shimada, uiwata* and the *momoware* which is also known as *ofuku.*

Traditional geisha makeup was, and still is, a white face, red lips and black lined eyes.

21

ANCIENT INDIA

- **Create** a design for mehndi for the feet and hands
- There was and still is a strong tradition of class division in India. Investigate the complexity of the caste system then form two teams and **debate** this question 'Class divisions provide a sense of belonging'
- It is still traditional for Indian brides to have a mehndi application. **Investigate** how this is carried out today. **Create** a mood board with different designs that are used at weddings
- Married Hindu women wear a bindi which is placed between the eyebrows. The place for the bindi is related to yoga philosophy. **Investigate** this philosophy and **investigate** the seven spiritual energy centres in the spine
- **Create** a hairstyle inspired by those of Ancient India

ACTIVITY

ANCIENT JAPAN

- **Investigate** the steps that are used for the entire geisha makeup application
- Use stage paint to **create** a geisha look
- **Create** a geisha hair style
- A rite of passage in ancient Japan for young boys between the ages of 10 and 16 in a ceremony known as genpuku or kakan. Carry out some **research** and find out how the hair would look
- **Find out** about other rites of passage in your own and other cultures

6,8 www.4to40.com
7,11,17,18,20 Wikipedia Commons
9 Image Provided Courtesy of Maiko Kawase, San Jose State University
10 fotosearch.com/AsiaStock
19 iStockphoto.com/nicoolay
21 iStockphoto.com/© Nuno Silva

Top tip You can learn more about the different ancient civilisations at **http:/www.show.me.uk/topicpage/Ancient-Civilisations.html** or the interactive website of the British Museum **http:/www.ancientcivilizations.co.uk/home_set.html**

We can tell what people looked like and the fashions for hair and beauty from statues, paintings and coins. Studying the ancient history of hair and beauty can tell us a great deal about the culture, society and even the politics of times long ago.

The hair and beauty history of Britain

Britain has a population that is made up of a mix of people from different civilisations, races and cultures. This is because, unlike other countries of the world, Britain has never been truly isolated. Over the centuries our lands have been invaded and populated by people of many different backgrounds. The mix of people that have lived, and continue to live, in this country has a direct effect on fashion, hair and beauty.

The Roman baths, Bath

In Britain there is no one single hair type or skin colour. There is a wonderful mixture of hair types from very curly to very straight and skin colours that range from very dark to very pale. You will discover more about this when you read Chapter 4, The Science of Hair and Beauty.

Because of the mixed races and cultures, those who work in the hair and beauty sector have to be very versatile and able to work on a wide range of different clients. Perhaps this is why British hair and beauty is said to be the best in the world.

By following the timeline of hair and beauty in ancient Britain you will be able to see that some of the trends for hair and beauty can be traced back to a particular time in our own history.

Bring your learning to life     

This piece of work can be a whole class project, carried out in small groups. Each group in the class should choose a period of time from the 'Hair and beauty of Britain' timeline on the next page.

You will need to carry out some more research for the era of your choice. Once you have completed your research work, make a plan for the tasks below and outline the roles and responsibilities for the people in your group.

- Create a mood board with images of the era of your choice
- Work in pairs to recreate a hairstyle and makeup from the era of your choice, using each other as models – you could even dress in clothes that represent the same era of time to provide a *total look*
- Photograph the results and bring together all the images together into a *style file.* The style file should be a collection of images, placed in a folder, which would be left in the reception area of a hair or beauty salon from the era you have investigated. The style file would be used by clients visiting the salon to help them choose a new look.

Social identity

Social identity is about being part of a group that has *shared* values. It is about how people place themselves into categories. For example you might share the same interests as your friends because you support the same football team or like the same music. Social identity is also about how people connect and relate with certain groups. For example you may have a certain group of friends that you see every day at school or college, and while you might socialise with others, it is with your own group of friends that you share the most values.

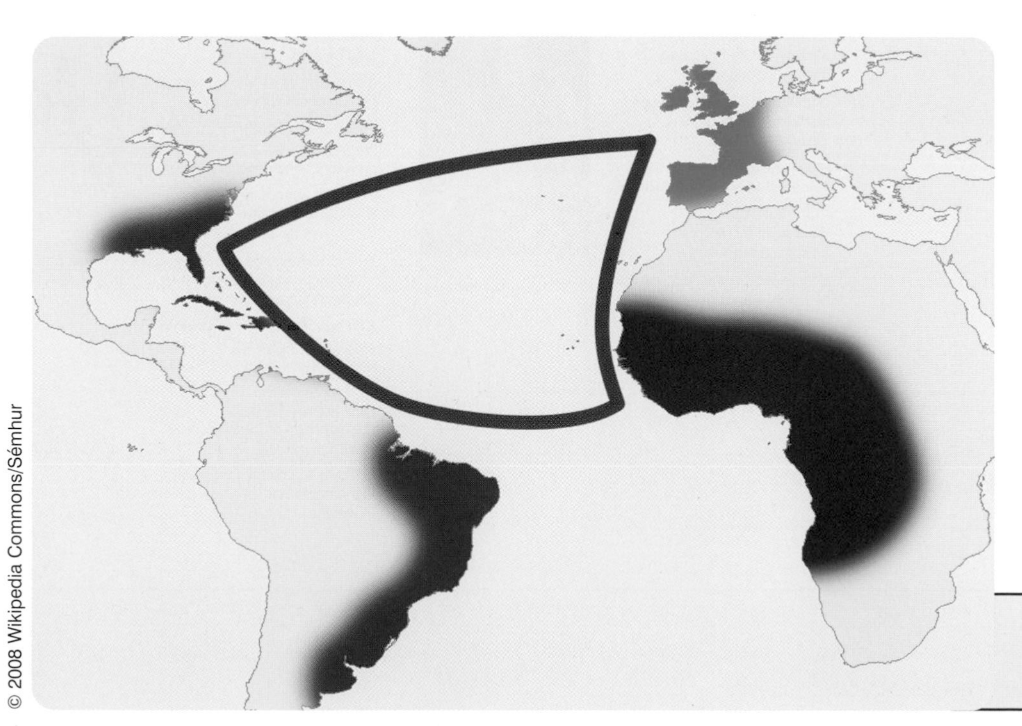

Map showing the route of the slave ships (see p.24)

History of Britain hair and beauty timeline

ACTIVITY 

MEDIEVAL 100–1400

- **Compare** the hairstyle of Carrie Fisher in the first Star Wars film with that of medieval hairstyles
- **Investigate** the barber organization known as the 'Worshipful Company of Barbers'
- Perfume was carried in pomanders. **Research** how they were used and what they looked like.
- Use a head block to **create** a medieval themed hairstyle
- **Create** a mood board which illustrates the fashions for clothes, makeup and hairstyles from this period of time

ACTIVITY 

RENAISSANCE 1400–1700

- **Explore** the hairstyles of Queen Elizabeth I
- **Research** different type of ruffs, how they were made–and how they grew in size! Use some fabric and **make** a ruff
- Research the ill-effects of the lead-based makeup
- Use a head block to **create** an Elizabethan themed hairstyle
- **Create** a mood board which illustrates the fashions for clothes, makeup and hairstyles from this period of time

ACTIVITY 

1700s

- **Investigate** which profession wears wigs based on those worn in the 1700s
- **Investigate** the source of cochineal
- Use a head block to **create** a 1700s' themed hairstyle
- **Create** a mood board which illustrates the fashions for clothes, makeup and hairstyles from this period of time

1,2,3,4 Wikipedia Commons

100 1500 1700 1800

Medieval 100–1400

Privileged women wore long hair, servants had their heads shaved or wore their hair short.

Short hair was directly related to religion.

Nuns wore their hair very short and hid what remained under a headdress called a wimple.

A fashionable hairstyle was to twist the hair to create buns on either side of the head.

High foreheads were an attractive feature. Women would shave or pluck out their hair at the forehead and remove their eyebrows to create a smooth and very high highline

Pale skin was a sign of wealth and beauty so women began to use white lead-based makeup.

1

Renaissance 1400–1700

Women's hair was worn long and straight, with a centre parting, but often covered by a hood or headdress.

High foreheads can be seen by the hairstyles of Queen Elizabeth I.

High ranking men wore their hair short to suit the fashion of wearing a ruff.

Wigs worn by men were loosely curled.

Beards were made fashionable by Henry VIII.

The makeup fashion was for pale skin, red lips and cheeks.

2

1700s

Wigs were very popular for men and women. Those for women included miniature constructions such as boats and even gardens.

Men's wigs were tightly curled or alternatively, the hair of the wig was gathered together in a pony tail at the nape of the neck, tied with a bow and powdered.

Black patches were placed on the face of men and women to cover scars or worn as an adornment.

Skin was pale white, cheeks coloured with carmine, which is a red colour extracted from cochineal.

Men and women tweezed their eyebrows to leave a thin, arched line which was coloured in black.

3

1800s

Hair styled into loose buns at the nape of the neck. Known as a psyche knot.

Men's hairstyles were neat and held in place with oils.

Men's beards and moustaches were grown, cut and shaped into a variety of different styles.

Hair was worn in ringlets and was depicted by the heroines in the novels by Jane Austin.

Women's hair was kept very neat by plaiting and wrapping the lengths into coils.

Soft pre-Raphaelite curls were created by wrapping hair in rags and left loose for a very romantic look.

New fashion for waves following the invention of the Marcel wave.

To have a pale face was still fashionable and seen as a sign of wealth.

1900

1920

5

Flapper fashion bobs in the 1920s. Lips were painted into red 'cupid bows'.

1930

6

1940

7

From clean lines to curls – Hollywood inspired looks in the 1940s.

1950

8

Makeup in the 1950s became softer with the introduction of pink, frosted lipsticks and nail varnish.

In the 1950s the beehive was created with a great deal of backcombing.

1960

9

1960s' geometry and unisex hairstyles created by Vidal Sassoon reflected the fashions by icons such as Mary Quant.

1960s: eyes were emphasised with long false black eyelashes, black mascaras and eyeliner. Lips were very pale in colour – sometimes white.

1970

10

1970s: punk was a statement of social revolution.

1970s: disco makeup was the trend and makeup for multi-racial skin tones became available.

1980

11

1980s: Afro and 'big' hair reflecting social attitudes.

Trevor Sorbie created the chops and the wedge in the 1980s.

1980s' makeup was bold with bronzed faces, bold blushers, bright eye shadows and strong lips.

1990

12

2000

13

Straight hair of the 1990s inspired by TV and film stars.

2000

ACTIVITY

1800s

- **Investigate** the origins of the psyche knot
- **Investigate** the life of Monsieur Marcel Grateau, the inventor of the Marcel wave
- **Research** the different fashions for beards and moustaches in the 1800s
- **Investigate** how wealthy Victorian women kept their skin pale
- Use a head block to **create** an 1800s' themed hairstyle
- **Create** a mood board which illustrates the fashions for clothes, makeup and hairstyles from this period of time

ACTIVITY

1900s

- Between 1900 and 2000 the fashion for skin colour changed from pale to tanned. Some people with naturally dark skin used products to make the skin paler. Form into two groups and **discuss** 'You should not try to change the natural colour of your skin'
- **Investigate** the influence of Coco Chanel on the fashion for tanned skin and **discuss** why tanned skin was a sign of wealth in the 1960s
- **Compare** the hairstyles of Amy Wine-house with those of the 1950s
- **Research** the film *Saturday Night Fever* to see the fashions for hair and makeup. **Organise** a 1970s disco inspired event
- **Research** and **discuss** why hair was 'big' in the 1980s
- **Investigate** the influence of the TV and film stars Meg Ryan and Jennifer Aniston on hair styles
- **Research** the work of Mary Quant. Discuss how the fashions are copied today
- Use a head block to **create** a hairstyle from a time between 1900–2000
- **Create** a mood board which illustrates the fashions for clothes, makeup and hairstyles from this period of time

EXTEND YOUR LEARNING

The slave trade, which many countries all over the world were involved in, including Britain, is an important piece of world history. There is a great deal on information about the events of the slave trade. Use you research skills to investigate it.

Black identity

For people of African descent there is a direct link between social identity and **black identity**. As a result of the transatlantic slave trade, which continued from the sixteenth to the nineteenth century, millions of black people were taken from their home lands, many from the west African coast, to other countries where they were forced work as slaves. Slaves lost their social identity through being removed from everything they related to. They lost their homes, their families and, often, even their real names.

Black identity in Britain

At the end of the nineteenth century there were relatively few people of black African descent in Britain. Those who had settled here were former slaves or their families. Between 1914 and 1918 citizens of African Commonwealth countries fought for Britain and many of those who were wounded stayed here after the First World War. Then, in 1946, a ship named Empire Windrush brought 492 men – the first of many – from the Caribbean to help rebuild Britain after the Second World War. This was the real start of an increase in the British population that had African type hair and darker skin colours.

Empire Windrush

It's a fact! Assimilated is the process of a minority group adopting the customs and attitudes of the existing culture. In this case, many people of African descent were trying to fit into a population of European descent.

In the early days of resettlement into Britain those people with African type hair tried to become *assimilated* into Britain because they wanted to fit in.

These immigrants had to get used to a different culture and the idea of what was considered to be 'beautiful'. One way they tried to fit in was to make their hair appear more 'white'. That is, they tried to style their hair in the same way that those with straighter Caucasian hair styled theirs. At the beginning of the twentieth century this was quite a difficult thing to do. The products we have today for African type hair were not available, nor was the technology. But, hair was straightened with chemicals, pressed with **hot combs**, ironed, **set** and **wrapped** in all manner of ways to achieve the hairstyles they wanted (or felt forced) to wear.

It was during the 1960s that there were changes in attitude and black identity was established. People with African ancestry wanted to relate to it and be proud of it. Instead of trying to fit into the European standards of beauty and imitating it, African ancestral beauty was promoted. One way of doing this was through hair styles. Instead of flattening and straightening their hair, its natural characteristics were used and the hair was dried by blowing it out from the head into what became known as an '**Afro**' hairstyle. This type of hairstyle was worn with pride and showed the world that 'Black is Beautiful'.

By the 1980s the fashion for the Afro had declined, but in its place came other hair styles that were directly related to the hairdressing practices and hair styles of traditional West Africa. Those with African type hair began to style their hair in **cornrows**, **plaits**, **locks** and by creating **patterns** and **fades** in short hair. This style in hairdressing has caught the imagination of those without African type hair – and the styles have become fashionable in their own right. Therefore, the trend for traditional West African styling today is as much about fashion as it is about black identity.

African type hair styled

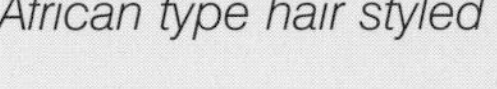

It's a fact!

It is very difficult to achieve some hair styles on African type hair because it is very curly. At the same time there are hair styles that cannot be achieved on straight hair, but which are easy to achieve on African type hair.

Braiding on African type hair

Black identity has been created to ensure those who choose to can celebrate their traditions. West African influenced hairstyles have become a fashion statement and people who do not have African ancestry or African type hair also like to wear them.

ACTIVITY

Research hair styles that are created using the cutting techniques to make 2D and 3D patterns in hair.

ACTIVITY

Research the different hair styles that can be created using cornrows, plaits and locks.

Subculture and identity

By studying the history of hair and beauty you can see how, in every civilisation, the way people looked provided a clue about who they were. The way people wore their hair and makeup gave them an identity. Sometimes the identity was chosen by them – they wanted to look like a nobleman or woman, or they may have chosen to live a religious life. At other times, identify was forced upon them because of circumstance – they were born to be a king or queen. Some were poor or were slaves and, because of this, the way they wore their hair, used makeup, hennaed their fingernails or wore a beard was dictated to them by others.

We can, by looking at some examples in recent British history, see how hair and beauty have formed the identity of a range of **subcultures**.

EXTEND YOUR LEARNING   

There has been a recent example of a girl with hair styled in cornrows being suspended from school until the plaits were removed. The suspended girl was white, with straight Caucasian hair. The parents of the suspended girl complained that in the same school, girls with African type hair were allowed to wear their hair in cornrows. The head teacher said this was acceptable as cornrows were part of their cultural heritage.

Debate the decision of the head teacher to have different standards in relation to the way hair is worn, based on hair type and race.

Manchester Evening News January 2007

It's a fact! The definition of subculture is where members of a group have *'certain norms, attitudes and values which are distinctive to them as a social group'.*

Source Sociology Themes and Perspectives

Subculture in Britain

Common interests in fashion and/or music, the way the hair is worn or makeup applied can create groups of people that have the same **norms**. This means a standard pattern of behaviour, attitudes and values that is considered to be normal.

In the recent history of Britain you can see examples of subcultures such as the following:

- Teddy boys 1950s
- Mods and Rockers 1960s
- Punks 1970s
- Goths 1980s

In each of these cases, it is the clothes, music and appearance that provide the subcultural group with its identity, and in addition a wish to be seen as different to others.

However there is one aspect of appearance which has been consistently used by all subcultures since the 1950s and that is hairstyle – or specifically the *length* of the hair. Long, short, cropped, shaved, coloured or natural – those on opposing sides of the look for hair were generally part of opposite subcultures.

Teddy boys

Teddy boys were so named because they liked to wear clothes that were inspired by the Edwardian period. The media of the time then shortened 'Edwardian' to 'Teddy' – and the Teddy boys (and girls) were born and became Britain's first 'teenagers'. The development of this subculture was quite shocking at the time. Their appearance was totally different to the men who, less than ten years before had been fighting one of the worst wars in history. As with any group of young people, the press picked up on any problems and those that were involved in fighting generally made the front page.

Teddy boys

The jackets worn by Teddy boys were long, with velvet collars and cuffs, and called 'drapes' due to the way they hung loosely from the shoulders in a long straight line that was not tailored. The loose, long jacket was worn with very tight and straight legged jeans called 'drainpipes'. They would wear a smart shirt and a very thin tie which was known as the 'Slim Jim' or 'bootlace'. Brocade waistcoats were also worn. The socks were bright and the shoes, suede with crepe soles, known as 'brothel creepers'.

The typical hairstyle was a large, greased **quiff** at the front of the head and what became known as a DA (ducks arse) at the nape. It was important for the hairstyle to be neat, so stainless steel combs were always at the ready.

The music linked to Teddy boys was rock and roll. Rock and roll was also enjoyed by Rockers in the 1960s.

EXTEND YOUR LEARNING

Investigate the fashions hairstyles and makeup for Teddy girls. Design a contemporary look based on the Teddy girl theme.

Mods and Rockers

Mods and Rockers were two subcultures formed in the 1960s that had totally different values and interests. They did not like the same music, clothes or hairstyles. They did not even like the same form of transport.

Mods were smartly dressed and had a 'good boy' image, wheras rockers wore motor biking clothes, and held the 'bad boy' image. You can see there was the every reason for major clashes …

The hairstyles of the rockers were similar to those worn by Teddy Boys, but not so groomed. Hair was often quiffed and greased, using 'Brylcreem', one of the top selling hair products of the 1960s. But in many cases, the hair was long and untidy which added to the bad boy, working class image. Rockers wore Levi jeans and heavy, black leather jackets, which were in fact a very sensible choice of clothing given that they rode motorbikes. The jackets were often decorated with studs spelling out where they came from or the name of their motorbike club.

Rocker

It's a fact!

Androgynous means having the characteristics of both sexes.

ACTIVITY

The Motown label in America was one of the largest recording companies of the 1960s. They captured a sound that is still popular today. Investigate the record label and, if you can, listen to some of the music that was produced at that time.

It's a fact! It was the 1979 film *Quadrophenia*, based on The Who's rock opera of the same name, which romanticised the Mod subculture.

Getty/Popperfoto

Mod boys with mirrored scooters

It's a fact! Anarchy means a state of lawlessness and disorder

Rockers liked rock and roll music as recorded by artists such as Elvis Presley and Eddie Cochran and they rode BSA, Triumph or Norton motorbikes.

The hairstyles worn by male Mods were neat, stylish and geometrically cut, although longer than those worn by other males of the time. Men at this time began to have their hair cut by hairdressers, rather than barbers, so many of the hairdressing techniques used for women's hair were used for cutting and styling the hair of Mod males. This resulted in hairstyles for Mod men and Mod women looking very similar, and the term **unisex** was used to describe the resulting **androgynous** look.

Mods liked the American soul music often recorded by artists on the Motown label and British groups such as The Small Faces, The Pretty Things and The Who.

Mods wore designer Italian suits with thin lapels and shiny pointed-toe shoes. They paid great attention to detail – such as the length of the vents in the back of the suit, or the fit of the Ben Sherman shirt. Parka jackets with fur trimmed hoods were also popular. These olive green, fish tailed coats were first worn by the American Army in 1951.

Mod girls were also fussy about their appearance. Their hairstyles were short and styled in a similar way to the boys. They also wore button-down collared shirts with suits and straight skirts. Some wore the *Carnaby Street*, London-led fashion designed by iconic fashion designers such as Mary Quant. Mini skirts and dresses with geometric designs – sometimes made of PVC – were fashionable then.

While Rockers were riding British made motorbikes, Mods were riding Italian motor scooters such as Vespa and Lambretta. The scooters were often decorated with lots of mirrors and chrome spotlights.

It was predictable that with such differences some groups of Mods and Rockers fought. The most famous clash was on Brighton Beach in 1964 when 3000 youths went to Brighton one Whitson weekend (now the Spring Bank Holiday). They caused chaos, using deck chairs and pebbles from the beach as weapons. This of course made front page news and gave Mods and Rockers a media image that was not true for the vast majority of young people. Most of them only wanted to listen to their music and wear their clothes to show that they belonged to their chosen subculture.

Punks

During the 1970s there was a movement which went against all that the Mods had stood for. This movement, which was deeply rooted in music culture, was about *anti-fashion*.

One of the first punk bands was led by Johnny Rotten and was called The Sex Pistols. His music contained political and anti-government lyrics. Their manager, Malcolm McLaren, owned a shop called Sex which specialised in what was considered to be outrageous clothing. The music and the look of punks was a statement of chaos and anarchy.

For mainstream Punks, the fashion for hair, for males and females, was brightly coloured and spiked. The spikes were arranged in various ways: a **Mohawk** where the hair stood vertically from the scalp in a fanned, narrow strip from the

© iStockphoto.com/Jerry Koch

Mohawk hairstyle

© iStockphoto.com/Scott Griessel

Punk hairstyle

ACTIVITY    

Investigate some of the designs created by Vivienne Westwood and design an outfit that is inspired by the same look.

EXTEND YOUR LEARNING  

The punk movement became very big, and within the subculture were other *subgenres* that all stemmed from early Punk days. Research the different movements, what they wore and how they looked.

© iStockphoto.com/Anna Yu

Punk with facial piercings

front hairline to the nape of the neck, the sides being shaved off completely, or cut very short, alternatively spikes were worn in what were known as **Liberty Spikes**, which was a look inspired by the Statue of Liberty.

Whichever way the spikes were worn, they took time and effort to perfect. The use of very strong styling products and hairsprays assisted in this. However, some were not strong enough and punks often used glue, egg white and gelatine to keep the hair as stiff as possible.

Punk makeup was as rebellious as the hair: bright eye colours, dark liners and strong lines were commonly used to ensure the wearer – male or female – stood out and looked different. Punks did not go for blending in their makeup!

Punk clothing was as outrageous as possible. Fashion designers such as Vivienne Westwood were associated with the punk movement, but clothes were

ACTIVITY  

Discuss the subcultures of the 1950s–1980s. Which do you think still have the most influence on the fashions of today?

Goth hair and makeup

often more DIY than designer. Many fashions were created from charity shop buys. Clothes were deliberately torn and then held back together with safety pins or chains. Tights were worn laddered. Jewellery was made from razor blades, chains and padlocks. Faces, lips, ears and eyebrows were pierced, and as well as studs and rings, chains were also worn. Many of these things seem mainstream now, but were considered to be shocking in the 1970s.

Goths

From the beginning of the 1980s and from within the punk subculture, a new movement was formed: Goths.

Like Punks, various individual groups of Goths developed, each with their own particular style. In general, the fashion for Goths was related to the revival of the Victorian Gothic era – black, morbid and dark.

The look of Goths and the way the media portrayed them was often totally at odds with their values. Although their choice of fashion was often as outrageous, Goths did not want to make political statements like punks. They valued individuality and tolerance for diversity.

Goth hairstyles were mainly defined by the colour – black. However, it was also common to see bright colours such as reds and purples. The look of the hairstyles was often long and feminine, but sometimes resembled the shaved, punk look.

As a general rule Goth makeup was a pale face, with dark lined eyes. Lips were dark and often lined to make a shape much larger than the natural lip line, and of course, black nail polish was almost compulsory.

Goth clothing was anything black and often related to a Dracula look. Some girls wore corsets and long dresses made from crushed velvet; others wore a harder look of bondage style clothing combined with spikes and studs. Men also wore Dracula inspired black and some wore corsets, lace and silk. This was not a sign of cross dressing, but intended to show that they were tolerant of diversity, challenging stereotypical views of what men and women should wear.

Bring your learning to life      

This can be a whole class project. Plan, prepare for and complete a fashion show to showcase 50 years of British subculture. You can use any of the examples from this chapter or you can investigate other subcultures. You will need to create the hairstyles, makeup and clothes for each of your chosen subcultures.

When you complete your research you can use *secondary* sources, such as books in the library or the Internet. But, because this fashion show relates to recent history, you can use *primary* research sources such as talking to people who lived through your chosen period of time, for example, your grandparents, parents or carers.

At the same time as you are gathering research and ideas for your fashion show, you could also find out more information from your grandparents, parents or carers about why they belonged to a particular subculture, what their values were and what it was like for them to be a teenager.

Technology within hair and beauty

The hair and beauty treatments and services carried out today are often based on those that have been practised for hundreds of years. But, with modern technology, hair and beauty treatments are now easier to carry out, safer for the client and much more predictable and reliable.

This section will look at three technological advances that have had a big impact on the hair and beauty sector. They are:

- foundation makeup
- razors
- hair colour

Foundation makeup

Today, makeup applied to the face to even out skin tone – known as foundation – comes in a variety of forms: liquid, cream, medicated, anti-ageing and gel. The makeup is specially designed for different skin types, such as normal, oily and dry. The wide range of colours available means they can be matched to the exact shade of the client's skin, providing a natural, flawless appearance. But it hasn't always been like this.

It is known that cosmetics have been used for over 5000 years by both men and women in almost every civilisation of the world.

Margaret Chute/Getty

Max Factor making up a Hollywood movie star

For centuries, women, and sometimes men, have changed the natural colour of their skin, often because the colour of the skin was directly linked with the social status of the person. Until recent times the main aim was to ensure the face was as pale as possible. For example, those who were of a lower social status and had to work outside would naturally have a darker skin due to the result of tanning in the sunlight. So, some people did all they could either to remain inside, or to protect themselves from the sun. Throughout history there is evidence that pale skin was achieved artificially by the use of white, lead-based, poisonous powders.

White or very pale makeup only went out of fashion in Britain during Victorian times, when the use of makeup in general was frowned upon. The only skin colouring the Victorians allowed themselves was the pinching of the cheeks to make them pink.

At the end of the 1890s (sometimes referred to as the 'naughty nineties'), women began wearing face makeup – foundation for the skin and rouge (what we call blusher today) for the cheeks. Initially, women would buy the makeup in secret and would not admit to wearing it, but by 1909 Selfridges in London sold makeup openly at a cosmetics counter. The fashion for foundation then was still pale: cream or ivory.

The rise of the film industry meant that makeup artists were very much sought after for their skills in making actresses' skin look flawless on the big screens. Originally, the foundation makeup used for movie stars was heavy and it broke up, cracking on the face. A makeup artist of the 1900s, Max Factor, developed a new type of foundation that would give a natural look to the skin. It was known as 'flexible greasepaint'. Movie stars began to wear the makeup off screen as well as on screen, which made ordinary women want to buy makeup so they too could feel like a movie star. In 1920, Max Factor began to sell a foundation makeup range known as 'Society' makeup. He also introduced the idea of 'Colour Harmony' – he identified a range of makeup colours that could be used on women to suit their hair and eye colour.

There was another challenge for the film industry when movies were filmed in colour, instead of black and white. Once again, Max Factor came to the rescue with 'Pancake', a foundation that looked good in colour. And then, another makeup problem in the late 1930s – television. For this, Max Factor developed a product called 'Pan-stick'. Pancake and Pan-stick are still available today.

The development of foundation makeup may have been primarily for the film and television industry and only afterwards for general consumers, but good things have come from what might be seen as vanity.

Much of the technology used for making foundation was subsequently used to develop camouflage makeup. Initially used to help cover the terrible burns and other skin wounds of service men injured in war, it was then made available for those not connected with the armed forces. Camouflage makeup is now used daily by some people to cover a range of skin disorders, such as birth marks, uneven pigmentation and even tattoos – helping to make these people feel better about their appearance.

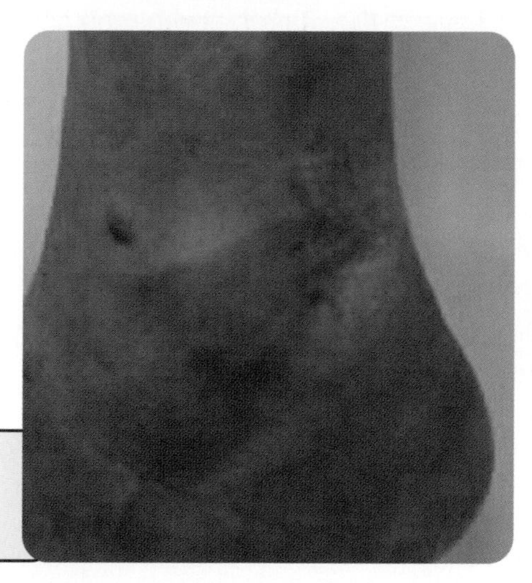

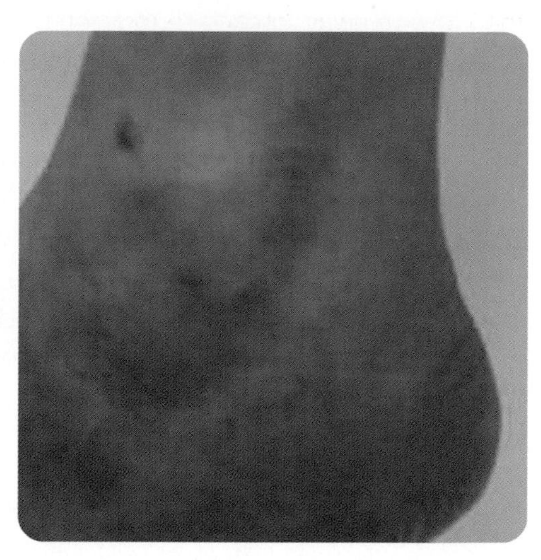

Makeup to camouflage bruising on the ankle

Razors

Have you ever thought about how convenient it is to have a razor that can be used relatively safely and then, when it is not sharp enough to shave comfortably, be thrown away?

It is known that man has shaved, or at least tried to shave, his face since the Stone Age. There are cave paintings which show men clean shaven and evidence has been found of items such as clam shells, which could be used as tweezers, as well as flints that could have been used as an early razor.

During the Bronze Age, man developed the ability to work metal, and razors were made from copper and bronze, and later in the Iron Age, from iron. None of these razors would have been at all comfortable to use.

Early barbers travelled from Greece to Italy around 300BC bringing with them a new type of razor. These were *thin* iron razors that could be sharpened. Then a whole new fashion began for clean shaven faces that lasted for nearly 400 years.

The next real development in razors came from a Frenchman in the 1770s. His name was Jean-Jacques Perret and he designed what was then considered to be a safety razor. The razor blade was held in place by an L-shaped wooden guard.

In the 1800s Michael Faraday invented a new steel making technique known as 'silver steel'. The edge of the blade was made very sharp by a process known as 'hollow grinding'.

The razors, known as straight razors, were sometimes known as 'cut throat' razors. The blade of the razor would have to be re-sharpened at regular intervals, which was very skilled job, and the reason why many men at this time went to the barbers to have a shave instead of doing it themselves.

However, the major technological development did not arrive until the beginning of the 1900s when in 1904 a patent was given to King Camp Gillette, an American who invented the very first 'safety' razor. Gillette's idea was for a safe, sharp razor that would have disposable blades. The blades would only be used once and then thrown away, otherwise they went rusty. Despite the cost of new blades, the razor was a great success and by the end of the First World War they were used by millions of men.

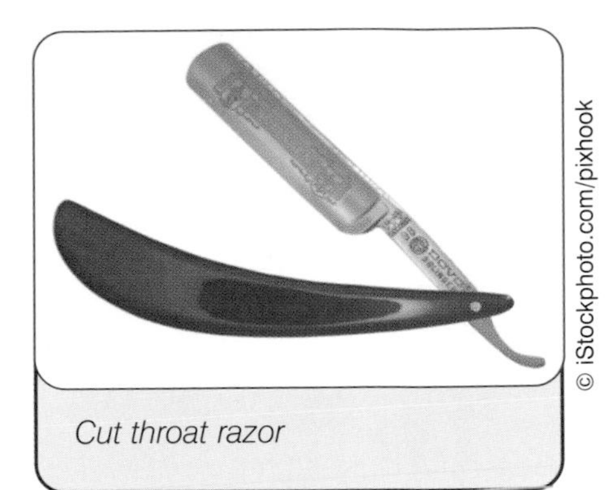

Cut throat razor

It's a fact!

Silver steel is steel that is bright in appearance (hence its name), but its most important property is that it can ground to make a very fine edge.

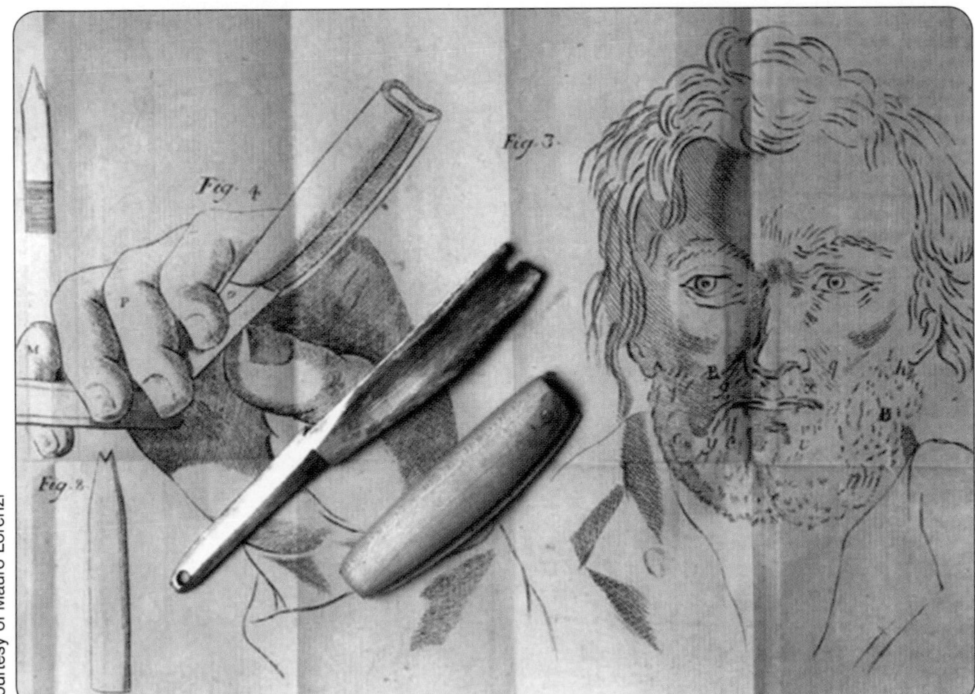

Perret safety razor (and plate from The art of Shaving Oneself)

First Gillette safety razor

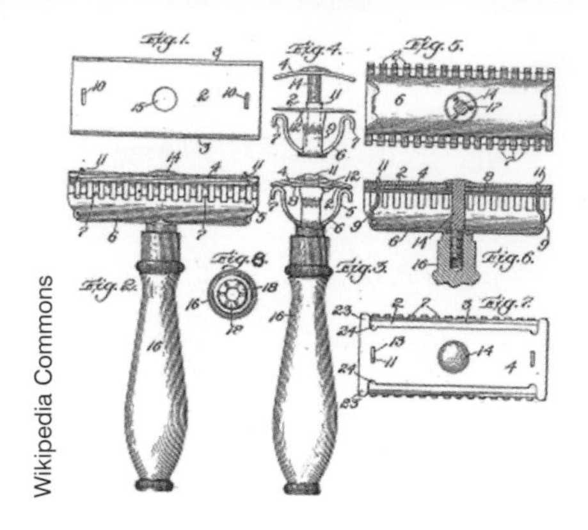

Wikipedia Commons

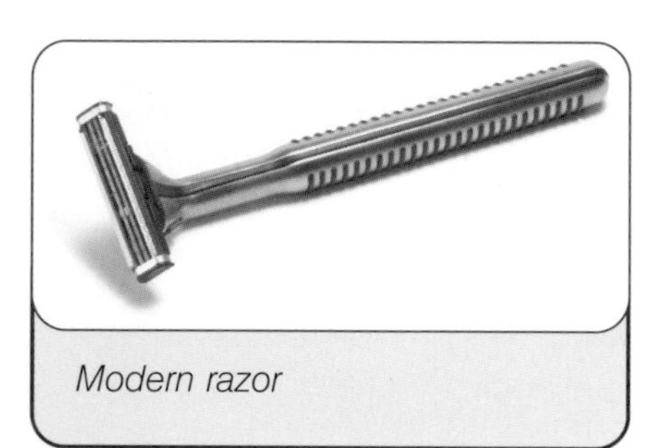

Modern razor

It's a fact! Barbers today still learn the art of shaving. The male grooming business is growing and many men are willing to pay for the experience of a traditional shave with a cut throat razor by an expert.

It's a fact! There are many different types of colour available for the hair: **temporary colour** (lasting for one wash), **semi-permanent colour** (lasting for up to six washes), **quasi colour** and **permanent colour** (colour which grows out).

In the 1960s stainless steel razor blades became available and were made by the company Wilkinson in Sheffield. Because the blades did not rust and could be reused, this was cheaper for the consumer.

From then on, in the last 50 years, the technology for razors has changed very quickly. Razors with two, three and even four blade cartridges became available as well as the true disposable razor – no changing of the blades – the whole thing can just be thrown away.

Hair colour

Have a look around your class or the members of your family and see how many people have colour on their hair. The colour market in hairdressing salons has always been a major part of business, but even more so since the demise of perming in the 1990s and the fashion for straight hair.

Why do you think people colour their hair? One reason is because changing the colour of your hair can actually affect your personality. Have you ever heard of the saying 'Blondes have more fun'? Some people really believe this and feel dull and uninteresting with 'mousey' brown hair. Another reason for colouring hair is to make a statement about your identity. So by colouring your hair, you could make a statement that says 'I am not dull, I am interesting', or 'I am not gentle, I am aggressive'.

One of the most commonly used colours throughout history and is still used today is the vegetable colour henna. The colour pigments of henna can make the hair various shades of auburn, red, copper and gold, depending on the natural colour of the hair. Hair that is very dark will only change to a dark, warm auburn. However fairer hair will become copper or gold. If the hair is naturally white (this means that the hair has no natural pigment in it at all), then an application of henna will turn the hair a very bright orange – a bit like Ronald McDonald!

Henna is also very good for the hair – it has great conditioning properties – and in days when hair conditioners did not exist, henna was an excellent alternative.

However, henna and other vegetable dyes, such as indigo, which was used to make brown and black colours, are not permanent.

It was not until the nineteenth century that artificial colours were developed. Dr August Wilheim von Hofmann identified the dye properties on **para-phenylenediamines (PPD)**.

Following on from this discovery by Dr von Hormann, in 1907 the French chemist Eugene Schuller developed a chemical-based colour that was adapted from the colours that were first used to dye fabrics. The colour was marketed under the brand 'Aureole'. The company he formed was called L'Oréal.

Schuller's technological development meant that all black, brown, red and yellow pigments which form the basis of all the hair colours from the very darkest to the very lightest could be recreated. Schuller also discovered that if you mixed the colour with **hydrogen peroxide** the colours became locked inside the hair shaft, making it permanent. The use of different strength hydrogen peroxide meant that hair could be lightened as well as darkened and the range of colours available meant that the hairdresser could create any colour desired.

This range of colours also meant that there had to be careful control over the production of the colours to ensure that every application provided a predictable result. Therefore, an **International Colour Chart (ICC)** was created. As a result, whichever company manufactured the colours, hairdressers could reliably identify the outcome of the colour application.

Each colour was given a number with 1 being the very darkest – black – and 10 being the very palest – lightest blonde.

Coloured hair

It's a fact!

PPD dyes are the main ingredients in all permanent and quasi permanent hair colours. The PPD is particularly good as the properties of the chemical means that it can enter the hair structure easily enabling the colour mixture to develop. However, PPDs are also linked to allergies, which is why anyone having a colour that contains these chemicals must carry out a skin test to ensure the colour is suitable for them.

Bring your learning to life

Next time you are in the hairdressing salon, ask to look at a colour chart and see how the ICC system works. Try to identify which number your hair colour is.

So, have we moved forward with hair colouring? In the past, vegetable colours were the only option. The vegetable colour range was very limiting, but safe. However, with chemical colours there is a risk of allergic reactions.

EXTEND YOUR LEARNING

Chose a hair or beauty product and investigate the technological advancements that have been made. For example, nail polish, hair spray, relaxing or perming products or skin care products.

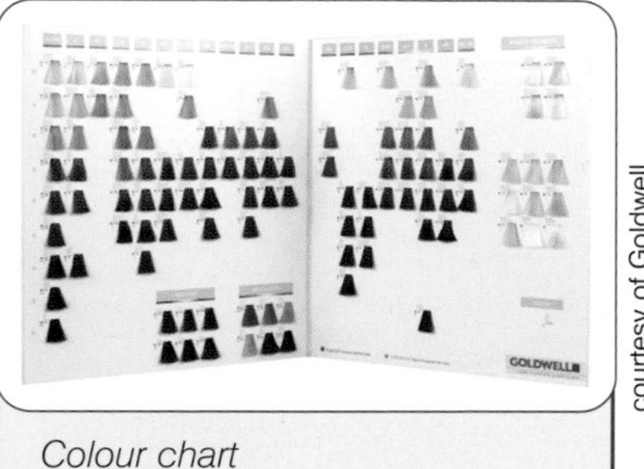

Colour chart

EXTEND YOUR LEARNING

Research the affects of allergic reaction to chemical-based skin colours.

Icons in the hair and beauty world

The world of hair and beauty and the history from which it has grown can be credited to a wide range of factors. History has shaped the way hair is worn and the way beauty is represented today. The beauty industry has been created by thousands of years of civilisations, their politics, economics and rules of their societies. But is has also been influences by a few iconic people.

Certain individuals make a contribution to the world of hair and beauty that have long lasting effects. For example, in this chapter you have seen how the chemist Eugene Schuller made it possible for us to colour our hair safely, reliably and predictably and how King Camp Gillette changed the morning routines of men with the invention of his disposable blade razors.

Other iconic figures in the world of beauty are:

- **Max Factor**
- **Vidal Sassoon**
- **Madame C J Walker**

Image courtesy of The Advertising Archives

Max Factor commercial for Crème Puff

Max Factor

Max Factor was born Max Faktor in Poland in 1877 and was apprenticed to a dentist-pharmacist. It was during this time that he became fascinated by the creams and potions. He later opened his first shop which sold skin crème and wigs to theatre companies. He left Poland and went to America with his wife and three children in 1904. His arrival coincided with the start of the movie industry in Hollywood.

Max Factor perfected the makeup used by actors and actresses for film and, later, for television. His innovative makeup was made available to the general public in the 1920s. From gaining fame for the flawless finishes his foundations produced, he went on develop a range of other beauty products that we still use today. He invented false eye lashes, lip gloss, the eye brow pencil and the mascara wand, as well as waterproof mascara – to name but a few of his innovations.

Max Factor died in 1938, but his company still lives on. Today the Max Factor company is owned by Proctor and Gamble who bought the brand for $1.5 billion in 1991.

Vidal Sassoon

Vidal Sassoon was born in London in 1928 and was 14 when he began an apprenticeship with Cohen's Beauty and Barber shop. Following his apprentice-ship and a time fighting in the Israeli war, he set up a small salon on Bond Street.

Vidal Sassoon wanted to revolutionise the hairdressing scene. He was innovative and did not want to replicate the hairdressing of the 1950s. The heavily lacquered and stiff hairstyles were replaced by the angular, expertly cut classic bob instigated by Sassoon. Sassoon used club-cutting techniques to create straight, precision cut lines on hair. The haircut was carried out in an exacting and methodical way, which still provides the basis of many of the cutting techniques used today.

When Vidal Sassoon created geometric shaped haircuts in the 1960s they were said to be the start of a new revolution in hairdressing. The new cuts were a reflection of the street fashion at that time, particularly those of Mary Quant who was a leading fashion designer in the 1960s. Hairdressing and fashion went hand-in-hand. Geometric shapes in clothing were replicated in the asymmetric and angular shapes of the hairstyles. Hair in the 1960s had social power. Fashion was 'swinging' and so was hair.

© Getty\Terence Donovan Archive

Sassoon bobs

The bob worked best on straight hair, which, when cut, moved freely and automatically fell into place. For the first time the *hairstyle* was the *haircut*. The haircut was the very foundation of the image – any mistakes in the haircut could not be disguised by styling. Therefore, the skill and art of hair cutting took on new importance.

> *Hair is nature's biggest compliment and the treatment of this compliment is in our hands. As in couture, the cut is the most important element … haircutting simply means design and this feeling for design must come from within*. Vidal Sassoon

Sassoon became most famous for his bob and five-point haircuts, which he had achieved by 1963.

Today, there is a Vidal Sassoon products range and salons all over the UK, as well as in America, Canada and Germany.

Getty

Mary Quant and Vidal Sassoon

Madame C J Walker

Madame C J Walker was born Sarah Breedlove in December 1867. She was the daughter of former slaves. Married at 14, she was widowed with a daughter by the age of 20. In the early 1900s Sarah began to lose her hair. She tried everything from home made products to shop bought products to try to alleviate the

Madame C J Walker

problem. Sarah went on to work with a pharmacist to develop a range of hair products, one of which was called the 'Wonderful Hair Grower', which conditioned and healed her scalp. It is said that the formula for the Wonderful Hair Grower came to her in a dream. She also developed other products such as vegetable shampoo which were specially formulated for use on African type hair.

As well as being known for having an innovative approach to the development of products for the African type hair market, which she sold door to door, she also became a good business woman and marketer. She was so successful that she was the first woman (black or white) to become a millionaire in America through her own accomplishments.

By 1910 Madame C J Walker had her own factory to produce her products. She also opened a hair and manicure school. She used the hairdressing school to show black women that they too could be successful business women. Some of her students opened their own salons. Others became agents for Madame C J Walker, selling her products all over the country.

Once the business was settled, Madame C J Walker transferred her energies to supporting human rights projects to make the life of black people better, both by financial help and by deeds. She worked to abolish the injustices of racial inequality and took her petitions to the White House.

Madame C J Walker was a pioneer in the world of African type hair products. She died aged 51 in 1919.

At a National Negro Business League Convention Madame C J Walker said of herself:

> *I am a woman who came from the cotton fields of the South. From there I was promoted to the washtub. From there I was promoted to the cook kitchen. And from there I promoted myself to into the business of manufacturing hair goods and preparations … I have built my own factory on my own ground. There is no royal flower-strewn path to success. And if there is, I have not found it for if I have accomplished anything in life; it is because I have been willing to work hard.*

EXTEND YOUR LEARNING

Choose an icon of your choice from the world of hair and beauty. Research them and then produce a timeline of their life and achievements.

What you have learnt

The influence of civilisations and culture on hair and beauty

- Many of the hair and makeup techniques we use today were used thousands of years ago
- The status of a person in different civilisations determines how they look
- Personal appearance is an important aspect in all civilisations

The historical influences of hair and beauty

- In every period of time throughout history, people have followed fashions for hair and beauty

- Some fashions of today are based on themes from history

The social factors that affect the way individuals look

- Occupation can dictate how hair is worn and how makeup is applied
- Race, culture, religion and class or caste can affect outward appearance

How identity is created and what influences it

- People who share values and interests like to look similar
- Identity is as much about values and interests as it is about fashion, hair and beauty
- Cultures and subcultures exist in every civilisation

Iconic leaders of the hair and beauty sector

- Many individuals have had an impact on the hair and beauty sector
- The skills and talents of some people that have worked in the hair and beauty sector create trends and fashions throughout the world

The technological developments of hair and beauty

- Technology plays an important part in the hair and beauty sector
- Discoveries and inventions lead to safer and reliable treatments and services in the hair and beauty sector

Assessment activities

Crossword

Across

1 A hairstyle worn by children in Ancient Egypt (4, 4, 2, 5)

3 These people removed the facial hair from men (7)

6 Used to house dead pharaohs (8)

9 This makeup was applied to the eye (4)

12 The Ancient Egyptians believed in this (4, 5, 5)

13 Men and women did this to their hair to keep cool (6)

14 This vegetable colour was used to dye hair in Ancient Egypt (5)

15 A period of time in Ancient Egypt (6, 7)

Down

1. These people were right at the bottom of the social order in Ancient Egypt (6)
2. These symbols were used to record events in Ancient Egypt (11)
4. This was used to colour the lips and cheeks (3, 5)
5. This colour of hair was considered to be beautiful in Ancient Egypt (5)
7. A way of preserving a dead body (13)
8. These people had to bathe every day to remain pure (7)
10. Pharaohs were seen to be one of these (4)
11. This body of water is thought to have healing powers (4, 3)
12. The clothing in Ancient Egypt was made from this fabric (5)

Multiple choice: Culture, subculture and identity

1 Social identity is a group of people with shared
- **a** values
- **b** clothes
- **c** money
- **d** jobs

2 During the slave trade, many people were taken from
- **a** America
- **b** England
- **c** Africa
- **d** Australia

3 Black identity is a celebration of
- **a** being identified
- **b** being black
- **c** being African
- **d** being Asian

4 Teddy Boys were a subculture in the
- **a** 1950s
- **b** 1960s
- **c** 1970s
- **d** 1980s

5 There is one thing about hair that separates people on opposite sides of a subculture and that is its
- **a** style
- **b** colour
- **c** width
- **d** length

6 Who were said to be the first teenagers?
   a Goths
   b Punks
   c Mods
   d Teddy boys

7 Leather jackets were worm by
   a Goths
   b Rockers
   c Mods
   d Teddy boys

8 Unisex hairstyles were worn by
   a Goths
   b Rockers
   c Mods
   d Punks

9 Mohawks were worn by
   a Teddy boys
   b Rockers
   c Mods
   d Punks

10 Black hair was favoured by
   a Teddy boys
   b Goths
   c Mods
   d Punks

Paul Hawes @ Review

2 the world of hair and beauty

Climbing to the top demands strength, whether it is to the top of Mount Everest or to the top of your career.

ABDUL KALAM B.1931, PRESIDENT OF INDIA

Introduction

You should not underestimate the world of hair and beauty. It is global. It has millions of clients worldwide. Almost every country in the world takes part in it.

The hair and beauty sector is made up of six, very different, separate industries. The hairdressing and barbering industries include a separate industry for African Caribbean hair. The beauty industries are beauty therapy, nail services and spa therapy. Each industry is quite diverse with different characteristics.

Those who work in the hair and beauty industries need to have a range of specialised skills that take many years to achieve. Can you think of any other job where you can make people feel better, without the need for medicine, where you can make people look younger without the need for cosmetic surgery and you where you can make people feel more confident about themselves without the need of a psychologist?

What you are going to learn

Throughout this chapter you will learn about:

- ★ The world of hair and beauty and related sectors from global to local
- ★ Career opportunities in hair and beauty
- ★ What employers expect from those who work in hair and beauty
- ★ The skills you will need to succeed in hair and beauty
- ★ The professional and trade organisations that support the hair and beauty industries
- ★ The size of the industries and the impact they have on the economy and society
- ★ How trends in hair and beauty are affected by influences from the world of fashion and celebrities
- ★ The environmental impact of the industries
- ★ Product design and development

Even when there is a down turn in spending, people still like to look good. Reports on consumer spending show that the sector is economically sound. The revenue of hairdressing and personal grooming establishments totals £5.25 billion. So, as you can see, the sector has a major impact of the economy of the country.

But, best of all, the standards we have in the UK for hair and beauty are considered to be the finest. Many countries in the rest of world use UK standards for the training and education of people working in their hair and beauty industries.

Welcome to the world of hair and beauty...

Introduction to the work of hair and beauty

There are six very separate industries that make up the hair and beauty sector.

The industries are:

- hairdressing
- barbering
- African Caribbean hair
- beauty therapy
- nail services
- spa therapy

Each of the six industries has different characteristics, yet all have many features in common.

Hair and beauty – from global to local

If you have read Chapter 1 'The history of hair and beauty in society', you will know that the practice of hair and beauty has taken place for centuries all over the world – and continues to do so. Even in areas that are remote and only recently discovered, men, women and children have been found who groom their hair and decorate their bodies.

The global size of the hair and beauty industry

Although the hair and beauty sector is very visible and you can see salons and spas all over the world, it is not easy to measure the global size of it. One reason for this is because when the number of hair and beauty businesses in the world is recorded, they are often mixed in with businesses from other sectors.

For example, in the United States, the statistics provided by the Organisation for Economic Co-Operation and Development (OECD) are only recorded in three broad areas: *agriculture*, *industry* and *services*. So where would hair and beauty fit into these categories? A good guess would be services, but there are many other service industries besides hair and beauty.

The information provided by the United States Bureau of Labor Statistics, which excludes self-employed people, shows that there are 345,000 hairdressers and **cosmetologists** employed in the USA. There are also 11,500 barbers, 47,500 manicurists and 15,580 shampooists.

Salon numbers and employment in the hair and beauty sector around the world

This table lists the number of hair and beauty salons and the number of people employed in salons around the world.

COUNTRY	NUMBER OF SALONS	NUMBER EMPLOYED
Canada	26,300	50,000
Mexico	40,000	120,000
Argentina	30,000 (estimated)	100,000
Brazil	60,000	1,000,000
Australia	21,400	65,000
China	1,200,000 (estimated)	6,000,000
Hong Kong	4,200	227,000
Taiwan	21,000	46,000
Japan	202,000	465,000

EXTEND YOUR LEARNING

Investigate the discovery of a remote tribe or community of people in any area of the world. Can you see evidence of participation in activities relating to hair and beauty? Present your evidence to other members of your group.

It's a fact!

A cosmetologist is someone who carries out both hair and beauty treatments.

Korea	86,000	200,000
Malaysia	8,000	35,000
United Arab Emirates	1,000	10,600
Turkey	54,700	107,000
Germany	65,400	253,000
France	58,500	144,000
Spain	48,000 (estimated)	70,000

Source: DR GSP 2004 Diagonal Reports GSP 2005 Market Sizes

The size of the hair and beauty industry in the UK

In the UK, all sectors are defined by **Standard Industrial Classification (SIC)** codes. The hair and beauty sector is made up of six very different industries, yet the SIC code does not identify them individually. For example, there is a SIC code, 9302, which is described as *Hairdressing and other beauty treatments*. Some of the industries in the hair and beauty sector also fall into the *Physical well-being activities* SIC code 9304. And another SIC code, 9309 includes *Other service activities*. So you can see that even in the UK, hair and beauty can be hidden within other industries.

Despite the complicated categories, it is recognised that the number of businesses in the UK hair and beauty sector is as shown in the table.

INDUSTRY	NUMBER OF BUSINESSES	NUMBER IN WORKFORCE
Hairdressing	35,704 (of which 302 are salons that specialise in African type hair)	200,000
Barbering	2,967	5,300
African Caribbean Hair	302	Included in hairdressing
Nail technicianss	1,512	Estimated to be up to 17,000
Beauty salons and consultants	14,054	33,500
Spas	400	6,000

Source: Habia Skills Foresight Report 2007

In total, across the UK there are nearly 250,000 people employed in nearly 55,000 businesses in the hair and beauty sector.

EXTEND YOUR LEARNING 

The number of people employed in the hair and beauty sector in the USA appears to be much lower (in relation to the population of the country) than in the UK. Discuss with others why do you think this is.

A Clue! Read the paragraph about the numbers employed in the USA again and find one reason why the number appears to be lower. (You will find the answer at the back of the book).

It's a fact!

There has been massive growth in the beauty therapy industry. In 1999 there were just over 6,000 businesses; this had grown to over 14,000 by 2006 – an increase of 133%!

ACTIVITY 

Count the number of hair and beauty salons you have on your own high street.

The profile of the sector

The hair and beauty sector is dominated by **micro-businesses** that are known as **Small and Medium Sized Enterprises**, or **SMEs**. SMEs are businesses that employ less than 50 people. However, despite the size of the businesses, the hair and beauty sector have a presence on every high street in the country.

Some of the salons you see on your high street will form part of a **chain**. The chain may be national, or local. Others may be part of a **franchise**.

It's a fact!

A franchise is a way of owning your own business as a *franchisee*, under the name of another, existing company, the *franchisor*.

ACTIVITY   

Investigate the opportunities for franchising in the hair and beauty sector. Tony & Guy, Saks, House of Colour, Rejuvalife International Ltd and The Francesco Group all offer franchise opportunities. Take the activity further by planning a career route that would enable you to become a **franchisee**.

It's a fact!

50% of beauty therapists and 71% of nail technicians are self-employed. However, only 1% who work in the spa industry are self-employed.

Many people in the hair and beauty sector are **self-employed**. Some are self-employed because they own their own salon; others work on a **freelance** basis.

What it is like to work in the hair and beauty sector

Standing

If you are considering a career in the hair and beauty sector, you need to be aware that most of the industries are tiring to work in – particularly when you first begin. You may be physically fit, but having to stand on your feet all day is different to being at school or college where you spend lengthy periods of time sitting. This is

It's a fact!

The nail service industry is the only one in which you will be able to work in a sitting position. This is because of the types of treatments and services that are offered.

why your posture is very important. You can read about posture and the effects of standing on the muscles of the body in Chapter 5 'Safe working practices'.

It's a fact! There are many opportunities to enter competitions for body painting and nail art. You can also enter competitions for hairdressing. And, you don't have to wait until you are fully qualified to enter competitions, as there are categories available for learners.

Creativity

You will have the opportunity to be creative in all industries in the hair and beauty sector. For example, in hairdressing and barbering, you will be able to design hairstyles by cutting, sometimes cutting 3D patterns into hair. You will also be able to demonstrate your creativity when you use hair colour and style hair. Nail art is an important service in nail services. Creative skills are required if you work in beauty therapy when applying makeup or body paint.

Dyslexia

Some creative, successful and intelligent people in the hair and beauty industry are also dyslexic. Having **dyslexia** is not a barrier to entering any of the industries – in fact, it is an advantage! While written communication may sometimes be a problem, dyslexics are often very creative and, amongst other skills, many have the ability to visualise form and shape, particularly in 3D, which is a very useful skill in the hair industry.

It's a fact! The D stands for *dimensional*. Hairdressers and barbers need to be able to visualise what a haircut or hairstyle will look like on the rounded surface of the head.

Colour blindness

Some people may have difficulties working in the hair industry if they have colour blindness. When colouring hair, you have to be able to identify very subtle differences in the **depth** and **tone** of natural and artificial colour. However colour blindness is not such a barrier in the beauty industry.

It's a fact! *Depth* is how light or how dark a colour is. For example, black, medium brown or light blonde. *Tone* is the colour you see. For example, copper, gold or ash.

Skin conditions

You will have to work with a range of chemicals, lotions and other products in most of the hair and beauty industries. Because of this, some people develop skin conditions such as dermatitis. Some people are more likely to do this than others – especially if they have a history of skin or other allergies. However, with correct training, the careful use of chemicals and the appropriate use of *personal protective equipment* (PPE), dermatitis can be prevented. You can read more about dermatitis in Chapter 4 'The science of hair and beauty'.

Communication skills

All the hair and beauty industries are client focused and provide a range of personal services. They all require skilled and knowledgeable staff, so as well as practical skills, you have a great deal of theory to learn. In addition, all the industries rely on repeat business, so the personal skills of stylist, therapists and technicians are critical. This means that all staff must have good verbal communication skills and enjoy working on a personal level, with people from a range of different backgrounds.

Later in this chapter you will learn about the specific employability skills that are required if you want to succeed in the hair and beauty sector.

About the industries in the hair and beauty sector

Hairdressing

Almost everyone would be able to describe what a hairdresser does, as most people will have had their hair cut at some time. As well as cutting hair, a hairdresser will provide hairstyling and chemical services. Chemical services are colouring, where the natural colour of hair can be changed or enhanced, and perming, where the structure of the hair can be changed to make it curlier or relaxed to make it straighter than it is naturally. Some hairdressing businesses also provide services such as hair extensions, where the length or density of hair can be increased.

The majority of hairdressing salons are usually open plan, but each business will have its own characteristics. Some salons can be very noisy places as they play loud music; others have a calm and relaxing atmosphere. Many are between the two extremes. The design and atmosphere of the hairdressing salon is designed and planned to meet the needs of the majority of clients that the salon owner wishes to attract. Some salon designs are modern, some are elegant or luxurious, while others are more clinical and minimalist looking.

Hob Salons, Temple Fortune, London

Hairdressing salon

It's a fact!

83% of recruits to the hairdressing industry are aged under 26. Males make up 23% of the industry.

EXTEND YOUR LEARNING  

Investigate the range of hairdressing salon designs on the Hairdressers Journal website **www.hji.co.uk/blogs/business/interiors/**

The hairdressing business can be very diverse and many salons offer more than just hairdressing. Some salons are termed 'unisex' which means that both men and women can have hairdressing services. Specialist barbers can also be found working alongside ladies hairdressers. Beauty therapy services frequently take place in hairdressing salons – especially the smaller treatments such as skin care, makeup and lash and eyebrow treatments. Many hairdressing salons have a 'nail bar' where a nail technician would work.

Barbering

Barbering is quite different to hairdressing, although some of the skills required can be transferred from one industry to the other. Barbers work on the hair of men and boys. The services they perform include traditional hair cutting, clippering and shaving. Barbers also carry out face and head massage. Some barbers will provide chemical services of colouring and perming.

Although some businesses may provide services for both male and female clients, many barbershops can look very different to hairdressing salons. Barbershops frequently have a very traditional look, which many men prefer. The decor is often

Barber's pole

EXTEND YOUR LEARNING  

While the red and white barber's pole is traditional, some barbers poles are red, white and blue. Investigate the history behind the three-coloured poles.

It's a fact! Those who work in the barbering industry are well qualified. 85% of staff offering technical services hold a Level 3 qualification.

Barber's shop

© iStockphoto.com/Shirly Friedman

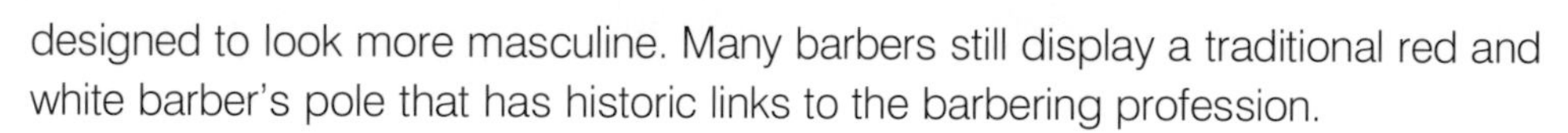

designed to look more masculine. Many barbers still display a traditional red and white barber's pole that has historic links to the barbering profession.

African-Caribbean hair

There are many different type of hair, one of which is African type. You can read about the variation in hair type in Chapter 4 'The science of hair and beauty'. The distinct characteristics of this hair have led to the development of specialised businesses to carry out services for clients with African type hair.

In addition to hair cutting, salons that work on African type hair will offer services such as chemical relaxing, which is a process that permanently straightens very tight curls. Styling techniques include thermal styling where hot curling irons are used to temporarily straighten hair. However, in recent times, there has been a move away from straightening techniques, which are seen by some as trying to get

Locks on African type hair

© iStockphoto.com/poco_bw

It's a fact! The word *locks*, not *dreadlocks* is now used to describe the technique of twisting strands of African type hair, as the hairstyle is worn by many who are not Rastafarians.

EXTEND YOUR LEARNING  

During the 1970s there was a rise in the popularity of the Rastafari religion. Followers of this religion cultivated their natural African type hair into twisted strands that were known as **dreadlocks**. Research the Rastafarian faith and investigate why the hairstyle is so significant.

African type hair to mimic Caucasian hair, to a growth in the number of salons which focus on *natural* African type hair. In such salons, chemical treatments would not be used to straighten or reform the curls in African type hair. Instead, styling techniques are used that work with and enhance the natural appearance of the hair type.

It's a fact!

The term *faradic* comes from the name of Michael Faraday (1791–1867) who was an influential English scientist and physicist.

Beauty therapy

From what was once considered to be a luxury, the services that beauty therapists provide have now become commonplace. Beauty therapists provide treatments to enhance the appearance, well-being and relaxation of clients. The treatments carried out include manicure, pedicure, makeup, waxing and massage. Other treatments are electrotherapies.

One example of an electrotherapy treatment is **faradic**. This is a treatment where an electrical current is used to stimulate muscles to contract, thus improving the muscle tone of the body.

EXTEND YOUR LEARNING

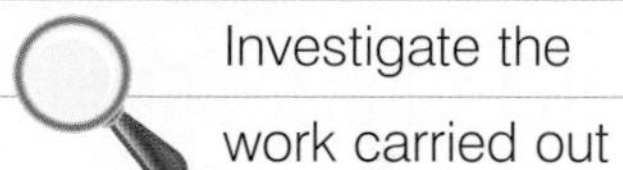

Investigate the work carried out by Faraday in both physics and chemistry.

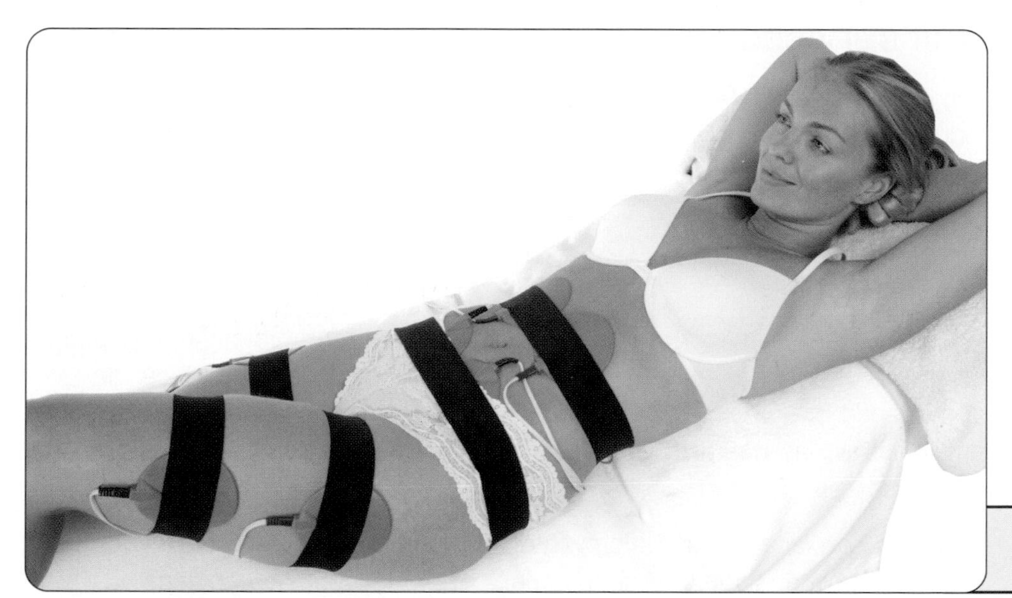

Faradic treatment

There are many other electrotherapies that are carried out by beauty therapists, such as **galvanic**, **high frequency**, **microcurrent** and **vacuum suction**.

It's a fact!

Some beauty therapy treatments are considered as being almost medical, such as **laser hair removal**. This treatment uses the heat energy from the laser to damage cells at the root of the hair, preventing further growth. This is a very specialised treatment that requires further training after qualifying as a beauty therapist.

EXTEND YOUR LEARNING

Research the effects and use of each of the electrotherapies.

The environment of a beauty therapy salon is usually very calming and tranquil, often with restful music being played to soothe and relax the client. Some beauty salons can look very clinical, while others are decorated in soft muted tones with candle, or dimly-lit treatment rooms to aid relaxation during massage.

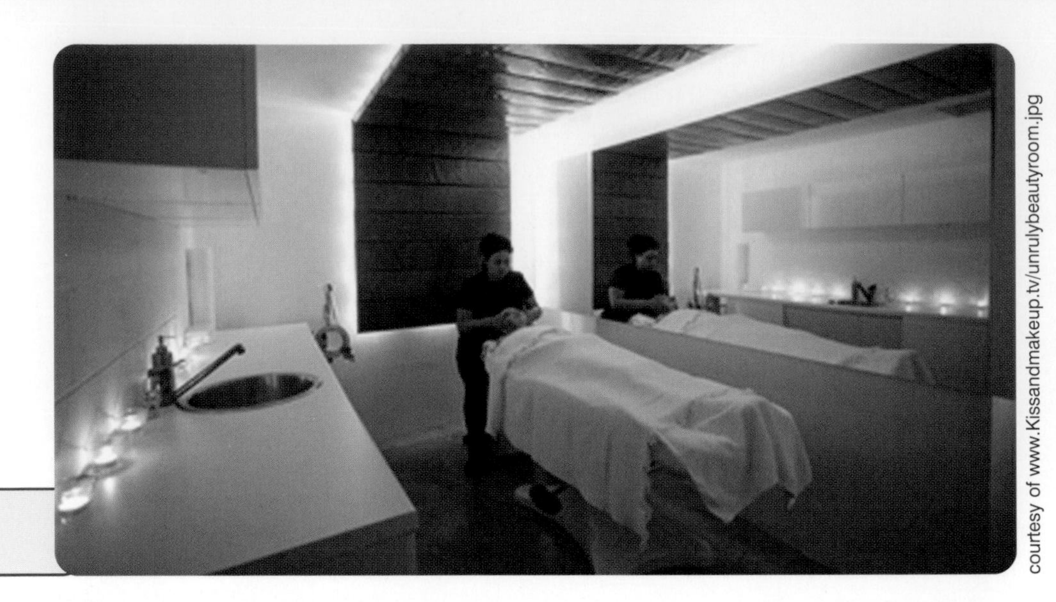

Beauty therapy treatment room

courtesy of www.Kissandmakeup.tv/unrulybeautyroom.jpg

EXTEND YOUR LEARNING

Research the three main systems for nail extensions: gels, acrylics and wraps.

Nail services

The growth of the nail industry in recent years is impressive. Prior to 2004, the nail industry was just one small part of the beauty therapy industry. It is now estimated that there are 17,000 businesses which carry out nail services treatments. Nail services are carried out in specialised nail salons, hairdressing salons, beauty therapy salons and spas. The people who carry out nail services are known as **nail technicians**.

Nail technicians carry out manicures and pedicures to improve the appearance of nails on the hands and the feet. They also lengthen and enhance the appearance of nails with nail extensions. Decorating nails is also carried out and is known as **nail art**, where **stencilling**, **freehand** and **air brushing** techniques are all used.

Part of the explanation for the growth of the nail industry can be linked to both fashion and technology. Having long nails has been seen for centuries as a sign of wealth as a person with long nails would be unable to do manual work. Today it is fashionable to have longer, well manicured nails. The ability to produce these well groomed, extended nails stems from the technology that was originally developed for dental technicians who used polymers and adhesives to create crowns and other dental devices. By experimenting with the dental materials, it was found that the properties of the products meant that they could be moulded into an extended fingernail shape which was strong when the products hardened.

Spa therapy

Within the spa environment it is possible to find most, if not all, the industries in the hair and beauty sector. At a spa you may be able to have your hair styled and receive a beauty therapy and nail service, yet, spa is an industry in its own right.

Spa therapists improve the appearance of the face and body and enhance health and well-being. In addition to this, one distinct characteristic of the spa environment is that the treatments are water based. The treatments that are carried out include heat and wet treatments, **hydrotherapy**, **flotation**, **steam**, **sauna** and **jacuzzi**.

It's a fact!

There are currently around 400 spas in the UK

Jon Arnold Images Ltd / Alamy

A traditional spa

EXTEND YOUR LEARNING

There are two major organisations which offer information about the spa industry. Investigate their websites and find out more: the British International Spa Association **www.spaassociation.org.uk** and the Spa Business Association (SpaBA) **www.britishspas.co.uk**

It's a fact!

The spa industry has the highest use of Information Technology in the hair and beauty sector. 100% of businesses use a computer for business purposes.

Job roles in hair and beauty

Within each industry in the hair and beauty sector, you have the opportunity go progress from Level's 1 to a Master's degree.

Progression in the world of hair and beauty

ACTIVITY 

Download care leaflets for hairdressing and barbering, African Caribbean hair, beauty therapy, nail services and spa therapy from **www.habia.org**

While many may think they know what happens in hair and beauty industries, fewer would be fully aware of the broad range of skills, both academic and creative, a person needs to be successful. And because many of the job roles that can be found are not *visible*, the progression opportunities are often underestimated.

In each of the industries it is possible to go from a Diploma in Hair and Beauty Studies through to a Master's degree. In addition to this, it is possible to get there through many different routes. The routes are also interchangeable, so at any stage, all career options are always open to you.

Career progression in the world of hair and beauty

The table below shows you the progression pathways from entry level to a Master's degree. You can move from the bottom to the top in a vertical direction, or you can cross between the pathways.

Master's degree in Salon or Spa Management	Master's degree in Salon or Spa Management	Master's degree in Salon or Spa Management	Master's degree in Salon or Spa Management
Honours degrees in Salon or Spa Management	Honours degrees in Salon or Spa Management	Honours degrees in Salon or Spa Management	Honours degrees in Salon or Spa Management
Foundation degree in Salon or Spa Management	Foundation degree in Salon or Spa Management	Foundation degree in Salon or Spa Management	Foundation degree in Salon or Spa Management
GCE A Levels	Advanced Diploma in Hair and Beauty Studies	Advanced Apprenticeship	NVQ Level 3
GCSE	Higher Diploma in Hair and Beauty Studies	Apprenticeship	NVQ Level 2
Foundation Diploma in Hair and Beauty Studies or NVQ Level 1 combined with GCSEs	Foundation Diploma in Hair and Beauty Studies	Young Apprenticeship* in Hairdressing combined with GCSEs	NVQ Level 1

* Young Apprenticeships are Level 2

Qualifications in hair and beauty

There are a series of very structured qualifications designed for specific job roles for those who work in the hair and beauty sector.

National Occupational Standards (NOS)

National Occupational Standards (NOS) are used to describe the skills and knowledge that is required to carry out a job role to a *nationally* recognised standard. Each occupation in the hair and beauty sector has a set of NOS, which are written by Habia. In order to write the standards, Habia works with specialised groups of people, such as employers and industry experts, from each of the six industries to determine what the standards will contain.

EXTEND YOUR LEARNING

Visit the Habia website **www.habia.org** to read the National Occupational Standards for the industry you are interested in. Reading the standards will provide an outline of the exact work you would be expected to do at each level from Level 1 to Level 3.

Learning pathways in the hair and beauty sector

There are two different types of qualifications relevant for the hair and beauty sector. One type of qualification leads to *readiness* for working in one of the industries, the other *prepares* you for it. They are known as ready for work qualifications or preparation for work qualifications.

Preparation for work qualifications in the hair and beauty sector

The Diploma in Hair and Beauty Studies is known as a *preparation for work* qualification. This is because the qualification provides an opportunity for you to investigate each of the six industries in the hair and beauty sector, and to try out some of the basic skills that are required to work in it. During the time you spend studying you will also develop the **employability skills** that are required.

There are other preparation for work qualifications known as **Vocationally Related Qualifications (VRQs)**. Unlike the Diploma in Hair and Beauty Studies, these learning programmes will be focused on just one industry. If you choose to complete a VRQ you will have the opportunity to develop more of the skills directly related to the industry in which you are interested.

It's a fact!

The employability skills developed through the Diploma in Hair and Beauty Studies are relevant for many other industries.

Ready for work qualifications in the hair and beauty sector

There are qualifications for the hair and beauty sector that are known as *ready for work* qualifications. One example of this type of qualification is a **National Vocational Qualification (NVQ)**. NVQs are **competence based** qualifications which are based on National Occupational Standards (NOS). Because NVQs are designed for specific job roles in industry, they are assessed in the workplace. Unlike other qualifications where you may have to take an exam at the end of a certain length of time, NVQs are continuously assessed.

It's a fact! According to the Oxford English Dictionary, competence is defined as *having the required ability, knowledge or authority*. For the hair and beauty industry, to be competent means that you are able to carry out a job related skill at any time, under any circumstances, on any client, under the commercial pressures of a busy salon or spa. So, for example, in hairdressing, it is not sufficient to be able to style short, straight hair. You also have to be able to style long curly hair and every other length and type of hair in between. In beauty therapy, it is not sufficient to be able to apply makeup on a young client with a pale skin tone, you have to be able to apply makeup to all ages of clients with a range of skin tones.

It's a fact! There is no defined junior level job role in spa therapy. Therefore, if you want to work in the spa industry, you would have to complete a Level 2 qualification in beauty therapy or nail services before beginning Level 3. However, as the spa industry is so diverse, you may also enter it with a Level 2 qualification in other industries, such as hairdressing, nutrition, fitness or even a pool attendant.

NVQs are also known as **learner centred** qualifications. This means the you will set the pace and speed at which you progress through the qualification. If you are someone who can learn skills and knowledge very quickly, then you will progress through the qualification at a greater speed than someone who may need more help and support. However, you need to be aware that learning skills and knowledge for the hair and beauty industry is not an easy option. It can take up to five years before you would be considered by employers to be fully qualified. But the good thing is, as you are progressing through your qualifications, you can successfully work at a lower level until you complete your NVQ Level 3.

NVQ Level 1

The NVQ Level 1 is designed for those who would like to work in an *assisting* role in the hair and beauty industry. It is also designed for those who are not yet ready to go directly to NVQ Level 2. It can be used as a stepping stone to the next level. You do not have to take NVQ Level 1 – if you are able and ready, you can go directly to NVQ Level 2.

It's a fact! An NVQ at Level 2 is equivalent to 5 GCSEs at Grade A*–C.

NVQ Level 2

This qualification is designed for those who want to work at a *junior* level in the hair and beauty sector. This qualification is used as a stepping stone to gain experience, skills and knowledge before progressing to NVQ Level 3.

It's a fact! An NVQ at Level 3 is equivalent to 3 GCE A Levels.

NVQ Level 3

All those who wish to work at a *senior* level in any of the hair and beauty industries will be expected to gain an NVQ at Level 3. It is at this level that you will have gained all the skills and knowledge required to complete the full range of treatments and services.

There are Level 3 qualifications available for all industries in the hair and beauty sector.

Gaining a ready for work qualification in the hair and beauty sector

There are two ways to gain an NVQ: either through an apprenticeship or through a college based learning programme. The route you choose is entirely up to you. The work based learning route of the apprenticeship is for those who feel ready to be employed as an apprentice. The apprenticeship can begin at anytime between the ages of 16 and 18. However, some people may not feel ready for employment at this age, and so they may prefer the college route.

Apprenticeships in the hair and beauty sector

To be an apprentice means that you are employed in a salon or spa and, during your employment, you work towards an NVQ in the industry of your employment. At the same time as studying for your NVQ, you will also develop skills in communication, numeracy and information technology, which are required for you to be successful in any industry.

The training for an NVQ is completed in a partnership between you, your employer and a training provider. There will be an agreement, which is usually prepared by the training provider, known as an **Individual Learning Plan**, which outlines how you are going to learn, who has responsibility for your learning and identifies any support that you may require to complete your apprenticeship.

There are two levels of apprenticeship:

- Apprenticeship
- Advanced Apprenticeship

Apprenticeships and Advanced Apprenticeships are available in all six industries in the hair and beauty sector. It typically takes between one and two years to complete an Apprenticeship and a further one to two years for an Advanced Apprenticeship.

Apprenticeship

During an Apprenticeship, you will study for:

- NVQ Level 2
- Communication, numeracy and information technology skills at Level 1
- Employment Rights and Responsibilities

Advanced apprenticeship

During an Advanced Apprenticeship, you will study for:

- NVQ Level 3
- Communication, numeracy and information technology skills at Level 2
- Employment Rights and Responsibilities

College based learning programmes

You can study for an NVQ at Levels 1–3 at a College of Further Education. During your time on the learning programme, you will spend some time with an

It's a fact!

The skills of communication, numeracy and information technology included within an apprenticeship are known as *transferable* skills. This means that even if you decide to leave the hair and beauty sector, the skills learnt can be used in another industry.

It's a fact!

An Advanced Apprenticeship is known as a Modern Apprenticeship in Wales and an Apprenticeship is known as a Foundation Modern Apprenticeship. The names may be different, but the learning programmes are the same.

It's a fact!

Employment Rights and Responsibilities (ERR) ensures that both you and your employer are aware of each other's right and responsibilities during employment. For example, you will learn about Contracts of Employment, holiday entitlement and the actions you can take if you have work related problems.

employer on work placement. This gives you a real idea of what a commercial salon or spa is like.

Because the NVQ has to be assessed in the workplace, you will learn your skills in a salon known as a **Realistic Working Environment (RWE)**. This is different to the **Realistic Learning Environment (RLE)** salon that you use for the Diploma in Hair and Beauty Studies.

EXTEND YOUR LEARNING

Write to, email, telephone or call in to see your local training provider and ask for a prospectus of courses in hair and beauty. Investigate the options that would be available for you in your own city or town.

Differences between a Realistic Working and Realist Learning Environment

REALISTIC WORKING ENVIRONMENT (used for *ready for work* qualifications)	REALISTIC LEARNING ENVIRONMENT (used for *preparation for work* qualifications)
Based on a *commercial* salon or spa environment	Based on a salon or spa environment
Assessment takes place on fee paying clients, which excludes family members or peer group	Assessment takes place on models which can include family members or peer group
Assessment of skills to confirm *competence* in a wide range of techniques	Assessment of skills to confirm *understanding* of limited range of techniques
Assessment for skills is based on commercially recognised time limits	There are no time limits for the assessment of skills

Employability skills for hair and beauty

Employability skills are different to the technical skills that are required to carry out a job role. Employability skills are important throughout your working life, but especially at the very beginning of it.

When you first leave school or college, the only skills a prospective employer will be able to make a judgement on will be your employability skills. This is because you will not, at this stage, have developed the job-ready technical skills and knowledge. This is what the employer will help you with during your training.

The hair and beauty sector is unique in the vast range of skills that are required from individuals who work in any of its industries. While the six industries are quite different, there are many employability skills that are common to them all. Therefore, it does not matter if you work in hairdressing, barbering, on African type hair, in nails services or spa therapy, the employability skills are all the same.

Identified employability skills

The important employability skills, which have been identified by employers in the hair and beauty sector, are:

- communication
- willingness to learn
- self manager
- team work
- customer care
- positive attitude
- personal ethics
- creativity
- flexible working
- leadership

Communication

Having good communication skills is probably the most critical of all the employability skills. In Chapter 6 'Communication and client care', you will see that communication is more than having the ability to hold a conversation. In the hair and beauty sector, verbal, non-verbal and what is known as physical communication are all equally important.

Whichever industry in which you work in the hair and beauty sector, you will have to work with clients. All the industries rely on repeat business. Clients are only likely to return for treatments and services if they have enjoyed their experience.

ACTIVITY

Do you have good communication skills? Think of examples of where you can find evidence that you have communicated successfull with others. Perhaps you have had to ask for feedback following a test or other school or college work. You will be asked to use the example in another activity at the end of this section.

Willingness to learn

The knowledge and technical skills you will develop to work in any of the industries in the hair and beauty sector can take a great deal of time to learn. When you first begin your training, you may think that you will never be as good as the experts in the industry, as some technical skills are very difficult.

However, if you are have the drive and determination to practise and study, then you will find that you can overcome the difficulties. You will not be able to learn the skills in just one week, not in just one month, or in just one year. And, even when you have completed your initial training and can work on clients, you will have to keep updating your skills for the rest of your working life. People who work in the sector say that this is one of the reasons why they find their jobs so interesting – they never get bored.

ACTIVITY

Think of an example where you have demonstrated you have a willingness to learn. Perhaps you are learning a skill outside school or college, or you have used research skills for projects or assignments. You will be asked to use the example in another activity at the end of this section.

Self manager

When you work in the hair and beauty sector you will spend a great deal of time on your own with a client. The client is totally dependent on you to ensure that the treatment or service they have requested will be carried out within the expected time, safely and competently. In addition to this, you may have more than one client at the same time. But, even though you may have two or even three clients, they all need to feel that they have your undivided attention. To

ACTIVITY

Think of an example where you can demonstrate that you have shown you have the skill of self management. Perhaps you are good at organising your own activities or are able to work under pressure. You will be asked to use the example in another activity at the end of this section.

ACTIVITY

Think of an example of where you can demonstrate that you have successfully worked as part of a team. Perhaps you have been involved in organising an event at school or college, or taken part in team sports. You will be asked to use the example in another activity at the end of this section.

ACTIVITY

Think of an example where you have experienced good client care, or where you have given good client care. You will be asked to use the example in another activity at the end of this section.

be able to do this you require the skill of self management – you have to manage your time effectively.

Being a self manager will help you to overcome difficulties and setbacks as you will develop the ability to *self assess*. This means *you* will be able to identify what the problem is and then plan and implement a solution to overcome the problem.

Team work

You may have noticed if you have visited a busy salon or spa, that there are a number of different people who look after you on your visit. You may have been greeted by a receptionist. A junior stylist or junior therapist may have prepared you for the treatments or services that were carried out by a senior stylist or senior therapist. At the end of your visit the receptionist may have booked another appointment for you. This is just one example of team work. Each person in the salon or spa is working with others to ensure that clients have a pleasurable experience. Working in a team means that the business runs efficiently and profitably.

Team work is also about having respect and consideration for, and empathy with, others.

Customer care

Have you ever been kept waiting for an appointment without knowing why? Have you ever experienced or witnessed poor service in a shop, restaurant or salon? How did you feel? Perhaps you felt uncomfortable or unhappy. However you felt, it is unlikely that you would return. Client care is very important. Without clients in the hair and beauty sector, you would not have a job at all. Client care can be anything from providing a full treatment or service to simply asking if the client is comfortable, or offering to make them a drink. By doing this you are demonstrating that you have respect and consideration for others and that you have social awareness and sensitivity.

Client care is one employability skill that is linked to many of the others. For example, you cannot achieve good client care if you have poor communication skills or there are members of the salon team who do not work well together.

Positive attitude

To succeed in the hair and beauty sector you need to have a positive attitude. The training is long and sometimes difficult. You will have to deal with clients who may not always be as polite as you. Therefore, you need to demonstrate that you are patient, tolerant and have a good sense of humour.

Personal ethics

Working in the hair and beauty sector means that you will come into direct contact with clients, on a personal level. Once a client gets to know you, and builds up their trust in you, they sometimes talk to you about very sensitive subjects. Anything that a client tells you must remain confidential. You must never tell others about the personal conversations you have with your clients. You must be sensitive to their needs and respect their privacy.

Personal ethics is also directly related to your work ethic. The hair and beauty industry is a service industry. Therefore, you need to demonstrate that you are honest and reliable.

Creativity

Being creative is a major advantage if you want to work in the hair and beauty sector. Hairdressing in particular is very much related to the fashion industry and, like clothing, is subject to change. Seasonal collections are developed by leading hairdressers. These collections are often a prediction of what the hairdressing fashion will be in the following year.

Being creative does not mean that you have to be an artist who can draw and paint. It can be the ability to see *form* and *shape*, to *visualise* in three dimensions and to be brave enough to experiment with different types of colours and media. It also means that you are innovative and have the ability to inspire others.

ACTIVITY 

Think of an example where you can demonstrate that you are creative. Perhaps you are good at art and design, or like to make your own clothes. You will be asked to use the example in another activity at the end of this section.

Flexible working

The hair and beauty industry is not a 9–5 job. You will not be able to finish work at exactly the same time every working day. Your work cannot end until the client is finished. You will not be able to have weekends off and you may be expected to work in shifts, which can include working in the evenings. This is particularly true of the spa industry. Spas operate 7 days a week from early morning to late evening – often because they are attached to hotels, holiday or leisure complexes. You may also find that some times of the year are much busier than others. For example, working in a hairdressing salon at Christmas time is very busy as people want their hair doing for the party season.

Being able to demonstrate flexible working means that you have the ability to **multi-task**. When working in a salon or spa, you may often have more than one

ACTIVITY 

Think of an example where you can demonstrate that you can work flexibly. Perhaps you have a part time job that you combine with your studying. You will be asked to use the example in another activity at the end of this section.

ACTIVITY 

Think of an example where you can demonstrate a positive attitude. You may have been faced with problems that you have successfully overcome, or you may have had to react to some criticism about work you have produced. Explain how you dealt with this – did you have a positive attitude? You will be asked to use the example in another activity at the end of this section.

ACTIVITY 

Think of an example where you can demonstrate that you are someone that other people can trust. You may have a babysitting job, or help other people with errands. You may be a Prefect or Mentor in your school or college. You will be asked to use the example in another activity at the end of this section.

client to deal with, or have a list of instructions to carry out on behalf of a more senior member of staff.

ACTIVITY 

Think of an example where you have demonstrated leadership skills. Perhaps you have inspired others or helped and supported others. You will be asked to use the example in another activity at the end of this section.

Leadership

There are many opportunities in the hair and beauty industry for those with the ability to lead others. You do not have to wait until you reach management positions to demonstrate this. Some leadership is required right at the very beginning of your training. For example, you need to demonstrate that you have dedication to learning, and to carry on learning continuously. Leadership is also about seeking new challenges and solving problems. When working in a salon or spa, you can encounter problems. You need to be able to develop the skills to deal with problems and identify how to solve them.

Bring your learning to life

Writing your first Curriculum Vitae (CV) can be quite daunting as you may have little actual work experience to record, making the CV look rather incomplete. However, employability skills are vital and are something that prospective employers will be looking for. Update your CV by adding a new section called *Employability Skills*. Use the evidence from the other activities in this section to complete it. Completing the CV is another example of self-management. Self managers have good planning skills, which includes planning for a new career.

Bring your learning to life

If you get the opportunity to complete your work experience in one of the hair and beauty industries, make an appointment to speak to the salon or spa manager/employer to carry out an interview to find out what employability skills they are looking for when recruiting a school or college leaver. You may find that the skills required for creating a good impression, ensuring personal appearance is appropriate, communication or time keeping are as important as the technical skills to carry out a job.

Once you have recorded the skills required, complete a self analysis. Compare the skills required with your own skills. Do they match up? If not, create an Action Plan to show how you can develop your employability skills further.

Salaries in hair and beauty

There is an assumption that if you work in the hair and beauty industry, you will not earn very much money. To some extent, this is true of many professions, particularly while you are training. When you first begin training or during an apprenticeship the pay, like other sectors, is low. In England an apprentice will earn, on average, between £95 and £120 per week.[1] The amount of pay you earn is a reflection of the contribution you can make to a business, which at the beginning is limited. However, very soon you will be able to make a financial contribution as your skills develop, and your pay will reflect this.

As you progress through your qualifications and take on more responsibility in your job role, your pay will increase. Today the average salary across the hair and beauty industry is £229 per week.[2] This means that some people earn less than this – and some earn more.

The full happiness rankings

POSITION	PROFESSION	POSITION	PROFESSION
1	Beauticians	9 =	Engineers
2 =	Hairdressers	9 =	Architects
2 =	Armed Forces	13 =	Journalists
4	Catering/chefs	13 =	Mechanics/Automotive
5	Retail staff	13 =	Human Resources
6 =	Teachers	16	Call centre
6 =	Marketing/PR	17 =	IT specialists
6 =	Accountants	17 =	Nurses
9 =	Secretaries/ Receptionists	17 =	Banker/Finance
9 =	Plumbers	17 =	Builders/construction

EXTEND YOUR LEARNING

To calculate a *mean average*, a sum of numbers is divided by the number of items on the list. Carry out a few exercises to work out some mean averages.

It's a fact!

A survey to find the happiest workers was carried out by City & Guilds.[3] Beauty therapists and hairdressers were at the top of the scale and secretarial, banking, insurance and finance workers were the least happy in their work.

© JUPITERIMAGES/Brand X/ Alamy

Many employers pay their staff on a commission basis. This means the employee will have a percentage share of the payments made by their clients. Therefore, the more clients you have and the busier you are, the more you will earn, both in commission and in tips and gratuities from your clients.

However, while everyone has to earn a salary to live, job satisfaction is also very important and cannot be quantified in monetary terms. Hairdressers and beauty therapists have topped the scale for happiness in a job role.

Many people in the hair and beauty sector earn much higher salaries than the mean average. If you look at the career progression pathways in this chapter, you

1. Typical apprentice pay at the time of publication August 2009.
2. Skills Needs Assessment of the Hair and Beauty Sector January 2008.
3. City & Guilds Happiness Index 2007.

It's a fact! To be successful in salon ownership, you need to develop management skills as well as technical skills.

will see that there are high level job roles in all industries. For example, management and teaching will attract the same level salaries for the hair and beauty sector that are found in other sectors. The sector has a history of self employment and salon ownership. Here your salary will reflect the success, efficiency and profitability of your own business.

Higher Education opportunities in hair and beauty

There are many Higher Education opportunities in each of the six industries in the hair and beauty sector. All of the industries require people who can function in high level job roles, such as management. In addition, there are some technical skills that are above Level 3.

There are five levels of Higher Education:

- Doctorate
- Master's degree
- Honours degree
- Foundation degree, ordinary (Bachelors) degree
- Certificates of Higher Education

You can progress into Higher Education directly from the Advanced Diploma in Hair and Beauty Studies, from an NVQ Level 3 or an Advanced Apprenticeship. Alternatively, you can progress from GCE 'A' Levels or employment. Typical progression from the Advanced Diploma in Hair and Beauty Studies would be to a Foundation degree, on completion of which there is automatic progression onto an Honours degree, for those who choose to progress further.

Examples of the Higher Education programmes currently available for the hair and beauty sector are:

- Hairdressing and Salon Management
- Beauty Therapy Operations
- Management in Hairdressing Salons
- Salon and Spa Management
- Professional Practice, Hairdressing and Media
- Small Business Management
- Professional Practice Beauty Therapy
- Beauty Therapies Management
- Spa and Therapy Management
- Cosmetic Science

In addition to Higher Education programmes directly linked to hair and beauty, on completion of the Advanced Diploma in Hair and Beauty Studies you may also consider a career that is related to the hair and beauty industry, such as:

- Fashion Styling (Makeup and Hair design)
- Makeup and Hair Design for Music, Film and Photography
- Media Styling and Promotion (Makeup and Hair Design)
- Spa Management with Hospitality
- Spa and Holistic Therapies
- Complementary Therapies
- Health, Fitness and Holistic Therapies Management

There are other progression opportunities in Higher Education that are not directly related to the hair and beauty sector, although some aspects are covered within the Higher and Advanced Diplomas in Hair and Beauty Studies:

- Marketing and Sales
- Manufacturing Technology
- Media Studies
- Product Design and Development
- Fashion Styling and Photography
- Physiotherapy
- Nutrition, Food, Science and Health

All of the above are just examples; there are hundreds of Higher Education programmes directly or indirectly related to the hair and beauty sector.

EXTEND YOUR LEARNING

Investigate the content and entry requirements for a programme in Higher Education that you may be interested in. Useful websites are the University and College Admission Service (UCAS) **www.ucas.ac.uk** and Foundation Degree Forward (FDF) **www.fdf.ac.uk**.

Career progression outside the hair and beauty sector

The Diploma in Hair and Beauty Studies will give you the opportunity to research and investigate the six industries of the sector. You may decide that you would like to progress to the Advanced Diploma in Hair and Beauty Studies, or work in one of the hair and beauty industries. However you may decide that the hair and beauty sector is not for you, but you do like some parts of it.

For example, when completing your work for the science of hair and beauty, you may enjoy the scientific experiments and research, the human biology, anatomy and physiology and the nutrition. In which case you may like to explore careers in:

- Cosmetic science
- Trichology
- Physiotherapy
- Nutrition and related areas

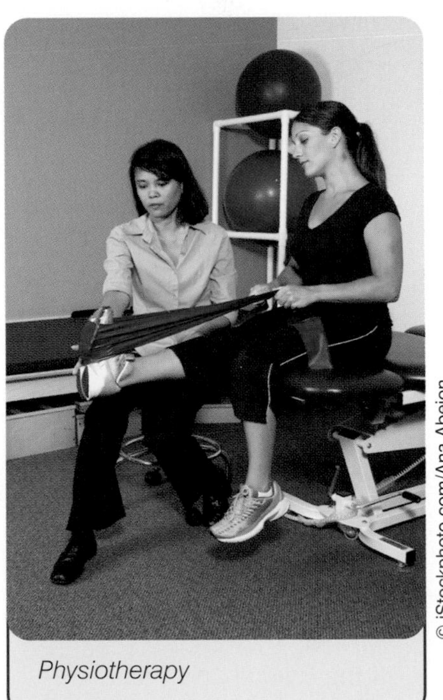

Physiotherapy

If you preferred the units about promoting and selling products, you might consider a career in:

- Marketing or sales
- Retail
- Customer service

When studying for the unit is salon business systems and processes, you may be able to see the link between this unit and the following occupations:

- Management (salon, spa or other businesses)
- Receptionist

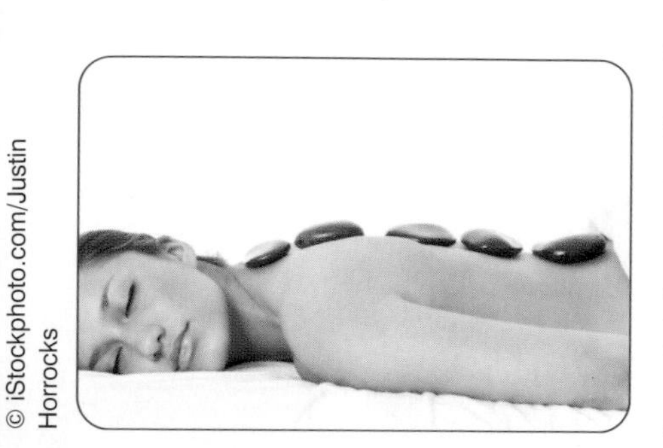

You may have enjoyed all aspects of the Diploma, but still may not want to be a hairdresser, beauty or spa therapist, barber or nail technician. In which case, all your hard work and study will not go to waste as the knowledge you have gained can lead into any of the following occupations:

- Holistic and complementary therapies
- Media studies
- Manufacturing technology
- Product design and development
- Creative studies and creative advertising
- Photography
- Fashion photography
- Photojournalism
- Fashion
- Public relations
- Events coordinator

EXTEND YOUR LEARNING

Investigate any of the alternative occupations that can be followed on completion of the Diploma in Hair and Beauty Studies. Find out what other skills or experience you need to enter them and make an action plan to guide your career development.

The impact of image on the world of hair and beauty

In Chapter 1 'The history of hair and beauty in society' you will have read about the development of the sector across the world and in this country. You will have read that personal image has always been important. How hair was worn or styled, or the way in which makeup was applied, projected an image to others about the place of that person in society.

EXTEND YOUR LEARNING

Search on Google images for examples of the Rachel and Pob.

Therefore, you can see that the hair and beauty sector was, and still is, moulded by trends and fashions. It only takes one new haircut on a well-known personality to create a new trend. There have been many examples of this in recent years. In the 1990s Jennifer Aniston made famous the long layered haircut she wore in the TV series *Friends*. Everyone wanted a 'Rachel'. Victoria Beckham has started many trends over the years with her different looks – from long hair extensions to the short 'Pob'.

In the world of beauty where tanning was once seen to be fashionable, fears related to skin cancer have led to the development of new types of equipment and products for providing a safe, tanned appearance. At the other extreme, there has been an increase in the fashion for paler skin.

The trend for extended nails has led to an increase in the number of nail bars and salons.

Increased leisure time has meant that people have more time to relax and so there is greater take up of the relaxing, therapeutic treatments that take place within spas. In the world of spa, there has been a trend for a more holistic approach to health and well-being. Many of these trends are set as a result of the increased amount of travel by clients to countries that have a different approach to beauty and spa treatments.

ACTIVITY 

Who or what influences the way you look? Analyse you own personal look and create a mood board with images that influence the way you create your own image.

EXTEND YOUR LEARNING

Use the Internet to find out what the trends in hair and beauty are going to be for next year.

Setting trends – the good and the bad

While celebrities may be instrumental is setting a new trend, all the hair and beauty industries also set their own. For example, top hairstylists and makeup artists will produce a collection each season, in the same way that fashion designers do with clothing. The collections are often very high fashion, but will be toned down so the hairstyle or makeup technique appeals to as wide a range of people as possible.

Therefore, trends in hair and beauty are actually very good for the sector. They lead to increased business.

While trends in hair and beauty do very little to harm people, there are some trends that can actually have an adverse affect. It would seem that everyone wants to be 'perfect'. However, what is perfect? Who determines the criteria?

Many images you see of people in magazines or in advertisements show skin without blemishes and bodies without unwanted lumps and bumps. Yet, even though it is known that many of them are airbrushed to remove any 'flaws', some people still try to copy these images. A further suggestion of 'perfection' is seen through the very slim, size zero, 'super models'. All this can lead to some people being dissatisfied with their bodies and appearance. Sometimes this dissatisfaction can have devastating results.

It's a fact!

The size zero debate came to the forefront in the media when the organisers of the Madrid Fashion Week in 2006 refused to use models who had a **Body Mass Index (BMI)** below 18. A BMI below this figure is considered to be unhealthy by the World Health Organisation.

EXTEND YOUR LEARNING  

Form into groups and debate whether you think size zero models should be used by fashion designers. You may ask, what is the point of seeing what clothes look like on a size zero model, when the vast majority of the clothes will be bought and worn by people who are not this size?

ACTIVITY 

Form a discussion group and discuss the dangers of trying to follow fashions and trends. You could use the examples such as slimming to achieve a size zero body, body piercing or tanning.

Wanting to achieve a size zero appearance has led to an increase in the number of people who have diet related conditions, such as *anorexia nervosa*, which is an eating disorder. Those with anorexia nervosa, male and female, typically have low body weights and a distortion of their own body image. Many have a fear of gaining weight and choose to limit their intake of food. In addition to the psychological problems associated with anorexia, the lack of nutrients through starvation, or a restricted diet, leads to damage to the body such as stunted growth, thinning of the hair, deficiencies of minerals in the body, reduction in the immune system function, and even infertility. In extreme cases, the end result has led to the death of people who have starved themselves trying to maintain the image.

Keeping up with trends

EXTEND YOUR LEARNING

Research the website of a product manufacturer of your choice. Investigate how they carry out their research, and the products that evolve.

Because the hair and beauty sector is continually evolving with changing trends, those who work in these industries have to continually adapt their existing skills and develop new ones to meet the needs of the new fashions. To assist with this there is a requirement for **Continuing Professional Development (CPD)**. CPD provides the opportunity for workers in the industry to learn new techniques and allows them to keep ahead of the industry, resulting in more profitable businesses. Those who do not keep up to date will eventually lose their credibility and their business.

Product manufacturers and those who produce equipment also react to changes in trends. Manufacturers invest heavily in **research and development (R&D)** to ensure that they are able to provide the right products, tools and equipment for the trends and fashions to be carried out.

Consumer spending in hair and beauty

It's a fact! Disposable income is a term that is used to describe the amount of money left over for spending after you have excluded essential spending such as taxes and living expenses. For example, mortgage, rent, food, household bills and essential clothing.

The money that consumers have to spend is known as **disposable income**. The more disposable income people have, the more money is spent on goods and services that, in times of hardship, may be considered to be a luxury.

Disposable income is important. For example, if fuel bills soar, or essential clothing costs rise too much, then, unless wages rise, the amount of disposable income that people have will fall. This means that there is less money available to spend on non-essential goods and services, including hair and beauty. A reduction in spending can lead to failing businesses and job losses. Job losses lead to a rise in those who are unemployed and having to live on benefits and have less disposable income. So, you can see that having disposable income is essential if the country is to have a strong economy.

ACTIVITY  

Calculate the amount of disposable income you have.

Research is continually being carried out that shows how consumers spend money in the hair and beauty sector. In the UK, overall, the amount of money spent in hairdressing salons and on personal grooming is £5.25 billion, and the spending for beauty therapy is £904 million. This amount has increased by 25 per cent since 2002.

When you investigate further you can find some interesting facts about the use of toiletries by males and females between the ages of 11 and 74 years of age:

- 93% of females use shampoo each week, compared to 80% of males
- 72% of females use skin care products, compared to 20% of males
- 36% of females use moisturisers, compared to 9% of males
- 4% of females use gel on their hair, compared to 13.5% of males

Source: ETCD GB TNS Worldpanel usage 12 months ending December 2006

From a report in 2007:

- The average household expenditure for hairdressing and beauty treatments was £161
- The average household expenditure for hair products, cosmetics and electrical appliances was £171.60

Source: Family spending, National Statistics/Marketing Pocket Book 2007

EXTEND YOUR LEARNING 

You can find more information and details about the size of the hair and beauty sector from the Habia website **www.habia.org** and download a document *Skills Needs Analysis for the Hair and Beauty Sector October 2007*. Investigate which years, from the period 2002 – 2006 had the highest growth in consumer spending in the hair and beauty industries.

ACTIVITY 

Investigate the amount of money you and your peers spend on hair and beauty treatments and services. You could identify total spending, or separate your research categories. For example, find out how much is spent on hairdressing services, beauty services and how much is spent on hair and beauty products. Work out the proportion that is spent in professional hairdressing and beauty salons and compare this to the amount spent on home, do-it-yourself products.

ACTIVITY 

Compare the amount of money spent by females in your consumer research study, with that of males.

The environment and the hair and beauty sector

Did you think about the environment when you last bought a shampoo, moisturiser or facial scrub? Every hair and beauty product you purchase will have made some impact on the environment. The ingredients used will require a degree of manufacture, some more than others. The finished products have to be packaged and transported to a place where they can be sold. Then, at the point of purchase, even more packaging can be added.

Every industry in all countries are now being asked to look carefully at the way manufacturing takes place in order to reduce damage to the environment.

There are some companies in the UK that have always been aware of the environmental impact of the hair and beauty sector. Anita Roddick, who opened the first Body Shop in Brighton in 1976, was one of the first people in the UK to link the environment with hair and beauty products. At that time few people appeared to be interested or aware of the environmental impact of the hair and beauty industry. Now every hair and beauty company that operates in the UK will have an action plan for reducing damage to the environment.

ACTIVITY 

Investigate the percentage of your total income that you spend on hair and beauty products and services.

It's a fact! L'Oréal ended testing on animals in 1989. The Research Team has now developed Episkin and SkinEthic which are reconstructed skin and tissue models. Since 2006, all skin and eye irritation tests have been carried out using reconstructed skin, eliminating the need for animal testing.

A typical action plan may include provision for:

- Ensuring the ingredients used are found from renewable plant sources that will not cause harm to people or the environment during manufacture or to the end user
- Finding alternatives to testing the safety of products on animals
- Making product containers out of bio-degradable materials that will not harm the environment when disposed of
- Reducing the amount of energy required for manufacture
- Planning the delivery of products to reduce the costs of transportation
- Disposal of the product after and during use

EXTEND YOUR LEARNING  

Download the report on sustainable development produced by L'Oréal from **www.loreal.com**.

ACTIVITY 

Think about how you can package a product to reduce waste and damage to the environment. You can do this activity by designing your own packaging for a product, or by showing how the packaging of an existing product can be improved.

Product design and development in the hair and beauty sector

When you look at the retail displays in a salon or spa you will see a wide range of professional products that are used there and that are also available for retail purchases by clients. If you look on the shelves of supermarkets and chemists you will see another range of products that are designed just for use at home.

Are you ever baffled by the choice?

When looking for a new shampoo, do you buy it from your hairdresser or from the supermarket? Do you choose it by the colour of the bottle, or do you read the features and benefits of the product. Have you ever been persuaded to buy a product after reading an advertisement about it?

All these types of questions are just some of those that will be considered by a manufacturer when they decide to design, develop and launch a new product or range of products.

Most new products are designed because there is a problem to solve. Perhaps an existing product is not selling well, or the packaging looks outdated. Perhaps a new fashion trend has developed and a product is required to meet the demands of the market. For example, prior to the use of straightening irons to smooth and straighten hair, you would not have found a product to protect hair from the intense, direct heat of the irons. But, as soon as straightening hair became fashionable, numerous products were available for this very purpose. And, even ten years ago, few people would have thought of using organic products.

Major manufacturers will employ people whose job it is to design and develop products or equipment.

Products for protecting hair when straightening

EXTEND YOUR LEARNING 

Research the L'Oréal website **www.loreal.com** and investigate the section on Science and Research. Note the number of people and the amount of money dedicated to cosmetic and dermatological research which can be found in 'Key Facts and Figures'.

The choice of products can be baffling

Designing a product

Successful design means that you have to be able to fully understand who the product is for – you have to know your market. So if you were thinking of designing a new makeup product, you would need to analyse, amongst other things:

- what products already exist
- who your product is aimed at – what is your market
- how much people would pay for it

Once you have decided what the product is going to be, it has to be made. You would need to think about how it can be made and the cost of manufacture – even at the earliest stages. You may find that the product you want to produce would be so costly to manufacture that you would not be able make a profit. If the product involved the use of chemicals you would have to check the safety of the products in both manufacture and use.

Putting a product into production

If you decide that you have a product that can go into production, you would need to make some models of how the end result will look. This means that you would create a mock up of the end result. When you have made your models, the next step is to carry out some market research with potential consumers. You have to be sure that the product is appealing and that consumers like the idea. Unless you get a positive result the idea may have to be abandoned.

Once you have completed your market research, decided how the product will look and how it can be made, you need to make a working **prototype**. The prototype stage is also when you would need to meet up with the people who are likely to make the product for you. You need to do this so that you can find out the likely costs of manufacture and confirm that production of the product is possible, affordable and profitable. The prototype would also have to include how the product will be presented and packaged to appeal to consumers.

The final stage of production would be to recheck that the end result meets the design brief.

EXTEND YOUR LEARNING

There are many marketing theories. One of the theories is known as the 4Ps. Investigate what the 4Ps are and why they are known as the *marketing mix*.

Once production is completed, the product will need to be marketed. A **marketing plan** would be put into place.

Marketing your product

You may not realise it, but throughout every day for most of your life, something has been marketed to you. When you watch television, go to the cinema, read a magazine, walk down the street or go into a shop – you will subject to marketing campaigns.

Marketing is more than selling a product, it is about getting your customer to notice your product, to buy your product and then to buy it again.

Working in a team produce a design brief for a new product, tool or piece of equipment for the hair and beauty sector that you think will be appealing to a chosen group of people. The design brief should include:

- what the product is
- what the product is called
- who the product is for
- what the product will do
- how the product will look
- how the product will be made
- the features and benefits of the product
- how the product will be marketed
- where your product will be sold
- how much the product will be sold for

It may be useful for you to refer to Chapter 4 'The science of hair and beauty' for information about how products work and testing products. You may want to consider environmental issues such as avoiding the excess use of packaging and the use of organic or environmentally friendly ingredients.

Set up a *Dragon's Den* and try to market your product to potential investors.

Bring your learning to life

Create an advertising campaign for your product. Think about the type of advertisement that would appeal to your target audience. Use the campaign to explain why your product is unique, its features and benefits.

What you have learnt

The world of hair and beauty and related sectors from global to local

- The hair and beauty sector is made up of six separate industries: hairdressing, barbering, African Caribbean hair, beauty therapy, nail services and spa therapy
- Almost every country in the world has had a hair and beauty sector

Career opportunities in hair and beauty

- You can progress from Level 1 to an Master's degree in the world of hair and beauty
- The career opportunities open to you are not restricted to the six in the hair and beauty sector. The skills and knowledge you learn for the Diploma in Hair and Beauty Studies can open more doors – in media, marketing, design, business management trichology, retail and much, much more

What employers expect from those who work in hair and beauty

- Employability skills are important in whichever occupation you choose to work in
- Good communication skills are vital for the hair and beauty industry. You also need to show that you have, amongst other things, a willingness to learn, can work in a team, have a positive attitude, are creative and show leadership qualities

The skills you will need to succeed in hair and beauty

- You will have to practise your skills for a very long time before you become competent enough to work on clients in the hair and beauty sector
- Once you have finished your initial training, you have to carry on training for the rest of your working life

The professional and trade organisations that support the hair and beauty industries

- There are professional and trade organisations for each of the six industries
- The organisations provide support, information and the opportunity for workers in the industry to meet and share issues and good practice

The size of the industries and the impact they have on the economy and society

- The true size of the industry is difficult to measure because of the way in which occupations are categorised
- The hair and beauty industries are continuing to grow both in this country and in others

How trends in hair and beauty are affected by influences from the world of fashion and celebrities

- Creative and talented individuals in the hair and beauty sector set new trends through their creativity
- Celebrities showcase and promote the new trends
- Trends ensure continual growth and business for the fashion related hair and beauty industry
- Not all trends are good – some can have a negative impact

The environmental impact of the industries

- All product manufacturers have action plans to ensure that the impact on the environment through the design, development and distribution of goods is reduced

Product design and development

- All new products and equipment begin with research into the need for the product or equipment
- The products or equipment are designed taking into account the cost of production and manufacture

Assessment activities

Crossword

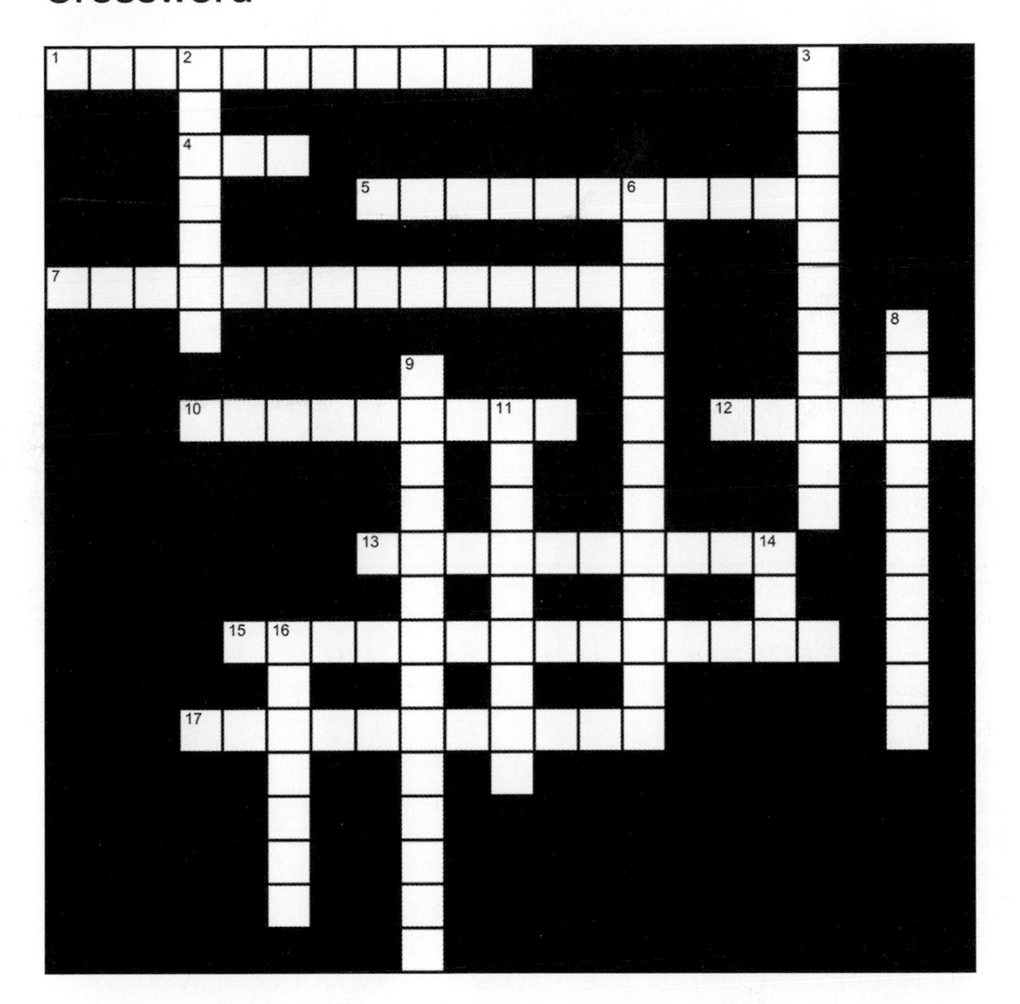

Across

1 If you are to be successful in the hair and beauty sector you must be able to do this well with a wide range of people (11)

4 The number of industries in the hair and beauty sector (3)

5 This is what you would be if you carried out a chemical relaxing service (11)

7 This learning programme means you are employed in a salon while you study (14)

10 This type of hair or beauty sector worker is not based in a salon or spa (9)

12 This person cuts the hair of men and boys (6)

13 The skin condition that can occur if personal protective equipment is not used (10)

15 The job role of a person who would carry out a pedicure (2 words) (4,10)

17 A psychometric test will identify this (11)

Down

2 A type of degree that can be studied for the hair and beauty sector (7)

3 The number of spas in the UK (4,7)

6 Employers rate these skills very highly (13)

8 This skill is useful for all the industries in the hair and beauty sector (10)

9 Gels, acrylics ad wraps are all types of this service (4,10)

11 The use of these in the hairdressing industry may cause discomfort to sensitive skin (9)

14 Hydrotherapy, flotation and steam treatments all take place in this environment (3)

16 Thermal styling is carried out on this hair type (7)

Wordsearch

```
N M M U Q N G D N O I T I R T U N R E C O N O M Y
R E C E P T I O N I S T Q U A L I F I C A T I O N
M J L J A R Q P L E C I N A G R O E R U T A E F C
L A I U S I E R W U R O V D Z S D E S I G N E D K
R M E A S C R O D I L T C O N S U M E R S L X E W
E T N H E H U T T A T T R I B U T E N S L Z Y Y S
Y A T O R O T O S L I A N Y T U A E B O B F H O T
C M S C V L C T I N G R E D I E N T S U D R W L Y
F O K B I O A Y M A N A G E M E N T O S O D Q P L
I U M B C G F P Y C X X E Y I M Q Z G W A T X M I
P G N P E Y U E T E C H N I C I A N S E N L E E N
T E N L L A N O I S S E F O R P P W M T Y E A A G
U N R I A E A I F Q E S Y S E L B A W E N E R R M
W P E S S S M R R K A K K S R U Z Y P C Y M J K Y
H V Q M O S A E I C N M N E B U Y G R D A Q H Q C
Y L L A T N E M N O R I V N E X R R K Y T S Y M I
Q A P S C A A R W T L S T I F E N E B V E W E L T
M S E H F L E L D L A F A S H I O N G D P D R B S
J V I U A M E R I R E R T U H R T E W A I O R A I
U S I B O D L K T T I Y Y B R L I Q X A N A V R L
E R O C G O S D W L Y A U V L I K D J S D A G B O
W L N E C T Z V R I J U H P H B C W A Y T Q M E H
G I H A O P A C K A G I N G T S I P A R E H T R Y
E B L Y E L B A D A R G E D O I B I L R B K O E W
E M P L O Y M E N T C R E A T I V I T Y U X A V A
```

attribute
barber
beauty
benefits
biodegradable
business
businesses
clients
complementary
consumers
creativity
designed
economy
employed
employment
energy
environment
environmentally
fashion
feature
franchise
global
hairdressing
holistic
income
ingredients
knowledge
local
management
manager
manufacture
media
nail
nutrition
organic
owner
packaging
personality
professional
prototype
qualification
receptionist
renewable
salary
salon
service
skill
spa
styling
team
technician
therapist
treatment
trend
trichology

Further research

Design a working environment for a hair and beauty industry of your choice. Describe the environment and the type of clients you think would be attracted. Provide examples of the colour scheme and the furniture that you would have in the salon or spa. Show your ideas on a mood board.

Multiple choice: The world of hair and beauty

1 Top hairdressers will produce one of these each year to predict fashion trends
- a collection
- b style book
- c hairstyle
- d haircut

2 A unisex salon is
- a a salon for men
- b a salon for women
- c a salon for men and women
- d a salon for men and boys

3 A galvanic treatment is an example of
- a a hairstyle
- b an electrotherapy
- c a nail extension
- d a massage

4 Typical progression from a Higher Level Diploma in Hair and Beauty Studies will be to
   a master's degree
   b young apprenticeship
   c advanced diploma in hair and beauty studies
   d foundation diploma in hair and beauty studies

5 Team work is important for the hair and beauty sector because
   a working as a team ensures the salon or spa environment is clean
   b working as a team ensures that you have chance to talk to your friends at work
   c working as a team ensures everyone likes each other
   d working as a team ensures the business runs efficiently and profitably

6 A conceptual model will be used to
   a design a new nail art technique
   b predict what a new product will look like
   c walk down the run way at a fashion show
   d design a piece of equipment

7 A competence based qualification
   a prepares you for work
   b prepares you for exams
   c ensures you are ready for study
   d ensures you are ready for work

8 Someone who carries out a manicure is most likely to be known as a
   a nail technician
   b hairdresser
   c beauty therapist
   d spa therapist

9 To work at management level in the hair and beauty sector you need to have
   a an NVQ Level 3
   b advanced diploma in hair and beauty studies
   c foundation degree
   d vocational qualification

10 Once a new product has been designed and developed, it has to be
   a sold
   b wrapped
   c priced
   d marketed

Viva: Sharon Cox at Sanrizz

3 salon business systems and processes

A complex system that works is invariably found to have evolved from a simple system that worked.

JOHN GALL B1925, SCIENTIST AND AUTHOR

Introduction

When you walk into any business that provides a service to the public you are likely to find a reception area. Because the reception area is the first area that clients and visitors see, it is important that a good impression is made. Therefore the environment has to be safe, welcoming and comfortable.

The receptionist is the first point of contact and is a key member of staff. The skills of a receptionist are as important as any member of staff in any business. For the hair and beauty sector, the skills of the receptionist are as important as the technical skills of stylists, therapists and technicians. The receptionist may be the

What you are going to learn

Throughout this chapter you will learn about:

- ★ Business systems and processes
- ★ The role and function of receptions and receptionists for any business and of hair and beauty receptions and receptionists
- ★ How the reception area plays a significant part in creating a positive and lasting impression of the business
- ★ How reception displays promote the business
- ★ How reception systems work
- ★ The different types of appointment systems and how they work
- ★ The significance of the Data Protection legislation
- ★ How stock control works
- ★ How to calculate the price of products, treatments and services
- ★ How to take payments

only member of staff who has a 'bird's eye view' of all events planned and the people who will visit the business on that day, and for the coming weeks.

Technology plays a vital role in more and more businesses and this is also true for salons and spas. So not only do receptionists have to be well organised people with outstanding communication skills; they also have to be computer literate.

The job role of a receptionist can be the key to a successful and efficient hair and beauty business.

It's a fact! The hair and beauty sector is made up of very many micro-businesses known as **small and medium sized enterprises (SMEs)**. You can read more about the size of the hair and beauty sector in Chapter 2 'The world of hair and beauty'.

Business systems and processes for businesses

In order to function efficiently and profitably, all businesses need to have systems and processes in place. The systems and processes will vary from one sector or business to another. The variety of different systems will be related to the size of the business. Small businesses have different needs to large businesses.

The size of the business and the skills of the staff will determine the type of business systems and processes that are required. Very small businesses can have the simplest of processes that may be operated by just one person. Other businesses may be so large that the processes have to be broken down into one person sized, job roles. For example, in a small beauty therapy business *one* person can source, purchase and pay for the supplies that are required. In a large spa business, *one* person may source supplies, a *second* may request the supplies and a *third* may actually authorise payment for them.

The systems and processes for *any* type of business may include general systems, process and methods for:

- ordering supplies
- maintaining the levels of stock
- calculating the time required for the production of products or to provide services
- receiving payments
- paying creditors
- selling products
- marketing products and services
- developing new ideas for products and services
- designing new products and services
- paying staff

ACTIVITY  

Work in a small group and identify other types of business systems and processes that need to be in place in any business.

Business systems and processes for the hair and beauty sector

All businesses in the hair and beauty sector, large and small, will need to have, as a minimum, a system and process in place to:

- schedule appointments
- receive payment for goods and services
- maintain and store client records
- control stock

Many of the activities related to the systems and processes for a business in the hair and beauty sector are completed in the reception area.

The reception area

The reception area of any business, which will include those in the hair and beauty sector, is likely to be the first area that visitors see. Because of this, the appearance of the area must provide a *positive and lasting impression*. The reception area should be well signposted so that visitors know where to report.

Reception areas can be found in many businesses

Reception areas for a business in the hair and beauty sector

Top tip

Use a visitors' book in a salon or spa so you have a record of people in the building who are not clients. For example, you may get visitors such as manufacturer's representatives and people who come to repair or maintain equipment.

Desk area

Most reception areas have a desk where reception stationery and equipment are kept. The desk must always be clean and tidy. The personal belongings of those who work on the reception desk should be out of sight for security and visual purposes. At the desk of a general business you will find a **visitors' book**, which must be signed by all those who are visiting the business. This not only provides a record of who has entered the premises, but it is a health and safety requirement. In the event of a fire or other evacuation procedure, the receptionist will take the visitors' book to check that all the visitors have left the building.

Computers are required to operate a reception management system

It's a fact!

Flowers or other arrangements are often displayed on a reception desk.

It's a fact!

If there was an evacuation in a salon or spa, the receptionist can use the Appointment Book as a record of people in the building.

Communications

You will find a computer at many reception areas. The computer for the reception area must only be used for business purposes. To use it for personal purposes would be unprofessional and will not create a good impression. Imagine how it would look to a client or visitor if the receptionist was checking out a social network site! There will normally be a telephone in the reception area, or in the case of larger companies, there may even be a switchboard. The telephone should only be used for professional purposes.

Top tip

Receptionists will ensure that the reading material is suitable for the age and gender of the clients and visitors to the business.

Waiting area

There will often be a waiting area where visitors can sit. The seating area must be clean and comfortable. Any reading materials such as magazines must be up to date and in good condition.

It's a fact!

The reading material provided at the reception area in the hair and beauty sector can be used to reflect the image of the salon or spa. For example, you will usually find magazines about fashion, health, well-being, personal appearance and hair styles.

Waiting area

ACTIVITY

Create a hairstyle or makeup file that could be kept in a reception area for men and/or women. The file should be of a professional standard that waiting clients could look through to give them ideas for a hair or beauty treatment or service.

Displays

The reception area is often used to display the products, and sometimes equipment, for clients to purchase for home use. The displays must be kept tidy and free from dust. In a salon or spa attractive displays can be used to promote products, services and treatments. Displays to promote products can also reflect the time of the year. For example, gifts at Christmas, tanning products in the summer time or protective face and hand creams in the winter.

Top tip

Many salons and spas will have a file of press cuttings at the reception area which illustrates success stories about their business. Some will have hairstyle files or examples of the work that is produced by the staff who work there.

ACTIVITY

Work in a team to design a promotional poster and create a display using hair and beauty products that could be used in a reception area. Ask other people in your group to evaluate the poster and display – would they be persuaded to buy the products?

ACTIVITY

Discuss other times of the year for promotional displays

Promotional display in salon or spa

Qrt / Alamy

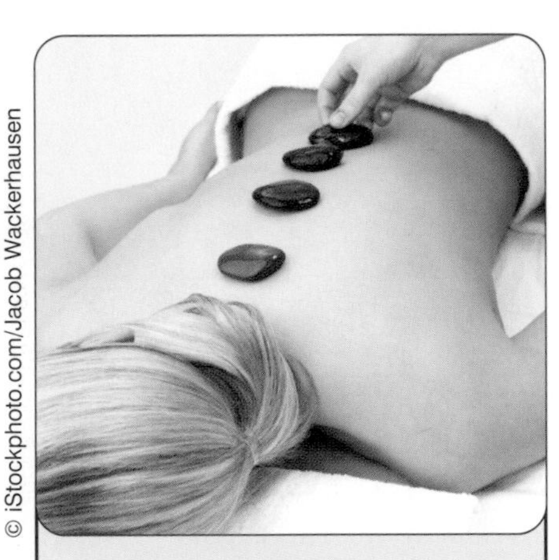

© iStockphoto.com/Jacob Wackerhausen

Hot stone therapy

Images

Images are used in the reception area to promote and advertise the work that is carried out and to reflect the image of the business.

Salon or spa images

In a spa reception you may see images of the treatments that take place, such as stone therapy or Indian head massage. In hairdressing or barbering reception areas you will see images of hairstyles. It is important that the images are kept up to date to illustrate the changes in fashion and technology. Manufacturers will also provide posters and other advertising materials that can be displayed in the reception area.

Certificates

In a salon or spa you will often find framed certificates for the qualifications that are held by staff displayed on the wall in the reception area. This promotes the expertise of the staff in the business and provides clients with confirmation that they are attending a salon or spa where staff are well trained and qualified.

Price list

The price list is normally displayed in the reception area. The price list should be clear to read and easy to understand. Many salons or spas also have leaflets that can be taken away by the client or other visitors. The leaflets will include the price list and other information to promote the business.

Insurance certificates

Insurance, public and treatment liability certificates, as well as relevant health and safety notices are also displayed in the reception area. Some Local Authorities require hair and beauty businesses to register with them. Some

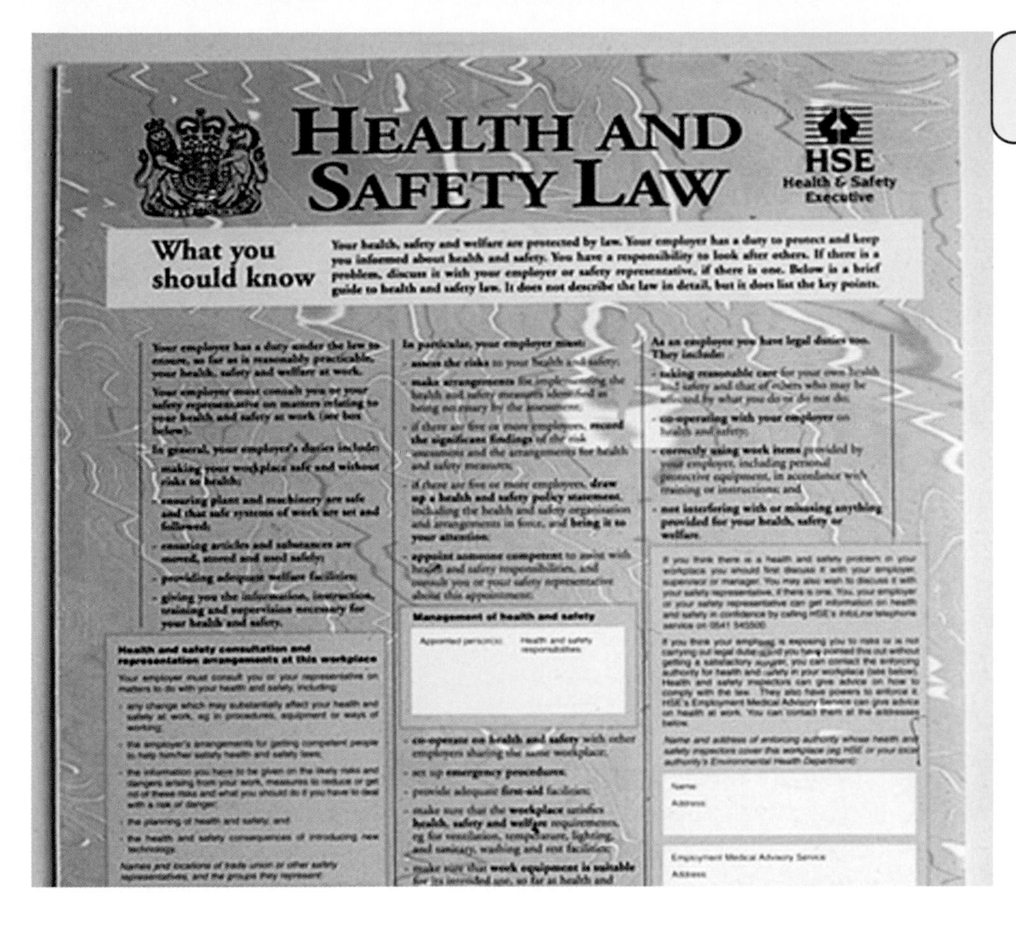

Certificates can be displayed in salons and spas

salons may need a special licence to carry our certain treatments such as ear piercing. These licences will also be displayed at the reception area.

SALON TREATMENTS

WAXING

Full leg and Bikini line	£25.00
Full Leg Wax	£21.00
Half Leg Wax	£13.00
Brazilian	£15.00
Hollywood	£20.00
Bikini Line	£8.50
Under Arm Wax	£5.00
Lip/Chin Wax	£5.00
Forearm wax	£9.00

PROPIL

Progressive and lasting hair removal. Applied after waxing the results are fewer and finer hairs. Waxing becomes less painful with a real delay in the hair re-growth making waxing less frequent. After 15-20 treatments areas may be hair free*.
*Natural forms of hair growth

5 minutes	£10.00

ELECTROLYSIS

10 minute sitting	£10.00
15 minute sitting	£15.00
20 minute sitting	£18.00

JESSICA - THE NATURAL NAIL COMPANY

Manicure	£14.00
French Manicure	£16.00
Shape and Varnish	£8.00
French Polish	£9.00
Pedicure	£20.00

PARAFFIN WAX TREATMENT

A hydrating, relaxing, warm mask. Applied to the hands or feet, leaving the skin soft. Helps relieve arthritic pain.

£12.00

Price list

Refreshments

Waiting visitors to a business should be offered refreshments. The receptionist may make the visitor a drink, or sometimes there is a drinks machine where visitors can choose and make their own. All refreshments must be hygienically prepared and presented.

ACTIVITY

Hair and beauty reception areas are frequently visible from the street. When you walk past one, make an observation about the impression that is given about the business. Would a client gain a good impression about the business by looking at the reception area? Is the reception area clear to see? Does the receptionist give a positive, first impression? Compare several reception areas and write a short report of your findings.

EXTEND YOUR LEARNING

Research a range of drink machines that could be found in a reception area. Which would you buy if you were a salon or spa owner?

Bring your learning to life

This can be a whole class project, or you could work in small groups, or if you choose, on your own.

Design a reception area for a chosen industry. It can be for an industry in the hair and beauty sector or it could be for any other business of your choosing.

You should prepare a **design brief** which indicates what the requirements are for the reception area. The design brief will be used as an indicator that will show if the end result has met the initial plans.

A mood board can be used to show the colour scheme, furnishings, fabrics and reception furniture.

The reception area should be designed taking account of health and safety requirements and client/visitor comfort. It should include all the key features that should be found in a reception area.

Present your finished design ideas to others and explain your justification for the design.

Top tip

If you are working with others, you will need to outline the roles and responsibilities for each person in the team. You may need someone to carry out research on reception furniture, another to find suitable fabrics. The choice of colour scheme may be decided after a group discussion and negotiation.

ACTIVITY

Discuss with others the different places where a receptionist can be found.

The role of a receptionist

A receptionist's job can be very interesting as they will meet a range of new people every day. The role is not limited to the hair and beauty sector. Receptionists work in other sectors, for example medical receptionists in hospitals and doctors' surgeries. You will also find receptionists in many offices and schools.

Although businesses may be different, the role of the receptionist is very similar. All receptionists are the first point of contact, either face to face or by telephone. Because of this they have to ensure that they make a good first impression, both for them and for the business.

All receptionists, in any business will:

- answer the telephone
- deal with enquiries
- take messages
- greet visitors
- assist visitors

Some office based receptionists will normally work from Monday to Friday. However those who work in the hospitality, leisure, hair and beauty sectors will work whenever customers and clients need the services of the business. For the hair and beauty sector this will include weekends and, sometimes, evenings.

The skills of the receptionist

As the first point of contact, receptionists in any type of business must be confident, friendly and have a suitable personality for the business they work in. Some receptionists will work in a calm, quiet environment, others in a busy bustling business. They have to be good organisers as they have to manage time and work schedules for themselves and for other people.

Good communication skills are vital for receptionists. This will include verbal and non-verbal communication as well as written communication. You can read more about communication skills in Chapter 6 'Communication and client care'. Receptionists often have to deal with cash handling, so numeracy skills are also important. More and more receptionists have to use information technology as part of their daily work, so computer skills are also required.

A receptionist

Receptionists for the hair and beauty sector

Salons and spas that are large enough will have a dedicated receptionist. Other businesses would have too few staff to justify this, so all staff are expected to help with the role. However, this does not mean that the role is less important.

The job role for a receptionist in the hair and beauty industry will include the following:

- creating a positive and lasting impression of the business
- handling client enquiries
- being the first point of contact for client complaints and disputes
- communicating with clients and visitors to the salon or spa, face to face, by telephone or electronic means such as email, and sometimes SMS
- ensuring the waiting area is well maintained, safe and secure
- taking responsibility for client payments by cash, credit and debit cards, cheques and vouchers
- meeting and greeting clients and visitors to the salon or spa
- scheduling appointments

It's a fact!

The receptionist's role is frequently carried out by a member of staff who also has additional management responsibilities for the business, which illustrates the importance of the job.

- assisting clients and customers with retail sales
- displaying and promoting salon and spa products, services and treatments
- monitoring stock by stock rotation
- ordering stock
- liaising with product manufacturers and their representatives

Scheduling appointments

One of the main roles of a receptionist in the hair and beauty sector is the scheduling of client appointments. This is an important function that has to be completed carefully and accurately. The appointment system ensures that those who work in the salon or spa have a well planned working day. This helps to ensure that there is a calm and efficient working environment.

A salon receptionist will need to be aware of the following in order to schedule appointments:

- the types of treatments and services available
- the members of staff available and capable of completing the treatments and services
- the time it takes for stylists, therapists or technicians to complete each treatment or service
- the length of time the client will be in the salon or spa
- the cost of each treatment or service
- how to record the treatments or services

If appointments have been inaccurately made the results can lead to unhappy staff, dissatisfied clients, and in the worst cases, loss of clients. To avoid this, when scheduling appointments, a receptionist will:

- record the name of the client
- record a contact telephone number; this could be a work, home or mobile number – it should be the one that the client is most likely to respond to
- record the service or treatment the client requires
- allocate the client to the member of staff of the client's choice, or if there is no preference, then to a member of staff who is qualified to carry out the treatment or service requested
- make the appointment for the date and time most convenient to the client and the salon or spa

When scheduling appointments a receptionist must:

- listen carefully to the client's request
- allow adequate time for the treatment or service

Top tip

Once the appointment is made, it is important for the receptionist to repeat the recorded information back to the client in order to confirm the appointment has been made correctly.

- make sure the client is aware of how long the treatment or service is likely to take
- suggest alternative times for appointments if the time the client requests is not available
- check if the client has a preferred stylist, therapist or technician

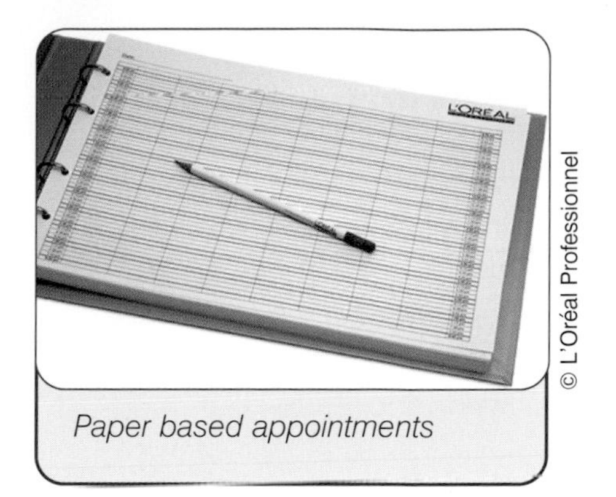

Paper based appointments

Recording appointments

Appointments can be recorded using a paper based system or using computer software. The use of the two systems varies between the industries in the hair and beauty sector.

Paper based appointment systems

Many businesses in the hair and beauty sector use paper based appointment systems. The systems work well and are easy to learn and use.

Standard appointment pages are divided into vertical columns which represent each member of staff, and then horizontally subdivided into 15 minute segments of time. This means that the time allowed for all treatments and services has to be calculated in 15, 30, 45 and 60 minute slots.

It's a fact!

The spa industry is most likely to use Information Technology for business functions, whereas the African Caribbean hair industry is the least likely to do so.

Computer based appointment systems

The use of IT is continually growing in all businesses in the hair and beauty sector. Therefore computer literacy is a useful employability skill for all members of staff.

EXTEND YOUR LEARNING

Download the Skill Foresight Report from the Habia website **www.habia.org** and investigate the use of IT by all industries in the sector.

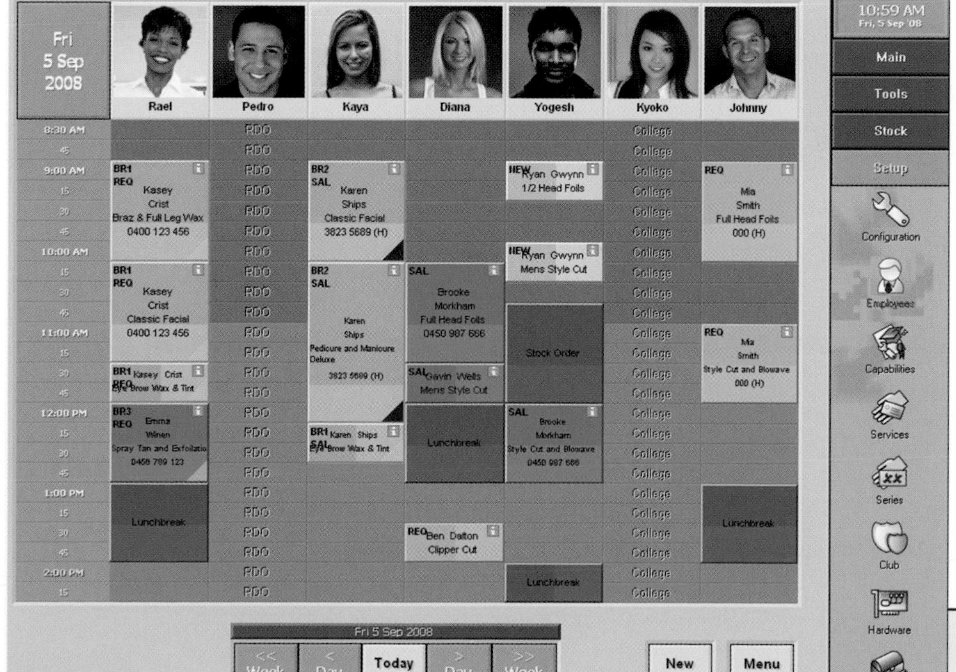

Appointment screen from Shortcuts

ACTIVITY  

Investigate an on-line demonstration for making an appointment in the hair and beauty sector at www.shortcuts.com.

When using a computer based appointment system, the same routine has to be followed as that used for making appointments with a paper based system. The receptionist will ask the same questions and use the same criteria for allocating a client to a particular stylist, therapist or technician. This system still has columns representing each member of staff, and time is divided throughout the day. The receptionist makes the appointment by blocking out a period of time, using the software in a similar way as blocking time out on paper.

Paper based versus information technology appointment systems

While paper based appointment systems have worked well for many years, there are limitations in the ways in which these types of systems can be used to generate other, additional and useful management information for the business.

All businesses have to be as competitive and efficient as possible to ensure profits are made. A computerised reception system can not only fufil the requirements for making appointments, but can also create additional information and reports about clients, that is lost, or more difficult to create using a paper based system.

Shortcuts is just one example of a **reception management system.** The methods for making appointments are linked to other information that is important for business planning. For example, from an appointment made by an individual client, it is possible to see the history of their visits, the treatments they have regularly, the products they buy and the amount of money they spend. By looking at this information, it is possible to target certain clients for promotions and special offers. They may like a particular brand of cleansing products. So, when the products are on special offer, you can use the information you hold to promote the offer to the client.

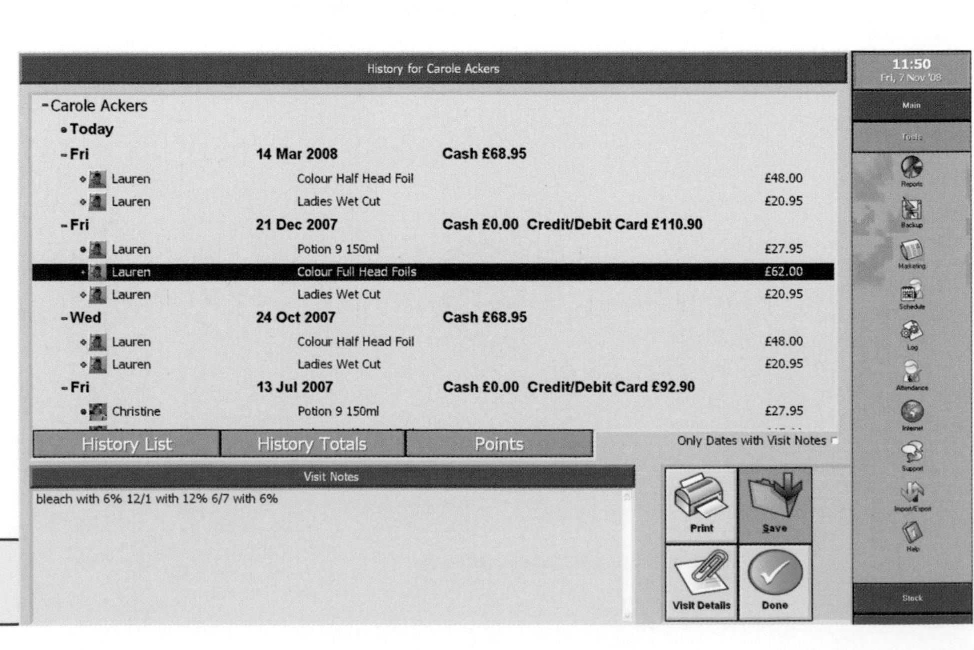

Shortcuts client history

It's a fact!

Information technology is not limited to the use of computers in the salon or spa. SMS is now being used to communicate with clients. For example, it can be used to remind clients that they have an appointment. Clients who fail to turn up for an appointment cost the business lost income and wasted staff time. The message can be sent one or two days before the appointment and the system allows the client to accept or decline the appointment.

Top tip

If an appointment is cancelled, the receptionist will rub out the appointment with an eraser on a paper based system or delete on a computer based system. It is very important that this is done in order to see that the appointment time has become available again.

Treatment and service abbreviations

There is not a great deal of space to write on the appointment page, therefore, apart from the name and contact details of the client, all other details relating to the appointment are abbreviated. To avoid confusion or misunderstandings, the same *short hand* abbreviations for treatments and services must be used by anyone recording an appointment. This is particularly important if the business does not have a dedicated receptionist so that the appointment page is easy to read and be understood by all.

Each business will have their own way of abbreviating the treatments and services carried out. Some commonly found abbreviations are:

c/b/d cut and blow dry

col colour

e/b/s eye brow shape

man manicure

b/m body massage

EXTEND YOUR LEARNING

Research the reception management systems available for making appointments and other reception functions. Compare the systems and determine which system you would be most likely to purchase if you were a salon or spa owner. List the reasons for your potential purchase.

ACTIVITY

Discuss how you would abbreviate the following treatments and services with others. Do you all agree how it should be done? If not, ask the person who made the suggestions for their logic.

- permanent wave
- shampoo and set
- pedicure
- back massage
- makeup
- face mask
- highlights
- eyelash tint
- nail extensions

It's a fact! Due to the development time of chemical services in the hairdressing and barbering industries, the stylist can work on a second client while the chemical is developing on the first client.

It's a fact! The differences in time will sometimes be a special feature of the salon or spa. Some businesses charge much higher prices based on the fact that clients will have more individual attention from staff. Some hair and beauty businesses do not have individual prices for treatments and services, but charge by the hour that the client spends in the salon or spa.

ACTIVITY  

If you are able to have a work placement in a salon or spa, check the times that are allowed for the treatments and services.

Treatment and service timing

Every client who books an appointment for a hair or beauty treatment or service will need to have time allocated for them with a stylist, therapist or technician.

The time spent by the client in the salon or spa is not the same as the time that is allocated for an appointment. For example, when a client has a hair colour, the time required to apply the colour may be as little as 15 minutes. But, the colour then has to have time to develop and then more time is needed to shampoo it from the hair. Then, even more time is required for the hair to be conditioned. Added to this is time allocated for any follow on services, such a cutting and styling. This means that the total time spent in the salon by the client can be up to 2 hours, although only around 1 hour of this time is spent with the stylist. However some treatments and services are very labour intensive. For example when creating scalp plaits or hair extensions, a stylist will be with the client for the whole service, which can take up to a full working day, and a body massage also requires the continual presence of a therapist.

Appointment times

The times allowed for treatments and services will vary according to the treatment or service. They will also vary from one salon or spa to another. However, there some times that can be used as a general guide for hair and beauty treatments and services that are carried out by competent and experienced staff.

Examples of appointment times for the hairdressing and barbering industry

The time allowed for a haircut is around 30 minutes, although a complete restyle may take up to one hour. A beard trim will be allocated 15 minutes. Colouring services can take from 15 minutes, or 2 or more hours of time by the stylist for a colour correction service. In the African Caribbean hair industry, some individual services can take a long time. For example, it can take 2 hours to complete a full head of scalp plaits with added hair.

Examples of appointment times for the beauty therapy industry

The receptionist should allow 45 minutes for a makeup service and 15 minutes for an eyebrow shape.

Examples of appointment times for the nail services industry

The time allowed for a manicure or pedicure is 45 minutes and for nail art approximately 5–10 minutes for each nail.

Examples of appointment times for the spa industry

An Indian head massage takes 45 minutes and for a full aromatherapy head and body massage, 75 minutes is required.

Answering the telephone

A receptionist will answer most, if not all the calls that are received by the business. However, if there is no dedicated receptionist, it is important for all staff to be trained in the skill of using the telephone.

The tone of voice that is used to answer the telephone is as important as body language for a face to face greeting. The response used when answering the telephone should be standardised and the sound of the voice should be welcoming. When speaking on the telephone, a receptionist will speak clearly. They will ensure that they do not mumble or speak too fast and will alter the tone of their voice so that they always sound interested in the caller's enquiry.

It is important that a ringing telephone is answered promptly. How long are you prepared to leave a telephone ringing? Perhaps 8, 9 or 10 times – or less? A lost telephone call can result in lost business.

Receptionists can be very busy people, they may have a number of people waiting at the desk for attention, but the client on the telephone will not know this. Therefore, the receptionist will always excuse themself from the people at the desk to answer the call. If they are very busy and they know that the call will take some time, they will take the caller's number and ring them back as soon as they can.

Top tip

Smiling when answering the telephone will result in friendly tone of voice.

It is important to answer the telephone promptly

ACTIVITY    

Role play the activities at a busy reception area. One of the group should act as the receptionist and the others as impatient clients waiting for attention. Use the following scenarios: a client is waiting to pay and he has a bus to catch; a client is waiting to check in for an appointment; the telephone is ringing; a client would like some advice about a retail product; another is waiting for a drink to be served. Discuss how the receptionist deals with the situation. What do you think is the correct order for the clients to be attended to?

Bring your learning to life 

When you are in the training salon or work placement, ask if you can have a go at the following tasks:

- making an appointment for a client
- cancelling an appointment
- answering the telephone
- meeting and greeting clients

Top tip

Remember that messages may contain confidential information, so other people should not be told the content of the message.

Taking messages

Receptionists will often take, record and pass on messages. Message taking is a form of communication and must be completed accurately in order to maintain effective communication within the salon or spa.

Messages must be clearly written and include, as a minimum, the following information:

- who the message is for
- who has taken the message
- the date and time the message was taken
- what the message is
- any action required
- if the message is urgent
- how to reply to the message (contact telephone number, address, email)

EXTEND YOUR LEARNING

Investigate the different options for taking and passing on messages.

Top tip

Receptionists and other message takers will ensure that the message is given to the appropriate person as soon as possible. If the person is not available, other people should be told that there is a message waiting. They will keep checking when the person will be available so the message can be passed on.

ACTIVITY

Design a form that includes all the criteria that should be covered when taking messages.

Taking payments

The role of the receptionist in a salon or spa will include the taking of payments from clients for services and treatments. There are advantages to having a dedicated receptionist as just one person is taking payments, therefore, any discrepancies that may occur with payments can be more easily identified. It is important to be aware that where there is no dedicated receptionist, not all of the staff who work in the salon or spa will be authorised to take payments from clients and that only those who are authorised should do so.

Most salons and spas will accept the following payment methods:

- **cash**
- **cheque**
- **credit card**
- **payment card**
- **gift voucher**

Messages should be written clearly

If the payment process is linked to the appointment system as it is with a reception management system, other activities will automatically take place at the same time as payments are made. For example, the treatment or service the client had will be recorded, and so will the products the client has

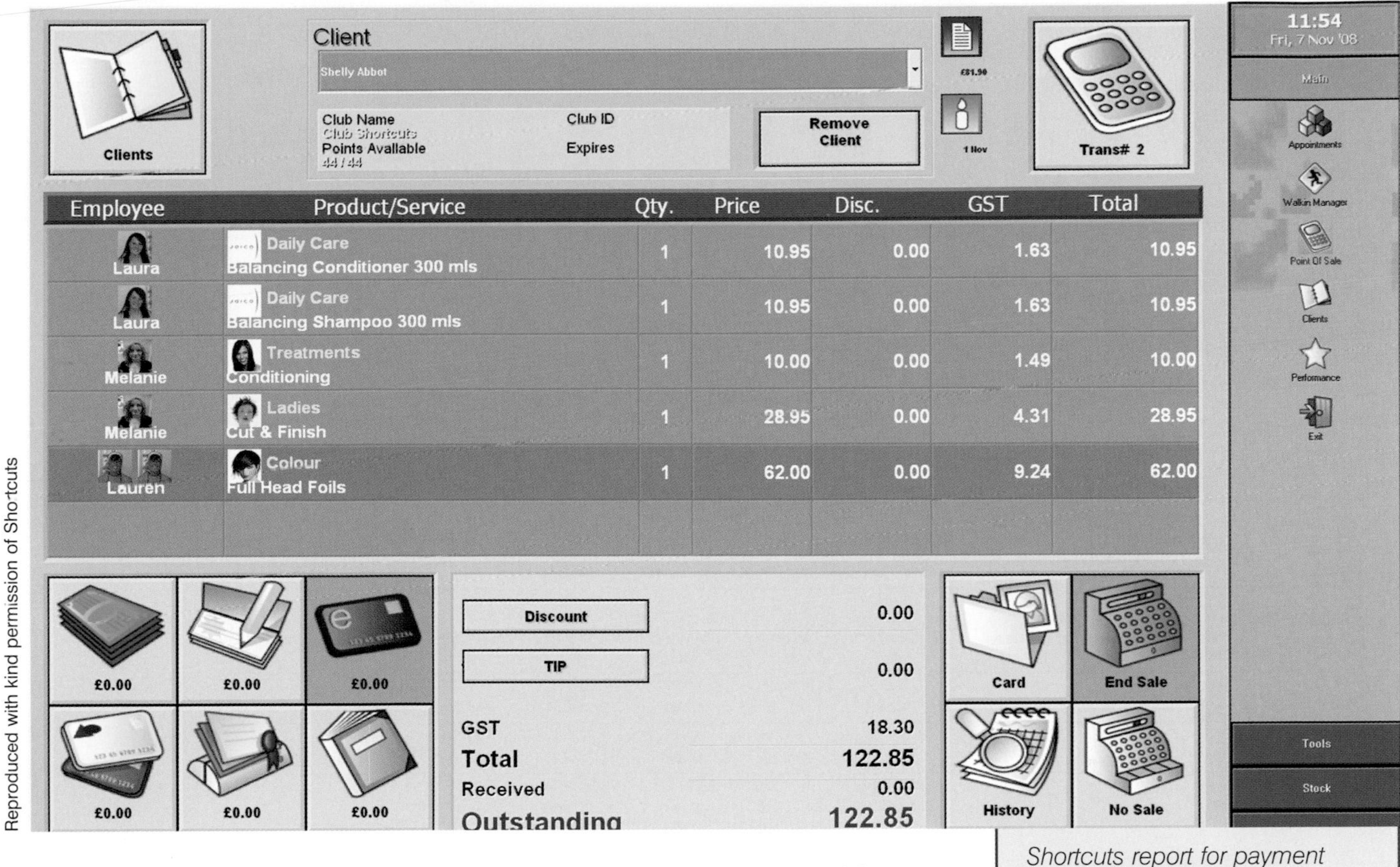

Shortcuts report for payment transaction

purchased. The products that the client bought are then also tracked for stock control.

The software used for payment transactions will also allow the receptionist to create reports for the value of the money taken by the business on a daily, weekly, monthly and yearly basis. As well as this, the value of client treatment, service and sales can be tracked for each individual member of staff. This will quickly highlight members of staff who are working well, and those who are creating insufficient profits for the business.

How to take client payments

The methods of calculating and storing payment will vary from one business to another. Most businesses will have an electronic till, even if they do not have a full reception management system. Having an electronic till enables the amount that the client has to pay and the change required to be accurately calculated. The till also provides a safe and secure place for payments to be stored.

Taking a cash payment

When taking cash payments a receptionist will:

- calculate the bill, ensuring the amount to be charged is correct
- inform the client of the total amount
- take the client's money and count it in front of the client

It's a fact!

Many of those employed in the hair and beauty sector receive **commission** as part of, or for their entire wage. Commission is based on the amount of money taken by the stylist, therapist or technician. This is one reason why it is important to accurately calculate sales activities of individual members of staff.

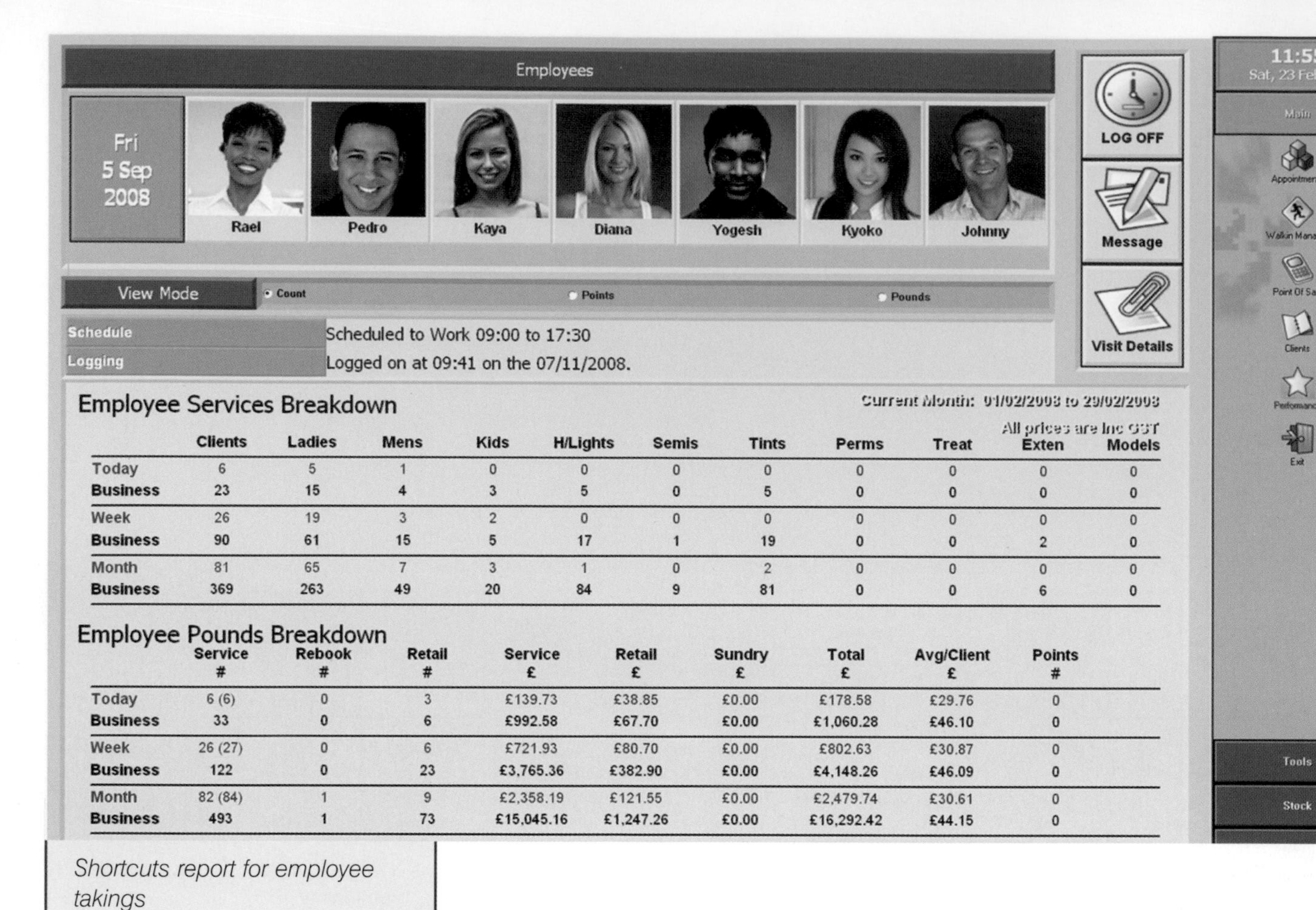

Employee Services Breakdown

	Clients	Ladies	Mens	Kids	H/Lights	Semis	Tints	Perms	Treat	Exten	Models
Today	6	5	1	0	0	0	0	0	0	0	0
Business	23	15	4	3	5	0	5	0	0	0	0
Week	26	19	3	2	0	0	0	0	0	0	0
Business	90	61	15	5	17	1	19	0	0	2	0
Month	81	65	7	3	1	0	2	0	0	0	0
Business	369	263	49	20	84	9	81	0	0	6	0

Employee Pounds Breakdown

	Service #	Rebook #	Retail #	Service £	Retail £	Sundry £	Total £	Avg/Client £	Points #
Today	6 (6)	0	3	£139.73	£38.85	£0.00	£178.58	£29.76	0
Business	33	0	6	£992.58	£67.70	£0.00	£1,060.28	£46.10	0
Week	26 (27)	0	6	£721.93	£80.70	£0.00	£802.63	£30.87	0
Business	122	0	23	£3,765.36	£382.90	£0.00	£4,148.26	£46.09	0
Month	82 (84)	1	9	£2,358.19	£121.55	£0.00	£2,479.74	£30.61	0
Business	493	1	73	£15,045.16	£1,247.26	£0.00	£16,292.42	£44.15	0

Shortcuts report for employee takings

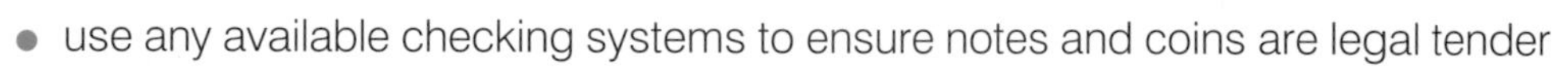

- use any available checking systems to ensure notes and coins are legal tender
- place the money on or near the till, where both the receptionist and the client can clearly see it
- calculate the change and count the change required into the client's hand
- place the money the client gave into the till
- give the client a receipt

Taking a payment by cheque

Some clients prefer to pay by cheque. Most salons accept this form of payment but cheques must be accompanied by a **cheque guarantee card**. Most cheque guarantee cards have a credit limit and this is usually found printed on the guarantee card. A cheque guarantee card is also a **debit card**, which is why many businesses prefer clients to use the debit facility. The payment transaction for a debit card occurs on the same trading day. This means that the bank clearance time for cheques is avoided.

When taking a cheque a receptionist will ensure:

- the date written on the cheque is correct
- the cheque is made payable to the salon or spa business name
- the words that describe the amount match the figures in the box

- the signature on the cheque matches the signature on the guarantee card
- the date on the guarantee card has not expired
- the sort code number on the cheque guarantee card matches the sort code on the cheque
- the card number and expiry date is written on the back of the cheque
- any mistakes made on the cheque are corrected and initialled by the client
- the cheque is placed into the till
- the client is given a receipt

It's a fact!

Credit card companies charge the salon a percentage of the bill value, therefore some small businesses may not accept this type of payment.

Taking a debit and credit card payment

We are living in an increasingly cashless society. Many people prefer to pay for goods and services using debit or credit cards to avoid carrying large amounts of cash. Payment by a debit card allows money to be transferred electronically from the client's bank account to the salon or spa account. The transaction for a debit card occurs almost immediately. For credit card payments, the salon or spa will receive payment from the credit card company 4–10 days after the transaction. The credit card company then sends the bill to the client.

To use a debit or credit card, the card is swiped or inserted into a terminal that is connected by a telephone line to the bank's central debit and credit card centre. The receptionist will input the amount to be charged. The client will be asked to check the amount and, if correct, will enter their PIN. The card centre will confirm that the transaction can go ahead and issue an authorisation number.

Credit cards can be used to pay for hair and beauty treatments

If the card has been reported stolen or the value of the bill is over the credit limit for the client, then the salon or spa will be notified that the transaction is invalid.

An invalid payment can occur if:

- the card is stolen/fraudulent
- the account is over the credit limit
- a stop has been placed on the client's account
- the card is damaged

Gift vouchers can be used for payment in place of cash

Taking a gift voucher payment

Gift vouchers, which are bought from the salon or spa, are used in the same way as a cash transaction. However, there will be a limit to the amount of change that can be given to the client if the treatment or service is less than the cost of the gift voucher. This often means that the value of the gift voucher that remains unspent is returned to the client as another voucher, rather than cash.

ACTIVITY

Design a gift voucher that can be used in a salon or spa.

Keeping client payments secure

Whatever the system that is in place for client payments, the payments must be kept safe and secure.

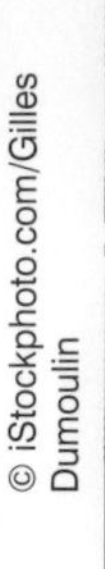

The till should always be kept locked

To do this a receptionist will:

- never leave the reception unattended
- keep cash in a lockable till that is securely fixed to the reception desk
- never leave the till draw open
- never leave cash in the till overnight
- transfer large amounts of money from the till to a secure safe or take the money to the bank.

Fraudulent payments

A client is carrying out an act of fraud if they try to pay using stolen cards or counterfeit cash. Fraud is a criminal offence and a deceptive practice. The client, who knowingly uses stolen credit cards or suspect tender, is intentionally deceiving the business for personal gain.

Stolen or fraudulent payment methods may be recognised by the following:

- the cheque may not have the same name on it as the client
- the cheque card and the cheque may not match
- the debit or credit card may not match the name of the client
- the debit or credit card may be out of date
- the debit or credit card may be damaged
- the client may not know the PIN for the account
- the cash may look or feel different
- the metal strip may be missing from the bank note
- the water mark may be missing from the bank note

Salon and spa stock

All salons and spa businesses will carry and use stock. The stock is required to carry out treatments and services. Some stock will be professional retail products that can be sold to clients.

The stock control process

Stock control is an important task in any hair and beauty business. **Stock taking** is the term that is used to describe the process of checking the amount of stock held and making a judgement about how much stock is required in the future.

Sufficient stock must be available to carry out treatments and services. However, if there is too much unused or unwanted stock, money that could be available for the business is restricted.

Stock control is a process that can be carried out manually, or by using a reception management system.

Manual stock control

The method of recording the level of stock can be completed very simply using a paper based system. Each product is listed in a table, a minimum amount to be kept in stock is recommended and the actual amount of the product found to be in stock on a given day is recorded. A simple calculation will show how much needs to be ordered.

Computerised stock control

Stock control is a function of a reception management system – and using such a system has advantages. The control of stock can be directly linked with other functions of the software.

To carry out stock control, a minimum requirement of stock is recommended and the amount of stock held is recorded. Each time a purchase is made, or a treatment or service is carried out, the products used or sold are recorded by scanning the bar code. The software will automatically adjust the recorded amount of stock that is held in the salon or spa. A report can be generated at any time which will tell the receptionist how much stock is held without having to manually count the products.

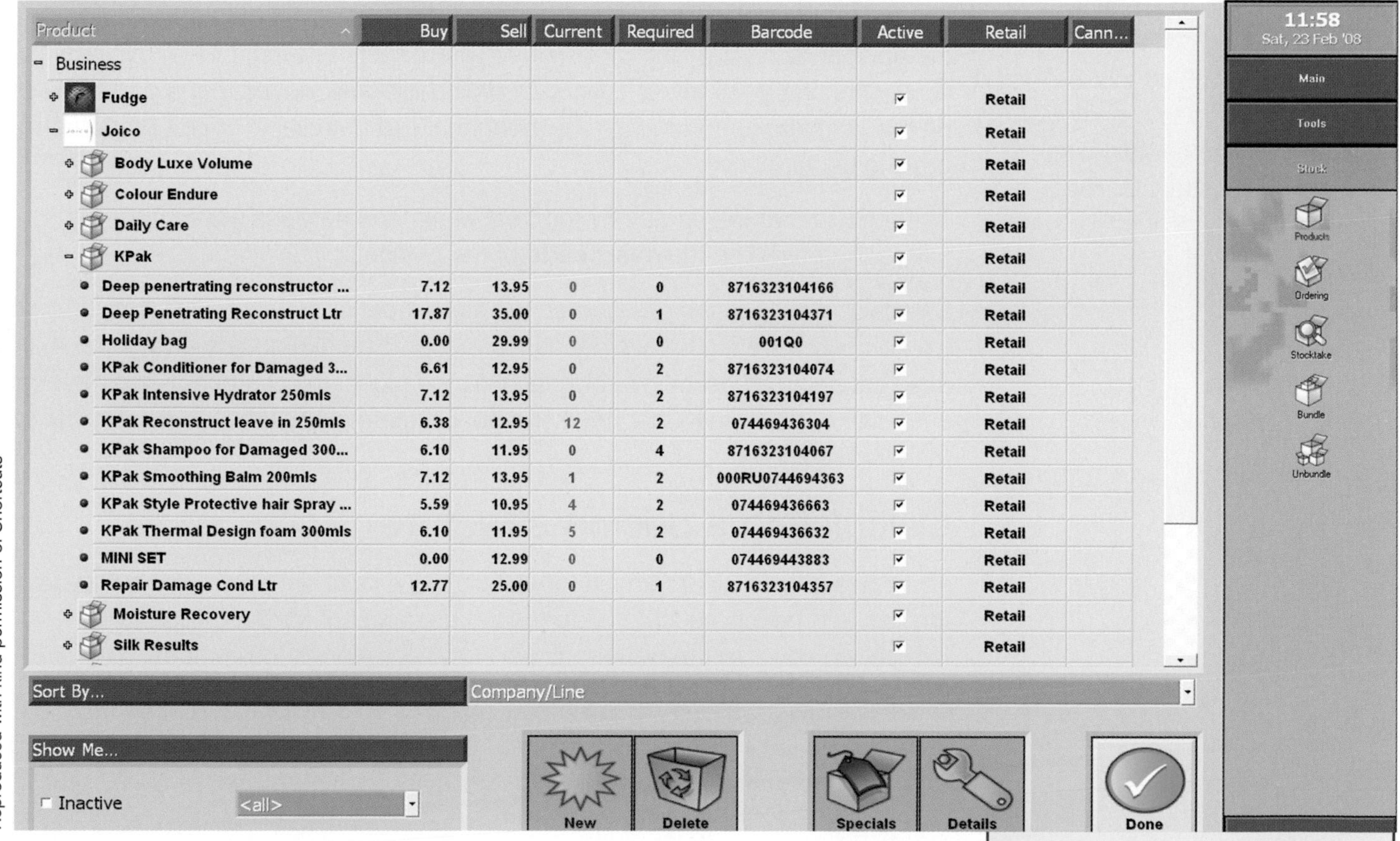

Product	Buy	Sell	Current	Required	Barcode	Active	Retail	Cann...
Business								
Fudge						☑	Retail	
Joico						☑	Retail	
Body Luxe Volume						☑	Retail	
Colour Endure						☑	Retail	
Daily Care						☑	Retail	
KPak						☑	Retail	
Deep penertrating reconstructor ...	7.12	13.95	0	0	8716323104166	☑	Retail	
Deep Penetrating Reconstruct Ltr	17.87	35.00	0	1	8716323104371	☑	Retail	
Holiday bag	0.00	29.99	0	0	001Q0	☑	Retail	
KPak Conditioner for Damaged 3...	6.61	12.95	0	2	8716323104074	☑	Retail	
KPak Intensive Hydrator 250mls	7.12	13.95	0	2	8716323104197	☑	Retail	
KPak Reconstruct leave in 250mls	6.38	12.95	12	2	074469436304	☑	Retail	
KPak Shampoo for Damaged 300...	6.10	11.95	0	4	8716323104067	☑	Retail	
KPak Smoothing Balm 200mls	7.12	13.95	1	2	000RU0744694363	☑	Retail	
KPak Style Protective hair Spray ...	5.59	10.95	4	2	074469436663	☑	Retail	
KPak Thermal Design foam 300mls	6.10	11.95	5	2	074469436632	☑	Retail	
MINI SET	0.00	12.99	0	0	074469443883	☑	Retail	
Repair Damage Cond Ltr	12.77	25.00	0	1	8716323104357	☑	Retail	
Moisture Recovery						☑	Retail	
Silk Results						☑	Retail	

Stock control sheet for shortcuts

ACTIVITY  

When you are in your training salon or work placement, read the manufacturer's instructions for a range of products. Find out what are the different conditions for storing stock.

The reports can also reveal which products are more popular than others, and which are not sold very often. Having this knowledge means that a receptionist or salon manager can investigate why the product is not selling or being used. Sometimes, this is because staff may have insufficient knowledge about the products, so staff training can be instigated. Alternatively, the product can be promoted.

Individual client record information will reveal which product the client purchases. Each time a stylist, therapist or technician refers to the record card, they can clearly see the spending patterns and product preferences of their client.

Storage of stock

Stock must be safely stored following the manufacturer's instructions. Some stock must be kept in cupboards that are resistant to fire, other stock has to be kept out of direct sunlight. Stock must be rotated. This means that old stock must be used before new stock.

Pricing structures

It's a fact! The term *overheads* refers to the routine costs for operating a business which cannot be directly related to a particular activity within the business, but are necessary for the business to function.

All businesses have to make a profit in order to survive and to pay the wages of the people who work in them. Profits for the hair and beauty sector are generated by charging clients for the treatments and services carried out by the stylist, therapist or technician and by selling retail products to clients. Determining the amount to charge clients is critical. Charging too little means that a profit cannot be made, charging too much may mean that too few clients will be prepared to pay the higher prices.

The amount that clients pay for the treatments and services will be carefully calculated based on the **overheads** of the business.

Salons and spas that are based on the high street or in major shopping centres will normally have higher overheads than those based in streets away from the main shopping areas, or in rural locations. The higher the overheads, the more an employer or salon manager must charge for treatments and services in order to make a profit.

Calculating a pricing structure

There has to be a clear formula for calculating a price structure for a business in the hair and beauty sector. The formula must account for the costs that are required to cover all the overheads and allow for a profit to be made.

There are many ways to calculate how much to charge for the treatments and services in a salon or spa. As a minimum, a salon manager will take the following overheads and factors into consideration:

Salaries

Salaries are the largest expense for a hair and beauty business. The costs of salaries for all members of staff regardless of whether they carry out treatments and services must be calculated when creating a pricing structure. This will include senior management staff, stylists, therapists and/or technicians, the receptionist, apprentices, cleaning and maintenance staff. Some members of staff will be more productive than others. Some stylists, therapists or technicians will be more popular with clients and busier than others; therefore, they will take more money for the business. Others will be new to the salon or spa, or have only just qualified, and so will need time to build up their clientele before becoming more profitable.

Salons or spas that do not employ apprentices to assist the more senior members of staff must charge higher prices. This higher charge is required to cover the costs of senior staff completing routine tasks such as client preparation, preparing refreshments or tidying the salon or spa, which could be completed by a less experienced member of staff.

You can read more about salaries in the hair and beauty sector in Chapter 2 'The world of hair and beauty'.

Stock

The stock that will be used on clients for treatments and services and that required for retail purposes must be accounted for when calculating a pricing structure. The type and brand of stock used will reflect the image of the salon or spa. Some stock is more expensive and exclusive than others. The employer or salon manager will choose a brand that complements the image of the salon or spa.

Some stock is known as *consumables*. Consumables are items that have to be purchased to carry out treatments and services, but are thrown away after use. For example, makeup applicators, waxing strips, cotton wool and couch roll.

Other stock will include refreshments such as tea, coffee and other drinks. Some salons also serve alcoholic drinks such as wine. The costs of this type of stock must be considered when calculating a pricing structure.

Rent/mortgage

The cost for the rent or repaying a mortgage of a hair or beauty property is an overhead. The amount paid will depend on the location. Good locations in shopping centres or high streets will normally cost more that businesses away from the high street, on housing estates or in rural locations.

Insurance

All businesses must be insured for the likelihood of loss, theft, damage or injury. Buildings insurance is required for the fabric of the business property, such as the roof or windows. Content insurance is required for everything that is kept inside the building which will include all tools and equipment. **Public liability insurance** is required to insure against accidental injury that may occur to clients and visitors to the salon or spa. **Treatment liability insurance** is required to insure against damage that may occur to the client as a result of a treatment or service.

Water, electricity and gas (utilities)

The amount of water, electricity and gas used by a business will be measured by meters and is an overhead that must be calculated when working out a pricing structure.

ACTIVITY

Research, compare and contrast two ranges of professional retail products for hair, beauty, nails or spa. One product range should be a basic, commonly used one. The second should be more exclusive or have a unique selling point, such as being organic or made from natural ingredients. Calculate how much a salon manager would have to pay for at least three of the product lines in each of the brands and how much they can be sold for. Then calculate the profit margin for the two ranges. Present your findings to a group.

EXTEND YOUR LEARNING

Properties can be freehold or leasehold – investigate the differences between them.

EXTEND YOUR LEARNING

Research the name of the licence(s) that is required to play music in public places.

It's a fact! The definition of *gross* is the total amount and *net* is the amount that remains after deductions.

EXTEND YOUR LEARNING

Hair and beauty businesses with a small turnover do not have to charge VAT. Research the current VAT threshold for businesses.

EXTEND YOUR LEARNING

Research the goods and services that are free from VAT and those that have VAT charged at a reduced rate.

Local/council/business rates

All businesses will have to allow for the costs of local and business taxes. These will vary from one area of the country to another.

Performing rights

Many salons and spas play music to create an atmosphere to match the image of the business. Business managers or employers choose music to play that they think their clients will enjoy. Some music may be very loud. Or, the music chosen may be played to create a more calming atmosphere. The majority of beauty therapy salons and spas will play very soothing and relaxing music to create a peaceful and restful environment in which treatments will take place. However, whatever the type of music played, all businesses are required to purchase a special license which allows music to be played to the public.

Value Added Tax (VAT)

VAT is a tax that has to be paid when certain goods and services are bought. When a client receives a salon or spa service, the salon owner will calculate the **net price** of the service, and then add the VAT to give a **gross price**. The costs for VAT are normally *included* in the price of goods or services that are bought. The salon or spa owner must pay the VAT proportion of the total price direct to the Government. The standard rate for the tax has varied over the years from as low as 10 per cent to as much as 17.5 per cent. When VAT stands at 17.5 per cent it means that if a client pays £50 for a treatment £7.45 goes directly to the Government.

ACTIVITY

Calculate the amount of VAT paid to the government for a £50 treatment if the VAT is 10 per cent.

Calculate the amount of VAT paid to the government for a £50 treatment if the VAT is 15 per cent.

Waste removal

Additional costs are incurred by businesses for the removal of waste. This can include general waste, removal of chemical waste as well as the safe removal of sharps such as razor blades and needles.

Laundry

Every client visit to a business in the hair and beauty sector will result in articles that have to be washed and dried. This will include gowns, sheets, towels and blankets. Some businesses have their own laundry facilities, where others use a professional laundry service which will collect dirty laundry from the salon or spa and return it freshly washed and laundered.

©iStockphoto.com/Rob Sylvan

The costs for laundering must be included in the overheads

Repair and renewal

All businesses must calculate the costs for repair and renewal into their overheads. Equipment will need to be repaired or replaced on a continual basis. Salons and spas must be redecorated and sometimes completely refurbished.

Professional fees

Employers frequently use accountants to assist them with the submission of business accounts for tax purposes. Some also use them for payroll purposes and to provide advice on employee pay and other enquiries such as maternity pay, pensions, sick pay, family tax credits and PAYE.

Some employers will also use the professional services of solicitors. Other professional fees may have to be paid to consultants for dealing with personnel issues, photography, advertising or marketing.

Many employers belong to professional bodies such as the National Hairdressers' Federation, SpaBa and CIBTAC and these costs must be calculated into the overheads. Professional bodies provide support on employment issues and an opportunity to *network* with other employers in similar businesses. You can read more about professional bodies for the hair and beauty sector in Chapter 2 'The world of hair and beauty'.

It's a fact!

You will be very familiar with the purpose of social networking sites such as Facebook, MySpace and Bebo. Through these sites you are able to keep in touch with people you like and who share the same interests as you. Professional bodies also allow people with similar interests in hair and beauty to keep in touch. Some professional bodies have a very strong and influential membership which means that they also try to influence the Government about issues that affect their businesses.

EXTEND YOUR LEARNING

Research and compare the costs of purchasing an industrial washing machine and tumble dryer against the cost of a professional laundry service.

It's a fact!

Employers can set the costs of membership of professional bodies against tax.

It's a fact! The continual training carried out by stylists, therapists and technicians is known as Continuing Professional Development (CPD).

Courtesy of Saks Hair & Beauty (www.saks.co.uk)

Continuing Professional Development (CPD) is used to keep up with the latest techniques

It's a fact! It is standard practice to have a range of prices in the salon or spa that reflect the expertise of the staff. For example, staff who have only just finished their training will charge lower process than more experienced staff.

Marketing budget

Marketing is the name of a process in which an employer of a business will identify and meet the needs and interests of their target clients. If they can successfully do this, their business is more likely to be more successful than their competitors. A budget should be set aside for this purpose in order to maintain a competitive business and this amount must be calculated into the overheads.

Training budget

The treatments and services carried out in the hair and beauty sector are linked to fashion and technology. Because of this, the skills of stylists, therapists and technicians have to be maintained and updated. Therefore, a training budget will be an overhead that must be considered when calculating the costs of treatments and services.

Decision making for the costs of treatments and services

Once a salon owner or employer has determined the overheads of the business, they then have to make a decision about the percentage of profit they wish to make. While an employer may want to make a vast profit, they must also consider:

- *The charges that are already being made in salons or spas in the same neighbourhood*. For example, if prices are going to be very much higher than neighbouring businesses, the marketing of the business will need to show what is special about the salon or spa in order for potential clients to justify spending more money

ACTIVITY    

Compare the prices for treatments and services from at least six different businesses from the hair and beauty sector. Ideally, they should all be from the same industry, so that you are comparing like with like. So, for example, look at six beauty therapy salons or nail salons, six hairdressing salons or spas.

Once you have completed your comparison, write a report about the pricing structures.

Include:

- which salon or spa charged the highest and lowest prices
- the percentage difference between the highest and the lowest prices
- the average price for similar treatments or services
- why you think the salon with the highest process charged so much – what was special about the business?

Bring your learning to life

If an employer correctly calculates the overheads of a business, and sets charges for treatments and services to cover the costs of all the overheads, a profit will be made.

The same principles apply to your own financial situation. You need enough money to complete the activities that make up your lifestyle. If you spend *more* money that you earn, then you will make a loss. If you spend *less* money than you earn, then you make a *profit.*

Calculate what your overheads are. You should include the essential costs of living, such as transport, rent and food. Then you need to calculate other expenses such as the amount of money used for clothes and socialising activities. Compare the money you spend with your income.

Are you making a profit or loss?

If you are making a profit, carry out some research to identify the best place for your savings. If you are making a loss, make an Action Plan to address how you will manage your income more carefully.

- *The level of staff expertise*. For example, if the business employs highly qualified staff, then higher charges can be made. Clients will know that they will gain better results for the treatments and services.
- *What the market will bear*. For example, in times of recession, when the spending power of clients is reduced or uncertain, charges may have to be adjusted to reflect this.

It's a fact!

A **contra-indication** is an existing condition that will prevent certain treatments or services from being carried out. For example, if the client has an infectious nail condition, then a manicure would be contra-indicated.

Keeping client records

Records are kept of all clients who visit a salon or spa. The records are a useful tool for recording information about the client. They are completed at the very first visit of the client, and then after each treatment or service.

At the first visit a lengthy consultation will allow the stylist, therapist or technician to obtain information that will determine the types of treatments and services that the client may have. Sometimes, during the first consultation, certain conditions are identified which mean that some of the treatments and services offered by the salon or spa are restricted. The restrictions usually occur when the client reveals an allergy or medical condition that is **contra-indicated**.

A client record can be paper based or linked to the reception management system. Paper based records are completed on record cards, which are kept in alphabetical order in a secure place. A client record that is linked to the reception management system will be saved and stored on the hard drive of the computer.

A typical client record will include the following:

- the name and contact details of the client
- the medical history of the client

Top tip

A stylist, therapist or technician will check that the information given by the client at the first consultation has not changed when they next visit the salon or spa. It is important to find out if there are any new contra-indications that will prevent the treatment or service being carried out.

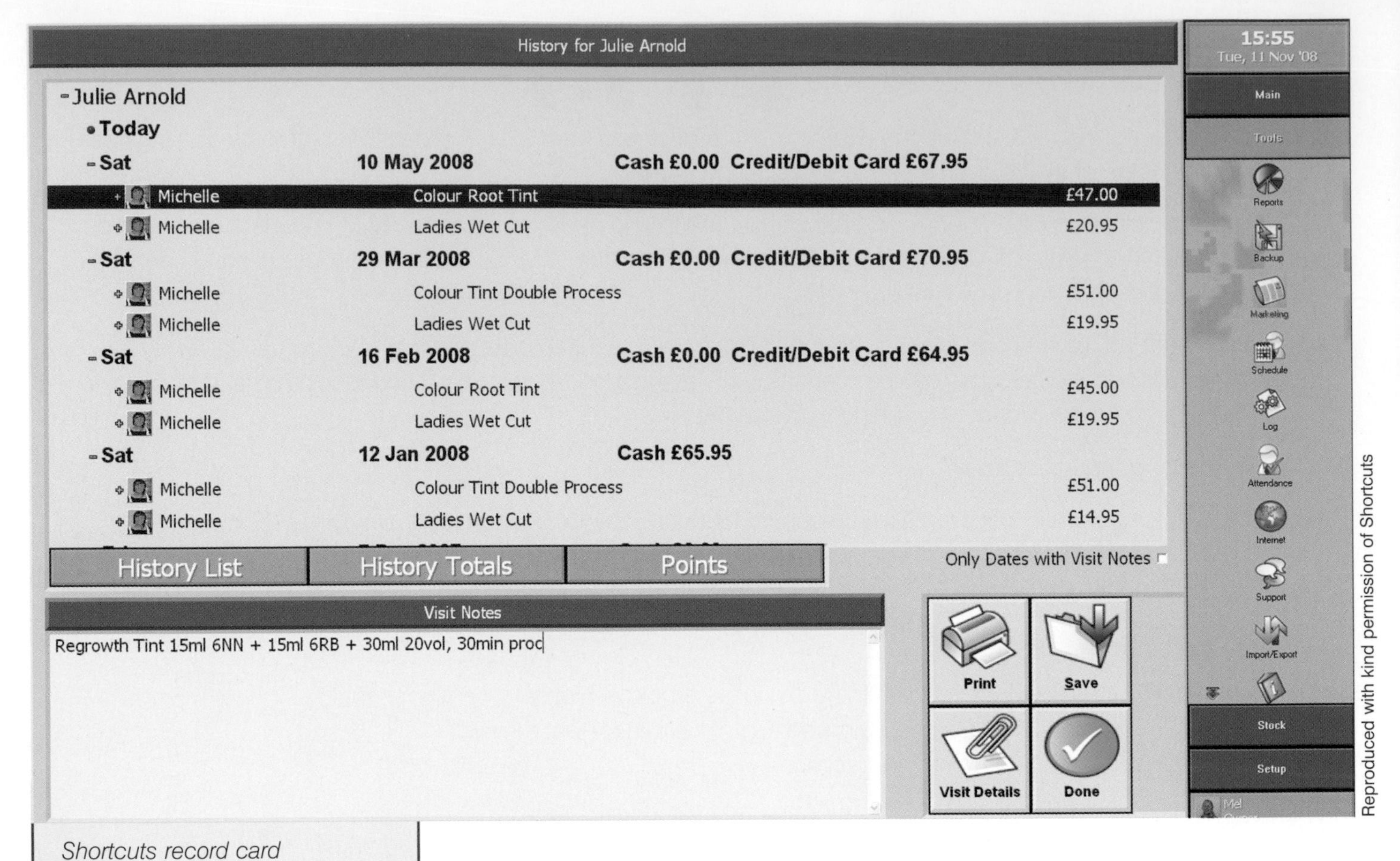

Shortcuts record card

- the treatments and services the client has received
- the results of the treatments and services
- the products and chemicals that have been used for the treatment or service
- the retail products that were recommended to the client

Bring your learning to life 

When completing work for the unit on hair care and styling, skin care and makeup or hand care and nail art, complete a client record card.

Client confidentiality

The information that is on a client record is confidential and falls under the remit of the Data Protection Act – whether they are paper or computer based.

It's a fact! In addition to information stored on computers or on record cards, receptionists, stylists, therapists and technicians will have many conversations with clients, either face to face, or on the telephone. Clients will reveal personal information about themselves and this information must also remain confidential.

The Data Protection Act

The Data Protection Act is the legislation that protects the use of personal data in the UK. The Act ensures that:

- Data is only used for the purposes for which it was collected
- The information must be accurate and up to date
- Data must not be given to a third party without the consent of the individual
- Individuals have the right to see information held about them
- Personal information should be kept for no longer than is necessary
- Information about individuals must not be transmitted outside the European Economic Area (EEA) without the individual's consent
- Those who hold personal information must have a secure place to keep the information, and staff training to ensure the requirements of Data Protection are met
- Those holding personal information must register with the Information Commissioner (although there are some exceptions to this)

ACTIVITY  

Find out if hair and beauty businesses have to register with the Information Commissioner.

It's a fact!

The Data Protection Act itself does not mention the word *privacy*, yet this is what the legislation ensures.

EXTEND YOUR LEARNING 

You can see the whole Data Protection Act on the Office of Public Sector Information Website. **http:/www.opsi.gov.uk/acts/acts1998/19980029.htm**.

EXTEND YOUR LEARNING 

Look at **http:/www.opsi.gov.uk** information website and find out more about the role of the Office of Public Sector Information.

What you have learnt

Business systems and processes

- All businesses must have systems and processes in place to ensure they are profitable
- The type of systems and processes used will be related to the size of the business

The role and function of receptions and receptionists for any business and of hair and beauty receptions and receptionists

- The receptionist in any business plays a key role in the organisation
- The receptionist is the first point of contact for clients and visitors
- The receptionist in a hair and beauty business will, amongst other things, schedule appointments, answer the telephone, take payments from clients and some have responsibility for stock control

How the reception area plays a significant part in creating a positive and lasting impression of the business

- The reception area is the first area a visitor or client will see
- The reception area must meet the requirements of health and safety, and for the comfort of the visitor or client

How reception displays promote the business

- The treatments and services offered by the hair and beauty business can be promoted in the reception area by the use of displays
- Professional retail products are displayed in the reception area
- The skill of those who work in the business can be illustrated with the display of their qualifications

How reception systems work

- The reception systems used by a receptionist will include
  - scheduling appointments
  - taking payments
  - storing client record details
  - maintaining stock
- The reception systems can be paper based or include the use of Information Technology with a reception management system

The different types of appointment systems and how they work

- Appointment systems can be paper based or computer based
- Appointments are scheduled according to the needs of the client, the skills of the stylist, therapist or technician and the time they take to complete

The significance of the Data Protection legislation

- All information provided by clients during consultations is confidential and under the remit of the Data Protection Act

How stock control works

- The number of products required to carry out treatments and services must be calculated
- The amount of stock held should be sufficient to meet the needs of the business
- Too much stock held will affect the cash flow of the business

- Insufficient stock held will affect the ability of stylists, therapists and technicians to carry out the treatments and services requested by the client

How to calculate the price of products, treatments and services

- The costs of overheads for a business must be accounted for when calculating the amount charged for treatments and services

How to take payments

- Payments can be made by cash, cheque, credit or debit cards and gift vouchers
- The receptionist calculates the payments and follows the correct procedures for the payment method used.

Assessment activities

Crossword

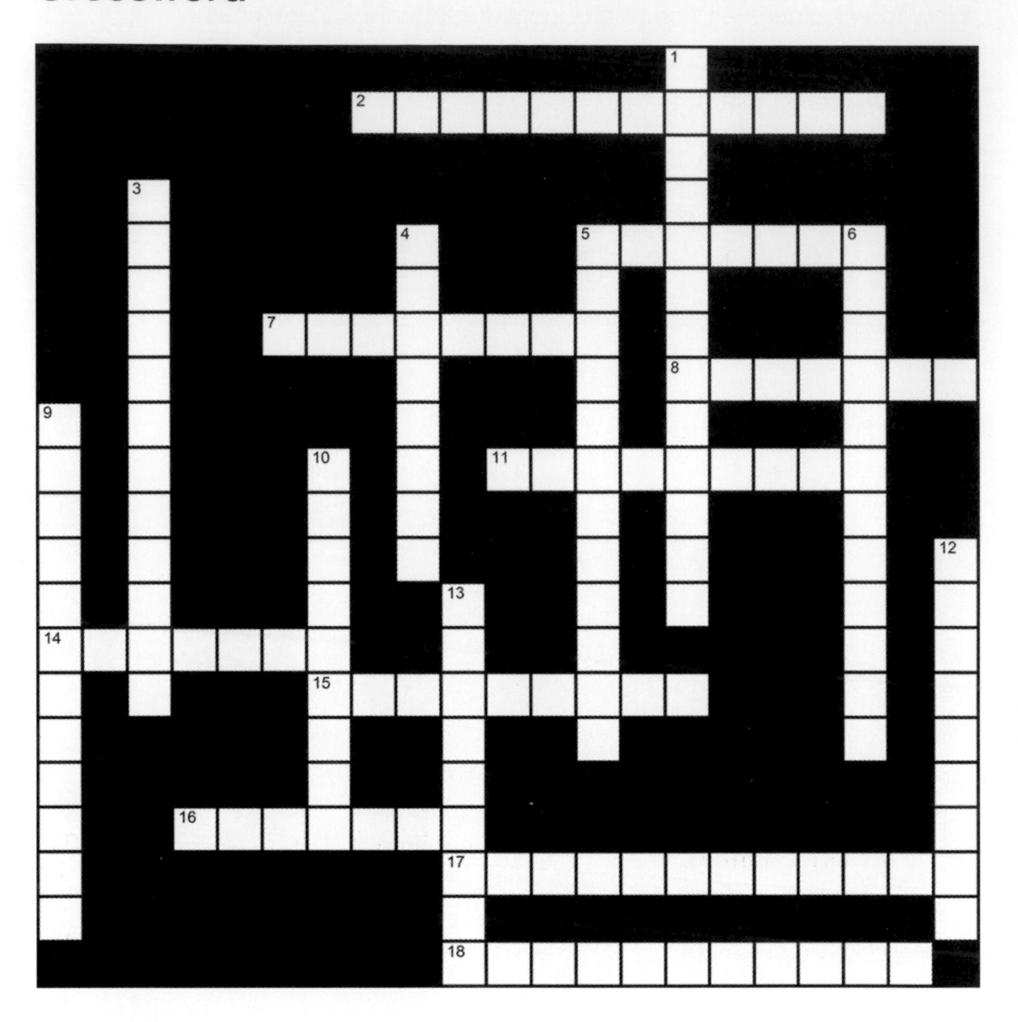

Across

2 The job title of a person who works in a reception area (12)

5 This can be used in place of cash by a client (7)

7 A receptionist will take these when a treatment or service is completed (8)

8 A receptionist must speak like this when answering the telephone (7)

11 The brand name of a reception management system (9)

14 You may find a display of these on the reception desk (7)

15 Used to call clients (9)

16 This must be passed on as quickly as possible (7)

17 A receptionist will schedule these to organise a working day (12)

18 The term used to describe the action of counting products that are held by the salon or spa (5, 6)

Down

1 These skills are essential for a receptionist (13)

3 One of the skills required by a person who works in a reception area (12)

4 Used to operate a reception management system (8)

5 Kept on the reception desk and a requirement for health and safety purposes (8,4)

6 A receptionist can offer these when a client is waiting (12)

9 A display of these will tell you that staff in a business are qualified (12)

10 A winter time theme for a product display (9)

12 This will tell clients what they have to pay for a treatment or service (5,4)

13 The term used to describe the routine costs of running a business (9)

Fill in the blanks

The ________ is the first area that all visitors and clients to a hair and beauty sector business will see. It is important for the reception area to be welcoming and ________ and to meet the requirements of health and safety and ________.

The receptionist is the ______ point of contact. Therefore, they must have outstanding ____________ skills to create a ______ first and lasting impression. Receptionists not only have to be well organised people, but they also need computer__________ skills as many businesses have a reception ____________ system. Receptionists also need __________ skills as they have to __________ the costs and take __________ for treatments and services. The skills of the __________ are as important as the skills carried out by stylists, __________ and technicians.

It is important for everyone training in the hair and beauty sector to learn reception skills as not every ____________ can justify the _____ for a full time receptionist. In some businesses all the staff will take some responsibility for working in the reception area.

communication	literacy	good	reception	costs
payment	comfortable	management	calculate	first
security	therapists	numeracy	business	receptionist

Multiple choice: Salon business systems and processes

1 The receptionist will require good skills in
- **a** hairdressing
- **b** communication
- **c** beauty therapy
- **d** window dressing

2 The reception area must
- **a** be well decorated
- **b** at the front of the salon

c meet health and safety and security requirements
d have a computer

3 A visitor's book is used for
a checking who visited the spa manager
b as a tool for health and safety
c checking when the manufacturer's representative last visited
d checking the date.

4 A good reception area will
a look clean, tidy, welcoming and comfortable
b have flowers on the desk
c have a computer
d look modern

5 A computer at the reception area is useful for
a checking the latest news
b finding information
c making appointments
d operating a reception management system

6 The telephone at the reception area must not be used for
a personal calls
b emergency calls
c business calls
d by clients

7 The magazines at the waiting area of the reception should be
a gossip magazines
b celebrity magazines
c up to date magazines
d weekly magazines

8 Reading material kept at the waiting area should be
a appropriate for males
b appropriate for females
c appropriate for all staff
d appropriate for all clients

9 Product displays should be
a free from dust and dirt
b attractive
c promotional
d in the window

10 The certificates that may be displayed in the salon reception are should be
a framed
b for the qualifications of the staff who work in the salon or spa
c recent
d for the qualifications of staff who maintain the building

4

the science of hair and beauty

Tracey Devine @ Angels, Aberdeen

Every science begins as philosophy and ends as art.

WILL DURANT 1885–1981, AMERICAN PHILOSOPHER, HISTORIAN AND WRITER

Introduction

The hair and beauty sector is made up of industries that create images and well-being. However, as an industry, we need to understand the different aspects of science and how it connects to the everyday activities that are carried out in salons and spas around the world to ensure that the best possible results can be achieved for our clients.

Anatomy and physiology play a huge part in a stylist's or therapist's end result, for example by understanding bone and muscle structure, the therapist will understand the different types of pressure and massage techniques that can be applied on different parts of the body to ensure that the massage becomes a treatment that benefits well-being. During the application of makeup, a makeup artist will work with the client's bone structure to enhance the overall effect either by highlighting and enhancing good features and toning down or softening less positive features.

Understanding the structure of skin and hair and nails enables the stylist or therapist to recognise any disorders or conditions that they need to take into consideration for the service or recommend alternative action such as visiting a doctor for medical advice. You will need to recognise how different factors such as the different systems in the body, the environment, products and other services, health, lifestyle and nutrition as well as age can affect the condition of hair, skin and nails.

This chapter will also look at an introduction to physics and chemistry in relation to the hair and beauty sector through the understanding of electric current and how that is used for different services. It will discuss what light is and why it is important to recognise different light, particularly for the application of makeup and hair colour. Understanding colour is essential to any good artist and that is no exception for the hair and beauty sector; we are artists working on living canvasses. The principles of colour, how light creates colour and how complementary and contrasting colour can be used to create different effects on the skin, hair and nails is what our industries are all about.

The main scientific principles governing how basic hair, beauty and nail products and their ingredients work, what the pH scale is and how it affects the use of products and the effect this can have on the hair, skin and nails will also be considered. How water type and temperature can impact on products, and the effectiveness of hair and skin treatments is a further aspect of this chapter on science.

Finally and most importantly we need to understand the importance of testing products prior to their use, the issues around the ethics of testing products on animals and processes for carrying out the common tests used in the hair and beauty sector.

What you are going to learn

This chapter will include:

- ★ **The basic structure and function of the skin and hair**
- ★ **The structure and function of nails**
- ★ **The basic anatomy and physiology of the head, neck and shoulders**
- ★ **The basic anatomy and physiology of the lower arm and hand**
- ★ **The basic anatomy and physiology of the lower leg and foot**
- ★ **Factors that affect the health and condition of the skin, hair and nails**
- ★ **How the different systems in the body can affect the condition of the hair, skin and nails**

- ★ How to recognise types of adverse skin, scalp, hair and nail conditions
- ★ Common tests used in the hair and beauty sector
- ★ The issues relating to the ethics of testing products on animals
- ★ The pH scale and how it affects the use of products and its effect on the hair, skin and nails
- ★ The basic scientific principles of how basic hair, beauty and nail products work
- ★ How electricity is used in hair, beauty and nail services
- ★ The principles of colour and how different lights can effect the appearance of colour
- ★ The effects of light and heat on the delivery of different services

The basic anatomy and physiology of the hair, skin and nail

The structure of the skin

The skin is our largest organ, yet we often take it for granted. The skin varies in appearance according to race, sex and age. Our skin will change from season to season and will reflect general health, lifestyle and diet. During puberty our **hormones** become more active causing the skin to become oily which often creates blemishes and spots on the skin's surface. During our twenties the skin is at its best as the hormone imbalance should now be stable. As we move into our thirties fine lines start to appear on the skin surface particularly around the eyes. At forty our hormone activity becomes less active and the skin starts to lose its strength and elasticity. The skin becomes drier and small lines and wrinkles appear on the surface of the skin. In our fifties discolouration, small brown patches start to appear on the temple area of the face and the back of the hands. All this is part of life and it is up to us to care and protect our skin from damage such as ultra-violet light from the sun.

The skin is made up of two main layers, the **epidermis** which provides waterproofing and serves as a barrier to infection and the **dermis**, which is home for the *appendages* of the skin and also the **basement membrane**.

The epidermis

The epidermis is the outer layer of the skin, the one that you can see and touch. The main function of the epidermis is to protect the deeper living structures within the dermis. The main type of **cell** found in the epidermis is the **keratinocyte**, which produces the protein **keratin**; keratin makes the skin tough and reduces the passage of substances in and out of the body. As the cells move closer towards the surface of the epidermis, they mature and then die and are constantly rubbed away or naturally shed. Did you know that between 70 and 90 per cent of the dust in a house is made up of dead skin cells that have been shed from the body? It is on these skin cells that dust mites feed.

There are five layers or *strata* of the epidermis, and each one has different characteristics.

The five layers are:

- Horny layer (*stratum corneum*) – In this layer, the skin cells are flat and resemble scales and are composed mainly from **keratin**. This helps to reflect ultra-violet light from the skin's surface. Black skin, which evolved to withstand strong ultra-violet light, has a thicker horny layer than that of Caucasian skin. The dead cells are rubbed off by friction and, if not removed, they form dry patches of scale on the skin's surface, making it look dry and dull.
- Lucid layer (*stratum lucidum*) – These cells do not have a **nucleus** and are clear in appearance. They are found in the non-hairy areas of the body such as the palms of the hands and soles of the feet. At the bottom of this layer is a fatty substance which prevents the absorption of liquids into the body.
- Granular layer (*stratum granulosum*) – within this layer there is the transition from living to dead cells. **Keratinisation** takes place here, which is the hardening of the skin cells. Excessive keratinisation can lead to a skin condition called **psoriasis**.
- Prickle cell layer (*stratum spinosum*) – named because the cells have fine, spiky projections. Chemical changes in this layer lead to the eventual keratinisation, or hardening of the cells, which makes the skin hard and durable. Two other important cells are found in this layer, the **langerhan cells** and **melanocyte cells**. Langerhan cells absorb and remove foreign bodies that enter the skin. Melanocyte cells produce the skins pigment **melanin**, which contributes to our skin colour. Melanocytes produce melanin by ultra-violet rays and their main

It's a fact! The word 'stratum' means 'layer'.

It's a fact! Excess shedding of dead skin cells on the scalp can be seen as **dandruff**.

Layers of the epidermis

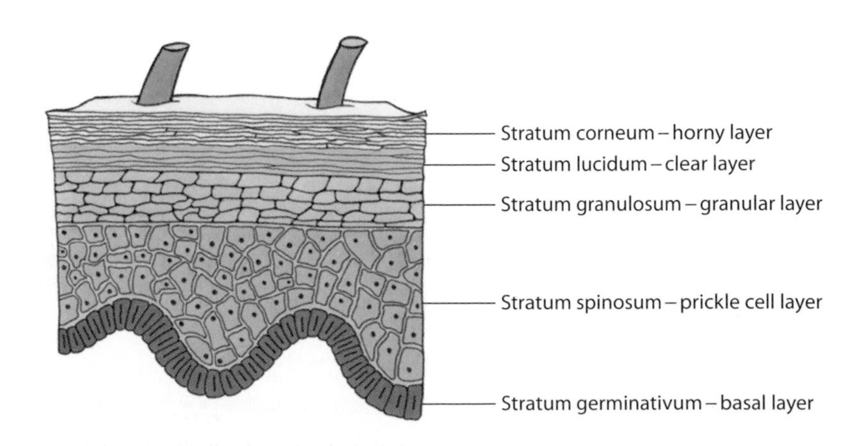

function is to protect other epidermal cells from the effects of ultra-violet light. The quantity and distribution of melanocytes are different depending on race. In white Caucasian skin melanin tends to be destroyed when it reaches the granular layer. In black skin melanin is present in larger quantities throughout all the epidermal layers. The increased protection allows less ultra-violet to reach the dermis which reduces the risk of premature ageing. People with darker skin also have less risk of developing skin cancer.

- Basal layer (*stratum germiniativum*) – this is the lowest layer of the epidermis. In this layer the cells are constantly dividing by a process known as **mytosis**. The cells then gradually make their way through the other layers of the epidermis until they die and are shed from the surface of the skin.

The dermis

The dermis is also known as the *true skin*, and it is within this section that the appendages to the hair, the blood and nerve supply are found along with other structures such as the **lymphatic system**, **blood vessels**, **hair follicle** and **nerves**. The dermis is much thicker than the epidermis and has two main sections: the **papillary** and the **reticular** layers.

- **Papillary layer** – This is the outermost layer of the dermis and extends into the epidermis to supply it with **nutrients**. Near the surface of the dermis are tiny projections called **papillae** that contain both nerve endings and blood capillaries.
- **Reticular layer** – The reticular layer is denser and is continuous with the **basement membrane**. In the reticular layer the dermis contains **protein fibres**, yellow elastin fibres which give the skin its elasticity and white **collagen fibres** which give the skin its strength. The fibres are made up from cells called **fibroblasts**. The basement membrane or **hypodermis** is not part of the skin, and lies at the base of the dermis. Its purpose is to attach the skin to underlying bone and muscles as well as supplying it with blood vessels and nerves.

Within the dermis a number of structures are based which we call **skin appendages**. These include:

- sweat glands
- sebaceous glands
- hair follicles
- nails

Sweat glands are also known as *sudoriferous glands* and are composed of *epithelial tissue*, which extends into the epidermis from the dermis. Sweat glands are found all over the body but are found in larger amounts on the palms of the hands and the soles of the feet. Their role is to regulate body temperature through the evaporation of sweat from the surface of the skin to stop the body overheating. There are two types of sweat glands:

- **Eccrine glands** are found all over the body and are simple sweat producing glands that respond to heat. The sweat duct opens on the surface of the skin through an opening called a **pore**.

It's a fact!

The dermis contains different types of **sensory** nerve endings, which register touch, pressure, pain and temperature. These nerve endings send messages to the *central nervous system* and the *brain* to inform us about what is happening on the surface of our skin.

EXTEND YOUR LEARNING

In medicine, the section concerned with the skin is called *dermatology*. Research more about dermatology and how new skin cosmetics and treatments are including ingredients such as collagen.

It's a fact! Pheromones are thought to create sexual attraction between individuals.

It's a fact! The **acid mantle** is the term given to the combination of sweat and sebum which creates an acid film on the skin; it is an acid with a pH of about 4.5 to 5.5. This film discourages the growth of bacteria and fungi.

Top tip To remember the six functions of the skin use the acronym 'SHAPES'.

Skin function – temperature control

- **Apocrine glands** are found in the arm pits, the nipples and the groin area. They are connected to hair follicles and become active during puberty. They are larger glands than those of the eccrine glands as they secrete a thicker fluid that is made from urea, fats, sugar and small amounts of protein. The gland increases in activity during times of stress, nervousness or excitement. Also found within the fluid are traces of *aromatic molecules* called **pheromones**.

Sebaceous glands appear as small sac-like organs. They can be found all over the body except the palms of the hands and soles of the feet. These glands are usually associated with the hair follicle and are found in large numbers on the scalp, forehead and the back and chest. They produce the skin's natural oil called **sebum**. Sebum is directly emptied onto the hair follicle. Sebum is composed of *fatty acids* and waxes that have **bactericidal** and **fungicidal** properties to discourage **micro-organisms** from settling on the skin's surface; it also helps to reduce evaporation of moisture to prevent the skin drying out.

The functions of the skin

The functions of the skin are:

- sense of touch
- heat regulation
- absorption
- protection
- excretion
- secretion

- *Sense of touch* – the dermis contains many *sensory nerve endings* which can transmit messages to the brain to ensure that you are aware of your surroundings, enabling you to detect the most delicate touch. At other times the sense of touch can be much more defined. For example, when cutting hair, you need to make direct contact with your client during the consultation. This type of touch is known as *physical* communication and is very important in gaining your client's trust and confidence. You will read more about physical communication in Chapter 3 'Salon business systems and processes'.
- *Heat Regulation* – within the dermis there lie many special nerve endings that can detect heat and cold. The organs of the body are designed to work at our normal body temperature of 36.8°C or 98.6°F, so it is important that this temperature is maintained. If you are too hot or too cold, the body can adjust the temperature in two main ways – one through the blood supply and the other by the production of sweat. If you get too hot, the sweat glands produce sweat, which then evaporates from the skin's surface, producing a cooling effect, in addition to this, the *blood vessels* expand – making you look pink – or sometimes very red, again allowing your temperature to be reduced. If you are too cold, the blood vessels contract making you look pale, and, in extreme cases, you can look very blue. By doing this, the blood vessels are reducing the amount of heat that is lost by the body. Also the muscles of the body can involuntary contract, causing you to shiver. This action helps to keep you warm.

- *Absorption* – although the skin acts as a barrier and prevents harmful micro-organisms entering the body, it is capable of a limited amount of absorption. The skin absorbs **vitamin D**, which comes from sunlight. Vitamin D is essential for the body as it helps the formation of healthy bones.
- *Protection* – the skin is the largest organ of the body and one of its functions is to protect other organs within the body. It does this by creating a barrier around the body which prevents the invasion of **micro-organisms**. In addition to the skin itself, another line of defence to micro-organisms is the *acid mantle*. The skin is also able to detect danger. It does this through the nerve endings that can track extremes of heat and cold as well as pain from something that may penetrate the surface of the skin – thus protecting the body from harm.
- *Excretion* – the skin excretes sweat, which helps to dispose of excess salts in the body as well as helping to cool the skin when you are too warm.
- *Secretion* – the skin also secretes sebum. Sebum helps to moisturise the skin and hair in order to prevent excessive dryness.

Skin function – sense of touch

Skin colour

In the world there are different types of people. To ensure survival we have adapted and we have evolved. This is apparent in the way we look and the colour of our skin illustrating different racial origins. The darker the skin and eyes the more protection there is from the sun's ultra-violet rays. Those living nearer the equator have darker skin and eyes as the sun is more intense. As we have developed over the centuries, races and cultures have mixed to influence the genes that may determine our skin colour. Skin colour can be categorised into six main skin colours:

- **White skin** – This skin colour is the most delicate, it has blue and pink tones that can be seen through the epidermis. The melanin content is low and the skin is prone to lines and wrinkles though the tendency of early ageing.
- **Mixed race skin** – This skin colour can be a mixture of different genes taken from the parents. The skin can take a combination of the skin colour and traits from both parents or can have dominance from one parent.
- **Asian skin** – This skin colour has a yellow tone but can be quite dark as the melanin content is quite high. The skin has many pores to help regulate the body temperature because of the heat. The skin is strong and flexible and has a smooth surface that ages well with very few wrinkles developing.
- **Black skin** – This skin colour has larger amounts of melanin that helps to protect it from ultra-violet rays. The epidermis is thicker and the skin is strong with greater elasticity than white skin, giving the skin more support and making it less likely to sag. There are more sebaceous glands that are larger, which give good lubrication and moisture, making it less prone to wrinkles and slowing down the aging process.
- **Chinese type skin** – This colour skin has a lighter yellow tone than Asian skin and tolerates ultra-violet rays well. The skin can have a tendency to be oily and can have a problem with open pores along the nose area. This type of skin does not wrinkle easily, delaying the appearance of ageing.

Skin function – absorption

Skin function – protection

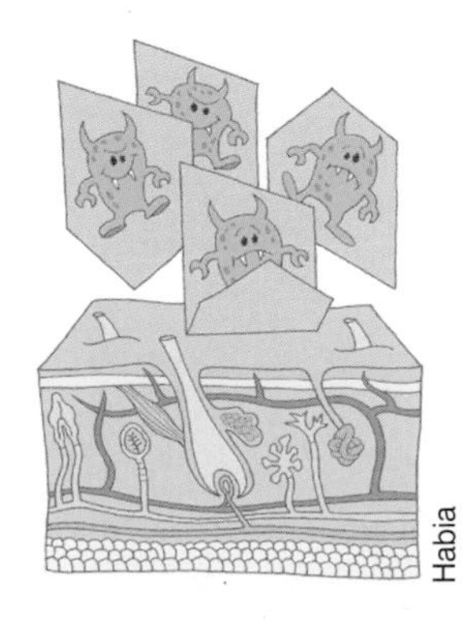

Skin function – excretion and secretion

Habia

It's a fact! Skin colour is determined by the amount of melanin in the skin.

It's a fact! Albinism is a condition characterised by the absence of melanin, were the skin and hair is very light or white.

ACTIVITY  

In groups or pairs discuss the different skin types. Can you identify each other's skin type?

- **Mediterranean skin** – This skin colour is olive toned and darker and tans easily. The skin tends to be oilier as the sebaceous glands produce more sebum to lubricate it in the heat to stop it drying out and developing wrinkles. The skin is strong and less prone to damage from ultra-violet rays.

Skin types

- *Normal* – This type of skin exists when the oil glands and sweat glands are working in *harmony* together. They give the skin a good balance of moisture to keep the skin soft and flexible. The skin has a fine texture that has even pore distribution and a soft even surface. It is quite rare for people to have normal skin – the majority of people will have a combination skin of normal to dry or normal to oily.
- *Dry* – This type of skin, as the name suggests, is *dehydrated* with a lack of oil and moisture, it is dry to the touch with a tendency to flakiness and early signs of fine lines and wrinkles, particularly around the eyes. The skin can be fairly sensitive and can often redden and chap in cold or windy weather.
- *Greasy* – This type of skin produces too much sebum. The skin pores are often larger than normal and can become blocked creating *infections* and *spots*. A greasy skin is shiny in appearance and is often connected with puberty, when there is an increase of hormonal activity that effects the production of sebum; this often corrects itself as hormone levels become more balanced.
- *Combination* – This type of skin is a combination of two or more skin types. The most common is that of normal or dry skin with a section of greasy skin running across the forehead and down the nose and chin, in the shape of a **capital T**, sometimes referred to as the *T zone*.

Within these skin types the skin can also be affected by a number of different conditions such as:

- *Dehydrated skin* – This is when the skin is temporarily lacking in moisture, which could be based on a number of reasons:
  - extreme weather such as to much sun
  - products that are too harsh for the skin
  - diet
  - dry atmosphere such as central heating
- *Sensitive skin* – This is when the skin can be very sensitive to external factors such as:
  - skin care products
  - perfume or fragrances
  - products or materials that lie on the skin such as clothing and washing powders
  - weather

- *Mature skin* – This is when the skin loses some of its elasticity, lines and wrinkles form and the skin will start to sag, particularly in certain areas on the face such as around the eyes and jaw line. The skin can also become dry from the slow down of sebum.
- *Sun damaged skin* – This is when the skin has been frequently exposed to the sun over a period of time. The skin will develop lots of wrinkles across all areas of the skin and face with patchy colour pigmentation. The skin will sag as it loses its elasticity and will look older than the person actually is. This type of skin can often be confused with mature skin.

ACTIVITY  

Research your family tree: where did your family come from? How has your family background influenced the way you look, how tall you are, the colour of your skin, eyes and hair or other distinguishing features?

The structure and function of the hair

Hair is a long, slender structure; each hair is made up of dead skin cells, which contain the protein called keratin. Hair grows all over the body, except the soles of the feet, the palms of the hands and on the eyelids. However, some types of hair have different characteristics to other types.

There are three types of human hair:

- *Lanugo hair* – This type of hair is soft and downy and found on new born babies. This hair is lost soon after birth.
- *Vellus hair* – This is the fine hair that is found all over the body.
- *Terminal hair* – This is the hair that is found on the scalp, arms, legs, pubic areas, ears, eyebrows and on the faces on men.

The hair structure and related skin

The hair is made up of three parts:

- The **root** is the section of hair that is found in the follicle
- The **bulb** is the enlarged base of the root. A gap at the base leads to a cavity which contains the papilla. The bulb contains the dividing cells that create the hair. As the hair grows it passes out of the bulb into the hair follicle
- The **shaft** is the section of hair that is seen above the skin surface

The skin around a hair has seven elements:

- *Follicle* – All the follicles you have are created before birth and it is a tubular down growth in the dermis that holds and supports the hair in place. Follicles vary in size, depending on the type of hair that grows from it. For example, a follicle containing a vellus hair will be smaller than that which contains terminal hair.
- *Sebaceous gland* – this is the gland that produces the natural oil of the hair and scalp called sebum. Sebum lubricates the hair to provide gloss to the hair and protection to the skin. Clients with an underactive sebaceous gland are likely to have hair that is dry in condition and it may look dull. However, if the sebaceous gland is overactive, too much sebum will be produced and the client will have oily hair.

Cross section of the skin

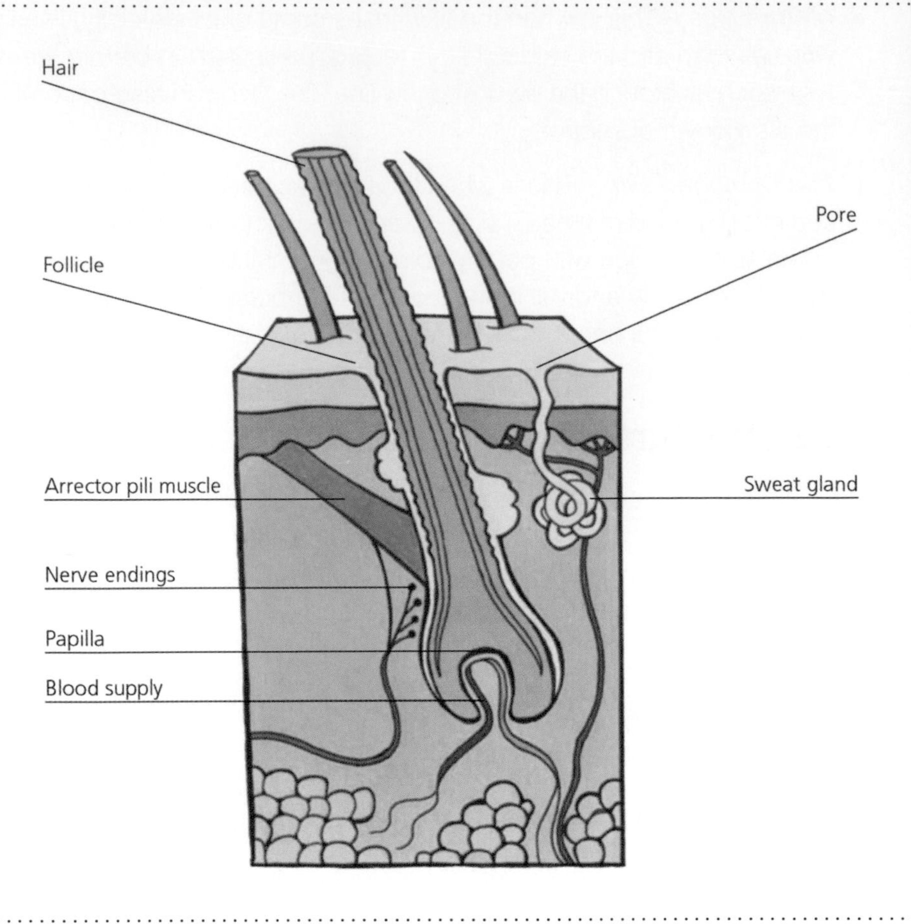

It's a fact! An extreme action of the arrector pili muscle can be seen on a cat or dog, who, when alarmed, raise their fur to make them look larger and more aggressive as a form of protection.

It's a fact! Nerve endings are designed to detect different sensations. For example changes in temperature or pain.

- *Sweat Gland* – the sweat gland is also known as the **sudoriferous** gland. This produces sweat which is made up of water, salts and other minerals. The release of sweat through the sweat duct onto the skin is used as a mechanism to cool the skin when you get hot.
- *Arrector pili muscle* – this is a muscle that works *involuntarily*. This means that you are not able to control the muscle yourself. If you get cold or frightened, the muscle will contract of it own accord and make the hair stand up. When the muscle is contracted it produces *goose pimples*. At the same time you get goose pimples, the hair (depending on its length) will stand on end, or be raised. This action helps you to either trap warm air if you are cold or act as a warning system if you are frightened.
- *Nerve endings* – although the hair does not have its own nervous system, and therefore, you cannot feel when the hair shaft has been cut, the follicle itself is surrounded by a network of nerves which enables you to feel any movement in the hair. In addition, the dermis contains a variety of nerve endings or **receptors**. Each one of the nerve endings is specially designed to detect different sensations, which occur on the skin.
- *Blood supply* – The hair itself does not have a blood supply – if it did, it would bleed when the hair was cut. However, the blood supply is very important, as it

carries nutrients that ensure healthy hair growth. The blood supply enters the *dermal papilla* through a series of fine small blood **capillaries**. The dermal papilla is the point from which all new cells for hair growth are produced. As well as supplying nutrients required for the development of new growth, the blood supply helps to removes waste products.

- *Papilla* – this is the point at which all new cells for hair growth are produced. When first formed, the cells produced are very soft, but they are hardened and shaped as they are forced into the follicle and out onto the surface of the skin. The hardening of the soft cells is known as keratinisation.

It's a fact!

There are 22 amino acids in the hair, which contain elements of carbon, hydrogen, nitrogen, oxygen and sulphur.

Chemical structure of hair

Hair has the same keratin structure as nails, horns, claws, feathers and fur. The main structure of the hair, the bundles of the cortex, is made up from molecules of **amino acids**. Amino acids are the basic structural building units of proteins. They form short chains called **peptides** or **polypeptides**, which in turn form into the protein keratin.

Cross-links within the hair

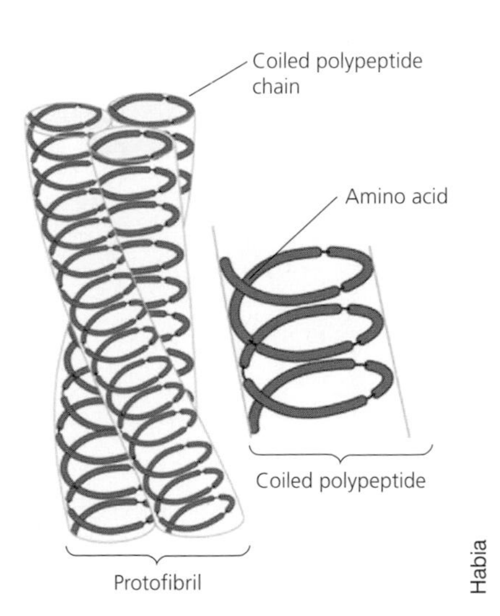

The structure of hair Hair is made up of three sections:

- cuticle
- cortex
- medulla

Cuticle The cuticle is the outermost part of the hair. It is made up of overlapping layers of **translucent** scales. The scales are sometimes likened to tiles of a roof in the way that each lays over the other. The scales of the cuticle play an important part in the condition of the hair. Hair that is in good condition will have a cuticle that lies flat and is smooth. A smooth cuticle makes it easier to brush and comb the hair and reflects the light to give a glossy appearance. If the cuticle is damaged the uneven or broken cuticle layers make the hair tangle easily and, because the cuticle does not lie flat, and smooth light does not reflect from it, makes the hair look dull.

There are a number of reasons why the cuticle may be damaged. It can be damaged by over processing with chemicals, physical damage through brushing, combing and using heated appliances without correctly protecting the hair with products, or tying the hair into unsuitable bands, or the hair can be damaged by the environment, for example excessive sun and wind damage. You can find out how good the condition of the cuticle is by carrying out a **porosity** test. The method for carrying out this test will be explained later in this chapter.

The hair showing the macrofibrils, microfibrils and protofibrils

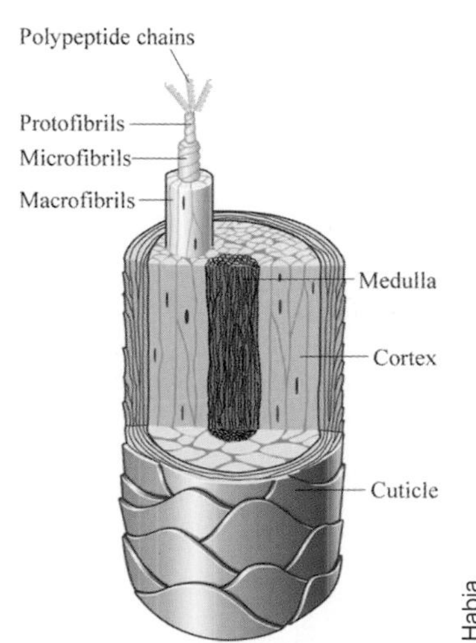

It's a fact!

The number of layers of the cuticle is one of the factors that determine the texture of hair. Hair that is fine will be smaller in diameter and have less layers of cuticle than hair that is coarse.

Cortex The cortex is the main section of hair and it is within this section that the properties *of elasticity* and *strength* exist and where the chemical changes take place when permanently colouring, bleaching, perming or relaxing the hair. The cortex is made up of intertwining, coiled bundles of elongated, cigar shaped cells

It's a fact! When hair is wet it stretches more than when it is dry.

that twist together. The bundles within the cortex are called **macrofibrils**, which are in turn made up from smaller bundles known as **microfibrils** that are made up of even smaller bundles called **protofibrils**.

The fibres are all held together by a series of linkages. Some of the linkages are very strong and can only be broken by the introduction of chemicals – such as when the hair is permed or relaxed. These are known as **sulphur bonds**. There are also some weaker bonds known as **salt linkages** and **hydrogen bonds** that can be broken by water.

The hair structure showing the salt linkages and hydrogen bonds

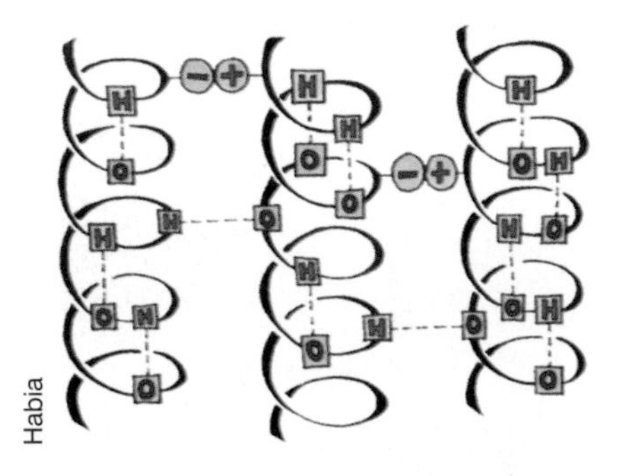

The linkages in the hair have an important role in the hair's ability to stretch and then return to its natural state. If the structure of the **cortex** is in good condition, the hair will stretch and return to its normal length. However if the cortex has been damaged, for example through excessive chemical treatments, the hair will break under tension, or remain in a stretched state. You can find out how good the elasticity is in the hair by carrying out an elasticity test. The method for carrying out this test will be explained later in this chapter.

Medulla The **medulla** is a space found within the central core of the hair that may or may not be present. It is normally found in coarse hair, but fine hair may not have a medulla. However, as the medulla is only made up of soft spongy cells with air spaces and has no function, it does not matter if the medulla is present or not.

Hair growth cycle

The hair on our head grows, falls out and grows again in a continual cycle of time that can last anything from 1.5 to 7 years and grows at an average rate of 1.25 cms each month. If the cycle is disrupted, the hair may fall out and not be replaced. When this happens, the hair becomes sparser, or in some case, bald patches will appear.

It's a fact! The colour pigment melanin is also found within the cortex. The natural and artificial colours of hair can be seen through the translucent cuticle cells.

There are three main stages to the hair growth cycle. They are known as:

- anagen
- catagen
- telogen

The three stages of hair growth

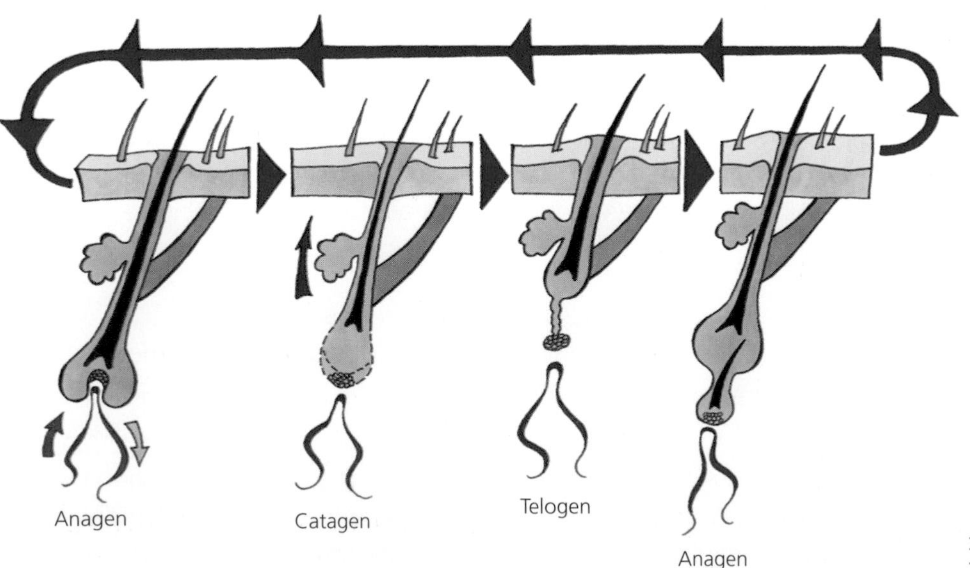

EXTEND YOUR LEARNING   

Although the hair grows, falls out and replaces itself, there are times when the growth cycle is interrupted, or the growth cycle stops completely. Research the hair growth cycle and find out why this happens and the results that occur.

Anagen Have you ever wondered why some people have very long hair, while others struggle to achieve a length that reaches past their shoulders? The reason for this variation is due to the active *growing stage* of the hair. This stage is known as anagen and can last between 1.5 and 7 years. Therefore, those people who have an active anagen stage of 7 years can grow their hair longer than those with an anagen stage of only 1.5 years. During the anagen stage, the hair is constantly fed by the blood supply to the dermal papilla.

The cuticle in good condition

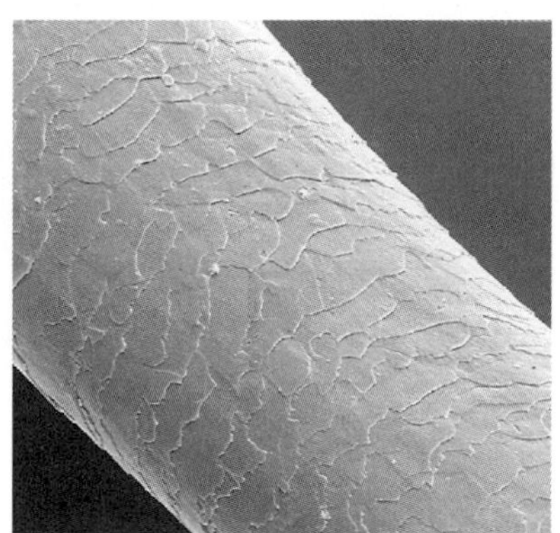

Dr John Gray

Catagen This stage is relatively short in length – it only lasts for around two weeks. During this stage the follicle rests and new cell production stops at the dermal papilla. The follicle begins to detach itself from the blood supply and begins to shrink away from the dermal papilla.

Telogen This stage can be described as the complete *resting stage* of hair growth. At this point the follicle completely separates from the papilla for a period of around four months. At the end of the *resting stage*, the follicle re-attaches itself to the papilla and the blood supply once again supplies the nutrients to allow new hair growth, starting a new anagen stage. If the follicle failed to reattach itself to the papilla, the new anagen stage would not begin and the client would experience hair loss – such as **alopecia** or as in male pattern baldness.

Factors affecting hair growth

Some people will have hair that grows at different rates to others. There are several reasons for this. They are:

- *Ethnic origin* – Some hair types appear to grow more quickly than others. The sleek straight hair of Asian origin does grow more quickly than African type hair, but the apparent slowness in growth is also because African type hair has a tendency to curl tightly at the roots.
- *Hereditary* – Male pattern baldness is hereditary, which means that if your father or grandfather (on both the mother or fathers side of the family) had hair loss, as a male, you likely to have a similar pattern of baldness.
- *Medication* – some types of drugs can inhibit or slow down hair growth – or in some cases, as with **chemotherapy**, cause the hair to fall out. However, there are some drugs, for example **steroids**, that cause excessive hair growth in unwanted places – such as on the faces of women.
- *Length of hair growth cycle* – some people have a longer anagen stage than others, thus they will be able to grow their hair for a longer period of time.

The cuticle in poor condition

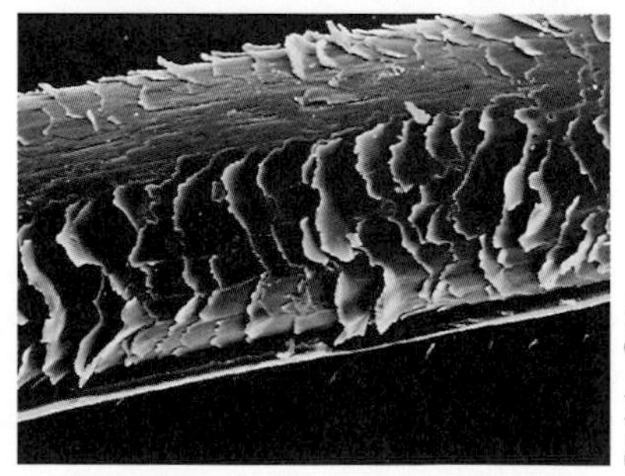

Dr John Gray

© iStockphoto.com/Izabela Habur

African type hair

Cross section of African type hair

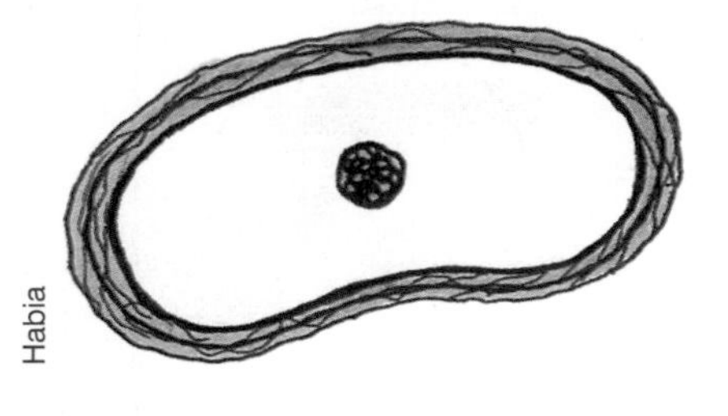
Habia

It's a fact! African type hair grows virtually parallel to the scalp.

Dr John Gray

Caucasian type hair

- *Diet* – a healthy balanced diet is essential for healthy hair growth. **Protein** is particularly important, as is iron. Drastic crash dieting can lead to hair loss.
- *Hormones* – changes in hormone levels are thought to be one of the causes of alopecia.

Hair type

Hair type refers to how straight, how wavy or how curly the hair is. Curly, wavy or straight hair can be natural or it can be chemically induced. For example, a person may have naturally curly hair, but they have straightened it with chemicals – therefore, the structure and appearance of the hair will have changed. Likewise, a person may have naturally straight hair, but has had a perm to increase the amount of body and movement in the hair. The change in the natural state of the hair can also be temporary. For example, if curly hair is stretched and smoothed when it is dried, it can look straight.

The type of hair you have is not only down to the direct **generic inheritance** from your parents, but also has a great deal to do with your ancestors.

Hair can be classified into three generic types:

- African
- Asian
- Caucasian or European

African type hair African type hair is sometimes known as *African Caribbean hair*. However, it is important to recognise that this type of hair is not restricted to those people who have originated from the Caribbean. African type hair is generally very curly, and often frizzy, but the type of curl can vary from soft, open curls to tight, woolly hair. This type of hair is not only found on people of African descent, but can also be found on people of mixed race. Sometimes, hair with similar characteristics to African type hair – tight, frizzy curls – can be seen on a client who is obviously European. African type hair is generally dark in colour – frequently brown, dark brown or black, but can also be red or blonde. Sometimes, African type hair may seem as though it does not grow as quickly as Asian or Caucasian hair, which is true to some extent. However, as the hair is very crinkled, it grows in a variety of directions before it appears to gain length. In addition to this, although the hair may look coarse, it is often very fine and delicate, meaning that the hair is likely to break before reaching a great length. Therefore, you have to treat this hair very gently when combing and brushing.

It's a fact! **If you look at African type hair under the microscope you will** see that the cross section of the hair is almost kidney shaped.

Caucasian or European type hair Caucasian or European hair has very many different characteristics. This type of hair can be straight, wavy or curly, coarse or fine in texture and vary in colour from black to the palest blonde. The reason for the differences in Caucasian hair is because people from all over Europe, and beyond, invaded or inhabited the British Isles for hundreds of years. Blonde, straight Caucasian hair is attributed to the Viking people who invaded Britain in 878AD. Red, and sometimes, coarser hair, can be linked to the Celts from Scotland, who were in turn invaded or occupied by five different ethnic groups during the Dark Ages. Dark brown glossy hair can be linked to the Romans who ruled in Britain from 43AD, while dark curly hair can be linked with the Roma Gypsies who lived in Britain at the same period of time. Thus, for these reasons, Caucasian hair is never the same from one person to another. It can be coarse and curly or fine and straight, it can have the characteristics of African type hair or those more associated with Asian hair.

It's a fact! If you look at Caucasian hair under the microscope you will see that the cross section of the hair is oval in shape.

Cross section of Caucasian type hair

Habia

It's a fact! Caucasian hair grows at an angle from the scalp.

Asian type hair Asian hair can be the dark glossy hair that you associate with India or Pakistan, or it can also be classed as hair that is much straighter Oriental type hair that can be found in the Far East – China and Japan. While Japanese hair is very straight, other types of Asian hair can also have some limited wave and movement in the hair. Asian hair is normally very dark brown or black in colour. This type of hair grows much faster than that of Caucasian or African type hair. Asian hair is often much coarser than Caucasian or African type.

You need to be aware that it is unlikely that you will have clients who have the exact characteristics of the three generic hair types that have been described. This is because, over many thousands of years, the different hair types have been mixed up – leading to the melting pot of hair types.

It's a fact! The 2001 national **census** counted 680,000 mixed race people, accounting for 1.2% of the overall population and nearly 15% of the ethnic minority population, which illustrates the amount of mixed race hair in the population. And the amount of mixed race hair is expected to grow.

Asian type hair

iStockphoto.com

EXTEND YOUR LEARNING

The office of National Statistics provides information about the population of Great Britain. Investigate the website **www.statistics.gov.uk/census/**. you can even find out what the most popular names have been for the last 100 years.

It's a fact! Asian hair grows almost perpendicular to the scalp.

Hair texture

Hair can be divided into three main divisions and then subdivided again.

The three main categories for hair texture are:

- coarse
- medium
- fine

Cross section of Asian type hair

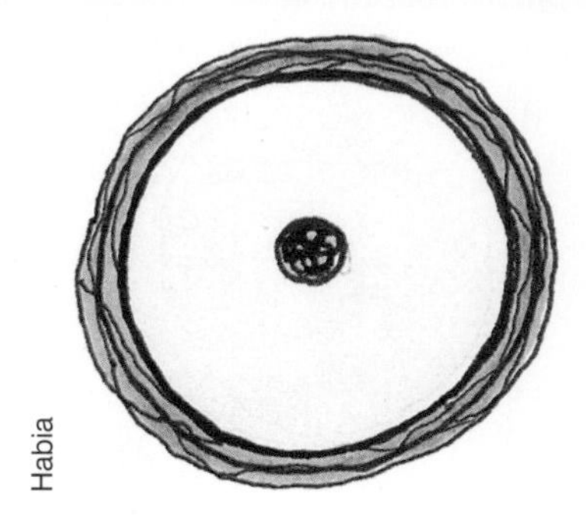

It's a fact! If you look at Asian hair under the microscope you will see that the cross section of the hair is round.

Coarse textured hair may have up to 11 layers

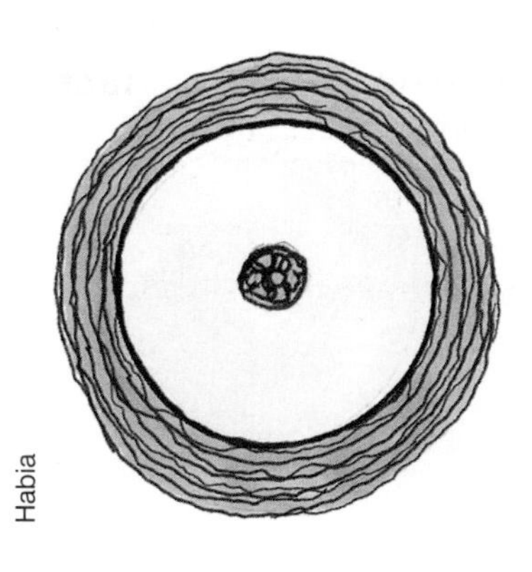

Fine textured hair may only have 4 layers of cuticle

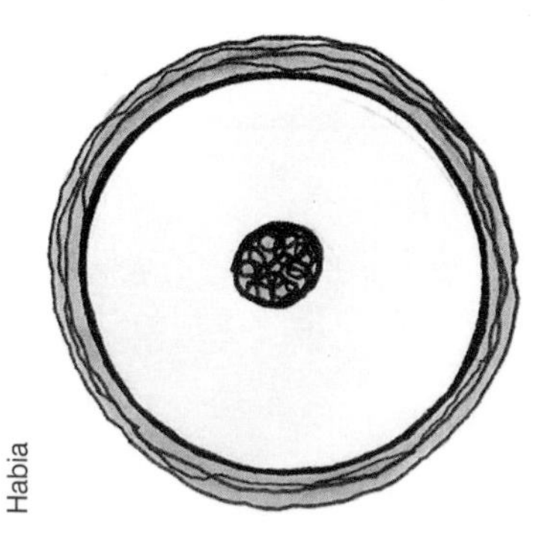

Then, the categories can be subdivided again into the following categories:

- **very coarse to coarse**
- **coarse to medium**
- **medium to fine**
- **fine to very fine**

Coarse hair One of the characteristics of coarse hair is that it quite often feels dry. People with coarse hair normally have less hair per square centimetre than those with fine hair. An average head of hair has 100,000 individual strands. People with fine hair can have as many as 150,000, while those with coarse hair may have only 80,000. Therefore, some people with coarse hair may also have sparse hair and people with fine hair, may have an abundance of hair.

The physical appearance of the diameter of coarse hair is larger than that of a fine hair and may have up to 11 layers of overlapping cuticle layers. Coarse hair normally has a medulla.

Fine hair Fine hair may only have four layers of overlapping cuticle layers and as a result may be much more liable to damage and breakage. Fine hair is often associated with sparse hair, although it is equally possible to have lots of fine hair.

Medium hair Medium hair falls between the characteristics of coarse and fine hair. It normally has around 7 layers of cuticle. The medulla in medium hair can appear and then disappear; although this does not have an effect on the hair.

It's a fact! An instrument known as a *micrometer* can measure the diameter of a single hair. The hair is placed within the anvil and spindle of the micrometer and its size is measured in **microns**. A micron is one millionth of a metre. Fine hair would be less than 50 microns, whereas very coarse hair would be around 120 microns.

Hair density

Hair can be described as being dense (or abundant) or it can be sparse. Abundant hair means that a person will have a greater number of hairs on their scalp than clients with sparse hair.

The texture, type and colour of hair can be directly related to density. The human scalp is approximately 770 square centimetres in size and research carried out by Drs Erasmus Wilson, Withof and Stelwagon found the following:

- Caucasian blonde hair was found to be more abundant with around 146,000 hairs
- Caucasian black hair was sparser with a density of 110,000 hairs
- Densities of red hair were between 86,000 and 100,000 hairs
- Densities of African type hair were between 50,000 and 110,000
- Asian hair had densities of between 80,000 and 140,000.

Some sparseness of hair can be isolated to particular areas of the scalp. It is common to have sparse areas at the temples on both men and women. Male pattern baldness can affect the crown area and, for some women, hair may also be thinner on the top of the head from the frontal area to the crown.

Alopecia Sparse hair can also be attributed to alopecia. No one really knows what causes alopecia, but the most common reasons connected to hair loss through alopecia are stress and changes in hormone levels.

The term 'alopecia' covers a variety of conditions. **Alopecia areata** means that the hair loss occurs in circular or oval patches which can be seen on any area of the head. If the alopecia areata condition continues, the bald patches can join together and eventually lead to a condition known as **alopecia totalis**, which means that there may be hair loss over the whole of the scalp.

Medium textured hair will have 7 layers of cuticle

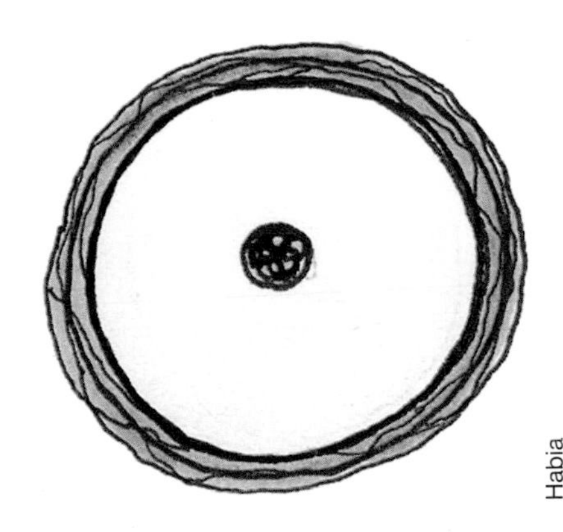
Habia

Hair elasticity

The elasticity in the hair allows you to temporarily change the look and structure of your hair. The ability of the hair to stretch and return to its original length depends on the structure and condition of the cortex. Within the cortex are a series of linkages or bonds that lie horizontally and vertically between the **cortical cells**. Some of the bonds, the sulphur bonds, are very strong and can only be broken by chemicals that are used to permanently curl or straighten the hair. However, water or applying gentle heat can temporarily break the weaker bonds of salt bonds and hydrogen bonds.

It's a fact!

Male pattern baldness can be inherited from the mother as well as the father.

It's a fact!

Hair is hygroscopic. This means that the hair can absorb moisture into itself from the atmosphere, and explains why your hair does not retain its styled position on foggy, damp days, or in a humid atmosphere.

It's a fact!

Alopecia areata can occur anywhere on the body. Areas of hair loss can be seen on arms and legs and even on the eyebrows.

Bring your learning to life

When you are on your work placement or in a salon environment, collect different samples of hair from clients who are having their hair cut. Stick the hair samples on a card. Can you identify the hair type and texture?

Changes in the hair structure that affect styling and finishing

The properties in hair that allow the shape to be temporarily changed during styling are directly related to the formation and structure of bonds within the cortex. There are three different types of bond. They are:

- sulphur bonds
- salt bonds
- hydrogen bonds

The change from alpha to beta keratin

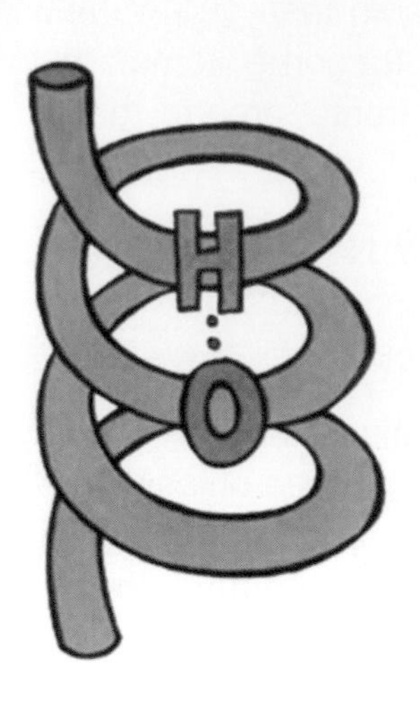

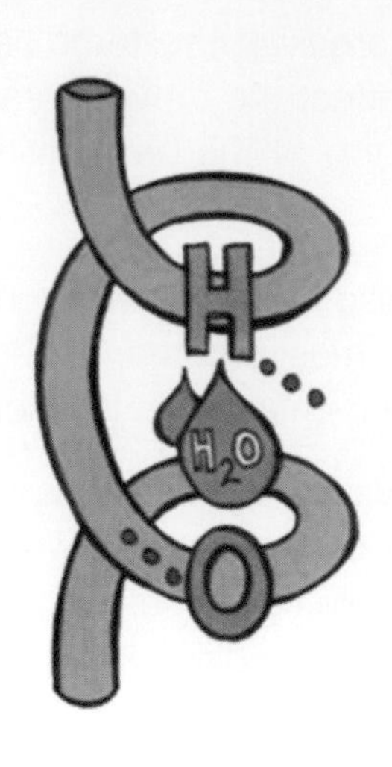

Habia

Structure of the nail unit

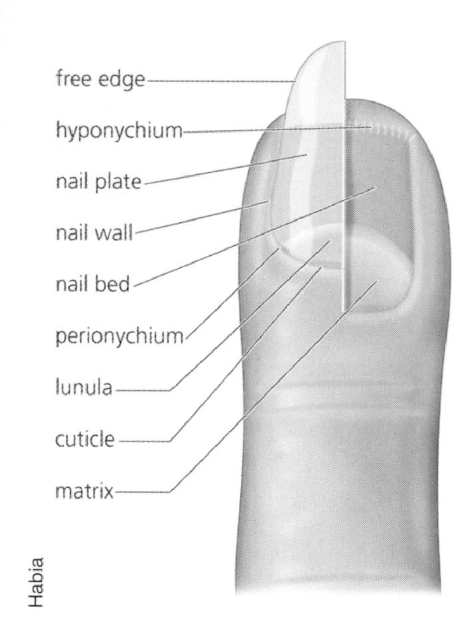

Habia

Chemicals, such as perm lotion, can only break the sulphur bonds, but the salt and hydrogen bonds are weaker and are broken by water, atmospheric conditions and gentle heat. This means that the hair can be stretched and shaped into a new temporary position when we style the hair.

When hair is in its natural state, the formation of keratin is called **alpha keratin**. When the hair has been stretched and dried, the keratin formation is known as **beta keratin**. The new position remains in place until the bonds are broken again by water or moisture in the atmosphere. When this happens, the hair goes back to its natural state and the formation of the keratin is once again known as alpha keratin.

The structure and function of nails

The nails are on the ends of our fingers and toes and provide a solid *rigid* support to protect the ends of our fingers or toes and the small bones from endless knocks and damage. Nails help us to pick up objects, particularly if they are very small and delicate. The nail is made from keratin, which is the same protein that is found in the hair and skin. Keratin is a protein composed of amino acids formed together in long chains. A large number of these chains are found in the nail, which is the reason why the nail is a lot harder than that of the skin and hair. The nail unit is made up of three main parts, the:

- nail bed
- matrix
- nail plate

It's a fact! Nails are formed very early in the development of an unborn baby and will be fully formed by week 20.

Nail bed

The nail bed is the living skin on which the nail plate sits. The nail bed is supplied with blood vessels that gives the nail plate a pinkish appearance. The nail bed is supplied with many nerves and is attached to the nail plate by a thin layer of tissue called the **bed epithelium**. The bed epithelium acts as a *seal* against infection for that area of the nail and also helps to guide the nail plate along the nail bed as it grows.

Matrix

This is the most important area in the nail unit. The matrix is where the nail plate is formed. The matrix is composed of *matrix cells* that form cells that become the nail plate. The matrix contains living nerves, lymph and blood vessels to feed and nourish the matrix cells to enable the matrix to continue to create and supply new nail cells. The matrix extends from under the nail fold at the base of the nail plate. The visible part of the matrix which can be seen at the base of the nail plate is called the **lunula**; it is a lighter colour than the rest of the nail plate and is seen as an curve or *half moon* shape.

Cross section of the nail unit

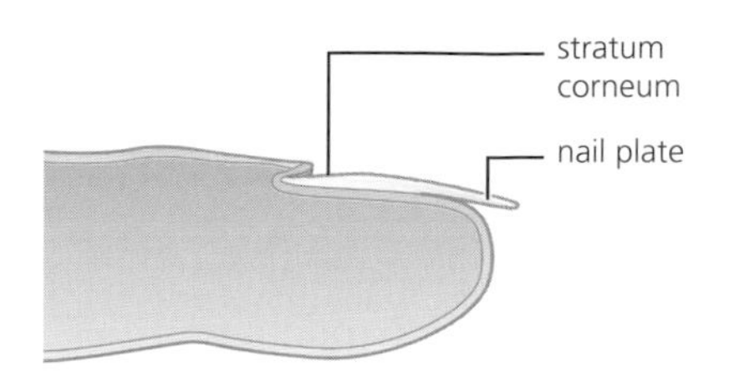

It's a fact!

Nails grow at the ends of the fingers and toes and their purpose is to help protect the fingers and toes and also help to pick up small objects. The nail plate is made up of compact layers of epidermal cells. To find out more information about the nail continue to read the section on the nail structure.

Nail plate

The nail plate is the visible and functional part of the nail unit. It is a hard keratin plate that is based on top of and slides along of the nail bed. The nail plate is made up of many layers of nail cells. The nail can absorb more water than the skin, however, when your hands have been in water for any length of time, the nails will become soft and flexible, which can easily cause the nail plate to become weak and cause the cell layers peel. The section of the nail plate that extends past the bed is called the **free edge**. Attached around the edge of the nail plate is the dead colourless tissue called the **cuticle**. The cuticle comes from the underside of the skin and its job is to seal the space between the nail plate and living skin to prevent the entry of any foreign material and micro-organisms, to help prevent any injury or infection.

The **eponychium** is the living skin at the base of the nail plate covering the matrix area. Sometimes people can confuse the eponychium with the cuticle but they are not the same. The cuticle is the dead tissue on the nail plate, the eponychium is living tissue. The **hyponychium** is the slightly thickened layer of skin that lies underneath the free edge of the nail plate to create a seal to prevent micro-organisms infecting the nail bed. Ligaments attach the nail bed and matrix to the finger bone, known as the **phalanges**. These ligaments are found at the base of the matrix and around the edges of the nail bed. Finally there are nail folds, these are folds of normal skin that surround the nail plate. They form the nail grooves, which are the slits or furrows that are on both sides of the nail on which the nail moves as it grows.

EXTEND YOUR LEARNING

Investigate the term *micro-organisms*, find out what they are and how they affect the human body.

Free edge

The free edge is the section of the nail that extends beyond the finger tip. It is this section of nail that is filed and shaped. Its function is to protect the fingertip.

Nail growth

The average rate that a nail grows in an adult is about 3.7 mm per month. The growth of the nail plate can be affected by nutrition and the person's health. Children's nails grow faster than adults as the growth rate usually slows down with age. Fingernails grow faster than toenails as toenails are thicker and harder.

It's a fact!

Nails grow faster in summer than they do in winter.

It's a fact! If disease, injury or infection occurs in the matrix, the shape or thickness of the nail plate can change.

It's a fact! If you lose a nail it will take 4–6 months to replace a fingernail and about 9–12 months to replace a toenail.

A normal, healthy nail can grow in a variety of shapes, depending on the shape of the matrix. The length, width and curvature of the matrix determine the thickness, width and curvature of the nail plate, a long matrix produces a thicker nail plate and a highly curved matrix creates a highly curved free edge.

The basic anatomy and physiology of different parts of the human body

Human beings are one of the most *complex* organisms on the planet. There are billions of microscopic parts with their own individual identity working together to form the human body. In other words the human body is a single structure made up of billions of smaller structures of four main types:

- *Cells* – These are the simplest unit of living matter that can maintain life and reproduce themselves
- *Tissues* – Tissues are more complex than cells. A tissue is an organisation of lots of similar cells with varying amounts and kinds of non-living intercellular substance between them
- *Organs* – An organ is more complex than a tissue. An organ is a organisation of several different types of tissues that when arranged together perform a special function
- *Systems* – Systems are the most complex. A system is an organisation of varying numbers and kinds of organs arranged together to perform complex functions for the body. There are ten major systems that make up the human body:
    - *Skeletal* – The skeleton has six main functions
        - **support** – it provides the framework which supports the body
        - **movement** – the vertebrate (back bone) is powered by skeletal muscles; without the skeleton to give leverage, movement would be restricted
        - **protection** – it protects many vital organs
        - **blood cell protection** – the skeleton provides haematopoiesis, which takes place in red bone marrow
        - **storage** – it stores calcium and the bone marrow can store iron
        - **endocrine regulation** – bone cells releases a hormone which controls the regulation of blood sugar
    - *Muscular* – This allows the body to move and different organs to work
    - *Nervous* – The nervous system is made up of two parts: (i) the central nervous system which is the largest part of the nervous system and includes

the brain and spinal cord and (ii) the peripheral nervous system which consists mainly of nerves. The nervous system is a highly specialised network of nerves called **neurons**. Neurons are sensors that send messages to the central nervous system (the largest part of the nervous system which includes the brain and spinal cord) which then sends messages back to tell them how to react, where the messages are finally sent back directly to the brain

- *Endocrine* – An integrated system of small organs that releases hormones, regulates our metabolism, growth and development and also plays apart of determining your mood
- *Circulatory* – This system moves nutrients, gases and waste to and from cells; it helps to fight disease and stabilise body temperature. It consists of two systems: (i) the cardiovascular which distributes blood and (ii) the lymphatic which distributes lymph. The cardiovascular system carries oxygenated blood from the heart to the body, skin, hair and nails. *Oxygenated* blood carries oxygen and nutrients' that diffuse from the blood into the cells surrounding the capillaries, and returns *deoxygenated* blood back to the heart. Deoxygenated blood contains carbon dioxide. The lymphatic system is the body's second system for collecting waste from around the body. It carries waste from the tissues that the blood cannot manage to carry. The fluid that is left behind is called lymph. The lymphatic system also protects the body against infection, as the lymph travels around the body past glands it is filtered of bacteria and germs and **antibodies** are produced to fight infection. Stimulating the circulatory system through massage will help the flow of blood and lymph which will:
  - remove toxins from the body faster
  - increase the absorption of waste matter
  - increase the flow of nutrients to the body skin, hair and nails, to improve condition and growth
  - help muscles to work more effectively

It's a fact!

Arteries carry blood away from the heart and veins carry blood to the heart.

- *Respiratory* – This consists of the airways, the lungs and the respiratory muscles and facilitates *oxygenation* of the blood by the removal of *carbon dioxide* and waste
- *Urinary* – This system produces, stores and eliminates urine. The system is made up of *two kidneys*, *two ureter tubes*, the *bladder* and the *urethra*. It also maintains the volume of water that it excretes in the urine and plays a role in maintaining normal blood pressure. Although the urinary system plays a major part in the excretion of waste, other organs contribute to this function: the lungs in the respiratory system, the skin and the liver

- *Reproductive* – This is a system of organs that work together for the purpose of reproduction
- *Digestive* – This system is made up of a digestive track, which is a series of hollow twisting organs that join from the mouth to the anus, and other organs that help the body break down and absorb food. Food and drink must be changed into small molecules of nutrients so that they can be absorbed by the blood and carried around the body
- *Immune* – This system protects the body against infection and disease by identifying and killing the invading organisms. The immune system has layers of defences, the skin being the first line of defence. If the invading organism gets through the layers of defence then the immune system adapts and remembers its response during the infection so that it can improve and respond quicker the next time

EXTEND YOUR LEARNING

The human body is a fascinating subject. Why not research and find out more about cells, tissues, organs and systems.

Before we can look at individual areas of the human body we need to look at the wider aspects that make up the skeletal system. **Bones** are the hard structure that makes up the basic framework of the **skeleton**. Where two or more bones meet a joint is formed.

The skeletal system also has tough connective tissue that forms a supporting structure; these different tissues are known as **cartilage**, **ligaments** and **tendons**.

- *Cartilage* – This provides the skeletal system with connection, support protection and flexibility. Cartilage is made up of firm connective tissue made from elastin and collagen fibres, it is flexible and durable. There are three types of cartilage:
  - **hyaline cartilage**, sometimes known as articular cartilage. This type of cartilage is used to cover the ends of the bones where they meet at a joint; it helps to prevent friction and the bones wearing away from the constant moving or rubbing against each other. This type of cartilage also helps in the attachment of some bones to others such as the ribs to the breastplate, and it also forms parts of the nose and windpipe
  - **fibrocartilage** is a tougher cartilage and less flexible; it is used to form ligaments and the pads between bones such as between the bones of the spine
  - **elastic cartilage** is very flexible and is used to form areas of the body such as the ear
- *Ligament* – These connect bones at joints to help movement between two or more bones. They are formed from fibrocartilage and link bones together, allowing them to move safely within a range of movement
- *Tendons* – These attach muscles to bones. They are made from bundles of collagen fibres which attach muscle to bone, such as at the Achilles tendon that attaches the calf muscle to the ankle

It's a fact! A ligament is a tough band of fibrous tissue that connects bones or holds organs in place.

Skeletal system

Bones

Bones are the most rigid structures of connective tissue that make up the skeleton. They differ greatly in shape and size but are similar in their structure and functions. Bones are made up of living tissue and contain:

- approximately 25 per cent water
- approximately 45 per cent inorganic material, calcium and phosphorus
- approximately 30 per cent organic material, comprising bone forming cells called osteoblasts along with a blood and nerve supply

Because they are living tissue, bones grow while we are children and we will feel pain if they are damaged. They are able to repair themselves when broken. As we grow older, a hardening process called **ossification** takes place. This makes the bone more solid in structure. In addition, bones contain **collagen**,

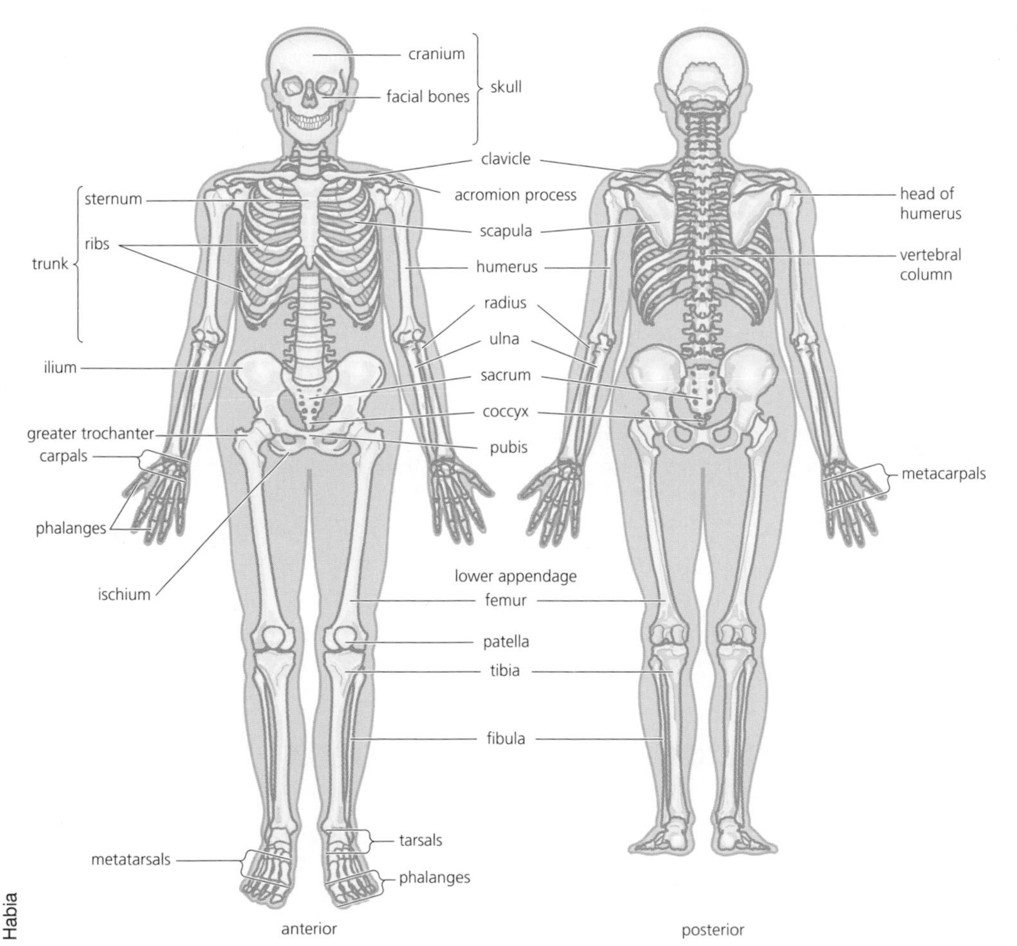

The human skeleton

which gives them resilience and **calcium** which gives them strength. Some bones have an inner cavity which contains **bone marrow**. Red bone marrow produces new blood cells and yellow bone marrow is used as a storage area for fat cells.

Bone can renew itself but this is a very slow process. Cells called **osteoclasts** break down old bone cells and form new bone cells. As the bone cells get older and mature, they are known as **osteocytes**.

There are two types of bone tissue: compact or hard bone tissue and cancellous which is a soft spongy bone tissue:

- *Compact bone tissue* – This has an almost solid structure making it hard and durable and is the outer structure of the bone
- *Cancellous bone tissue* – This has a looser inner structure giving a spongy appearance to the bone. It has larger canals, providing space for red or yellow bone marrow. Cancellous bone tissue is found in side of the bone

Muscular system

It's a fact! Muscles are incredible structures that are long lasting, self healing and have the ability to get stronger if we exercise and keep fit.

Muscles

It would be impossible for the human body to do anything without muscles. Muscles play a major part in the circulation of the blood. The *heart* is mainly comprised of a muscle tissue that makes it work by pumping the blood around the body. The skeleton supports and protects our inner organs, but it needs muscles in order to move about by turning energy from nutrition into movement. Muscles allow us to talk, walk, pick up objects and express our thoughts through facial expression.

There are three types of muscles:

- *Skeletal muscles* – We can feel and see this type of muscle working. We are able to control them and they are attached to the skin and nearly always work in pairs, one muscle moving one way and the other moving it back
- *Smooth muscles* – We are not usually aware of these muscles working. They are controlled by the brain sending signals directly to them. They are usually associated with our internal organs and blood vessels
- *Cardiac muscle* – This is only found in the heart and is controlled by the brain

The basic anatomy of the head neck and shoulders

It's a fact! The skull is made up of 22 bones.

The bones and muscles of the head and face determine the shape of the head and face and the individual features that a person has. Hair or beauty professionals need to know the position of bones or muscles so that you can identify and enhance good features on the face or head and camouflage other features.

When carrying out a facial treatment or massage to the head and shoulders it is important that you understand and use the correct techniques and routines to ensure that damage is not caused to the skin or muscles by applying too much pressure.

Bones of the head and face

The **skull** is made up of bones that form the head, also known as the **cranium**, and the face. The cranium creates an inner casing to enclose and protect the brain. Except for the **mandible**, all of the bones of the skull are joined together by sutures to make it rigid.

The cranium is made up of eight bones:

BONE	NUMBER OF BONES	POSITION OF THE BONES IN THE CRANIUM	FUNCTION OF THE BONE
Occipital	1	Located at the lower back of the cranium	The occipital contains a passageway called the foramen magnum, in which the spinal cord, the nerves and blood vessels pass through, linking the brain with the rest of the body
Parietal	2	Large bones located at the sides of the head	Forms the crown area (top and sides) of the head
Temporal	2	Located at either side of the head	Encased in the temporal bones are the six ear ossicles of the middle ears (these bones are not part of the skull)
Frontal	1	Located at the front of the skull to form the forehead	Forms the forehead and the upper walls of the eye sockets; it also contains two sinuses, one above each eye
Ethmoid	1	Located between the eye sockets	Forms part of the nasal cavities
Spheniod	1	Located at the base of the skull in front of the temporal bones	A butterfly shaped bone that joins the bones of the cranium together

Bones of the face

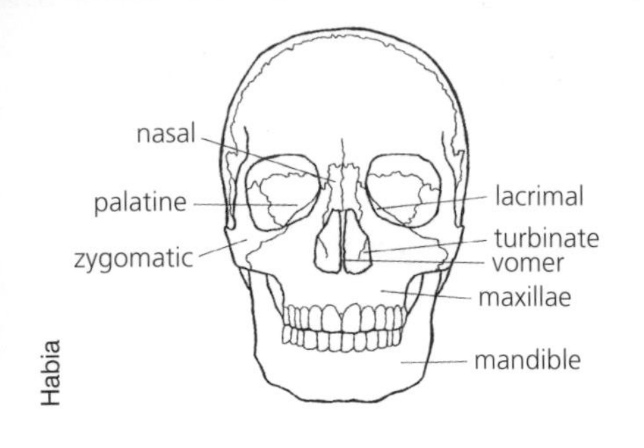

Bones of the skull and face

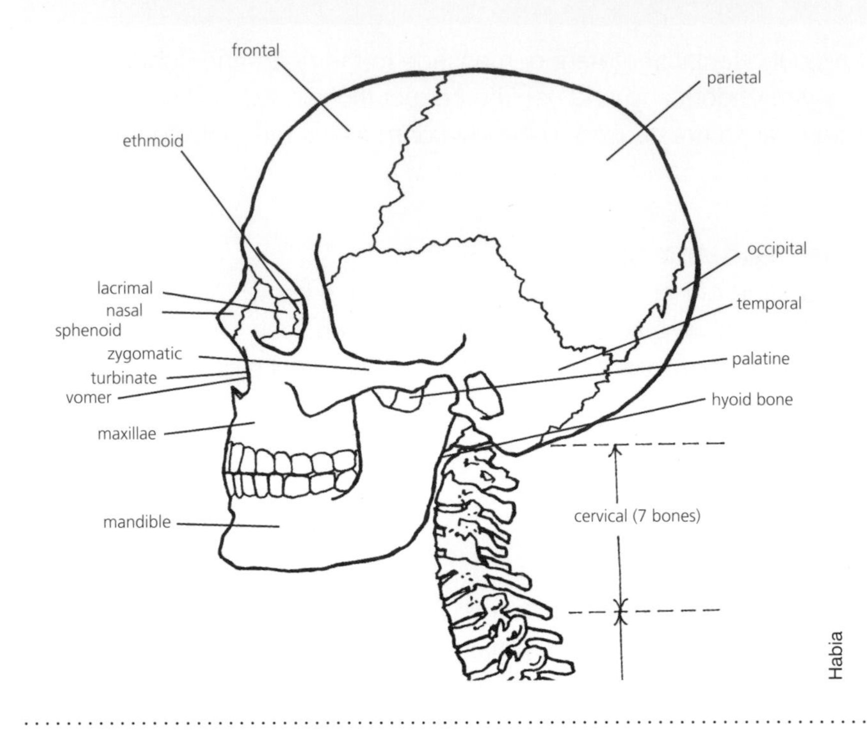

There are 14 bones of the face:

BONE	NUMBER OF BONES	POSITION OF THE BONES IN THE FACE	FUNCTION OF THE BONE
Lacrimal	2	Form the eye socket	Forms the inner wall of the eye socket that contains a passage for the tear duct
Turbinate	2	Located at the sides of the nose	Forms the sides of the nose
Vomer	1	Located on the nose	Forms the top of the nose
Maxillae	2	Forms the upper jaw	The two bones fuse together to form the upper jaw containing the sockets for the upper teeth
Mandible	1	Forms the lower jaw	It is the only movable bone in the skull enabling us to talk and chew; it contains the sockets for the lower set of teeth
Nasal	2	Located on the nose	Forms the bridge of the nose

Palatine	2	Located at the back of the nasal cavity	It contributes to 3 cavities: the wall of the nasal cavity, the roof of the mouth and the floor of the orbit
Zygomatic	2	Located on the cheek	Forms the cheek bones

Bones of the neck and shoulder

There are 12 bones that that make up the neck and shoulder:

BONE	NUMBER OF BONES	POSITION OF THE BONES IN THE NECK AND SHOULDER	FUNCTION OF THE BONE
Cervical vertebra	7	In the neck	Forms the length of the neck and forms the top of the spinal column. The first bone, the atlas vertebra, supports the skull and the second bone, the axis vertebra, allows the rotation of the head.
Hyoid	1	Located at the front of the neck	A U-shaped bone that supports the tongue
Clavicle	2	Located at the base of the neck	Also called the collar bone, the clavicle bones join with the sternum and scapula bones to allow movement of the shoulders
Scapula	2	Located in the upper back	Also called the shoulder blades, these bones enable arm muscles to attach allowing the arm to move. The shoulder girdle comprises of the clavicles and scapulae, allowing the shoulders to move

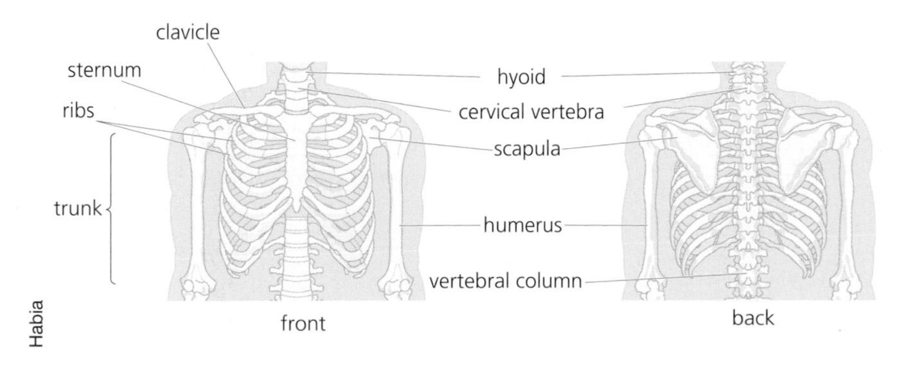

Bones of the neck, chest and shoulders

Muscles of the face, head and neck

Muscles of the neck and shoulders

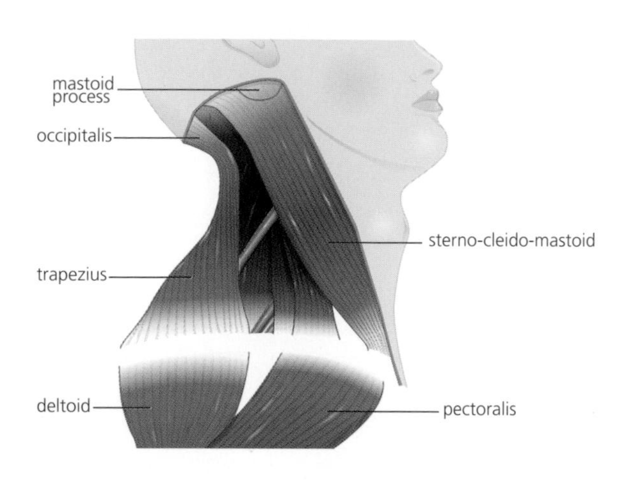

Muscles of the face

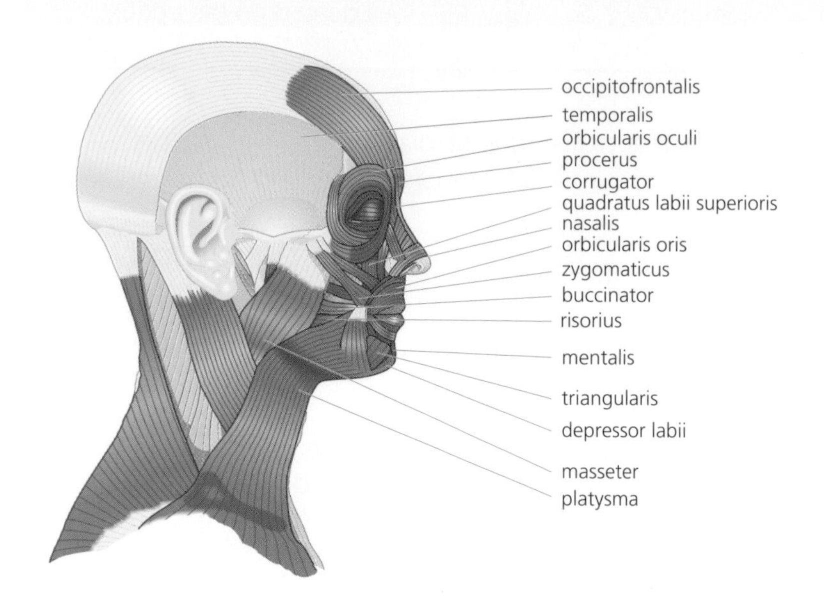

The muscles of the head and face are very small and are attached either to another muscle in the face or to the skin. When a muscle contracts, it moves the facial skin; this creates facial expression.

MUSCLE	EXPRESSION	POSITION	ACTION
Occipito frontalis	Surprise	Covers the occipital bone and the frontal bone that creates the forehead	Raises the eyebrows and creates horizontal wrinkle lines across the forehead
Corrugator (corrugator supercilli)	Frown	Located between the eyebrows	Draws them together to create a vertical frown line

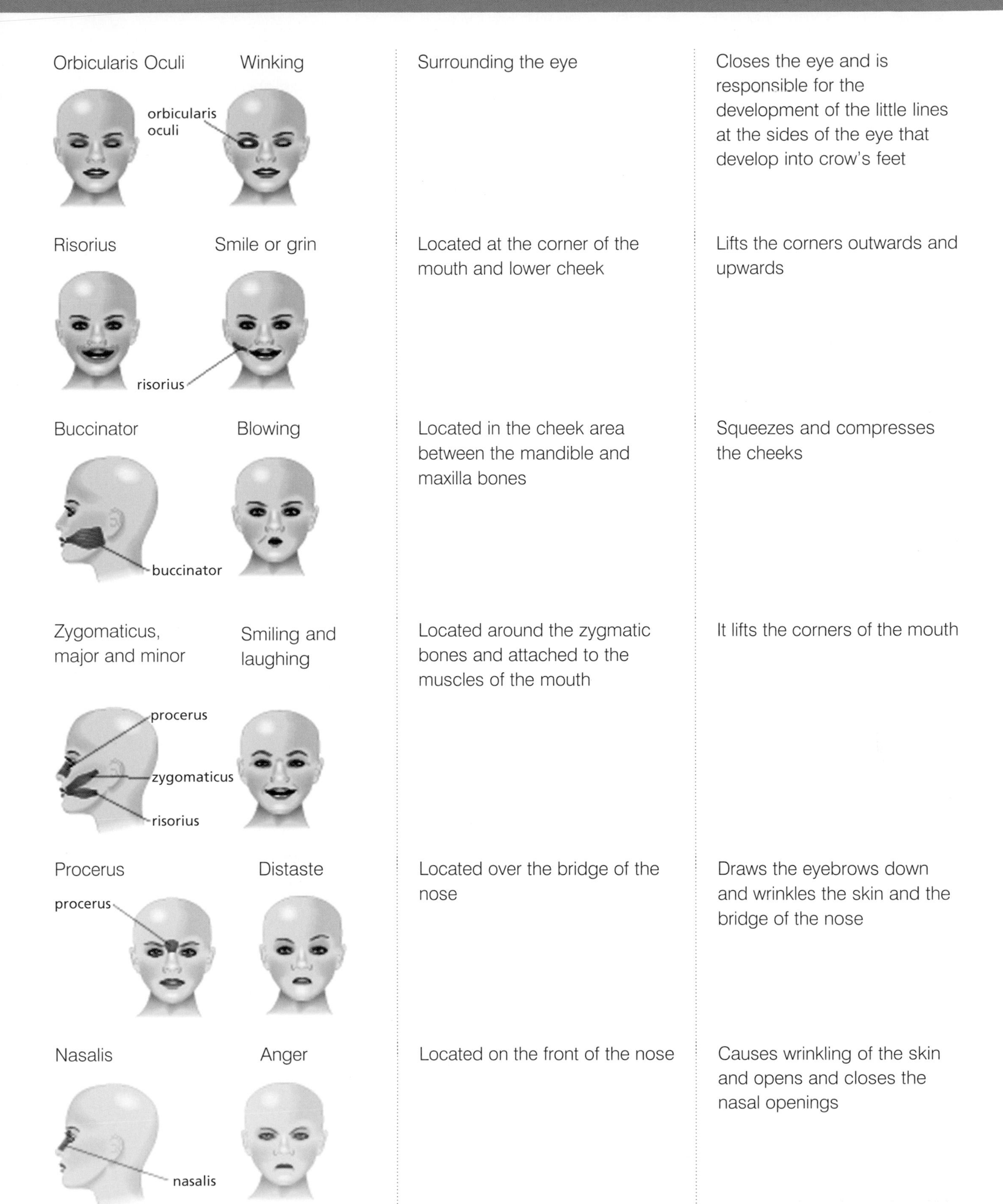

Orbicularis Oculi	Winking	Surrounding the eye	Closes the eye and is responsible for the development of the little lines at the sides of the eye that develop into crow's feet
Risorius	Smile or grin	Located at the corner of the mouth and lower cheek	Lifts the corners outwards and upwards
Buccinator	Blowing	Located in the cheek area between the mandible and maxilla bones	Squeezes and compresses the cheeks
Zygomaticus, major and minor	Smiling and laughing	Located around the zygmatic bones and attached to the muscles of the mouth	It lifts the corners of the mouth
Procerus	Distaste	Located over the bridge of the nose	Draws the eyebrows down and wrinkles the skin and the bridge of the nose
Nasalis	Anger	Located on the front of the nose	Causes wrinkling of the skin and opens and closes the nasal openings

Quadratus labii superioris — Disdain 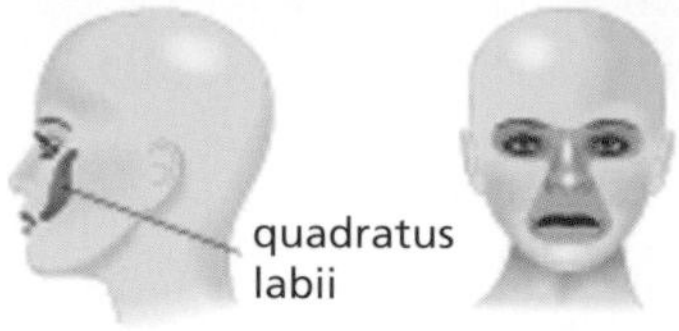 quadratus labii	Located around the upper lip	Draws back and lifts the upper lip and nostrils
Depressor labii — Sulking 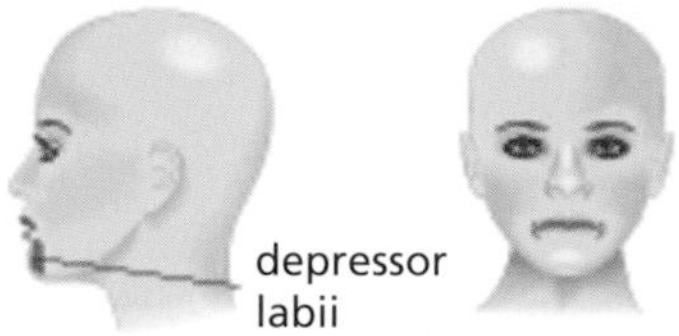 depressor labii	Located around the lower lip	Depresses the lower lip
Orbicularis oris — Pouting, puckering, kissing 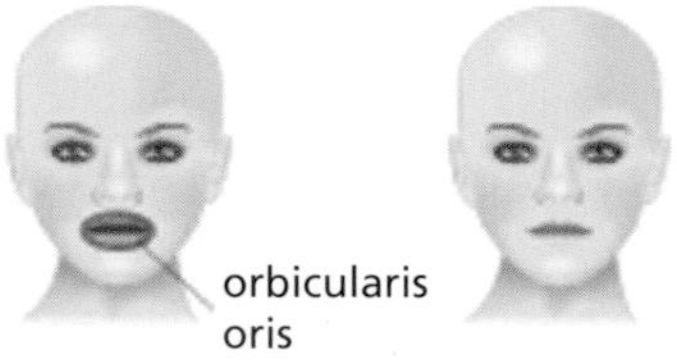 orbicularis oris	Located around the mouth	Purses the lips
Triangularis — Sulking or sadness 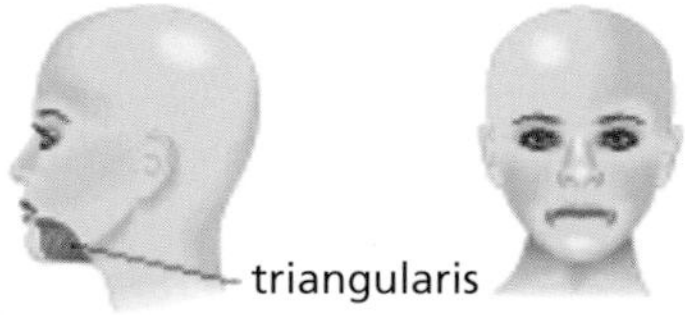 triangularis	Along the side of the chin	Pulls dawn the corners of the mouth
Mentalis — Doubt or displeasure 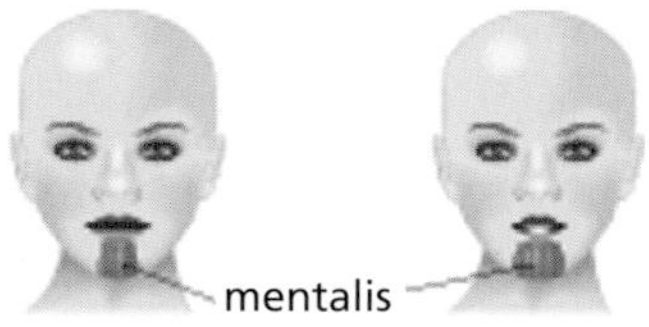 mentalis	Covers the front of the chin	Pulls the lower lip up which causes the chin to wrinkle
Platysma — Grimace or fear 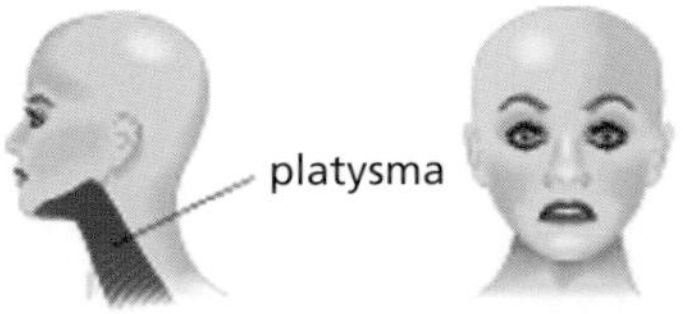 platysma	Located at the side of the neck and chin	Pulls the corners of the mouth downwards and backwards

Muscles of the neck and shoulders

MUSCLE	POSITION	ACTION
Sterno-cleido-mastoid	Located in the neck, they connect to the sternum, clavicle bone and the temporal bone	The two muscles work together to tilt and rotate the head and flex the neck
Trapezius	Located at the back of the neck and upper back	It is a large triangular muscle that works with the sterno-cleido-mastoid muscle to move the head from side to side and draw the head back
Occipitalis	Located at the back of the head	Moves the scalp
Deltoid	Located across the shoulders	A thick triangular muscle that draws the arm away from the side of the body

The basic anatomy of the hand and arm

As part of a manicure service, it is important that you understand the bones and muscles of the hand and lower arm so that you know what each bone and muscle is used for. You also need to know how much pressure should be applied during massage so that you do not cause any damage. The hands are intricate structures and the main organs for physically moving, holding and manipulating objects. Their function and skill is wide ranging from picking up and wielding a bat to threading a needle. The fingertips contain dense areas of nerve endings so they can provide us with tactile feedback – this is why our sense of touch is associated with our hands.

The bones of the hand and wrist

There are eight bones in the wrist, arranged in two rows of four. These bones fit into a shallow socket formed by the bones in the forearm. The eight bones are:

In the first row, nearest the forearm you have the:

- scaphoid
- lunate
- triquetral
- pisiform

In the second row, nearest the palm you have the:

- trapezium
- trapezoid
- capitate
- hamate

The palm is made up of five bones, one to each of the digits or fingers. These bones are called the **metacarpals** and finally the fingers are made up of 14 digit

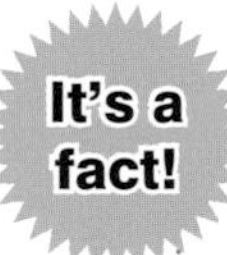

The human hand has 27 bones.

Bones of the wrist and hand

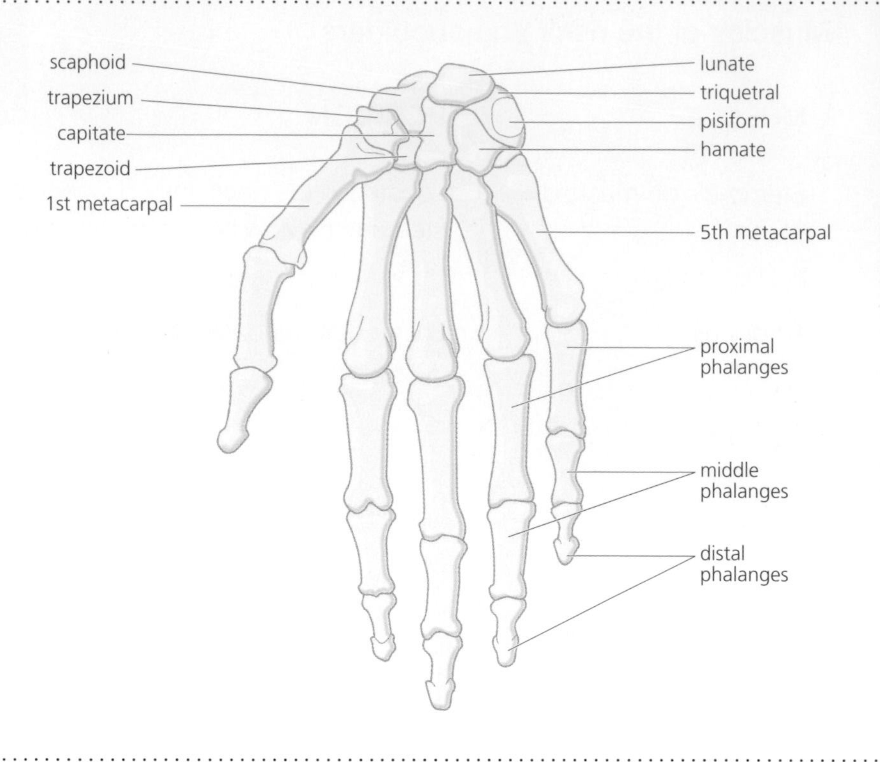

Muscles of the hand and arm

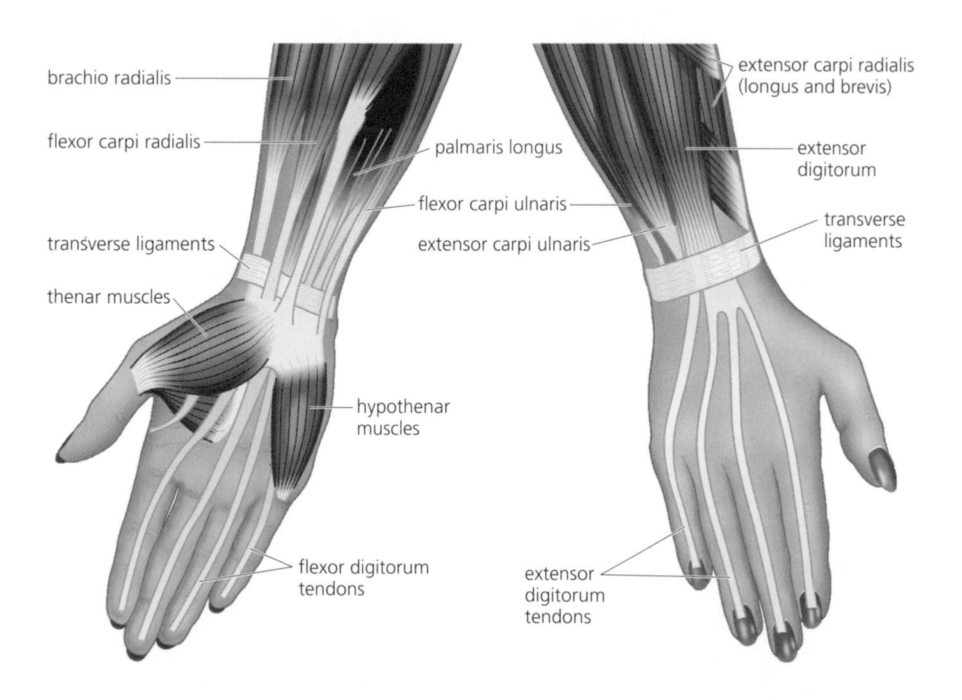

bones called **phalanges**, two on each of the thumbs and three on each finger. The distal phalanges carry the nail.

Bones of the arm

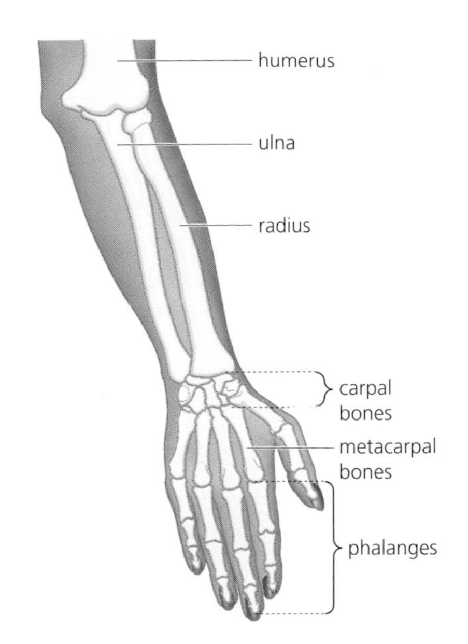

The bones of the arm

The arm is made up of three bones:

- Humerous – this is the bone of the upper arm from the shoulder to the elbow
- Radius – this is one of the two bones that make up the lower arm
- Ulna – this is one of the two bones that make up the lower arm

The radius and ulna lie beside each other and enables the wrist to rotate so that the palm of the hand can face upwards or downwards.

The muscles of the hand and arm

The hands and fingers are moved by muscles and tendons based in the forearm. When the muscle contracts, it pulls on the tendon that then moves the fingers. There are two types of muscles that move the wrist:

- Flexors – draw the wrist, hand and fingers towards the forearm
- Extensors – straighten the wrist, hand and fingers

Muscles of the hand and lower arm

MUSCLE	POSITION	ACTION
Brachio radialis	Located on the exterior or thumb side of the forearm	Turns and flexes the elbow
Flexor carpi radialis	Located on the inner side and middle of the forearm	Flexes the wrist
Extensor carpi radialis	Located on the outer side on the thumb side of the forearm	Straightens and extends the wrist and hand
Flexor carpi ulnaris	Located on the inner side of the arm or on the little finer side of the forearm	Flexes the hand
Extensor carpi ulnaris	Located on the outside of the forearm	Extends the wrist
Palmaris longus	Located in the middle of the inner forearm	Flexes the wrist and hand
Hyothenar muscle	Located in the palm of the hand near the little finger	Flexes the little finger
Thenar muscle	Located in the palm of the hand near the thumb	Flexes the thumb
Flexor digitorum tendons	Located on the front of the finger	Flexes the fingers
Extensor digitorum	Located on the back of the fingers	Extends the fingers

The basic anatomy of the foot and lower leg

As part of a pedicure service, it is important that you understand the bones and muscles of the foot and lower leg so that you know what each bone and muscle is used for. You also need to know how much pressure should be applied during massage.

The human foot combines mechanical complexity and structural strength. The foot can support enormous pressure and provides flexibility and resiliency. Think of the pressure you put your feet through every day when you walk and run, particularly if you do not wear practical shoes. The foot and ankle work together to provide the body with support, balance and mobility.

The foot has the following main parts:

- The *forefoot* – composed of the five toes and their connecting long bones, the **metatarsal** bones. There are fourteen **phalanges** bones which make up the toes and five metatarsal bones connecting to the phalanges bones.
- The *midfoot* – composed of seven irregular shaped **tarsal** bones that form the foot's arch and serves as a shock absorber. The foot's arches are supported

Bones of the foot

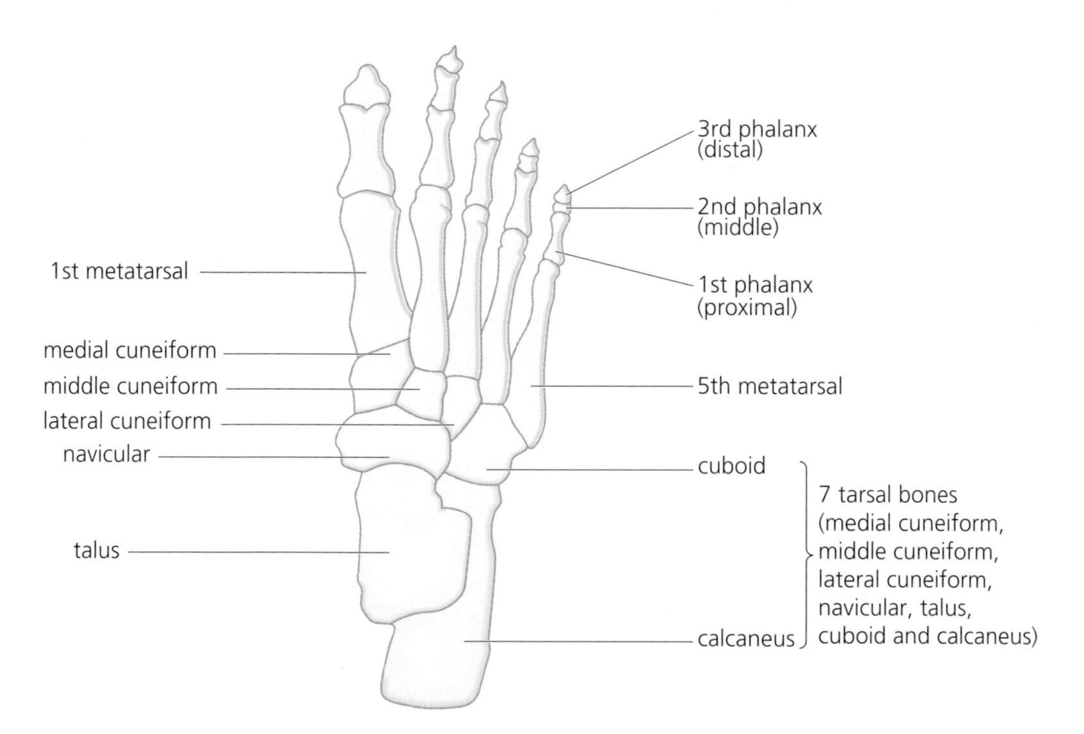

by ligaments. It is the arches the support the weight of the body and helps our balance when walking. These bones are called:

- medial cuneiform
- middle cuneiform
- lateral cuneiform
- navicular
- talus
- cubiod
- calcaneus

- the *hindfoot* – composed of three joints and links the midfoot to the ankle

Bones of the lower leg

The lower leg is made up of two long bones, the **tibia** and **fibula**. They are joined to the foot by the ankle and enable the ankle to have a wide range of movement; they are joined to the upper leg by the knee.

It's a fact!

The human foot and ankle contains 26 bones.

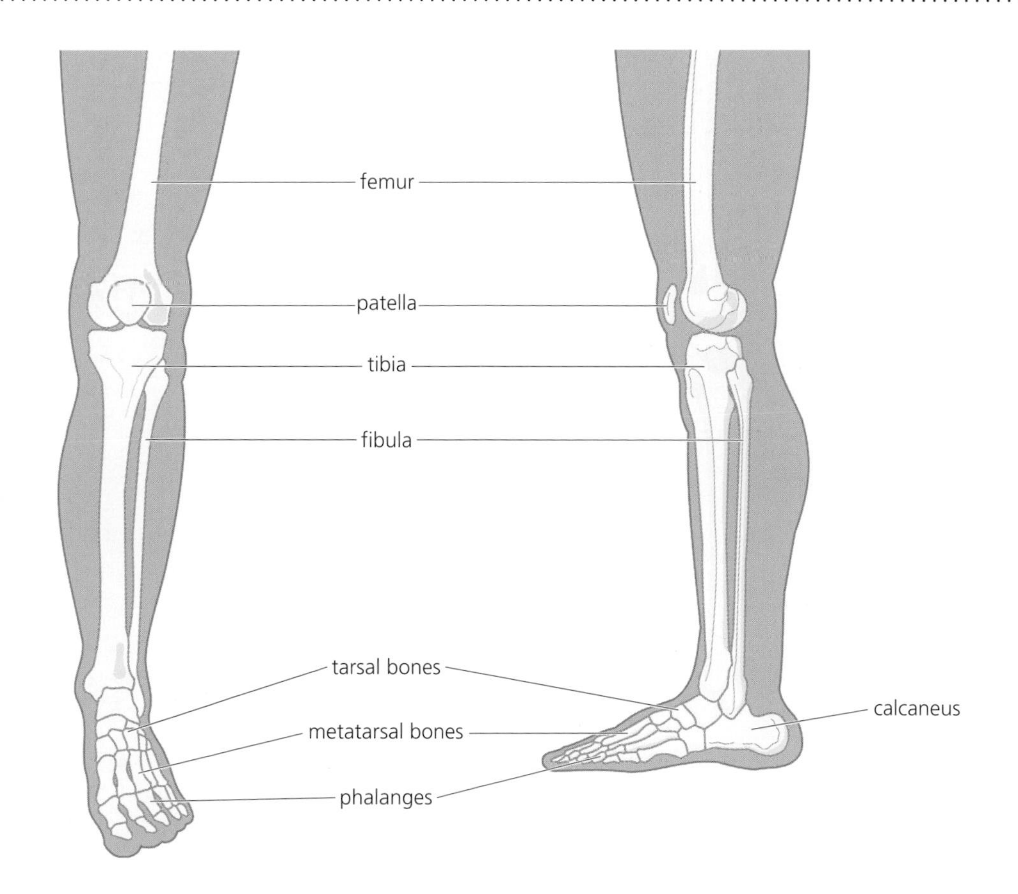

Bones of the foot lower leg

Muscles of the foot and lower leg

MUSCLE	POSITION	ACTION
Flexor digitorum tendons	Located underneath the toes	Bends the toes
Extensor digitorum tendons	Located on the top of the toes	Straightens the toes
Achillies tendon	Located near the ankle, it is attached to the soleus and the gastrocnemius muscles (calf of the leg)	Helps to raise the foot
Flexor digitorum longus	Located at the front of the lower leg to the toes	Flexes and inverts the foot
Extensor digitorum longus	Located at the side of the front of the lower leg	Flexes the foot and extends the toes
Peroneus longus	Located at the side of the lower leg	Flexes the foot and supports the foot arch
Soleus	Located at the calf of the leg below the gastrocnemius muscles	Flexes the foot
Tibialis anterior	Located at the front of the lower leg	Flexes and brings the foot up towards the leg, points the toes up and also helps support the foot arch
Gastrocnemius	Located at the calf of the leg down to the Achilles tendon at the heel	Flexes the lower leg and extends and points the toes downwards.

Muscles of the lower leg

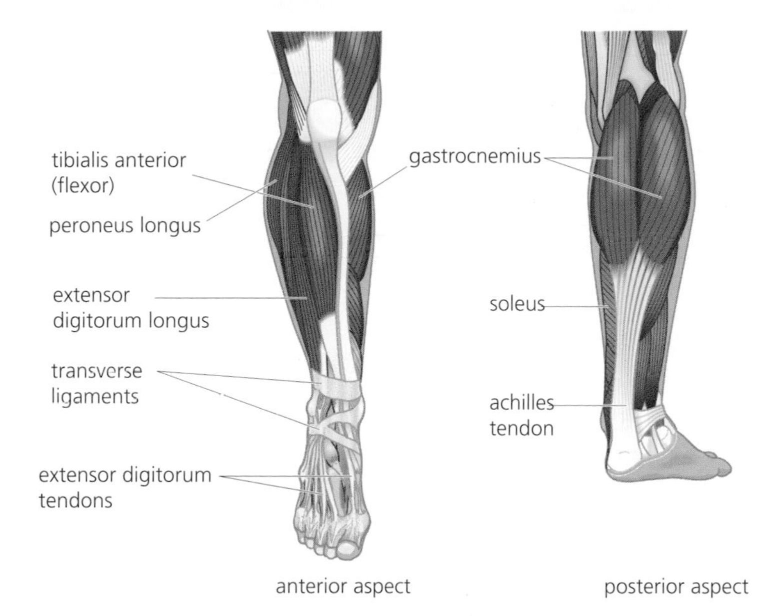

Muscles of the tendons of the foot

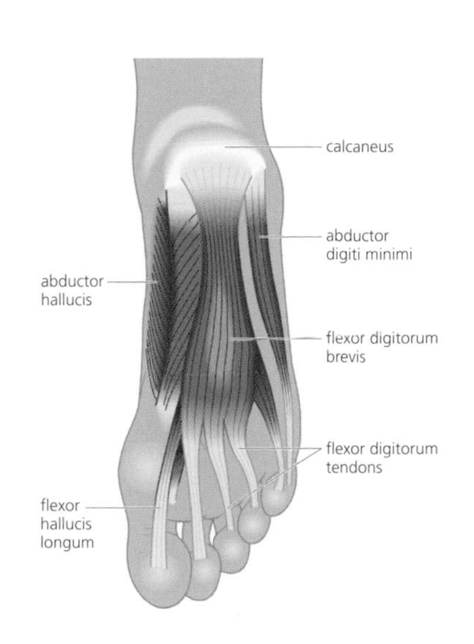

Types of adverse skin, scalp and nail conditions

Before beginning any service or treatment you need to examine the client's skin, hair or nails to make sure that they are healthy and in a suitable condition for you to carry out the service or treatment that the client has booked. This *examination* is part of the **consultation** process that you will learn about in later chapters. It is important that you carry out the examination so that you do not expose yourself or other clients to any possibility of cross infection, from bacteria, fungal or virus infection. These are often recognised by: swelling, irritation, redness, pain and tenderness to the skin or by dry dull looking hair. Different conditions tend to display different symptoms; in the charts below you will learn to recognise the different skin, hair and nails conditions that you may come across when carrying out a consultation.

Viral conditions

Viruses are groups of very simple organisms that are smaller than bacteria and can cause infections and disease.

CONDITION	CAUSE AND SYMPTOMS	TREATMENTS
Cold sores (Herpes simplex) 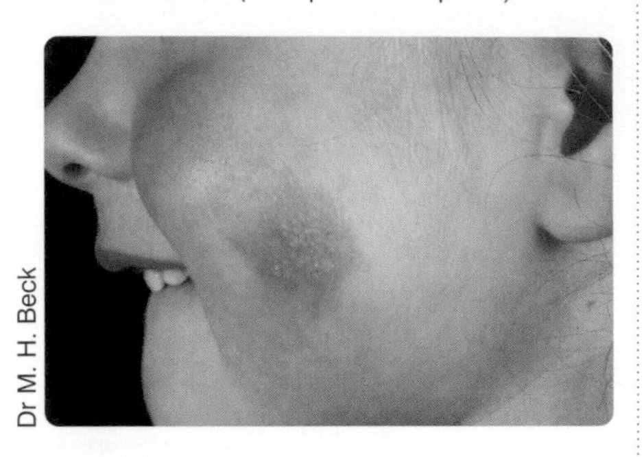 Dr M. H. Beck	An infectious condition that appears when the skin has been exposed to extremes of temperature or ultra-violet light (sunlight). It can also appear when a person's resistance is low through ill health or stress. At first the skin's condition appears inflamed and red in a localised areas such as on the cheek or lips. Then the area can become itchy and a crust forms that often cracks and weeps fluid.	This is a recurring skin condition that is difficult to treat. Medical treatment should be sought and treatments and services should not take place on the skin near to the area of infection.
Warts 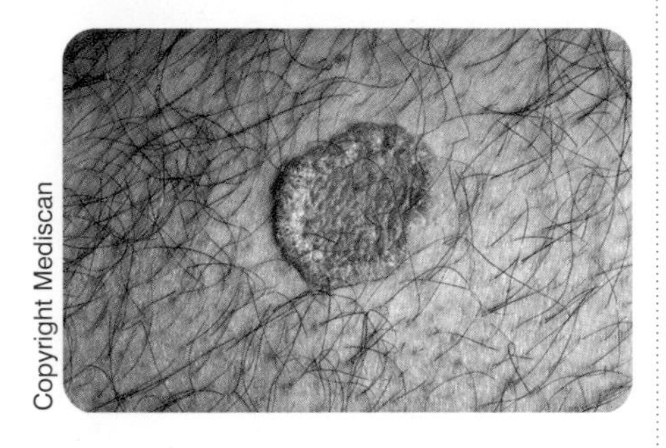 Copyright Mediscan	Warts are infectious outgrowths of the epidermis and can be found anywhere on the body. They appear as small roughened areas of skin that form lumps. They can vary in colour from a pale flesh colour to brown. The virus is more easily spread through water, so shampooing a client with warts on their head may lead to the transfer of the virus.	Medical treatment should be sought and treatments and services should not be carried out in the area infected.
Verrucas 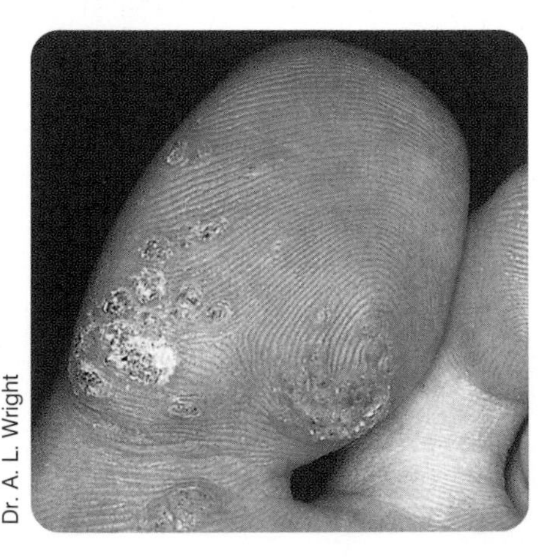 Dr. A. L. Wright	A verruca is infectious and found on the foot. They are similar to a wart except that they are ingrowing and usually have a black spot in the centre.	Medical treatment should be sought and treatments and services should not be carried out in the area infected.

Bacterial conditions

Bacteria are a large group of micro-organisms, many of which can cause infection and disease.

CONDITION	CAUSE AND SYMPTOMS	TREATMENTS
Impetigo 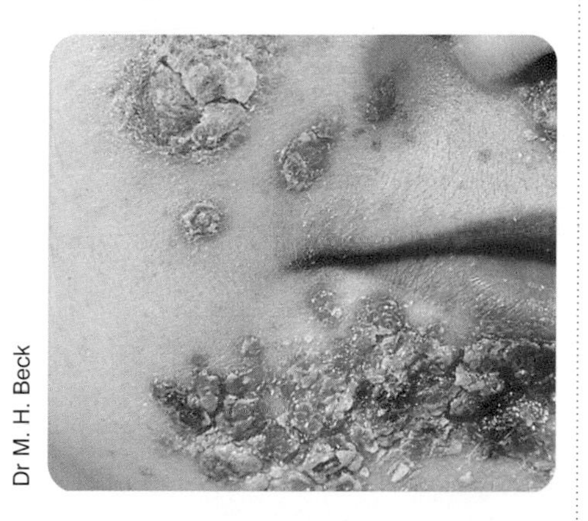 Dr M. H. Beck	Impetigo is a infectious condition where bacteria enters an opening of the skin causing a burning sensation, followed by yellow clear filled spots and pustules, which dry into yellow or honey coloured crusty formations. It can be found on any area of the body but is usually found on the face and scalp. Impetigo can be spread by direct or indirect contact by a person or through dirty tools and towels.	Medical treatment should be sought and treatments and services should not be carried out in the area infected.
Boils (Furuncles) 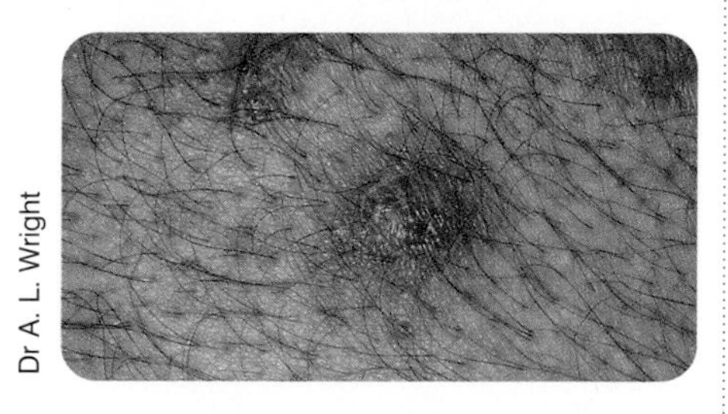 Dr A. L. Wright	Boils are infectious red painful swellings with a hard pus filled core that extends down into the skin. They are formed around the hair follicle and are usually located at the back of the neck, ankles or wrist.	Medical treatment should be sought and treatments and services should not be carried out in the area infected.
Conjuctivitis 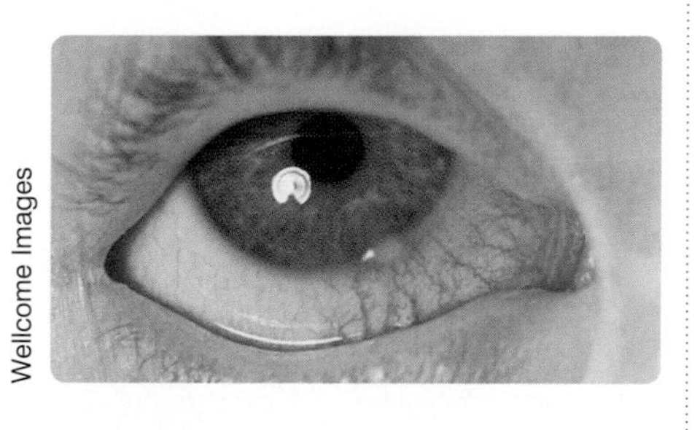 Wellcome Images	Conjunctivitis is an infectious condition of the eye, it inflames the mucous membrane that covers the eye and lines the eyelid. The eye becomes sore and red and pus can sometimes be excreted.	Medical treatment should be sought and treatments and services should not be carried out in the area infected.
Folliculitis 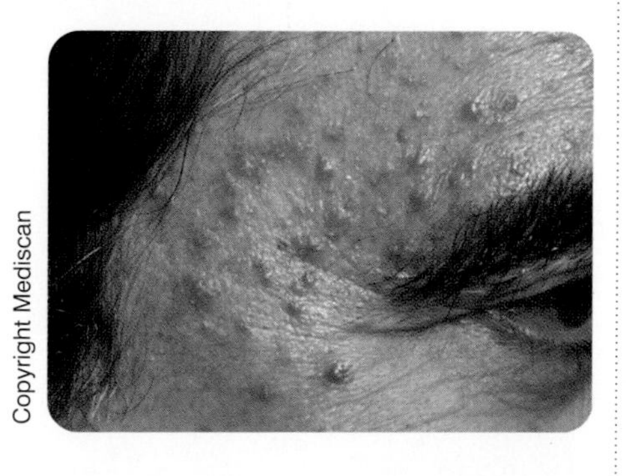 Copyright Mediscan	Folliculitis is an infectious condition caused when bacteria enters the opening of the follicle causing an infection. The opening of the follicle can become inflamed and painful. The condition can be found on any part of the body or scalp. It can be spread by direct and indirect contact with a person or by dirty tools and towels or by irritation from chemicals.	Medical treatment should be sought and treatments and services should not be carried out in the area infected.

Fungal conditions

Fungi are microscopic plants that do not have leaves or roots. Fungal infections of the skin live off waste products produces by the skin.

CONDITION	CAUSE AND SYMPTOMS	TREATMENTS
Ringworm 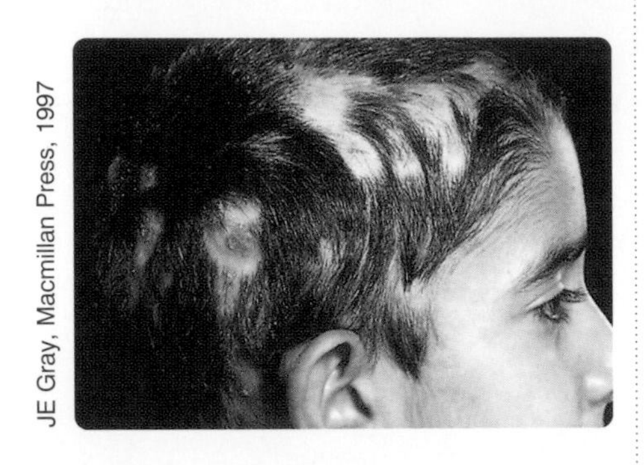 JE Gray, Macmillan Press, 1997	This condition is not caused by a worm, as the name suggests, but a fungus that lives on the keratin of the skin and hair. The symptoms are patches of pink skin surrounded by a red active ring. The centre of the patch is covered in grey scales of dead keratin and if on the scalp the hair will break leaving stubble.	Medical treatment should be sought and treatments and services should not be carried out in the area infected.
Athlete's foot (Tinea pedis) 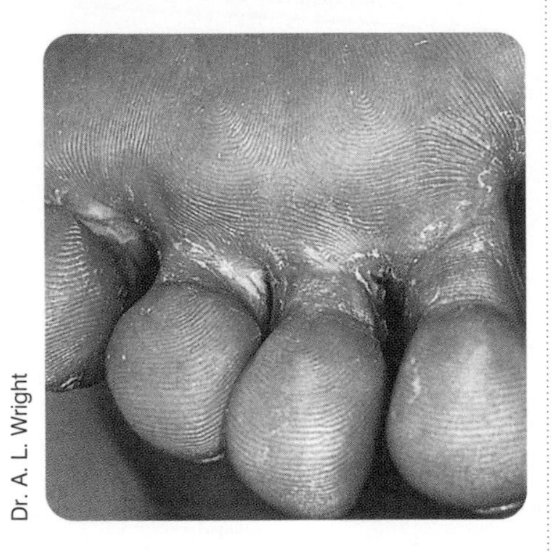 Dr. A. L. Wright	Athletes foot is a infectious condition that is found between the toes. It appears as small blisters which then burst. The skin can then become dry and itchy.	Medical treatment should be sought and treatments and services should not be carried out in the area infected.
Ringworm of the nail plate (Tinea unguium/onychomycosis) 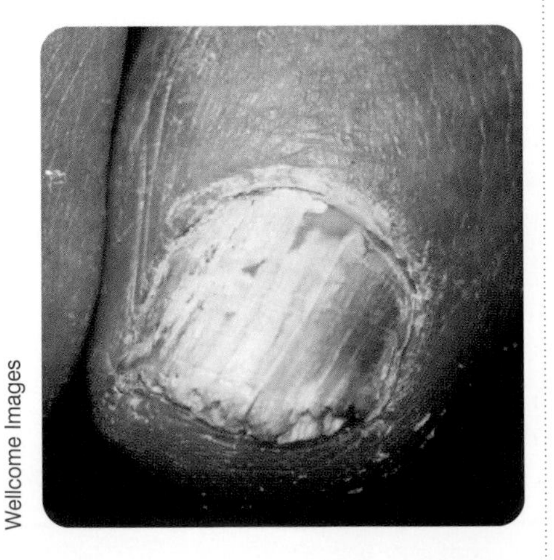 Wellcome Images	Ringworm of the nail plate, like all other forms of ringworm, is infectious. The nail plate will become a yellowish-grey colour, the nail plate will become dry and brittle and eventually separate from the nail bed.	Medical treatment should be sought and treatments and services should not be carried out in the area infected.

Onycholysis 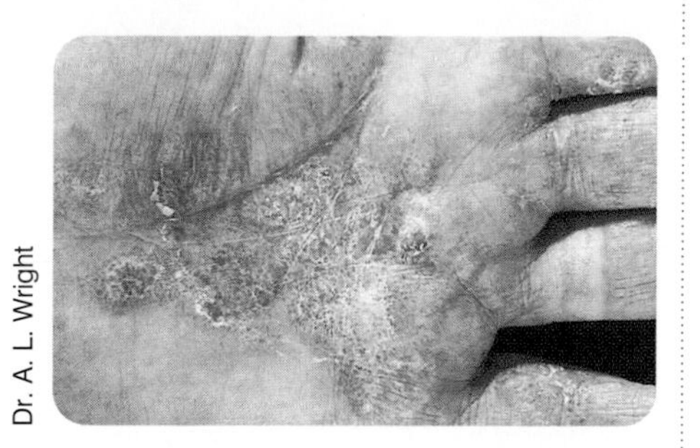 Dr. A. L. Wright	Onycholysis is the separation of the nail plate from the nail bed. It can be caused by skin disease such as psoriasis or fungal infection or from the result of an injury. Infection with bacteria gives the nail a yellowy green tinge. If the nail turns white it has a fungal infection.	Medical treatment should be sought and treatments and services should not be carried out in the area infected.

Parasitic conditions

This is when an animal or plant lives on or in our body so that it can feed.

CONDITION	CAUSE AND SYMPTOMS	TREATMENTS
Head lice (Pediculosis Capitis) 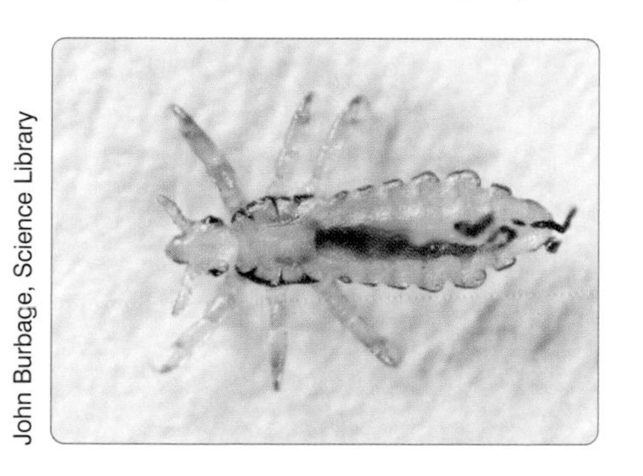 John Burbage, Science Library	These are small insects know as **parasites**, they live by sucking and feeding on the blood of their host. The lice live on the scalp and lay eggs called nits. The nits are glued onto the hair shaft with a special cement near the roots of the hair, or in areas where the hair is abundant, for example within the bands holding pony tails or under hair bands – anywhere the eggs will be least noticed and most protected. The nits are clear in appearance while the louse forms inside, but turn white and are easily visible once the louse has hatched and the egg shells have dried. Head lice are caught through head to head contact.	Pharmacist treatment should be sought and treatments and services should not be carried out in the area infected.
Scabies 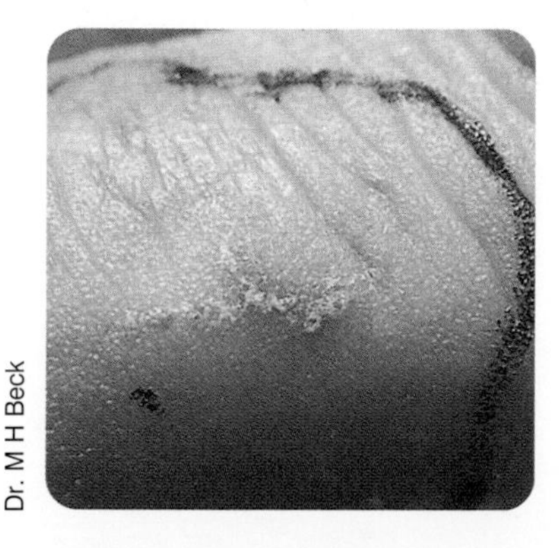 Dr. M H Beck	This condition is caused by the itch mite. The mite called Sarcoptes Scabiei burrows through the skin leaving greyish lines and reddish spots. The condition is extremely itchy, particularly at night. Scabies is contagious and can be passed on by close physical contact.	Medical treatment should be sought and treatments and services should not be carried out.

Skin defects that may restrict treatments and makeup application

There are many different skin conditions that we could cover but some of the most common ones are listed below.

CONDITION	CAUSE AND SYMPTOMS	TREATMENTS
Milia 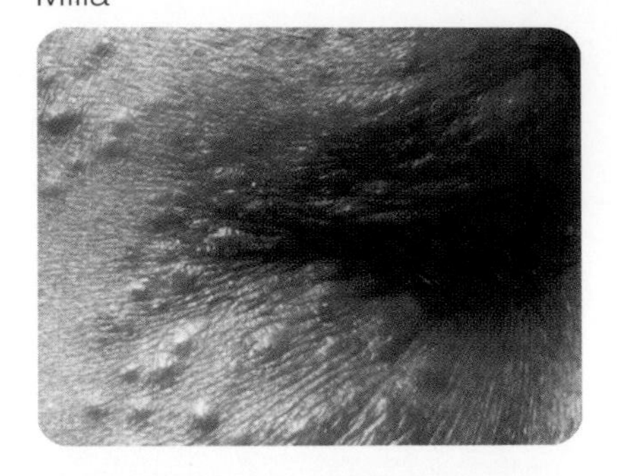	Milia is a non-infectious condition that causes keratinisation of the skin over the hair follicle, causing sebum to become blocked in the hair follicle. It appears as small, hard, pearly-white lumps or cysts and is usually found around the eyes or upper section of the face.	They can be removed by a physician or a specialist such as a beauty therapist depending on the location. A sterile needle is used to pierce the skin to unblock the follicle.
Blackheads (Comedones) 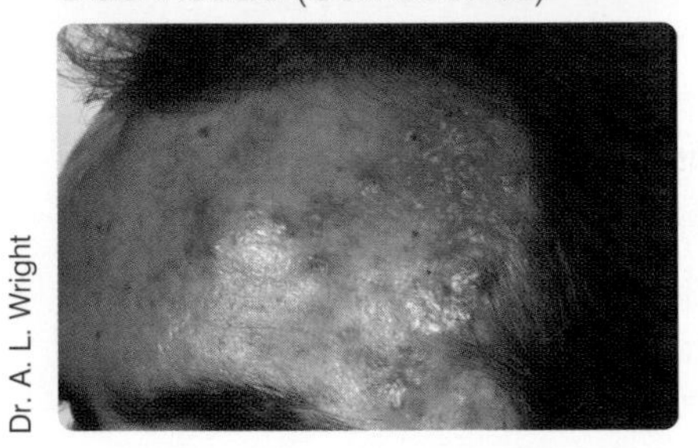 Dr. A. L. Wright	Blackheads are a non-infectious condition caused by keratinisation of the skin blocking the hair follicle. There may also be an excess production of sebum. The condition is usually located on the face, around the chin, nose and forehead or the upper back or chest.	Heat treatments help to relax and soften the skin around the hail follicle before using a piece of equipment called a comedo extractor to unblock the follicle. Using cleaning products will help limit the production of blackheads.
Seborrhoea (skin) 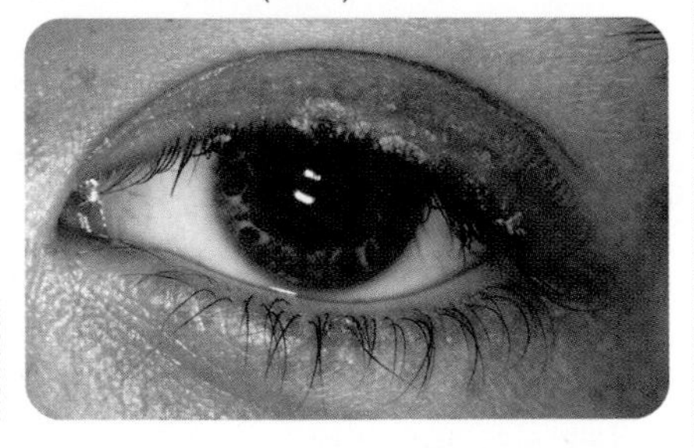 Mediscan	Seborrhoea affects the skin (face and back and chest) and scalp. It is a non-infectious condition created by the over-production of sebum. The skin can appear coarse and oily, with the added presence of both pustules and blackheads.	Medical treatment may need to be sought but, in addition, using cleaning products will help to remove excess oil.
Acne Vulgaris 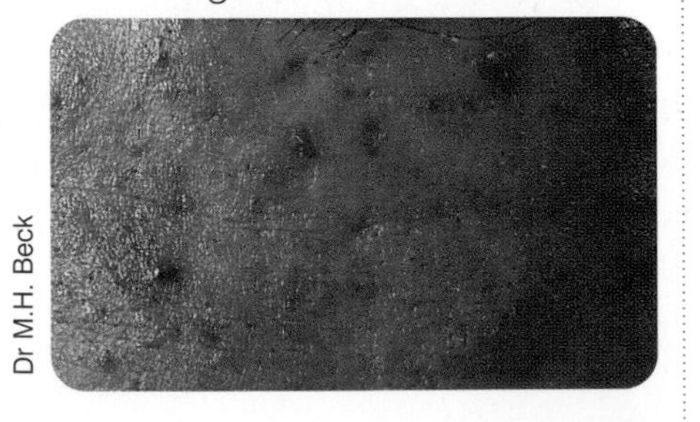 Dr M.H. Beck	Acne is often associated with puberty when there is an increase in the activity of the sebaceous gland, causing an over-production of sebum. The sebum may stay within the sebaceous duct creating a blockage and bacterial infection around the area. It is a non-infectious condition that inflames	Medical treatment may need to be sought to use antibiotics.

the skin and is accompanied by pustules and papules. The most common location is on the face around the nose, chin and forehead but it can also be found on the back and chest.

Eczma

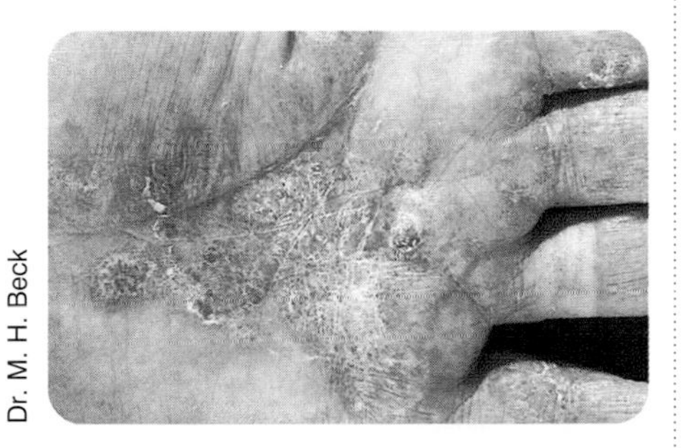
Dr. M. H. Beck

Eczema is a non-infectious condition that can effect the whole body. It appears as very dry, scaly and flaky skin which is red and sometimes broken; it can be very itchy and uncomfortable.

When the condition is most active the use of hypo-allergenic skin products is recommended.

Psoriasis

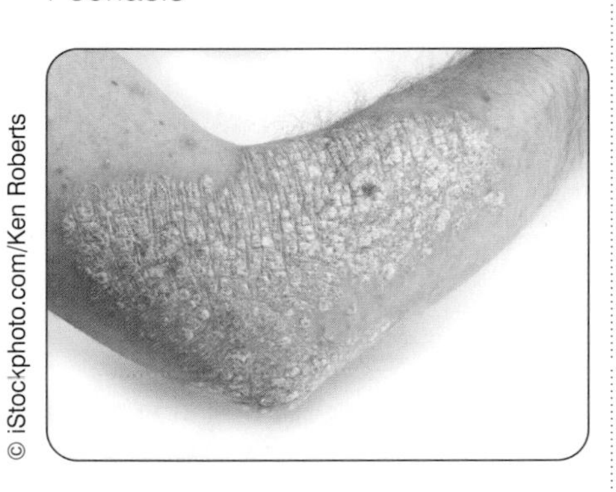

This non-infectious condition can be distressing for the person. The real cause is unknown, but is thought to be related to stress and the over-production of epidermal cells. The symptoms can be seen as raised red patches covered in white or slivery scales.

Medical treatment may need to be sought. Some specialised shampoos can help or the client may be referred to a trichologist.

Skin allergies

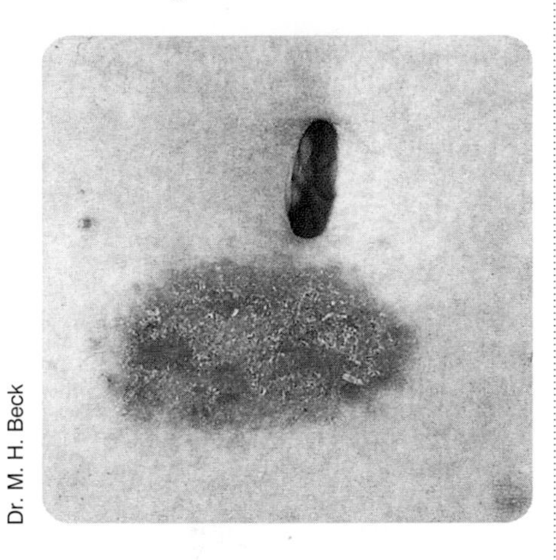
Dr. M. H Beck

An allergy is when the skin becomes sensitive to a particular item or when a particular substance touches or sits on or is absorbed into the skin. An allergic skin reaction causes redness and often swelling to the skin which can become hot and inflamed. There may be itching and irritation around the affected area and it is generally uncomfortable. Individuals have different levels of tolerances for different substances and some people are more sensitive and will react to many things whilst other people do not.

Medical treatment may need to be sought. Skin tests before product use should always be carried out particularly for clients known to have allergies or sensitive skin.

Seborrhoea (Scalp) 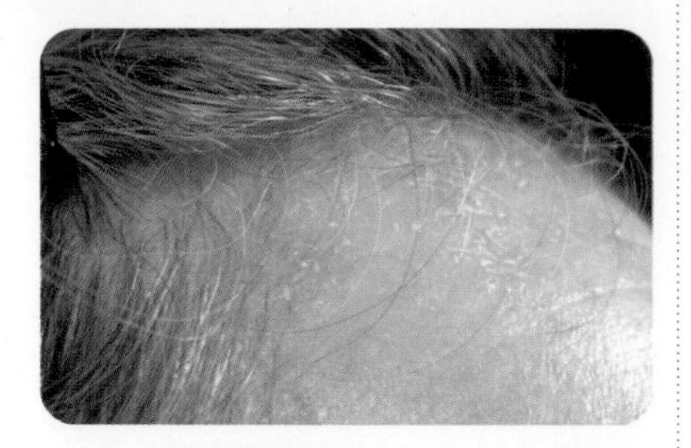	This non-infectious condition of the skin and hair is caused by the over production of sebum which makes the hair very greasy and lank. This condition can make the hair very difficult to work with as physical work such as blow-drying or chemical services can stimulate the production of sebum.	Regular washing with a specialised shampoo can help or the client may be referred to a trichologist.
Keloids 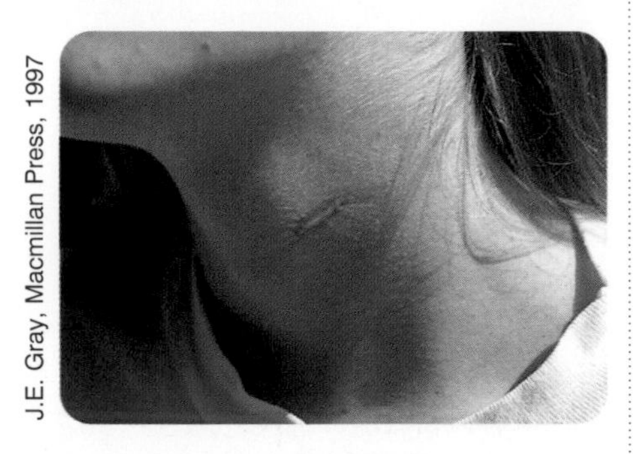 J.E. Gray, Macmillan Press, 1997	This non-infectious condition of the skin is most commonly found in clients who have African type skin. Keloids are small raised scars that can often be itchy. They are caused by cutting the hair close to the skin either when cutting around the hairline or when shaving.	Moisturise the skin regularly.

Pigmentation disorders

Pigmentation conditions are created because of irregularities in the production of melanin in the skin. They are not infectious and do not affect treatment or services. However they need to be taken into account when applying makeup to ensure even and good coverage. Camouflage makeup may need to be used.

CONDITION	CAUSE AND SYMPTOMS	TREATMENTS
Vitiligo or Hypopigmentation 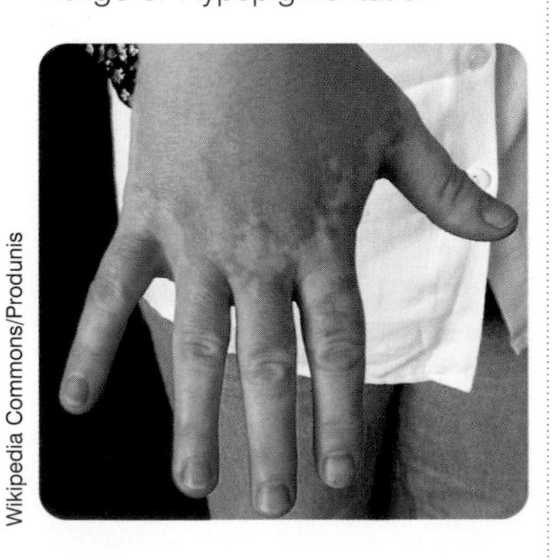 Wikipedia Commons/Produnis	A condition were small or larger patches of skin have lost their pigmentation. The skin will appear lighter; these lighter areas are more sensitive to the sun and will burn easily and will need protecting.	Use of makeup to disguise the difference in the skin's colour

Freckles  © iStockphoto.com/LizaMcCorkle	Freckles are caused by an uneven distribution of melanin. They are tiny, flat dark patches of pigment that are mainly present on light skinned people, usually people with red or blonde hair. If exposed to too much sun they become more prominent and often increase in size. People with freckles tend to burn from the sun more easily and should always wear a sun block.	The use of sun screens and sun blocks to protect from the sun. Makeup can even out the skin's colour variation.

Scalp defects that may restrict treatments

CONDITION	CAUSE AND SYMPTOMS	TREATMENTS
Sebaceous cysts 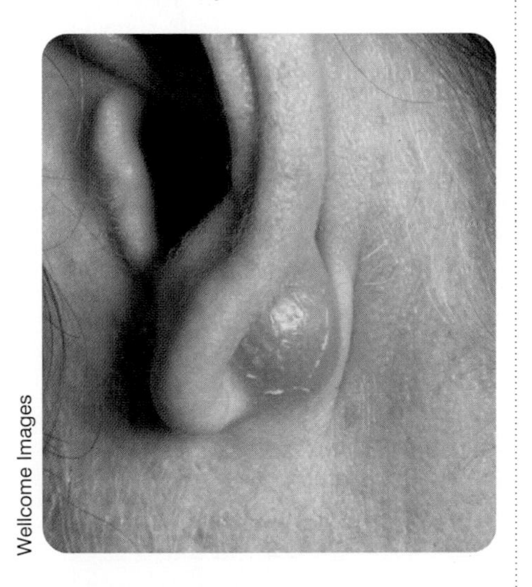 Wellcome Images	These are non-infectious lumps that appear on the scalp. The lumps are caused by a blockage of the sebaceous gland leading to excess sebum filling up under the surface of the skin.	Medical advice should be sought, but hairdressing services can continue.
Dandruff (Pityriasis Capitis) 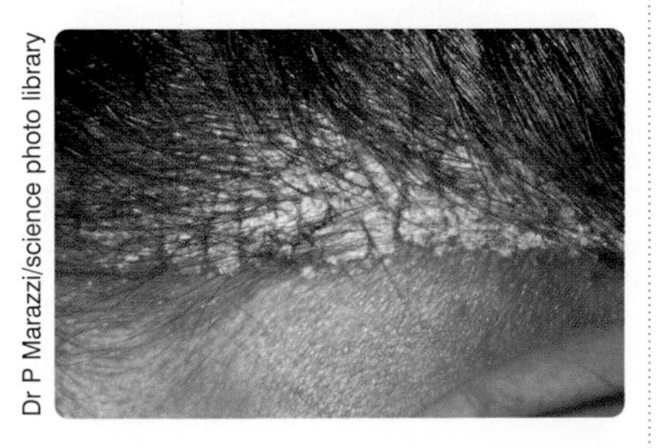 Dr P Marazzi/science photo library	This is excess shedding of the epidermis, which leads to small flakes of loose dry skin on the scalp that can drop and become visible on the shoulders. The dry scales are not infectious and can be caused by irritation to some hairdressing products or an excessively dry scalp. However, if the scales become oily and sticky, it is a sign that a fungal infection is present.	Providing a fungal infection is not present, dandruff can be treated by medicated shampoos and moisturising the scalp. Hairdressing services can continue.

Hair defects

CONDITION	CAUSE AND SYMPTOMS	TREATMENTS
Split ends (Fragilitis crinium)  J.E. Gray, Macmillan Press, 1997.	This condition is the splitting of the hair shaft at the ends of the hair. It is caused by chemical, physical or environmental damage to the hair and can be prevented by regular cutting and conditioning treatments.	Cutting to remove the split and damaged ends of the hair and using conditioning treatments to prevent future damage. Advise the client how to physically treat their hair during drying and styling.
Trichorrhexis nodosa  J.E. Gray, Macmillan Press, 1997.	This condition is similar to split ends, but the splitting occurs along the hair shaft, rather than the ends of the hair. It is caused by chemical, physical or environmental damage to the hair and can be prevented by regular cutting and conditioning treatments.	No treatment can cure this condition, but the client should be advised to have conditioning treatments to prevent future occurrences. Advise the client how to physically treat their hair during drying and styling.
Monilethrix 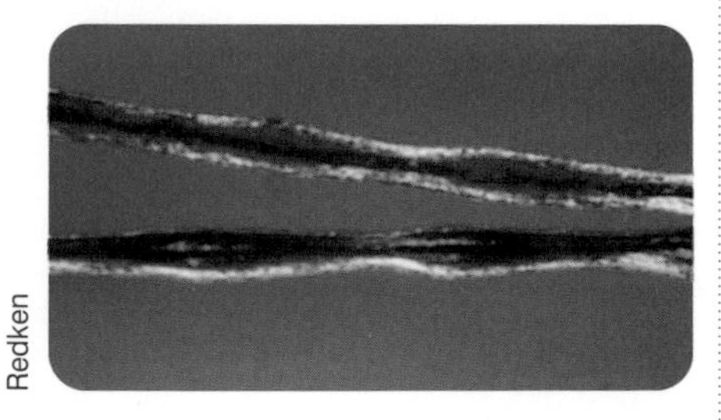 Redken	This condition is often referred to as beaded hair, this is because the hair has bead-like swellings and constrictions along its shaft. The hair can be very weak and often breaks close to the scalp. The condition is caused by irregular development of the hair within the hair follicle.	No treatment can cure this condition, but the client should be advised to have conditioning treatments that may help protect the hair. Advise the client how to physically treat their hair during drying and styling.

Damaged hair

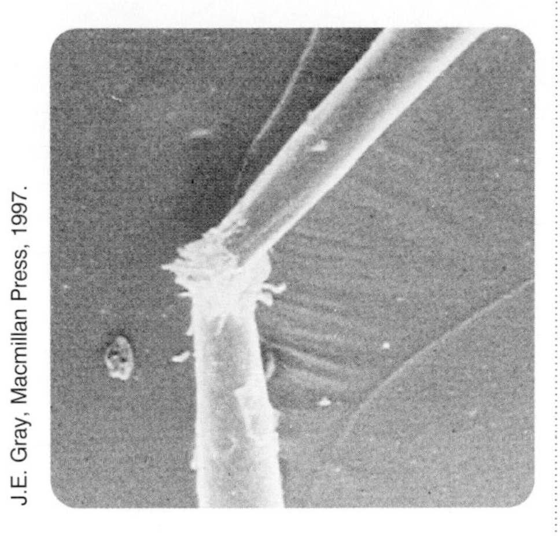

J.E. Gray, Macmillan Press, 1997.

This can be damage to the cuticle and/or the cortex. Some damage will become either split ends or trichorrhexis nodosa, but at other times the symptoms can be dull, rough, porous or dry hair.

Deep reconstructive conditioning treatments can aid this condition, and the client should be advised to have regular, follow up conditioning treatments to prevent future occurrences. Advise the client how to physically treat their hair during drying and styling.

Alopecia

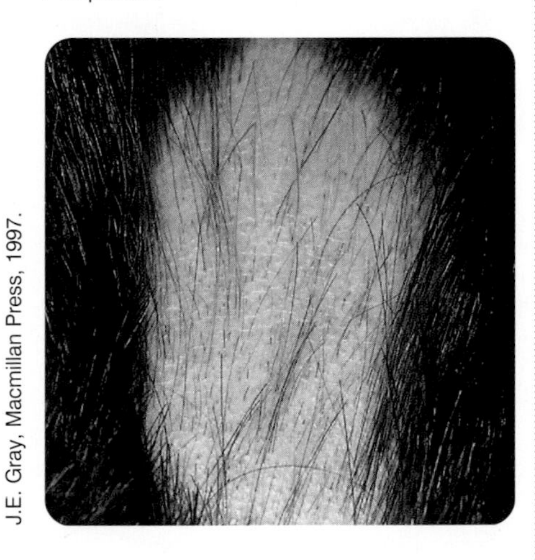

J.E. Gray, Macmillan Press, 1997.

The generic term for hair loss is alopecia, but there are different types that can affect the hair on the scalp and the body. The causes of some types of alopecia are unknown; they can often be linked to stress related illnesses and changes in hormone levels. **Alopecia areata** appears as small round or oval patches of hair loss, which can spread to total loss of hair on the scalp known as **alopecia totalis**. **Traction alopecia** is caused by excessive tension on the hair, leading to hair being pulled from the scalp leaving areas of baldness. This is commonly seen in hair braiding if they are too tight or with hair extensions if they have been incorrectly applied – especially around the front hairline were the hair is weaker. **Cicatricial alopecia** is caused by damage to the dermis following physical injury or damage. The hair follicle is damaged and scarring prevents the growth of new hair.

Clients with alopecia should be referred to a trichologist for specialised advice. Traction alopecia can be prevented by reducing the stress on the client's hair and providing advice about how long braids or hair extensions should be worn for.

Nail and skin conditions

CONDITION	CAUSE AND SYMPTOMS	TREATMENTS
Ingrowing nail (Onychocryptosis) 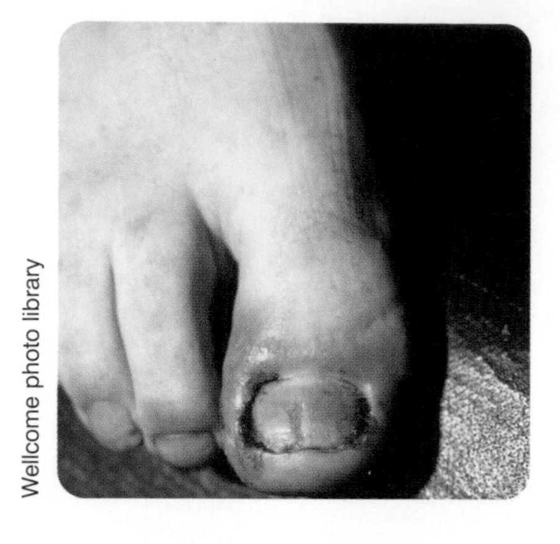 Wellcome photo library	This is often a painful condition were the nail grows into the side of the nail bed creating pressure and swelling in the affected area that, if not treated, will become infected. This condition occurs most commonly on the toenail. It can be caused by: • cutting the nail too short and rounding off at the tip • wearing shoes that are too small or too narrow, causing the nail to curl under and dig into the skin • damaging the toenails by stubbing the toes or dropping something on them • abnormal shaped nail bed	Treatments and services should not be carried out in the area affected.
Bruised nail 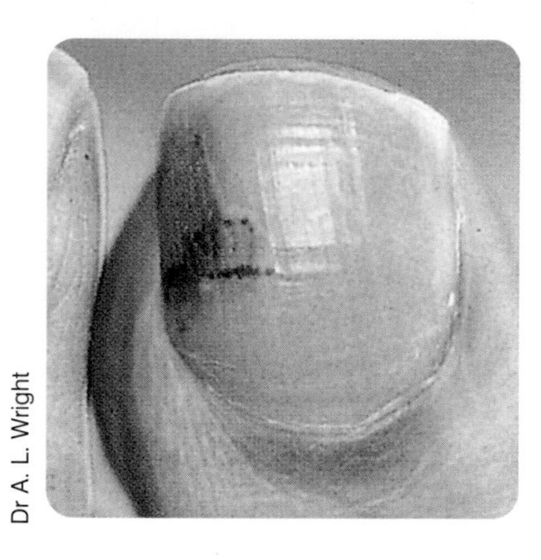 Dr A. L. Wright	A bruised nail is usually caused by damage or trauma to the nail bed. Dark spots of blood appear under the nail plate that can cause pressure and pain.	The bruised area will grow out and nail treatments can be carried out as long as the client is not in any pain.
Pitting 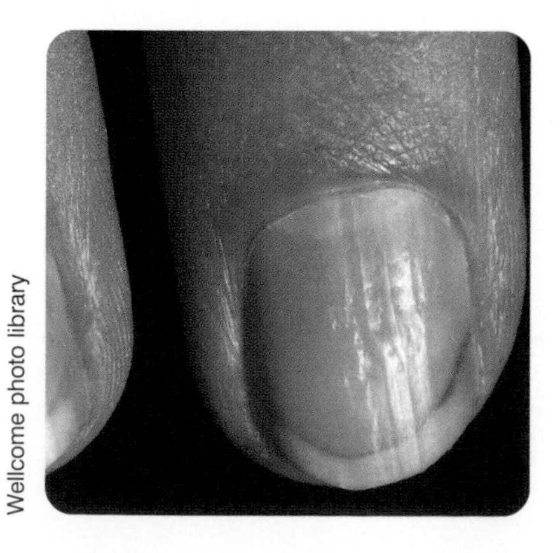 Wellcome photo library	This condition consists of small pits on the surface of the nail plate, this can be caused by psoriasis or dermatitis.	Nail services can be carried out on the nail but need to be worked gently.

Corns 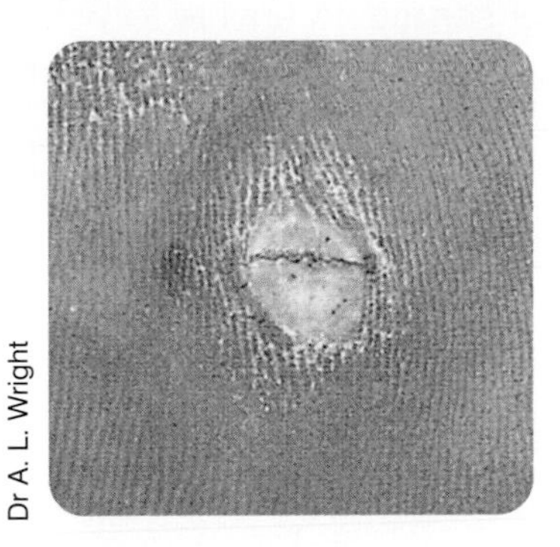 Dr A. L. Wright	Corns are areas of hard skin usually found on the top or sides of the toe. They are caused by pressure from ill-fitting shoes.	Treatment should be sought from a chiropodist.
Peeling or flaking nails (Lamellar dystrophy) 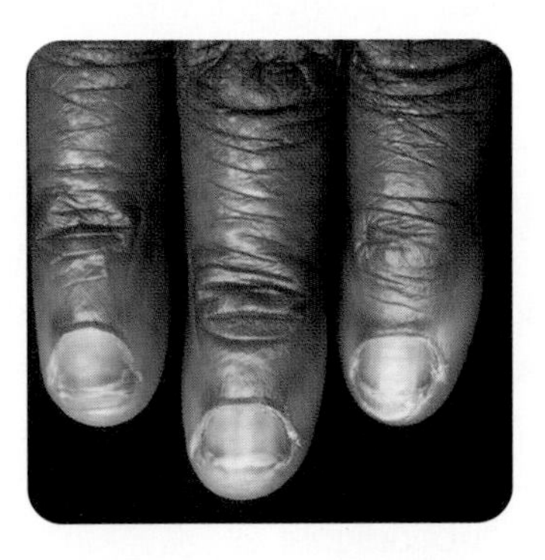	This condition is caused by a lack of moisture in the nail causing the nail to become dry and peel or flake.	The nail and cuticle need to be re-moisturised and detergents should be avoided.
Beau's lines 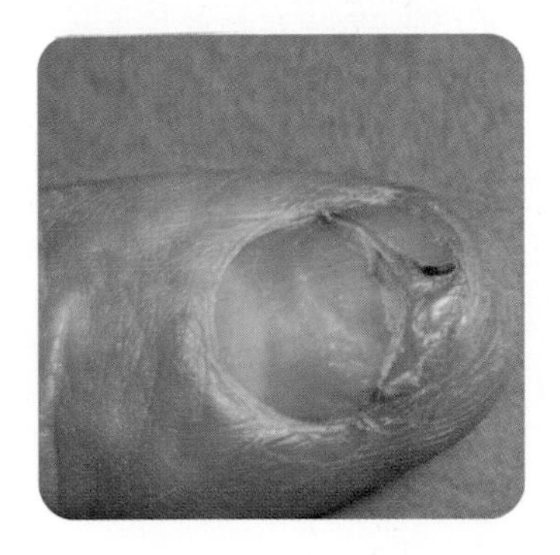	Deep horizontal ridges across the nail plate, caused by mechanical trauma such as artificial nails or over buffing, or it can be created from illness.	No treatment, the nail will need to grow out.

How to carry out the common testing processes used in the hair and beauty sector

It's a fact!

The term used for nail biting is *onychophagy*.

Before carrying out any treatment or service, it is important that you find out as much as possible about the skin, hair or nails of your client so that you can make the right decisions about the types of products and equipment you can use. You have read earlier in this chapter about the different skin, hair and nail conditions that you need to be aware of and recognise the signs of during the consultation.

The next important aspect of the consultation process is to ensure that you carry out any tests needed before a particular treatment or service, to ensure for example that you do not damage the hair or skin, or cause an **allergic reaction** to a chemical product you have decided to use. It is important that all tests are carried out and their results accurately recorded on the clients consultation records so that you can refer back to them when needed. There are different types of tests for the hair and skin.

It's a fact! The keratin structure on hair that is very curly, i.e. African type hair, can also feel rough when a porosity test is carried out and may not give a true indication of the condition of the cuticle.

Hair tests

Porosity

The porosity test indicates the condition of the hair. If the scales of the cuticle are laying flat and evenly down the length of the hair shaft, making the hair feel smooth and reflecting light, the hair is in good condition. However, if the cuticle scales are uneven, damaged or missing, the hair will feel rough and appear dull – the hair is in bad condition.

How to carry out a **porosity test** – a porosity test is carried out on the hair before it is shampooed. You need to take a small bundle of hairs, holding the ends of the bundle together with one hand. Using the thumb and forefinger of the other hand, you gently stoke the hair from the ends to the roots to feel the condition of the cuticle. If the hair feels smooth it means that the cuticle is lying flat and that the hair is in good condition. However, if the hair feels rough, it is an indication that the cuticle has been damaged and that the hair is in poor condition.

Elasticity test

The structure of the cortex, when it is in good condition, allows the hair to stretch under tension and when the tension is removed, to return to its normal length and position. However, if the cortex has been damaged, the properties of elasticity will be reduced, or in extreme cases, completely missing. Recognising the amount of elasticity in the hair will be one of the determining factors for the decision of the type of products and services that can be carried out.

How to carry out a **elasticity test** – to carry out an elasticity test, take a single strand of hair and, supporting it at the roots to ensure client comfort, gently stretch the hair, and then release it, observing how soon it returns to its natural

ACTIVITY

Carry out a range of tests on a variety of different hair conditions and types. For example, compare the amount of elasticity there is in very curly hair to that of very straight hair. Also, observe how much the elasticity is reduced in hair that has chemical treatments compared to virgin hair (hair that has had no chemical products on it to change the hair structure). Then compare the porosity levels on a whole length of hair from the roots to the ends. You may find the condition of the cuticle at the roots is in good condition, but that the condition of the cuticle at the ends of the hair is poor.

position. Hair that is in good condition will stretch and then immediately return to its normal position. If the hair has reduced elasticity, the hair may return to its natural position more slowly. However hair that is very poor condition may stretch and not return or may break under the slightest pressure.

Incompatibility test

This test is carried out prior to a chemical service. It will determine if other products containing metallic salts have been used. Metallic salts react with other chemicals and damage or destroy the hair.

How to carry out an **incompatibility test** – you will need to cut a small section of hair from the head. It is usually best to cut the hair from the back of the head so that it is not noticeable. Wearing your personal protective equipment (PPE), place the hair cutting into a plastic bowl and then add a mixture of 20 parts **hydrogen peroxide** and one part **ammonium hydroxide** (ammonium hydroxide is used to quicken up the process; using hydrogen peroxide on its own makes it a slower process). If the mixture heats up, discolours or bubbles, there has been a reaction and the service should not be carried out.

Strand test

A strand test is used to check the progress of a hair colouring or lightening service. If a hair colour or lightener is not left to develop for long enough, the development will be incomplete. The colour will not be fully developed or the hair may not be light enough, this is called under processed. If the lightener is left on the hair too long, the hair will be lightened too much, which will cause damage to the hair structure, and the hair may break off.

Strand tests are also used when relaxing hair to check the development of the relaxing product when straightening the hair. Relaxers, like hair lighteners, are very strong chemical products and if left on the hair too long will destroy it.

How to carry out a **strand test** – when using most hair relaxing or colouring products, the recommended time advised by the manufacturer for development must be followed. It is important the manufacturer's instructions are read and followed. However, if the hair is very porous or a lightening or toning product is being used, the development of the product will need to be checked. This is done by picking up a small section of hair with the product on it. The colour product is removed from a small section using the back of the comb or using cotton wool so that the hair can be clearly seen. The colour on the hair is checked to ensure it is the same (evenly distributed) along the hair shaft, and, if using a lightener, that the hair is light enough and enough natural hair colour has been removed. If the colour has developed correctly, it can be removed. If not, it can reapplied to the strand and left it to develop further before taking another strand test.

Curl development test

A curl development test is used in perming to check the development of the curl

How to carry out a **curl development test** – during the perm processing stage, when the perm rods are wound in the hair, at approximately 5 minute intervals (always follow manufacturers instructions), you will unwind the hair from the rod until it is about 2–4 inches in length from the scalp. Then holding the wound rod, you need to slightly push the rod towards the scalp, if the hair that you have unwound makes an 'S' shape, the hair has processed for enough time and you can stop the perm processing by rinsing away the perm lotion and continue with the next stage of the perm process, called neutralising the hair. If you do not carry out a curl development test, you may overprocess the hair, causing it to become dry and frizzy, or you may underprocess the hair so that the curl does not develop properly, leaving the hair either wavy or straight.

Skin tests

Sensitivity tests

There are a range of tests that come under the banner of sensitivity tests that are used in beauty therapy and spa treatments these include:

- Tactile or thermal test
- Pressure test
- Sharp and blunt tests

A tactile test checks reaction to temperature for beauty therapy treatments such as electrotherapy. You will use the test to check the client's reaction for temperature prior to the treatment so that you can make adjustments to suit individual clients.

How to carry out a **tactile test** – fill two cylinders such as test tubes, one with hot water and the other with cold water and lay on the skin to check the nerve response.

Sharp and blunt tests checks reactions against sharp and blunt objects on the skin.

How to carry out a **sharp and blunt test** – use a sharp and blunt object such as a safety pin. Ask the client to turn away their head. First place the sharp end of the pin on the skin and then the blunt end to test the nerve reaction – ask if the client can feel the difference. This test is used to check the nerve response to the types of current used in some electrotherapy treatments.

A pressure test checks the amount of pressure that is comfortable for the client and is often used before massage treatments.

How to carry out a **pressure test** – manually using your hands, use different amounts of pressure on an area of the body that may be sensitive, such as the back of the neck or were the client may have had an injury in the past or suffers muscle tension.

Skin test

A skin test is carried out to determine whether the client will have an allergic reaction to chemicals, such as those found in a hair colouring products. A skin test is sometimes referred to as *a patch test*.

How to carry out a **skin test** – clean an area of the client's skin behind the ear or the fold of the arm using spirit to remove any grease from the skin. Mix a small amount of the colour you are intending to use with the correct strength of hydrogen peroxide and apply a little of the mixture to the skin. Let the colour dry, and you could cover it with collodion, which will protect it. The colour test must stay on the skin for 24–48 hours. You then need to check the test to see if there has been a reaction. If there has been a positive reaction the skin in the area of the test will look red and inflamed, there may be some swelling and irritation or discomfort. If the client has a positive reaction, do not carry out a colour service with this product, if you do the client may have a very serious reaction affecting the whole body. If there is a negative reaction, you can carry out the service.

Skin tests should always be carried out when you are using chemicals on the skin, for example when eyelash perming or permanently colouring eyelashes and brows.

It's a fact!

Acidic solutions have a pH between 1 and 6.9.

Alkaline solutions have a pH between 7.1 and 14.

Pull test

The pull test helps to evaluate excessive or abnormal scalp hair loss.

How to carry out a **pull test** – section a small amount of hair and gently pull the hair whilst sliding the fingers down the hair shaft from roots to point. Carry out the test on at least three different areas of the head. If more than 12 hairs per section of hair that you have pulled are shed, it may be an indication of an abnormal hair growth condition. This test is usually carried out prior to a service that will put tension on the hair such as plaiting, braiding or hair extensions.

ACTIVITY

Collect together different hair and skin care products such as shampoos, conditioners, perm solution, relaxers, bar of soap, cuticle remover, skin cleaners and moisturisers. Test them for pH. Draw a pH scale and identify where each product sits on the scale and explain what effect that product will have on the hair, skin or nails. Find out why some shampoos string when they accidentally go in your eye.

The pH scale

The pH scale measures the amount of acidity and alkalinity in a substance. The 'p' stands for *potential* and the 'H' stands for *hydrogen*. The system is based on a measuring scale from pH 1 to pH 14. Numbers lower than pH 7 identify the strength of an acid, pH 1 being the strongest acid, the further up the scale you move towards pH 7, the weaker the acid becomes. The numbers higher than pH 7 are alkaline – pH 14 being the strongest alkaline and as you work back down the scale to pH 7 the alkaline becomes weaker. Neutral is pH 7. Distilled water is neutral.

pH scale

The acid mantle that protects the skin and hair has a pH of 4.5–5.5 which is acidic. This helps to slow down the growth of any bacteria on the skin. You can measure pH by using pH paper or universal indicator paper. The paper will identify whether something is acid or alkaline by turning the paper a different colour. You can match the colour to a chart that will indicate the strength of the pH.

Images courtesy of Goldwell

Shampoo

How shampoo works

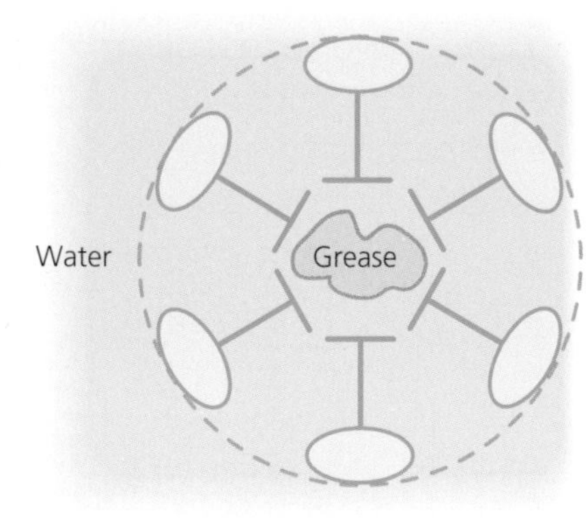

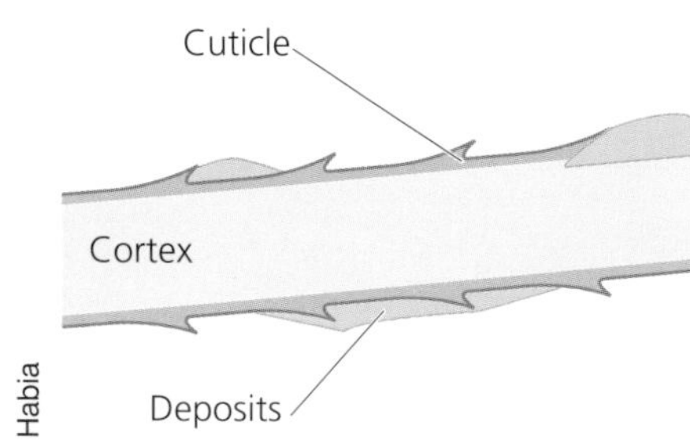

Habia

How products work

Today sales in hair, skin and nail care products add up to a multi-billion pound industry. Every product we use has been scientifically developed. Within each product, ingredients have been put together so that they do a specific job. Within hair and beauty industries, there are a wide range of products that are used, chemicals to change the colour and structures of the hair, proteins to add strength and moisturisers to add moisture. We are going to look at the some of the different types of products used within the hair and beauty industries and identify the main ingredients in certain types of product that make them beneficial to use.

Water does not easily spread over the hair and scalp but forms small droplets. This is because the molecules in water are attracted together by a weak electrical force. A **shampoo** is needed to reduce the **surface tension** of water allowing the water to spread easily and to wet the hair and scalp.

Shampoos are made up of different quantities of ingredients such as **surfactants**, **silicones** and **cationic polymers** along with perfumes, **preservatives** and sometimes added ingredients to control certain scalp conditions such as dandruff. Some shampoos will help preserve the colour and condition of artificial coloured hair. Shampoos will contain different ingredients to give different effects: *jojoba* is a non-greasy plant oil, which will help to moisturise dry hair; *coconut* contains an emollient that helps dry hair to regain some elasticity and feel smoother; *rosemary* is an antiseptic and helps to reduce scales on the scalp; while *camomile* is for greasy hair to give brightness and shine.

However the main ingredients in shampoos are:

- *Surfactants* – contain foaming agents and contain both **hydrophobic** ingredients that attract oil and **hydrophilic** ingredients that attract water. This allows the shampoo to emulsify the dirt, styling products and oil together on the hair and remove them when rinsing
- *Silicones* – these help to lubricate to hair making it easier to brush and making the hair look and feel smoother
- *Cationic polymers* – help to smooth down the cuticle and are used in higher concentrates in hair conditioners

Conditioners and restructurants protect the hair so that it keeps its condition or improve hair in bad condition. The main purpose of these products is to:

- rebalance the acid balance of the hair
- close and smooth the cuticle
- reflect light from the hair surface to make the hair look shiny and glossy
- make it easy to de-tangle the hair and stop tangles forming
- repair damaged areas within the cortex and cuticle

There are different types of conditioners, some stay on the surface of the hair cuticle and others go deep into the hair and penetrate the cortex. Both types of conditioners may contain **bactericides** and **fungicides** to help stop the growth of bacteria and fungi on the hair and scalp.

Surface conditioners stay on the surface of the hair and add gloss and shine by coating and smoothing down the cuticle with ingredients such as **cationic polymers**. Surface conditioners include:

- Wash out conditioner – these are the most common conditioners that we use every day. They help to smooth down the cuticle to add shine and make the hair easier to manage
- Leave in conditioners – these are designed to stay on the hair and not be rinsed away. They help to retain moisture and reducing static in fine hair
- Ph balancing conditioners – these readjust the hair's pH to its natural pH of 4.5–5.5 after a chemical service. The conditioner helps to reduces the swelling in the hair caused by the use of chemicals such as perms, relaxers and colouring products and closes the cuticle scales.

Penetrating conditioners are known as **restructurants** as they enter the hair shaft to the cortex of the hair and are designed to repair the damaged fibres that makeup the hair cortex. These types of conditioners may or may not also work as a surface conditioner. So a separate surface conditioner may be needed to close down the cuticle and make the hair shiny and manageable.

Conditioners may use the following ingredients:

- *Lanolin* – this a natural product extracted from sheep's wool which has moisturising properties with high water absorbing capabilities
- *Lecithin* – a natural product extracted from soy bean and found in egg yolks. Helps to protect the hair and skin and replenish the acid mantle. It is an antioxidant and a natural emulsifier
- *Citric acid* – contains vitamin C and found in citrus food such as lemons and lime. It has astringent and antioxidant properties and it can help to readjust the hair and skin's pH balance
- *Quaternary ammonium compounds* – derived from ammonium with hydrogen atoms replaced by organic groups. It is used as a surface active agent and softener
- *Emollients* – moisturisers that treat hair that is dry by increasing the hair's ability to hold water and prevent water loss. Many natural products are added to an emollient in order to give them their properties. Aloe vera is added to soothe dryness and jojoba keeps the hair moist
- *Protein hydrolysates* – solutions of amino acid and peptides used in penetrating conditioners to rebuild and add strength to hair
- *Panthenol* – a vitamin B complex used as a penetrating hair conditioner to strengthen and restore damage in the cortex as well as moisturising and plumping up the hair shaft to make it look thicker
- *Dimethicone copolyol* – complex natural silica which acts as a spreading agent and gives moisture and shine
- *Cetyl alcohol* – derived from the fatty acid of coconut oil, it helps the hair maintain its moisture and softens and smoothes the cuticle. It can also be used in shampoo as a lather booster.

EXTEND YOUR LEARNING

Identify a particular type of product you are interested in. Research when and how the product was first developed and used. Identify how and if the use of science and the understanding and development of ingredients have contributed to any improvement in your chosen product.

A perm

Perm process – disulphide bridges broken and reformed

Habia

Images courtesy of Goldwell

Hair conditioner

Perming is the name used to describe the service that changes the straight hair and makes it curly.

To perm the hair you have to change the hair's natural structure, this is done by the use of chemicals.

The hair is made up of **polypeptide chains** of hair keratin. Joining the chains together are cross links. Think of a ladder, the polypeptide chains are the long length of the ladder and the cross chains are the rungs of the ladder that keep it strong and stable. There are a number of different types of cross-links but the strongest and most important ones are the **disulphide bridges**. They give the hair its strength. A disulphide bridge is a bond linking two sulphur atoms together.

When we add the perm lotion to the hair when it has been wound round a perm rod, the disulphide bridges break leaving the hair soft and pliable and able to take the shape of the perm rod. When some of the disulphide bridges have been broken, and an '*S*' shape of the curl has been formed. The perm lotion is rinsed away and the hair is neutralised. The **neutralising** process joins the two sulphur bonds together to form a new disulphide bridge in the hairs new curled state.

The main ingredient in perm solution is **ammonium thioglycollate** and the main ingredient of a neutraliser is **hydrogen peroxide**.

Relaxing is the opposite of perming. Relaxing hair is the process of removing natural curl from the hair and making the hair straighter. The relaxing product is applied to the hair. The disulphide bridges are broken and the hair becomes soft and pliable enabling the new straighter relaxed shape to be formed. The hair is then neutralised to rejoin the disulphide bridges in the new straighter state.

The main ingredients of a relaxer - **ammonium thioglycollate** or **sodium**, **potassium** or **lithium hydroxide**

The main ingredients of a neutraliser used for ammonium thioglycollate relaxers is hydrogen peroxide.

There is no neutraliser for hydroxide relaxers as they break the disulphide bridges differently and can not be reformed. An application of an acid balance shampoo is used or a normalising lotion that removes any remaing hydroxide after rinsing.

It's a fact! The pH of a hair relaxer has an alkalinity between a pH 10 and pH 13.

A relaxer

Colour products

Images courtesy of Goldwell

Temporary colour on the hair structure

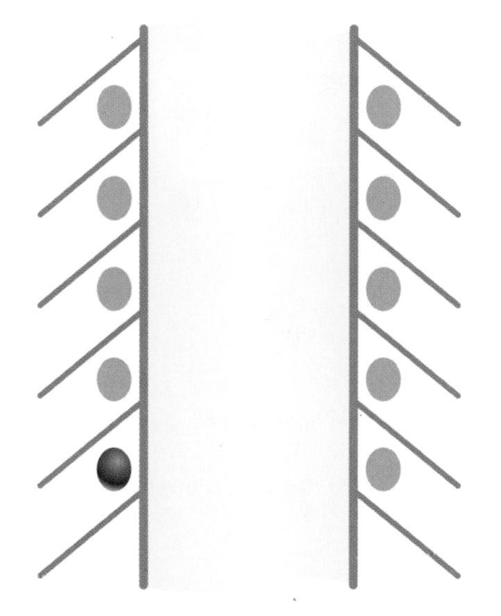

Semi permanent colour on the hair structure

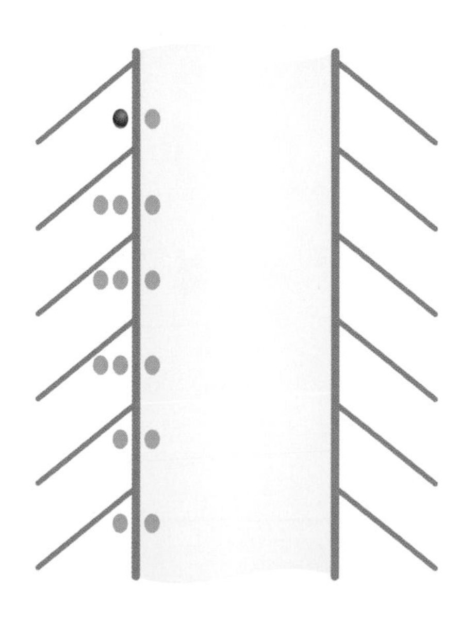

Hair colouring products are grouped according to how long they stay in the hair:

- **Temporary colours** – deposit colour and tone on the hair cuticle and are lost as soon as the hair is washed. They can come in a number of different formats such as shampoos, lotions, creams, mousses, gels, sprays, paints and crayons.
- **Semi-permanent colour** – deposit colour and tone on the cuticle and outer cortex. The colour gradually lifts each time the hair is washed and depending on the condition of the hair usually lasts between 6 and 8 washes.
- **Quasi-permanent colour** – these are longer lasting than a semi-permanent colour but not as long as a permanent colour. A developer is used to help hold the colour in the hair. They do not lighten the hair.
- **Permanent colour** – permanently colours the hair and can darken hair, add tone and depth as well as lighten the hair.

The main ingredients found in colouring products are:

- Natural vegetable colourings such as:
  - *Henna* to add red to the hair, *camomile* to add yellow and brighten light blonde hair, *indigo* used to produce a blue-black colour and *walnut* to produce a yellow-brown colour.
- Synthetic organic ingredients such as:
  - **azo dyes** are found in temporary colours. These are acid dyes that give bright intense colour and are added to a base such as shampoo and plastic resin to form the different forms of colour products
  - **nito dyes** are found in semi-permanent colour, the colours are made alkaline to help them penetrate the hair cuticle
  - **para dyes** are found in quasi- and permanent colour

Quasi permanent colour on the hair structure

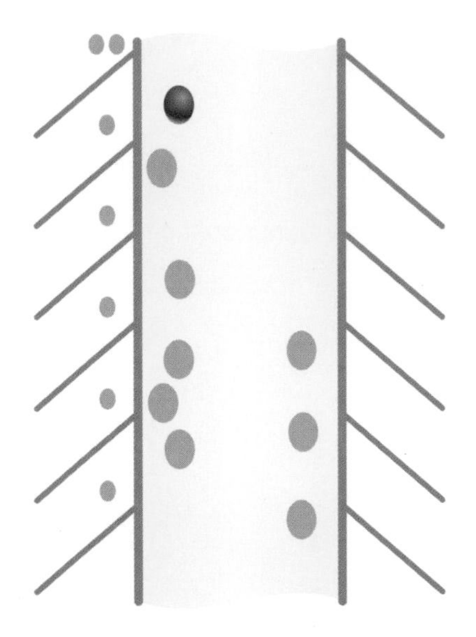

Permanent colour on the hair structure

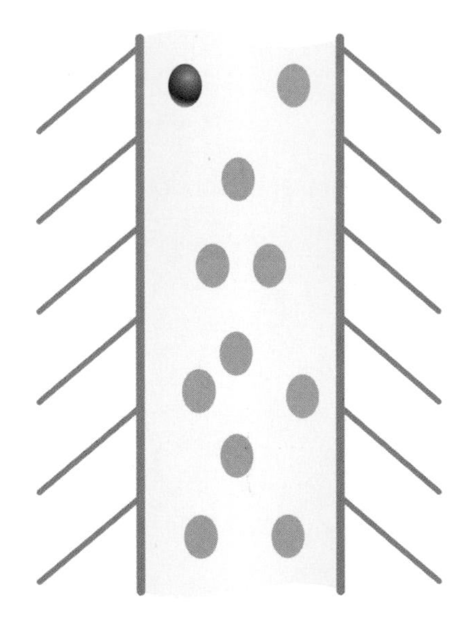

To produce a permanent colour additional ingredients are added: **ammonium hydroxide** used to lift and open the cuticle, **sodium sulphite** to prevent the colour oxidising to early, **lanolin** used as a conditioner and finally a foaming agent to help remove the colour.

Hydrogen peroxide is the oxidising agent mixed with the para dye to allow large colour molecules to form and become trapped in the hair cortex.

There is a wide variety of hair styling products available on the market for both professional and home use. Many products can be used in combination with each other to help you to provide the result you want to achieve.

Products range from styling and finishing sprays, mousses, waxes and crèmes, gels pastes and glaze to polishes and serums. They are all available to give different results such as:

- soft, medium and strong styling support
- moisture retention
- provide additional strength to the hair
- add shine
- environmental protection
- heat protection
- definition of the finished style.

To achieve these requirements the main types of ingredients found in different styling products are:

- *styling polymers* that form bonds between hair strands
- *plasticisers* and neutralisers that modify polymer properties to make them more flexible and easier to wash out of the hair
- *solvents* that are used to carry ingredients on to the hair and then evaporate
- *thickeners* that make products such as gel and crèmes easier to apply
- *conditioning* agents that help to protect the hair and provide softness and shine
- *surfactants* that are used to help ingredients work together, such as oil and water

Styling products

Images courtesy of Goldwell

- *propellants* that are pressurised gasses to push out products from their container such as hairspray
- *preservatives* that help to maintain the condition of the product and prevent the growth of micro-organisms
- *fragrances* used to prove a scent

Skin cleaners are used on the skin to remove makeup and grime from the face. A good cleanser should be easily removed from the skin without leaving the skin feeling greasy or clogging the pores. It should not dry or irritate the skin or burn the eyes, but should leave your skin feeling clean. Skin cleaners come in many forms such as bars of soaps to foams, washes, milks, lotions and creams.

The main ingredients found in skin cleaners are:

- surfactants that emulsify the dirt and skin debris
- water
- moisturisers to moisturise and protect the skin's acid mantle
- lathering agents
- fillers used to harden bars of soap and cleaners
- preservatives that help to maintain the condition of the product and prevent the growth of micro-organisms
- fragrances used to provide scent

Courtesy of Guinot

Cleanser

Skin toners help to cleanse the skin removing any trace of skin cleaner and shrink the pores.

Ingredients found in skin toners are:

- **alcohol** and water that helps to provide a cooling effect
- **humectants** to help keep the moisture in the upper layer of the epidermis

Astringents are strong forms of skin toners and can be drying to the skin, they contain ingredients such as witchhazel that is used on problem area such as spots

Moisturisers are used to help maintain the natural moisture and oil balance of the skin by locking in moisture. They can also be used to help protect the skin from environmental damage, relieve skin sensitivity and tautness, plump up skin tissue to help minimise the appearance of fine lines and provide a protective layer between the skin and makeup.

Ingredients found in moisturisers are:

- water
- oil
- humectants such as glycerine, *hylauronic acid* and *sorbitol* are used to attract water from the dermis and the atmosphere to give to the epidermis

Courtesy of Guinot

Toner

A face mask is a product that can be used to have a deep cleansing, toning, refreshing or nourishing effect on the skin. There are two main types of masks: those that set and those that are non-setting.

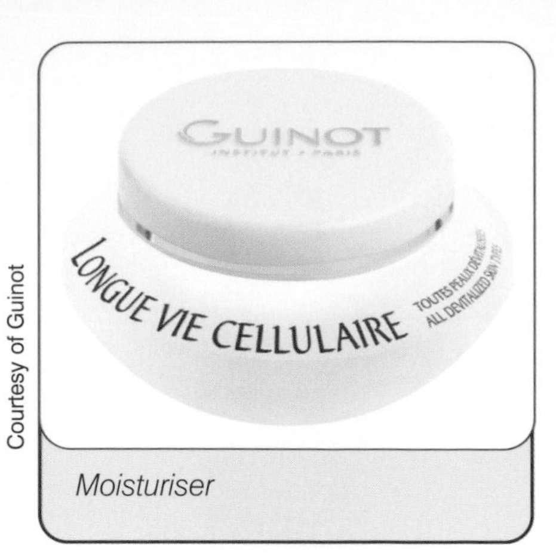

Courtesy of Guinot

Moisturiser

Courtesy of Guinot

Face masks are a popular retail product in the salon

Habia

Nail enamel

- *setting masks* include: clay, peel off masks and thermal masks
- *non-setting masks* include: warm oil made from plant oil such as almond or olive oil, natural masks made from natural fruit, plants and herbs which are rich in vitamins and minerals and cream masks

Ingredients found in clay faces masks are:

- *Fullers Earth* used to give a stimulating effect for oily skin
- *Calamine* used to sooth sensitive or delicate skin

Active lotions can also be used, for example: rose or orange water that give a mild stimulating and toning effect, witch hazel used to give an astringent effect but can also have a soothing effect on blemishes and oils such as almond for dehydrated and sensitive skin.

Peel-off masks are made from gel, latex or paraffin wax, which has a stimulating effect on the skin.

Thermal masks contain minerals that warm up when they make contact with the skin.

Pigments are the heart of colour in makeup. Pigment is a type of material which affects the colour of light reflection and absorption. It is the process of light interaction with a hard substance that creates the colour. Materials are chosen because of their ability to bring colour to other surfaces. A pigment material is actually insoluble and sits within a liquid instead of being absorbed like a dye. They are both natural and synthetic. The most important factor of a pigment that makes it useful in makeup is its low **toxicity**. Most makeup pigments come in a powder form and a binding solution is used to enable the colour to stay in place, for example eye shadow on your eye lids and lipstick for your lips.

Pearlescent pigments are good for using in eye shadows, nail varnish and hair products to give an impression of transparency and soft shimmering tone.

Aluminium pigment is used to give a metallic effect for intense decorative makeup such as gold and silver eye shadow.

Nail enamel consists of a pigment that is suspended in a solvent to create the colour of the enamel and a film former. The film former (*nitrocellulose* is the most common film former used) provides a shiny, tough, non-toxic film that adheres to the nail plate. *Resins* and *plasticisers* are added to increase the flexibility to help reduce chips and the nail enamel peeling. Special *fillers* can be added to create additional light reflection and *aluminium* can be added to give a metallic shine and fibres such as *nylon* can be added to add additional strength.

To remove the nail enamel from the nail plate a **nail enamel remover** is used. This is made from strong solvents, such as acetone, alcohol, ethyl acetate or butyl acetate. Conditioning agents such as lanolin and castor oil can be added to help moisturise the nail.

The nail cuticle can be removed manually or by using a cuticle removing product. Cuticle removers are usually liquid or cream based. They contain an alkali that breaks down the cuticle skin (keratin). They are made from *sodium hydroxide* or *potassium hydroxide* and humectants' such as *glycerine*.

ACTIVITY

Develop a mood board of different products. Your mood board can be based on a theme such as colour, or a particular type of product. In a short report explain how you came up with your idea, and what you have learnt about any of the products you have used for your mood board.

Cuticle remover

Courtesy of Creative Nail Design Inc, All CND products available from Sweet Squared

Bring your learning to life

When you are on your work placement or in a salon environment, make a record of the different types of products used in the salon. Explain how the product works, what it feels like and how it smells.

Testing products

The official testing of cosmetic products is subject to EU legislation. The *EU Cosmetic Directive* requires that cosmetics be safe for intended use prior to marketing. The *Cosmetic Directive* is regularly amended to adapt to technical progress. The *Directive* deals with checking the composition of products, labelling of ingredients and testing of products. The *Cosmetic Directive* forbids:

- testing of finished products and ingredients on animals
- marketing of cosmetic products and ingredients which have been tested on animals

However, until 2009, ingredients or combinations of ingredients to be used in cosmetic products could be tested on animals.

There are other methods of testing ingredients and cosmetic products other than animal testing, such as cell and skin tissue cultures, using corneas from eye

ACTIVITY

In a group discuss the ethical issues of product testing on animals, what do you feel are the pros and cons of animal testing. Key points that you could discuss are:

- Does animal testing work?
- Is animal testing morally right?
- What are the alternatives to animal testing?

EXTEND YOUR LEARNING

Find out more about product testing research information on the *EU Cosmetic Directive* and report your findings.

banks, and sophisticated computer and mathematical models. Some companies only use non-toxic natural ingredients that do not need testing or use ingredients that have already been approved.

How water, heat and electricity are used in the hair and beauty sector

Without these three main components we would not be able to deliver treatments and services to our clients. In this section you are going to learn about how water type and temperature impacts on skin and hair treatments and how electricity is used to support treatments and services.

Water

Water is a very important commodity, without it we would not be able to function or survive. Our body needs water to function. If we do not replace lost water we *dehydrate* and could die. Water is used in our everyday lives. We use it for everything we do from cooking our food, cleaning ourselves and our clothes, in the products we use and to carry out may treatments and services.

There are two types of water, hard and soft.

Hard water is water containing a quantity of dissolved minerals such as **calcium** or **magnesium** that has been collected as rainwater and has passed through limestone or chalky ground. **Soft water** contains fewer quantities of dissolved minerals because it has passed through ground that is made up mainly of **granite**. Minerals in water give it its taste. Some mineral waters are bottled and sold for their taste and supposed health benefits.

Hard water is not user friendly. It may shorten the life of equipment and not help products such as shampoo and cleaners to performance at their best.

Effect of hard water

On equipment: When hard water is heated it creates a reaction that forms a hard scale in pipes and around heating elements such as those in face and hair steamers and within spray fittings of showers and wash basins, the scale slowly reduces the ability for water to pass through making the equipment unsafe or unreliable to use.

On products: Soaps and some shampoos and cleaners are less effective in hard water because the water reacts with the product to create calcium or magnesium salts. These types of salts are not soluble and form a greyish scum and no lather. This then requires larger quantities of product to cleanse the skin or hair. If the scum is not removed completely, it can make the skin or hair seem duller and lifeless. However a **detergent** based product, like some types of shampoo, will create lather because the calcium and magnesium salts react enabling them to dissolve in water.

Hard water can be softened by removing the calcium from the water; this can be done with chemicals or by using an appliance that is plumbed into your water supply. The process is to remove the minerals, calcium and magnesium, and replace them with another, usually sodium. The process is called **ion exchange**. However, the sodium in water can leave the water tasting slightly salty.

Why we use heat

In beauty therapy and spa treatments it can be beneficial to pre-heat body tissue (muscle) prior to or as part of a treatment so that it makes the tissues of the body more receptive to manual, mechanical or electrical treatments. General heat can be applied through the use of saunas, steam rooms or baths, showers or jacuzzis. Direct heat or local heat can be applied to a certain area of the body by using equipment such as a heat lamp. The benefits of using heat are:

- soothing muscular tension
- soothing sensory nerves
- stimulating sebaceous and sweat glands
- promoting relaxation
- increasing circulation
- bringing blood closer to the surface of the skin
- increasing cell metabolism

In hair services, hot water helps the hair cuticle to soften and open to allow the penetration of products. Electrical equipment such as steamers can be used to open up the cuticle to allow conditioning treatments to enter the hair cortex. Heat created from equipment called *accelerates* can also be used to reduce the development time needed to process colouring or lightening products or when perming the hair. Heat can also be used to increase the intensity of some colour products and of course heat is used to style the hair. Using heat and stretching the hair by blow drying and using electrically heated equipment enables us to style the hair by temporarily changing the molecules in the hair to hold this new shape. This works by:

- breaking the hydrogen bond in the hair by wetting the hair through the shampooing process and then stretching and reshaping the hair with a brush or roller and drying the hair into its new shape
- using heat directly on dry hair to break the hydrogen bonds to stretch and reshape the hair

However hair is **hygroscopic** – it is able to absorb moisture. Moisture is absorbed through the hair structure by a process called **capillary action**, similar to ink being absorbed on blotting paper. As the hair absorbs moisture the temporary new shape of the hair starts to soften and revert back to its natural state. So curly hair that has been straightened will start to curl again and straight hair that has been curled will start to lose the curl. Every time we wash our hair we have to re-style it and use styling and finishing products to help retain the style, protect the hair from too much damage that can be caused by the constant use of heat and to stop the hair from absorbing moisture.

For nail services, heat is used to help soften the skin and nail as part of a manicure or pedicure treatment. Thermal mitts or boots are used to soften the skin and open the pores to help moisturising ingredients penetrate to a deeper level. Heated paraffin wax treatments are used to soften dry, rough skin and help improve blood circulation and heat can also be used to dry and harden the nail enamel after it has been applied to the nail.

Electricity

Electricity runs the lights, our technical equipment used to carry out treatments and services and our computerised systems needed in our everyday life. Could you image what life would be like without it?

What is electricity?

Electricity is energy. All **atoms** are made up of two different types of electrically charged particles. Positively charged particles are called **protons** and negatively charged particles are called **electrons**. The proton sits in the nucleus of the atom and the electron circulates around it. Atoms that make up different elements have different numbers of protons and electrons, but for each element there are always equal numbers; for example in a hydrogen atom there is one proton and one electron; in oxygen there are eight protons and eight electrons.

Simple electric circuit

Habia

When you use a nylon brush on freshly washed hair, the friction from the brush removes electrons from the atoms in the hair. The electrons are collected on the hair brush and the protons stay in the hair. The removal of the electrons leaves the hair positively charged, the positively charged protons repel each other and the hair separates, because positive and negative attract each other the hairs will separate from each other and be drawn to the brush where the negatively charged electrons are. This creates a form of electricity called static electricity, it is also called **friction**. When electrons can be made to move from atom to atom through a substance such as a copper wire, the flow of electrons is called an electric current. Substances that allow electric current to pass through easily are called good **conductors**. Examples of good conductors are copper and silver. Substances that do not allow electric current to pass through are called **insulators**. An example of an insulator is rubber or plastic. So copper wires are used to carry electricity and rubber is used to surround the wire to insulate the electricity and make it safe to handle and stop the electricity passing through our body when we touch an electric flex. Some electrical equipment such as hairdryers has plastic bodywork to make them all insulating and safe to use. It is very important that all electrical equipment is regularly checked and maintained by a professional electrician.

Contact with electricity can cause:

- *electric shock* – this is when the electric current passes through the body
- *burns* – electric current can burn the skin, nerves, muscles and tissues in the body
- *death* – a severe electric shock can cause problem with our breathing and heartbeat resulting in death

An electric current will only travel if there is a complete conducting path from the source of electricity. This path is called a **circuit**.

ACTIVITY

List all the different types of electrical equipment that can be used in skin, hair and nail services and explain what they are used for.

Mains electricity is generated at a power station and carried along cables to buildings. When we plug our equipment in to the socket on the wall and switch on, we have completed a circuit and we have power.

Colour and light

Colour has always been part of our lives; it enriches what we see, and affects how we feel and can sometime affect what we do. Colour has been used in the hair and beauty industries for thousands of years. The way we look and the use of colour has been part of every civilisation identifying wealth and status within society. Today colour is just as important and is one of the most important factors that we need to take into consideration when carrying out treatments or services. In hair services we use the colour in hair to help give definition to a hairstyle and add colour to create interest to the style. Colour is used to enhance the client's natural skin tone or give vibrancy and individuality. Not forgetting that we can also remove natural colour, making the hair lighter by using lightening products that remove the majority of natural pigments in the hair to leave it a very pale yellow/cream colour that we can then add additional tone to. In beauty therapy colour is used as a therapeutic treatment to create harmony and balance to our minds and body, in makeup services colour is the main ingredient to create the finished image the client wants to portray and the occasion it is required for. Light plays an important factor when we are working with colour because different types of lighting, natural or artificial, dark or light will affect the final overall look of the colour. Colour used in nail services is also used to enhance the natural nail or provide vibrancy and coordination with the client's total look. Nail art is an extension to the process of just adding colour to the nail; it enables more individuality and creative elements to be incorporated into an individual look.

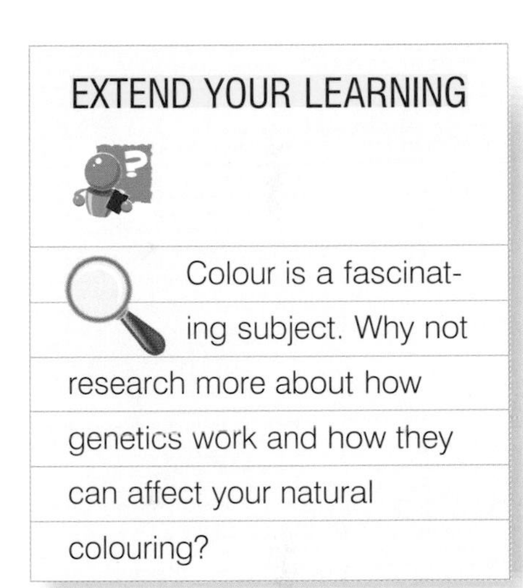
EXTEND YOUR LEARNING

Colour is a fascinating subject. Why not research more about how genetics work and how they can affect your natural colouring?

Hair and skin colour

Hair and skin colour are made from the presence of a pigment called melanin. There a two types of melanin:

- **pheomelanin** – which creates the red and yellow in colour
- **eumelanin** – which creates the black and brown in colour

Everyone has a mixture of the different types of melanin, but the more of one type of melanin that you have will determine your colouring for both your skin and hair. Genetics will also play a part in determining your hair, skin and eye colour, for example red hair is the least common of the hair colours, and is found mainly among people with a Celtic heritage.

When using colour in hair or beauty services, it is important to identify the natural colour and tone of the skin or hair. So that you can choice colours that work and enhance the client's natural appearance.

Natural light broken up by a prism to show different colours

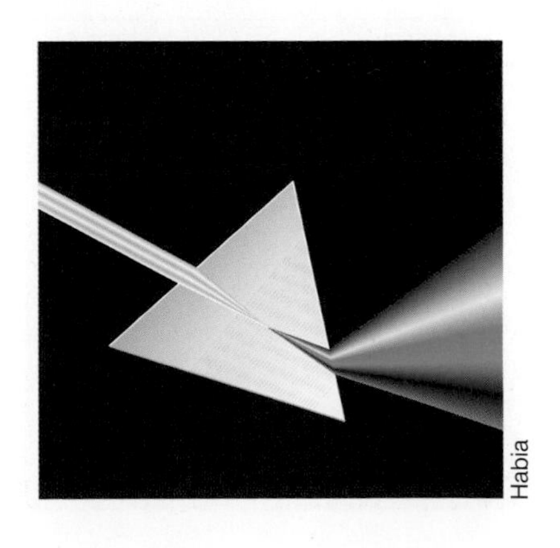
Habia

The principles of light and colour

Colour is a form of light energy; all the colours that we see are contained in natural light which is also referred to as *white light*. To be able to clearly see the individual colours of natural light, the light needs to be reflected off a flat, polished surface such as glass or crystal. **Prisms**, which are usually a triangular shape, can be used to break light up so that we can see the split of colour in light. The colours in natural light are referred to as the **colour spectrum**; we can see these colours in a rainbow.

There are seven colours: red, orange, yellow, green, blue, indigo and violet.

To remember the colours of the spectrum you can use a saying that identifies the first letter of each colour:

Richard **O**f **Y**ork **G**ave **B**attle **I**n **V**ain

Can you make up any more sayings that will help you remember the colours?

ACTIVITY 

In groups discuss how lighting would affect your choice of makeup application, think about the different occasions that people attend, how lighting is used in photography and how that needs to be taken into consideration when using makeup. Show examples of different makeup applications used for different lighting by producing a mood board or portfolio.

The molecules of a pigment or dye in an object either *absorb* or *reflect* colours of light. The colours that are reflected from the object are the colours that we see; for example a red lipstick will reflect red light and absorb all the other coloured light. White coloured nail enamel however will reflect all colours and black nail enamel will absorb all the colours and not reflect any. However, pigments rarely reflect a single colour from the spectrum, usually the colours either side of the main colour is also reflected, for example if orange is the main colour, small amounts of red and yellow will also be reflected. Different tones of orange can be seen depending on the varying amounts of red or yellow colour reflected. Colour can also appear to change tone, appearing lighter, darker, duller or brighter when viewed under different lighting. Natural light will give the truest colour. Therefore when colouring, it is important that hair salons have artificial lighting with a colour mix that is as near as possible to that of daylight.

Ordinary electric light bulbs have more red colour and less blue colour than natural day light, this will make red colour pigments more vibrant or deeper and blue colour pigments appear darker or blacker. Artificial warm white light gives the nearest match to natural daylight and salons will use this type of light when colouring hair. Some salons will also have a separate colouring area that is lightly coloured – usually white so that the surrounding walls and ceilings do not affect the choice or final appearance of hair colours.

Illustration of primary colours

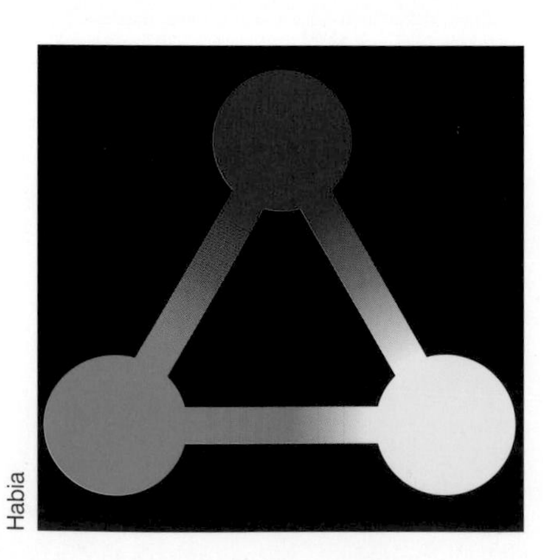

Habia

When carrying out makeup applications, it is important that during the consultation you find out the occasion that the makeup is to be applied for, so that the choice of colour and application technique will be suitable for the lighting. You would not want to have the same makeup application for a bride who will be having photographs done in the daytime, to that for a night out at a nightclub were the lighting will be darker and possibly multi-coloured.

Principles of colour theory

Colour is formed through the way objects absorb and reflect different colours within light. Colour theory explains how colour should be used to create different effects.

In makeup, hair colouring and nail enamels along with artists paint, colour is based on three **primary colours:** red, yellow and blue.

From these three primary colours you can create an infinite number of different colours. If you mix two primary colours together, you will make **secondary colours** of green, orange and violet:

- yellow and blue = green
- red and yellow = orange
- red and blue = violet

By mixing a primary and secondary colour together you will create a **tertiary colour**, for example mixing yellow and orange together will create yellow-orange and mixing blue with violet you create blue-violet. Tertiary colours are often referred to for the tone within a colour, relating the colour to warm or cool tones depending on their position on the colour circle in relation to the primary colour.

By understanding the relationship of colours in the colour circle, you will learn which colours work harmoniously together and those that contrast or clash. On the **colour circle**, the primary colours sit in a triangle, at an equal distance from each other. The secondary colours sit in the middle of two primary colours and then the tertiary colours vary in shade and tone as they sit between the primary and secondary colours. Colours that sit directly opposite each other *complement* each other but can be used in colour correction hair services to neutralise each other, for example if a colour with blue pigment has been applied to blonde hair it will give a green cast to the hair, because the yellow in the hair and the blue pigment together will create a green tone. To *neutralise* the green tone, a red tone will need to be applied to the hair. Red is used because on the colour circle it sits directly opposite green.

Illustration of the colour circle showing primary, secondary and tertiary colours

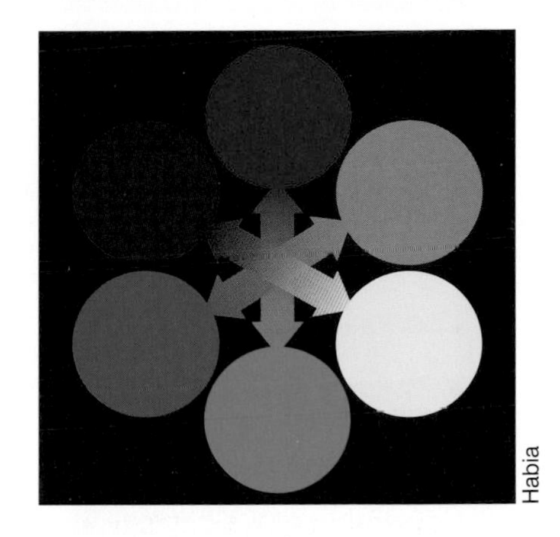
Habia

ACTIVITY

Use your imagination and create your own colour circle to explain how colour works

It's a fact!

A compound colour is a varied mix of all three primary colours that produce brown, khakis and earthy colours.

What you have learnt

The basic anatomy and physiology of the hair, skin and nails which has covered

- The basic structure and function of the skin and hair
- The structure and function of nails
- The basic anatomy and physiology of the head, neck and shoulders
- The basic anatomy and physiology of the lower arm and hand

- The basic anatomy and physiology of the lower leg and foot
- Factors that affect the health and condition of the skin, hair and nails
- How the different systems in the body can affect the condition of the hair, skin and nails
- How to recognise types of adverse skin, scalp, hair and nail conditions

How to carry out the different types of tests within the hair and beauty sector

- Common tests used in the hair and beauty sector
- The issues relating to the ethics of testing products on animals

Understanding the different types of products, how they work and the effects they have on the hair, skin and nails

- The pH scale and how it affects the use of products and its effect on the hair, skin and nails
- The basic scientific principles governing how basic hair, beauty and nail products work

How the use of electricity, water and heat play their part in the hair and beauty sector

- How electricity is used in hair, beauty and nail services
- The effects of light and heat on the delivery of different services

Finally you have learnt about colour and light and how it can influence out professional decisions

- The principles of colour
- How different lights can effect the appearance of colour

Assessment activities

Crossword

Across

4 Growing stage of hair (6)

6 Category of skin colour (5)

8 Type of bond in the hair (7)

9 Hair type (7)

10 A function of the skin (10)

13 A skin type (11)

15 Visible unit of the nail (5)

16 Factor that affects skin (9)

17 Nails grow faster at this time (6)

Down

1 Absorbs moisture (11)

2 A layer of the epidermis (7, 10)

3 Part of the nail unit (4, 3)

5 Muscle that makes hair erect (8, 4)

7 Protein of the hair (7)

11 Outer layer of the skin (9)

12 Outer layer of a hair (7)

14 Melanocytes produce these (7)

Wordsearch

R	E	Y	A	L	Y	N	R	O	H	Y	S	C	N	F	E	D
S	C	A	S	I	A	N	V	E	L	L	U	S	E	Q	N	H
N	R	Z	X	M	N	C	J	I	P	T	G	K	G	B	E	D
O	R	U	H	M	A	M	O	C	I	A	W	M	A	V	G	I
I	E	R	P	Y	G	C	K	C	N	D	A	A	L	I	A	P
T	A	P	U	G	E	E	L	O	O	T	Z	A	E	G	L	C
C	H	C	I	X	N	E	I	N	R	F	M	D	T	A	O	O
E	Y	J	I	D	D	T	Z	I	M	N	O	P	T	R	C	N
T	X	H	Z	D	E	F	X	P	A	D	Z	E	O	C	P	C
O	E	T	H	R	M	R	L	Z	L	S	W	B	G	T	Z	V
R	P	R	C	X	P	A	M	B	B	M	E	D	U	L	L	A
P	Q	X	M	A	R	N	N	I	E	C	Y	I	N	Q	Q	C
S	E	Y	L	I	D	S	W	T	S	L	G	L	A	B	K	J
Z	E	X	K	V	N	G	H	Z	L	E	J	H	L	Q	G	I
L	X	B	A	R	O	A	J	L	X	E	M	N	P	X	O	Q
R	A	E	U	T	F	J	L	X	E	T	R	O	C	O	J	X
I	O	R	D	M	A	B	S	O	R	B	T	I	O	N	A	X

Epidermis	Normal	Cortex	Excretion
Oily	Cuticle	Asian	Lanugo
Terminal	Telagen	Absorbtion	Anagen
Colagen	Acidmantle	Vellus	Matrix
Plate	Protection	Medulla	
Hornylayer	Sebum	Bed	

Assessment questions

Label the following diagram

1 Structure of the skin and hair

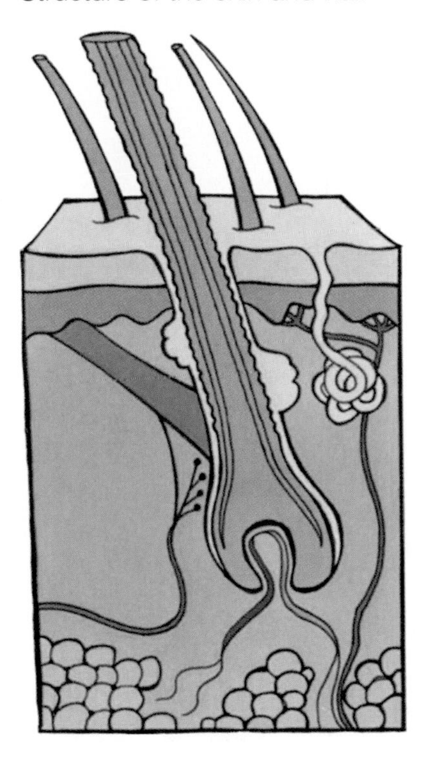

2 Structure of the nail

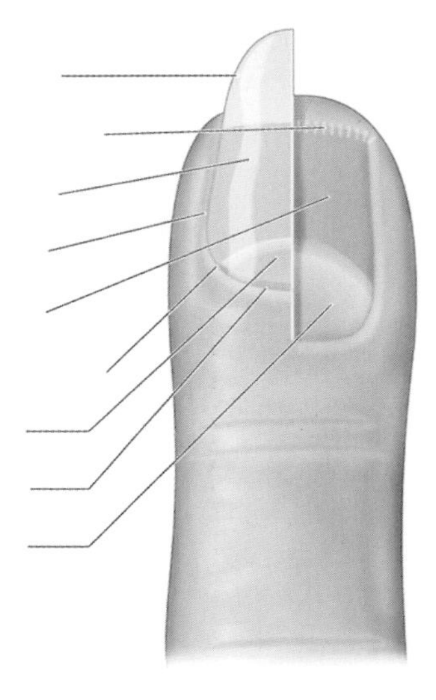

Short questions: Anatomy of the body – the systems of the body

1. Name the six main functions of the skeleton.
2. Name the different systems of the body.
3. What does a ligament do?
4. Which organ is made up of mainly muscle and pumps blood around the body?
5. Name the two types of bones found in the human body.
6. Bones are made from: 25% water, 30% organic material and 45% ....?
7. What do tendons do?
8. What do muscles do?
9. Name the three types of muscles.
10. If arteries carry blood away from the heart, what carries blood to the heart?

Tracey Devine @ Angels, Aberdeen

5 safe working practices

Safety is as simple as A B C – Always Be Careful

AUTHOR UNKNOWN

Introduction

You may think that health and safety is not the most exciting or sexiest subject to learn about, but it is one of the most important. Health and safety comes into everything we do. From a very early stage in our lives we are taught about the dangers we may come across and how to act to keep ourselves safe. Subconsciously we are aware of things that may harm us. Our bodies have defence mechanisms that help to protect us from harm. In society we have rules that are put in place so that we can learn the correct and safe way to behave. Safe working practices are part of those rules; they protect us from harm and set the guidelines that we should follow. In this chapter you will be looking at different aspects of safe working practices needed for the hair and beauty sector. It starts as soon as a clients enters a salon, spa or nail bar, it starts very simply with what they see. Is the salon clean and tidy? Are the staff well presented and have they taken pride in their appearance? Would you be happy to have a facial, manicure or hair cut if the salon environment was dirty, if no one had bothered to clean and tidy up from the last client; how would you react if there were dirty towels left on

What you are going to learn

This chapter will include:

★ Key aspects of health and safety legislation
★ Who legislation is for
★ Fire safety
★ Dealing with emergency situations
★ Client safety and expectations
★ Personal conduct, well-being and safety
★ Sterilising tools and equipment
★ The difference between a risk and a hazard
★ Disposal of waste

the side with dirty tools on a trolley that looked like they may be used on you. If the staff were wearing soiled clothes and their skin, nails and hair did not look cared for, how would you feel, would you want to stay?

Key aspects of health and safety legislation

Health and safety is for everyone. There is **legislation** for all aspects of safety when people are at work. The Health and Safety at Work Act (1974) sets down the requirements that everyone must follow when they are working. There are sections that apply to the employer and there are sections that apply to an employee.

It does not matter what job or position people have in a job, everyone needs to take responsibility for how they behave and the actions they take. Health and safety regulations and polices will ensure that everyone is aware of their own responsibilities for health and safety at work. When a person is employed, they will be given a job description and this will explain what they are expected to do in the job and it should cover health and safety aspects such as:

- behaviour
- working methods
- appearance
- security
- use of drugs, alcohol and food

In the next section of this chapter you are going to learn about the different types of Health and Safety legislation that an employed person should know about and the different responsibilities associated with them.

It's a fact! The Health and to Safety Executive (HSE) is the organisation appointed by the Government to enable employers to understand and implement health and safety. The HSE also ensures health and safety laws are followed by checking that employers are following all guidelines.

Health and Safety Regulations and Legislation

The Health and Safety at Work Act (1974)

The Health and Safety at Work Act (1974) is the main legislation which most other legislation is derived from. The Act places a general duty of care on the employer to ensure, so far as is reasonably practical, that the health, safety and welfare of their employees are maintained. However, everyone at work has a responsibility to comply with the Act, including employees, trainees and yourselves when you are on work placement.

In the Act Employer's have a responsibility to:

- provide and maintain safety equipment and safe systems of work
- ensure products and equipment are properly stored, handled and used
- provide information, training and supervision and ensure all staff are aware of and use manufacturers' instructions
- provide a safe place of work
- provide a safe working environment
- provide a written safety policy that will include risk assessments
- look after the health and safety of clients

And Employee's and trainees have a responsibility to:

- take care of their own health and safety
- take care of health and safety of colleagues and clients
- cooperate with the salon employer
- correctly use tools, equipment and products
- not interfere with or misuse anything provided for health and safety purposes such as fire extinguishers

Bring your learning to life

When you are on work placement or in a salon environment, write down each day the different tasks that you have carried out. Can you identify which health and safety Act or Legislation they relate to?

Health and Safety (First Aid) Regulations (1981)

People at work can have accidents or become ill. It is important that if someone becomes ill or has an accident that they receive immediate attention. The Health and Safety (First Aid) Regulations requires employers to provide adequate and appropriate equipment, facilities and people to deal with first aid incidents.

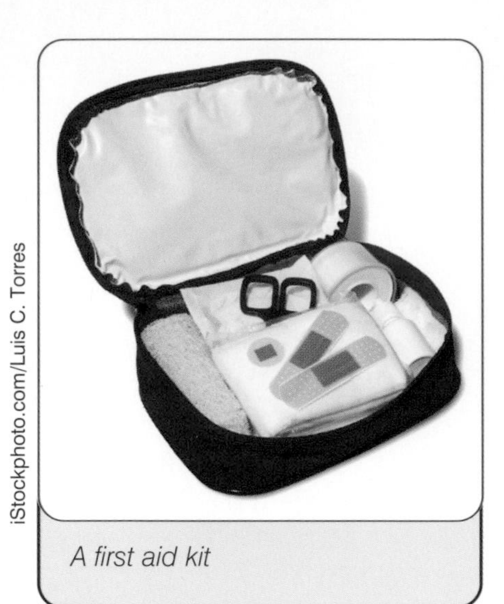
iStockphoto.com/Luis C. Torres

A first aid kit

The minimum requirement for an employer is to provide:

- a suitably stocked first aid box
- an appointed person to be responsible for first aid arrangements (but they will only attempt to give first aid if they have been trained)

First aid box. There is no standard list of items that should be put in the first aid box. It depends on the working environment and what an employer has assessed and decided is needed.

Record keeping. It is a legal requirement for the employer or an appointed responsible person in the salon to record in a book any incidents involving accidents, injuries and illness which have taken place and been attended to at work.

The following information should be included in the record book:

- the date, time and place of the incident
- the name and job of the injured or ill person
- details of the illness or injury and any information on any first aid given
- what happened to the casualty immediately afterwards, for example whether they stayed at work, went home or went to hospital
- the name and signature of the person dealing with the incident

Recording information can help employers identify any accident trends and help to improve systems for carrying out health and safety **risk assessments**.

The Workplace (Health, Safety and Welfare) Regulations (1992)

This regulation provides employers with a **code of practice** to maintain a safe, secure working environment. The requirements of this regulation cover:

- Maintenance of the workplace and equipment – To make sure that there are systems in place to ensure that the working environment is in efficient order and that equipment is maintained and in good working order for employees to use safely.
- Ventilation – To make sure that there is effective and suitable provision to ensure that the environment is ventilated by a sufficient quantity of fresh or **purified** air. This is very important when dealing with chemicals that give off fumes or for the nail industry where there is often a lot of dust created from filing nail fibre.
- Temperature – To make sure that inside the workplace the temperature of rooms are reasonable and comfortable to work in. This is particularly important in spa and beauty therapy businesses were clients can be in a state of undress.
- Lighting – To make sure that different environments have suitable and sufficient lighting so that people are safe, for example a stairway will need clear bright lighting whereas other spaces may suit muted lighting, such as a relaxation room.
- Cleanliness and waste materials – To make sure that the surfaces and floors inside a salon or spa are capable of being kept sufficiently clean and also that there is correct provision for the disposal of different types of waste be it **general waste** or **clinical waste**.

- Work areas – To make sure that work areas are suitable for the work to be carried out in them.
- Conditions of the floors and traffic routes – To make sure that the floor is suitable for the working environment, easy to clean and not slippery and that the floor is free from obstructions.
- *Windows and translucent doors and walls* – To make sure that windows and translucent doors and walls have been appropriately marked or contain features that makes them noticeable so that people do not walk into them.

The Manual Handling Operations Regulations (1992)

This regulation is about safe handling and manual lifting. It explains the procedures employers need to put in place to ensure the safety of employees moving heavy items. In the salon this could relate to the delivery of product from manufacturers or moving chairs during cleaning activities. The regulations require the employer to carry out a **risk assessment** of any activity that requires manual lifting.

The risk assessment should cover:

- the risk of an injury happening
- the type of activity required, such as strenuous pushing or carrying items over a long distance
- if the items could be heavy or difficult to handle
- the working environment, such as if there could be slippery floors or if the floor has variations in its level or if there are steps to negotiate

Top tip

Make sure your posture is correct to start. Your hips, shoulders and feet should be in line. Centre the object to be lifted in front of you. Bend from the knees. Try not to let your shoulders get in front of your knees. Grasp the object firmly and from the underneath. Use your legs to lift the weight of the object. Make sure you are holding it comfortably. Carry the object walking upright. Remember to use your knees again when you put the object down.

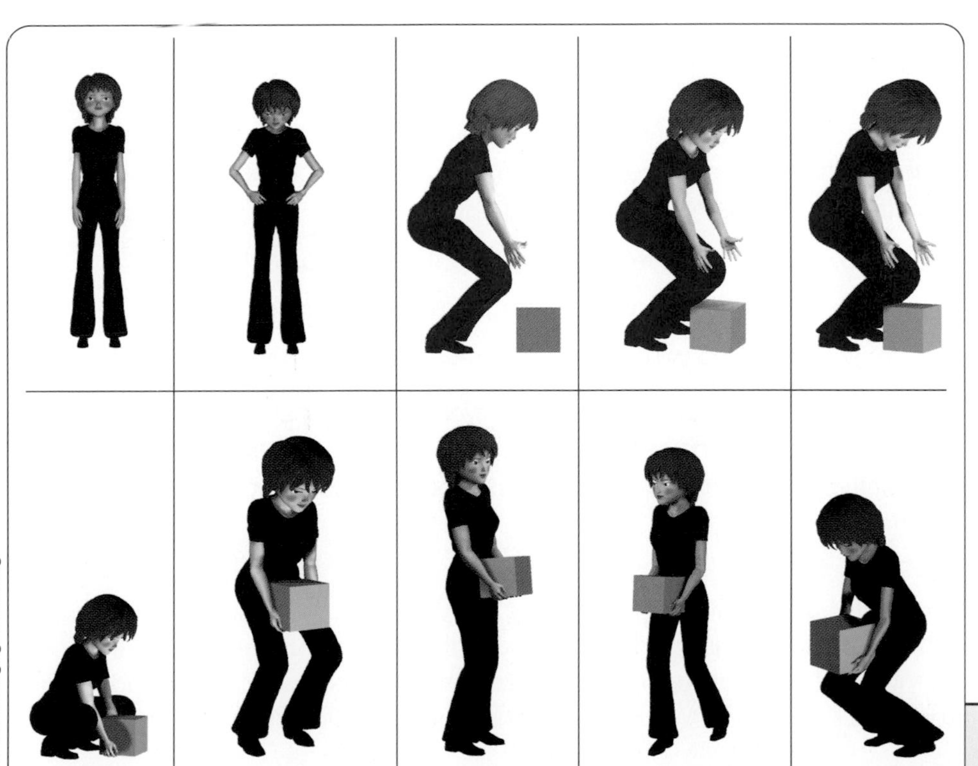

Safe lifting of boxes

- the staff's ability to handle and lift the objects
- training needs for employees who will be handling and moving items.

The Provision and Use of Work Equipment at Work Regulations (PUWER) (1998)

This regulation is for employers and requires that equipment provided and used at work is:

- suitable for its intended use
- safe to use, maintained and, if required, inspected to ensure it is safe for use
- only used by employees who have received the proper information, instruction and training

Personal Protective Equipment (PPE) at Work Regulations (1992)

This regulation requires employers to provide **personal protective equipment (PPE)** that is to be used in the salon by employees whenever there is a risk to health and safety, such as when using chemicals.

The regulations require that PPE is:

- properly assessed before used to ensure it is suitable for the job
- maintained and stored properly
- provided with instructions on how to use it safely
- used correctly by employees

Identify the occasions and the type of personal protective equipment (PPE) that would need to be worn when carrying out different beauty, hair and nail services.

Control of Substances Hazardous to Health (COSHH) Regulations (1999)

Using chemicals such as those found in hair, beauty and nail products can put an individual's health at risk, so the law requires employers to control the use and exposure to hazardous substances to prevent ill health. COSHH regulations relate to the safe handling, storage and use of products. If products are not used correctly they may harm people in the following ways:

- cause *skin irritation* or *dermatitis* as a result of skin contact
- cause asthma by developing an *allergy* to the substance
- cause the loss of *consciousness* as a result of fumes

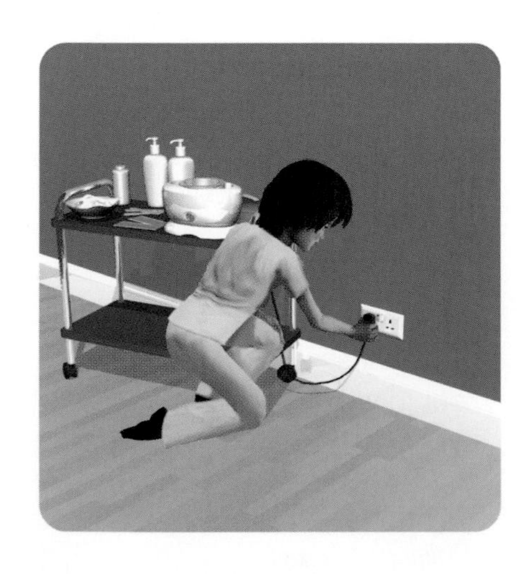

To make sure employees are safe, employers will carry out a risk assessment on the products used in the salon. Employees must follow the salon's policy and manufacturers' instructions on how to use, handle and dispose of the products safely.

Electricity at Work Regulations (1989)

Electrical equipment is used all the time in the hair and beauty sector. It is essential that electrical equipment is checked to make sure it is in good working order. The Electricity at Work Regulations require employers to maintain electrical equipment and have it checked by a qualified electrician every year. These checks must be recorded and the records made available for inspection. Employers must provide suitable training to ensure that employees know how to use the equipment safely.

Before equipment is used it is the individual's responsibility to make sure that they have *visually checked* the electrical equipment before it is use. For example: are the wires secure at the plug.

If the equipment becomes faulty during use, for example, over heating or cutting out, it must be reported to a responsible person and labelled as faulty before it is put away ready for repair.

Reporting of Injuries, Diseases and Dangerous Occurrences Regulations (RIDDOR) (1995)

This regulation requires employers to inform the Health and Safety Executive of work related accidents, diseases and dangerous occurrences.

These could include:

- an employee who has died at work
- a employee fracturing an arm or leg (not the hand or wrist or ankle or foot) spine, pelvis or skull
- an amputation of the hand or foot
- a serious eye injury (this also includes chemical accidents)
- an electrical shock requiring medical attention or loss of consciousness
- any injury requiring hospital admission as an in-patient for more than 24 hours
- an accident resulting in more than three days off work
- any work related diseases

Who is responsible for health and safety?

Within a working environment and depending on the size of the business, there may be a **designated person** or several people responsible for different aspects of health and safety, such as:

- the employer or manager who has overall responsibility
- a person responsible for first aid
- a fire warden
- a person responsible for security

It is important that within any type of business that all employees knows who to go to for help if an incident happens or to report a hazard or risk.

Fire triangle

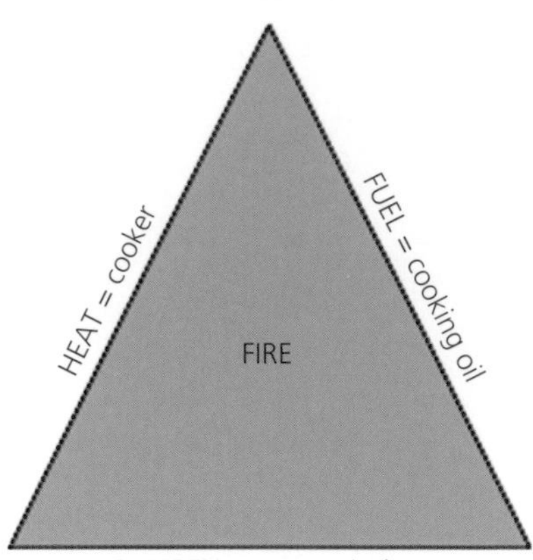

Fire safety

Although someone in an organisation or salon may have responsibility for fire safety, it is crucial for everyone to be *vigilant* and act responsibly towards the prevention of fire. It is important that everyone is aware of the safety procedures when it comes to dealing with a fire and has a clear understanding of the *evacuation* procedures. It is important that you understand the salon's safety procedures. Not taking the time to listen and learn about fire safety can result in your own death or be the cause of somebody else's.

Did you know that a fire is created when three things are present at the same time?

- fuel
- oxygen
- heat

The combination of these three things is often referred to as a *fire triangle*. If only two aspects of the fire triangle are present, then a fire will not occur. It is only when all three come into contact that a fire is created. Fires from different fuels react very differently – they are all individual and can behave a little differently.

EXTEND YOUR LEARNING

Fires created by different fuels all behave differently. Fire experts can often work out how and where a fire was started by reading the signs left by the fire and how it affected the surrounding areas. Research the role that a fire expert has and the type of training that would be needed to carry out the job.

Courtesy of Chubb Fire Ltd.

Fire extinguishers

There are three ways in which a fire spreads:

- **Conduction** – this is when heat is passed through a material such as wood or metal
- **Convection** – this happens when a liquid or gas is heated
- **Radiation** – this is when heat is transmitted without contact

There are six different types or *classes of fires*, each type has a fire extinguisher to help tackle and put out the fire:

- Class A – solid, organic materials
- Class B – liquids
- Class C – gases
- Class D – metals
- Class F – liquefiable solids such as fats and cooking oils
- electrical

Fire extinguisher symbols

Extinguishing a fire

There are three methods of extinguishing a fire:

- cooling – the fire is extinguished by reducing the temperature
- starving – the fire is extinguished by limiting or removing the fuel
- smothering – the fire is extinguished by limiting or excluding oxygen

Top tip

It is important that in the working environment all employees should know the different types of fire extinguishers available and were they are kept.

Types of fire extinguishers

TYPE OF EXTINGUISHERS	CLASSIFICATION OF FIRE	EXAMPLES OF TYPE OF FUEL	DANGERS
Water	A	wood, paper, textiles	Do not use on electrical fires or on burning liquids
Dry Powder	A, B, C and electrical	For mixed fire risk environments, good all round extinguisher that is also suitable for liquids such as methane, propane, hydrogen and natural gas.	Causes powder dust when used which could impair visibility
Wet chemical	A and F	Designed for tackling fires from cooking oil but can also be used for wood, paper, textiles.	Do not use in a fire that includes live electrical equipment
CO_2 (Carbon Dioxide)	B and electrical	Flammable liquids, oils, fats, solvents and electrical equipment	Do not use in confined spaces and be aware of possibility that the fire may reignite particularly if fire is very hot
AFFF (Aqueous Film Foaming Foam)	A and B	petrol, oil, fats, paint	Not generally used on fires with electrical apparatus

Dealing with emergency situations

Employers will have policies and procedures to deal with different emergency situations. Safety legislation is in place to protect everyone, employers review the legislation and identify how each Act relates to their business and from that they will produce policies and procedures, for example fire safety procedures and *evacuation* and *accident* procedures. They will use these procedures to ensure that all their employees know what to do in an emergency situation.

Fire safety policy and procedures

This will cover issues such as training requirements, smoking, switching off electrical equipment, safe use of fire doors, reporting procedures, evacuation procedures and fire fighting procedures, for example it may say that only individuals who have had fire fighting training should use a fire extinguisher and that the most important thing to do is think safety first, raise the alarm if you see a fire and then quickly follow the salon's policy for evacuating the salon.

Evacuation policy and procedures

This will cover issues such as the emergency exits to use, designated area and person to report to, what to do if you are one of the last people out.

Accident procedures

This will cover issues such as who the person responsible for first aid is, reporting systems, where to find emergency phone numbers and how to use the accident book.

All policies will explain people's responsibilities and the limit of responsibility that different people may have. It is important that individuals clearly understand their area and limit of responsibility so that it does not put people in difficult situations or danger.

Client safety and expectations

Being able to communicate well with clients to find out what they want is all well and good, but, if a treatment or service is carried out in an unsafe way, clients will not have *confidence* in you or the salon and they will probably not return. Clients want to be looked after and pampered during their visit. They will expect:

- to be placed in a clean and tidy beauty room or work station
- to be given a clean gown to wear
- to see that the towels used are freshly laundered
- that tools and equipment are cleaned and **sterilised** before they are used
- to be given a drink in a clean cup that is not chipped or stained
- Professionals to work *safely* and *responsibly* while carrying out the treatment or service

Clients are paying for a total experience. As professionals we need to ensure clients enjoy the experience and will look forward to their next visit. Part of the experience will be achieved by the way you conduct and present themselves to clients.

Personal conduct, well-being and safety

The way people conduct themselves at work will show their professionalism. Behaving sensibly and showing respect to clients and colleagues is essential. Being aware of what is happening around you is important but you will also need to concentrate on your own work to make sure you are doing it safely.

Many salons will have a work policy that will cover personal conduct and this will usually cover aspects such as:

- time schedules for working
- reporting in when absent due to sickness or personal issues
- the dress code
- the salon smoking policy
- the use of drugs and alcohol
- where and when eating and drinking can take place
- health and safety responsibility
- the use of tools and equipment

Preparation is often the key to success at work. A professional stylist, therapist or technician will always be prepared for their clients.

Top tip

Always read work policies and procedures. They will provide the information needed to work safely and responsibly.

Preparing for the client

A professional will always prepare for each new treatment or service in readiness for their client. They will make sure that:

- the work station has been cleaned and prepared for the next client
- their tools and equipment have been cleaned and sterilised and set up ready for use
- they have checked to see if the client has a record card or treatment plan
- they have the products available and close to hand

Preparing yourself

Becoming a professional within the hair and beauty sector is about preparing yourself for your clients and the treatments and services you will be carrying out. This includes the way you will present yourself to clients, the way to behave and the *discipline* required to work in a *client orientated business* that is *physically* and *mentally* demanding.

Being prepared for work in the hair and beauty sector is about how you act, the choices and decisions you make and about how you live your life, the food you eat and the way you look after your health. This will all affect how you perform in your work.

The hair and beauty business is about looking and feeling good, but working in the industry is also about working hard, physically you are on your feet all day, you are holding and manipulating equipment and stretching and using your body to carry out some of the treatments and services. Mentally you are listening, advising and making decisions with and for your clients. It is both physically and mentally tiring and you need to be *fit* and *healthy* to meet the demands of the job, so you need to look after yourself. Eating a balanced diet and getting regular exercise is essential to healthy living, a sensible attitude to the amount of sleep you need during a working week to enable you to work effectively is very important to building a successful career. You should understand the effects drinking alcohol or using drugs will have, not only on your body but also on your conduct and behaviour during work. That is not to say that you need to have a boring life just because you are working, it is about making sure that you can give your best at work but also that you have the time and energy to enjoy yourself outside of work, it is about getting the right work–life balance.

A balanced diet

A balanced diet contains:

- **Carbohydrates** – these give use our energy and can be found in potatoes, rice, pasta, bread and cereals
- **Proteins** – these are needed to enable us to grow and repair our bodies, they can also give use energy. Protein is mainly found in red and white meat, fish, eggs, cheese and milk.
- **Fats** – these are also used as a form of energy. Fat is important in your diet as it contains fat soluble vitamins; but you need to eat the right amount and the right kind. There are three main types of fats:
  - Unsaturated – found in fish such as tuna and salmon, olive oil, and peanut oil. This type of fat helps keep a healthy heart
  - Saturated – found in meat, butter, cheese and milk. We should not eat too much of this type of fat as it can raise cholesterol and increase the risk of heart disease
  - Trans fats – found in margarine, snack food and fried food. Again we should not eat too much of this type of fat because it can raise cholesterol and increase the risk of heart disease
- **Vitamins** – you only need a very small amount of vitamins each type to help different parts of the body, Different types of vitamins can be found in foods such as meat, vegetables, fruit, fish, nuts, rice, pasta, eggs and butter:

Food groups

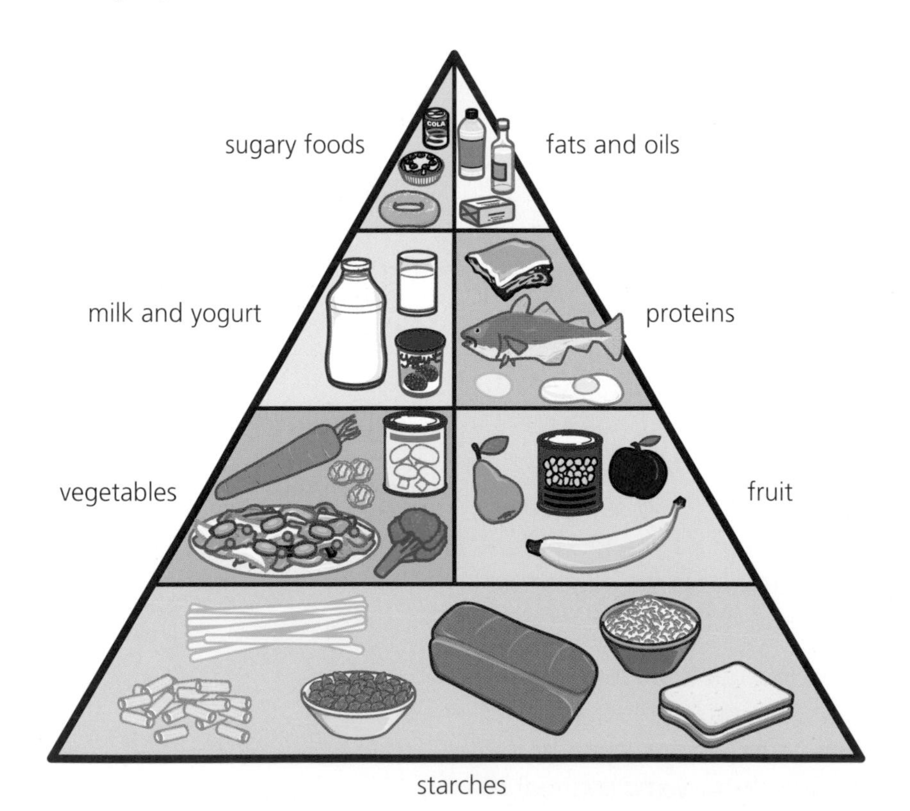

- Vitamin A – is good for your eyes
- Vitamin B – there are different types of this vitamin; they are good for our immune and nervous system and play an important role in cell metabolism
- Vitamin C – helps the body to repair itself
- Vitamin D – is good for the absorption of calcium
- Vitamin E – helps in reproduction

- **Mineral salts** – you only need a small amount of minerals; different minerals support the body. Different types of minerals can be found in fish, meat, milk, seeds, nuts, fruit and vegetables and salt:
  - Iron – this is needed to make haemoglobin in our blood.
  - Calcium – this is needed to give us strong healthy teeth, bones and muscles
  - Sodium – this is used in all our cells especially the nervous system
  - Iodine – this is used to make a hormone called thyroxin
- **Fibre** – this is used to help the digestive system work properly. Fibre can be found in fruit, vegetables, nuts, seeds and pulses along with rice and wholemeal or granary bread.

Top tip

The *five a day rule* recommends that to stay healthy we should eat five servings of fruit and vegetables every day. One serving can include items such as: 1 medium sized fruit such as an apple, half a cup of beans, chopped fruit or vegetables, a cup of leafy salad leaves or a small glass of fresh fruit juice. Remember, potatoes do not count because they are starches.

EXTEND YOUR LEARNING   

Nutrition and exercise is the key to a healthy life. Research the different types of food groups that we eat and the different types of exercise we can do. Review your findings against what you currently eat and the exercise you do. Then produce a healthy life plan that you could use, include the five a day rule in your plan. Follow the plan for a number of weeks, adapt it as you use it if needed and then review your findings. Do you feel healthier or not?

Personal appearance

In the hair and beauty sector, businesses will have an **image** that they want to portray to the outside world. They may want to attract a certain clientele – perhaps a certain age group or targeted on the amount of money individuals are likely to spend. This image will often be reflected in what the employer expects employees to wear in the salon and how they conduct themselves at work. This will usually be described in a job description or salon policy.

A salon policy may relate to the expected standards in **hygiene**, the wearing of jewellery and shoes that an employee must follow, for example that jewellery should not get in the way of work and it should not cause any discomfort to the client, by catching or pulling on them.

Habia

An unprofessional and a professional look for a stylist

Habia

An unprofessional and a professional look for a beauty therapist

Personal appearance portrays not only the salon image but also an individual's own personality. Even if a person wears a salon uniform, they need to take pride in their appearance. A clean and well presented outfit will give clients confidence. If clothes are dirty and soiled, not only does it give the client a bad impression of that person and the salon but it can also be embarrassing or upsetting to clients and colleagues if that person also smells sweaty.

Work on your own or in a group: identify a picture of a salon or spa that you like. Then design an outfit or a variety of outfits for the employees who may work there. Make sure the design is suitable for the work activities that will be carried out but also portrays the right image for your chosen salon or spa. Finally present your designs

Personal hygiene

It is vital that stylists, therapists and technicians maintain high standards of personal hygiene. Body hygiene is achieved through daily showering or bathing to remove stale sweat, dirt and any bacteria, which create **body odour (BO)**.

How to wash your hands

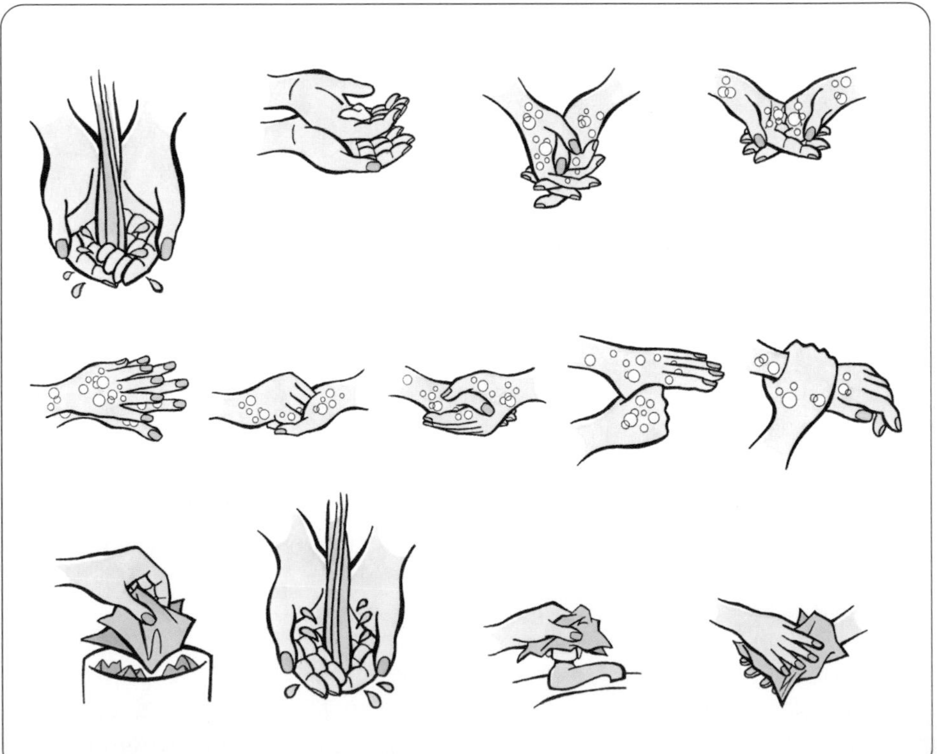

Habia

Clothes that are restrictive and tight do not allow the air to circulate around the body and causes perspiration leading to BO. Underwear should be clean and fresh each day. Teeth should be cleaned regularly, particularly after eating food. It is always more considerate to colleagues and clients for people not to eat strong flavoured food such as garlic and curry while working so that they do not breath the smell all over them. The use of breath fresheners or mouth wash to freshen the breath during the day is a very good idea when working closely with other people and *antiperspirants* or *deodorants* should be applied to the underarms to help reduce perspiration and the smell of sweat. Hands should be washed regularly throughout the day, especially after visiting the toilet and before eating food or carrying out a treatment or service on a client. Washing hands will minimise the risk of **cross infection** and washing them during a treatment illustrates to the client a hygienic, professional image.

Posture

Making sure that your body **posture** is correct is key to your long-term health and to your success in a career in the hair and beauty sector.

Working in the hair and beauty sector is a tiring job: professionals are on their feet for the majority of the day. It is important that you are aware of the correct standing position to ensure survival within the industry. Bad posture will lead to body fatigue and possible long-term injury. Standing incorrectly will put pressure and strain on both muscles and ligaments. This happens when the upper part of the body is out of line with the lower parts. Bad posture will create pain and discomfort but also gives the client an impression of laziness and an uncaring attitude.

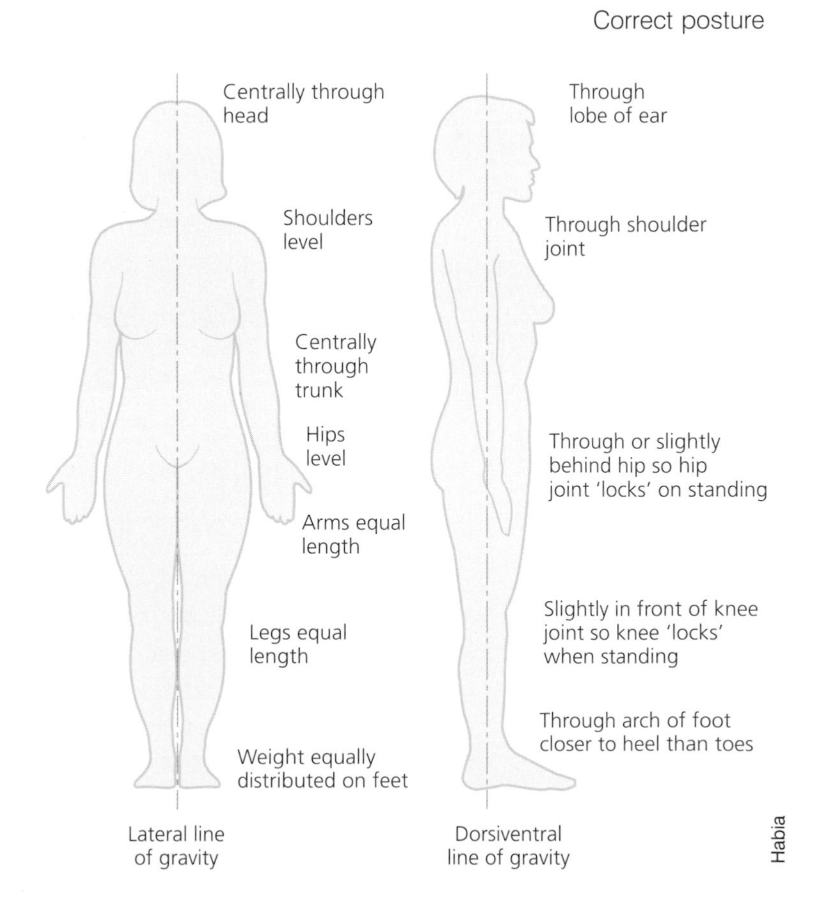

Like a professional in the hair and beauty sector, you will need to learn how to have good posture to ensure that your **stance** is even and that you have good body *balance* as you work around the client. During some treatments and services, particularly in the nail industry, stools are used to work at the correct height and to maintain body balance whilst working.

Correct posture is achieved when your head, shoulders, upper body torso and abdomen, thighs and legs distribute your body's weight evenly over your feet, which should be facing forward and slightly apart. If you move position and lower one of your hips, it will change the balance of your body and put more weight on that leg and foot. It will cause the spine to curve and put strain and discomfort on the lower part of your back.

It is important that you are aware of how to work safely to protect you health so that you can have a long and exciting future in the world of hair and beauty. Understanding how to stand and use your body balance to protect your bones and muscles is only part of protecting your health. Using the same movements and actions can also put strain on certain parts of your body. **Repetitive strain injury (RSI)** is a common problem, along with skin and breathing conditions. To protect yourself you must always be ware of the risks and how to avoid them, employers should include this information in their work policies and procedures, but also always use information included by manufacturers in there instructions of how to use and prepare equipment and products safely. Always use PPE and always work sensibly and responsibly.

Repetitive strain injury (RSI)

Repetitive strain injury (RSI) is a general term used to describe symptoms that occur when you have carried out a *repetitive task*, such as in the hands, wrist or fingers when holding a blow-dryer and hair brush or typing on a computer for long periods of time. Causes of RSI can be a combination of different elements that can include:

- doing something repeatedly for too long
- working with equipment that is too heavy or big for you
- working too fast
- not having breaks
- holding your muscles in the same position for long periods of time
- lack of training

The main outcome of RSI is damage to muscles, tendons and nerves. Damage to the nerves will give you a tingling sensation.

The symptoms can be any one of the following:

- burning, aching or shooting pain in an area of the body such as the wrist or arm
- tremors, numbness and also clumsiness
- weakness in the area such as the hand, arm or shoulder

Not everyone experiences all the symptoms and symptoms may not occur for several hours or longer after the activity which caused them. If you identify any soreness, discomfort or tingling in your neck, shoulders, arms, wrist or fingers, you should report it to your trainer so that your work practices can be reviewed and more training can be given along with any necessary alterations to equipment. A doctor may prescribe medication, or alternative medicine such as massage, physical therapy and exercise to rebuild muscle strength, flexibility and posture.

Skin sensitivity

Skin sensitivity is a condition were the skin is sensitive to many factors that cause the skin to react creating, redness, spots or pustules, bumps and skin erosion. Skin sensitivity can be related to inherited factors – gender, age and race – but certain characteristics can be identified, including:

- skin that tends to be thin or fine textured
- skin that is typically dry
- skin that is prone to flushing from temperature changes
- skin that easily sunburns or windburns
- skin that is prone to allergic reactions
- skin that easily irritates resulting in red blotchy patches

Sensitive skin tends to be irritated by many common items such as:

- sorbic acid found in cosmetics, glue, paints, rubber and varnishes
- chemicals found in fragrances
- wool and lanolin – Lanolin is found in cosmetic products
- alkalis in detergents
- rubber latex found in rubber gloves, it is always safest not to use PPE made from latex

Dermatitis

There are four common types of dermatitis or eczema

1. Atopic dermatitis – caused by dry sensitive skin which over reacts to allergies such as eczma, asthma or hay fever
2. Seborrheic dermatitis – is a condition that occurs in areas of the skin where there are large oil glands, mainly on the scalp, face and behind the ears. On the scalp it is referred to as dandruff
3. Actinic dermatitis – is a sensitivity to sunlight exposure
4. Contact dermatitis – caused by contact with an irritating material over a period of time

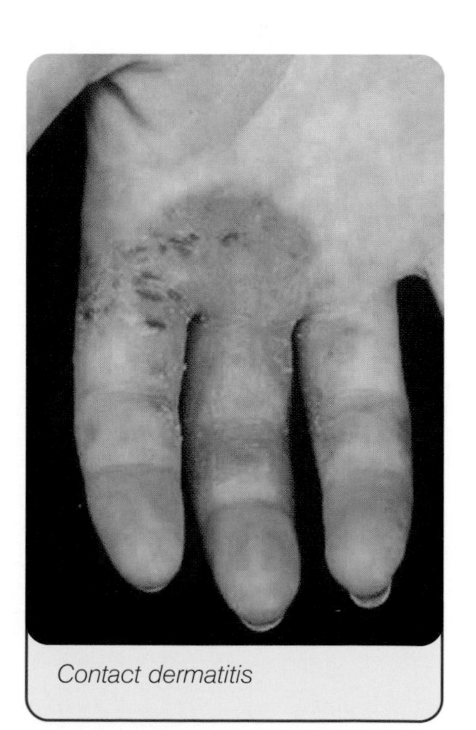

Contact dermatitis

Contact dermatitis

Contact dermatitis is a skin condition that can affect people working in the hair and beauty sector. It is an itchy skin condition caused by an allergic reaction to certain materials. Products such as shampoos that are in constant contact with the skin can cause irritation. In fact, one of the main causes of dermatitis for hairdressers is due to constantly having wet hands during the shampoo process. In some cases the condition can get so severe that the hairdresser may have to change their career. It is therefore important that after services such as shampooing hair you wash and dry your hands and apply a good hand cream to protect them. Wearing protective, disposable, non-latex gloves will protect the hands from water and chemicals, helping to prevent contact dermatitis.

Top tip Habia have produced a guide on dermatitis and glove use for hairdressers. An online version is available on **www.habia.org**.

Asthma

Asthma is a condition where the airways become irritated and inflamed so that they become narrower and produce extra *mucus*. There are a number of causes to asthma but the one that can affect you in the work place is called **occupational asthma** and is caused by chemical products or fine particles of dust from skin and nails. When mixing and using chemical products, you should always use PPE – this should include a wearing a mask.

There are three main ways that chemical products and dust can enter the body:

- **Inhalation** – breathing in **vapours** or dust. Many hair, skin and nail products produce vapours that escape into the air. It is essential that the salon environment has a good ventilation system to remove these vapours. Dust can be another problem in the salon. There are two types of dust: one that you can see and that is not to harmful, as it is heavier than air and settles on surfaces, and there is dust that you cannot see. This type of dust is more harmful because it floats around in the air and you can easily breathe it in. To reduce the risk of breathing in dust, extractors can be used and are often fitted to manicure stations as well as having good room ventilation. Masks should also be worn if you are susceptible to dust. This could lead to occupational asthma.
- **Ingestion** – through the mouth. Always make sure you wash your hands after using any product and before eating to ensure you do not *ingest* anything other than your food. Always keep your food and drink away from where you are working. This could lead to respiratory problems like occupational asthma or digestion problems.
- **Absorption** – through the skin. Every time we touch a chemical, some of it will be absorbed into our skin. After continual use and absorption of a chemical, the body may start to react causing irritation to the skin in the area that the chemical is absorbed. This could lead to contact dermatitis or other allergies.

It's a fact! You should always report occupational conditions to your employer.

Sterilising tools and equipment

A professional would never use dirty tools and equipment. They must be cleaned and sterilised before using them on clients. As part of the consultation, tools and equipment needed for the treatment or service will be identified for use. During your work experience and in training sessions it is up to you to ensure that tools and equipment are ready to use and fit for purpose.

It's a fact! Sterilisation is the complete eradication of living organisms.

Different tools and equipment are cleaned, **sterilised** or **disinfected** in different ways. There are three main methods of sterilising tools. These are:

- heat
- radiation
- chemicals

Within the hair and beauty sector this will relate to:

- heat = the use of an autoclave
- radiation = the use of an ultra-violet light box
- chemicals = the use of barbicide

An autoclave

Sorisa

Heat

Autoclaves are the most reliable method of sterilising but are not always used in every salon. They are used for sterilising metal tools such as scissors, tweezers and cuticle nippers. They work by building up steam pressure, creating heat that destroys all living bacteria.

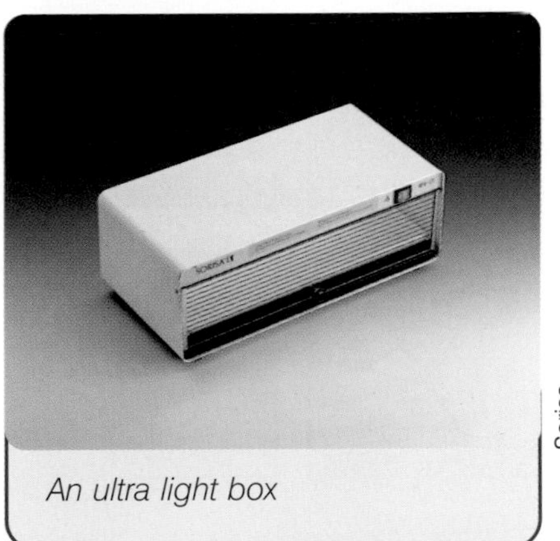

An ultra light box

Sorisa

Radiation

An **ultra-violet (UV) light box** is often used as a method of sterilising tools such as combs, brushes and nail clippers. The tools must be washed and dried before placing them in the box. The ultra-violet light will prevent bacterial growth on the tools, but complete sterilisation is not guaranteed as tools will only be sterilised on the areas the UV rays reach, so the tools must be turned over to ensure they have been exposed to the light on all sides. Because this method of sterilising is time consuming and sterilisation cannot be guaranteed, it is often better to use the UV light box as a hygienic method of storing tools that have already been sterilised by another method.

A barbicide jar and barbicide

Sorisa

Chemicals

The use of chemicals is the most common method in the salon to disinfect tools and equipment such as eyebrow tweezers and combs. In the hair and beauty sector we tend to use a chemical called **barbicide** – it is a clear, blue low level disinfectant. It does not sterilise tools, but reduces the probability of infection. Barbicide must be changed daily and all the tools must be totally submerged in the solution and left in the solution for the time recommended by the manufacturer.

Electrical tools and equipment should be wiped down to remove any debris or dirt after and before use and then stored correctly. Always follow the manufacturers' instructions for cleaning and storing tools and equipment.

Hazards and risks

It is the duty of everyone who works in a salon environment to be aware of potential hazards and risks. Professionals need to be alert to spot a hazard that may have the potential of becoming a risk to prevent an accident happening. If they can deal with the hazard it should be deal with quickly and safely however, if they spot a hazard or risk that they cannot deal with, they need to make sure they inform the person responsible for health and safety straight away.

Spot the hazards

Hazard symbols

- A **hazard** is something with the potential to cause harm
- A **risk** is the likelihood of (someone being harmed by the hazard) the hazard's potential being realised

For example: If a tap was leaking in the salon, it could be classed as a hazard. If that tap was at the backwash area in a hairdressing salon and the leak was creating a pool of water were stylists stand to wash hair, this would then be a risk as the likelihood is that someone will slip and hurt themselves.

ACTIVITY

Carry out a simple risk assessment – this could be of your home or in a salon environment. On a risk assessment form that you have produced or developed with help from others, list the hazards you have identified, the people who are at risk from the hazard, and identify if any existing procedures are in place or whether new or additional procedures are required.

Risk assessment

Every employer must carry out a risk assessment. It must cover all the activities that take place in their salon and the substances that are used within the salon.

A risk assessment is nothing more than a review of what is in the salon that could cause harm to employees and clients. The employer can then weigh up whether enough precautions have been taken to prevent harm from accidents or if additional precautions need to be put in place. The whole aim is to make sure that no one in the salon gets hurt, or becomes ill.

The main thing an employer needs to decide is whether a hazard is significant and if sufficient procedures have been put in place to deal with the hazard satisfactory.

How an employer will assess the risks in a salon:

- they will look for the hazards
- decide if any one could be harmed and how
- evaluate the risks and decide whether the existing precautions are sufficient or whether new ones are needed

- record the findings
- review risk assessment records and revise them when necessary. For example, when there are changes to the salon's equipment or products.

Trailing electrical flexes must be avoided

Disposing of waste

We all have to dispose of our waste. How we do that will depend on where we live and work in the country. In the UK around 330 million tonnes of waste is produced annually – a quarter of that is produced by us at home and by businesses. This is called controlled waste.

Each **Local Authority** is responsible for setting local policy for the removal of waste. Their policies vary but they usually follow similar systems for categorising different types of waste material and each waste type will have a different method of waste disposal. Waste disposal has a generic name: **waste management**.

Waste management is the collection, transport, processing, recycling or disposal of waste material. Waste management is essential; could you image what it would be like to live in a town or city where everyone dumped their rubbish on to the streets. The smell, the flies, the rats and the effect on the environment would be terrible, not to mention the health issue of disease.

Wherever possible waste management will try to cover environmental issues to reduce the use of landfills and incineration methods by recycling the waste.

- **landfill** involves burying waste to dispose of it
- **incineration** is the combustion of waste, converting waste into heat, gas, steam and ash
- **recycling** involves extracting and reprocessing waste into new products

Recycling is a term that is generally used to refer to the widespread collection and reuse of everyday waste material such as tins, glass, paper and plastic. The different categories of waste are usually collected separately by Local Authorities to be reprocessed into new products.

Waste management for businesses is the responsibility of the business owner. It is the owner's responsibility to ensure the waste material produced by the business is disposed of following the Government's and Local Authority policy at a commercial waste site.

In the hair and beauty sector the majority of waste produced is general waste, however, salons do produce clinical waste. Clinical waste must be kept apart from general waste and be disposed of separately by a licensed incinerator or landfill site. Clinical waste in the hair and beauty sector will include items such as:

- waste that consists of human tissue
- blood or other body fluids

- swabs, cotton wool or dressings
- syringes, blades or needles

The waste consisting of human tissue, blood and bodily fluids, swabs or dressings should be put in an approved separate sealed bag or container. Syringes, blades and needles need to be dealt with separately – they are known as 'sharps'. **Sharps** must be disposed of by putting them in a sharps box after they have been used. A sharps box is a sealed container provided by your local authority or licensed operator. Used waste products such as perm solution, colouring lightening products can be disposed of by diluting them and disposing of them down the sink.

What you have learnt

The key aspects of the health and safety legislation that is used in the hair and beauty sector

- Who legislation is for and why we need it
- The importance of following instructions and understanding different safety procedures
- The importance of record keeping and carrying out risk assessments

Fire safety

- The different types of fires and how to extinguish them

How to deal with different emergency situations

To understand the importance of client safety and the importance of meeting clients' expectations in relation to health and saftey

The effect our own personal conduct and safety has on others

- How you should look after you own well-being at work
- Understanding the importance of a healthy diet and how this can help you achieve the right work–life balance
- Why personal appearance and hygiene is important to the image and business of the salon
- Why it is important to understand body posture and the effect posture can have on your working life
- The importance of wearing personal protective equipment and working sensibly and responsibly
- Understanding what causes repetitive strain injury, skin sensitivity, contact dermatitis and occupational asthma

How to clean, disinfect and sterilise tools and equipment

- The different methods of sterilising tools and equipment

The difference between a risk and a hazard

- How to carry out a risk assessment

How to dispose of the different types of waste created within the hair and beauty sector

- The different types of waste disposal systems there are

Assessment activities

Crossword

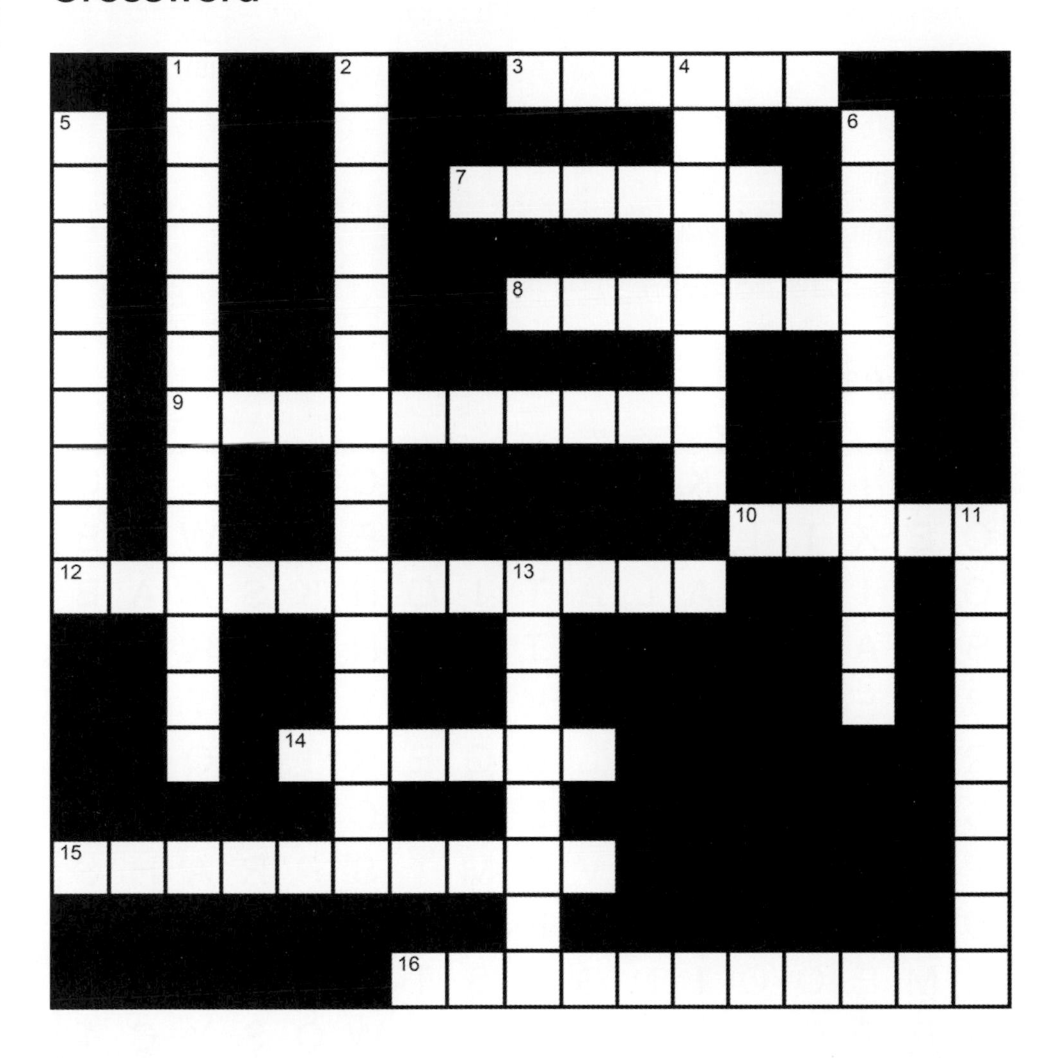

Across

3 Potential to cause harm (6)

7 Criteria set by employer (6)

8 Behaviour, you should be good at this (7)

9 A way of chemicals entering the body (10)

10 Not to be used on electrical fires (5)

12 Type of equipment used for putting out fires (12)

14 Keeps information (6)

15 Condition affecting the skin (10)

16 Rules set by Government (11)

Down

1 Method used to kill living organs (13)

2 Term used for disposing of waste (5, 10)

4 Whatever you think, there's always a cause for this to happen (8)

5 Solution used to sterilise tools (9)

6 Fresh air in, old air out (11)

11 Fire can spread this way (9)

13 One method of extinguishing a fire (8)

Wordsearch

E	Z	I	I	L	K	O	F	S	L	A	C	I	M	E	H	C
O	E	X	T	I	N	G	U	I	S	H	E	R	J	W	H	B
O	L	I	N	H	A	L	A	T	I	O	N	K	S	A	A	B
B	S	A	B	S	O	R	P	T	I	O	N	E	Z	R	N	L
R	I	E	C	E	L	C	M	K	K	C	Y	A	B	T	J	E
R	T	N	O	I	T	A	L	U	G	E	R	I	D	Q	T	G
S	I	Q	C	W	R	D	Y	B	I	D	C	O	B	K	V	I
E	T	H	L	L	S	T	V	O	M	I	S	P	R	A	H	S
C	A	G	A	V	I	Z	C	H	D	Q	A	M	Z	O	O	L
N	M	E	Q	C	I	N	G	E	S	T	I	O	N	F	T	A
A	R	Q	G	R	C	A	I	F	L	X	W	O	S	Y	C	T
T	E	L	Y	A	S	I	X	C	N	E	Y	J	M	B	K	I
S	D	K	Q	T	R	A	D	A	A	R	A	C	A	S	N	O
B	P	U	H	V	F	O	V	E	V	L	X	E	I	U	G	N
U	M	M	N	J	B	T	T	F	N	R	A	R	L	L	F	Q
S	A	O	Q	U	S	N	S	S	W	T	P	B	Z	Q	O	X
A	P	I	S	T	E	R	I	L	I	S	A	T	I	O	N	P

Policy	Sterilisation	Electrical	Ingestion
Hazard	Clinical	Absorption	Risk
Sharps	Asthma	Dermatitis	Regulation
Barbicide	Accident	Substances	Chemicals
Legislation	Extinguisher	Storage	Inhalation

Assessment question: Balanced diet

Link the boxes on the left under Balanced Diet with the appropriate Food Types on the right. You may use different coloured markers to show your connections.

Balanced diet	Food Type
Carbohydrates	Vegetables
	Meat
	Fish
Proteins	Olive oil
	Fried potatoes
	Nuts
Fats	Wholemeal bread
	Eggs
	Margarine
Vitamins	Fruit
	Cereals
	Liver
Minerals	Salt
	Pasta
	Cheese
Fibre	Milk
	Rice

Assessment question: Legislation

Link the legislation on the left with the reason for the legislation on the right. You may use different coloured markers to show your connections.

Legislation	Reason
Workplace (Health, Safety and Welfare Regulations 1992	Wearing gloves and apron
Health and Safety at Work Act 1974	Making sure there is enough ventilation
Provision and Use of Work Equipment Regulations 1992	Disposal of products
Personal Protective Equipment at Work Regulations 1992	Main Legislation in which nearly all other regulations are made
Control of Substances Hazardous to Health Regulations 2002 (COSHH)	Ensuring that equipment is used correct and in safe working order

6

communication and client care

Spectrum: Sanrizz artistic team

> **When people talk, listen completely. Most people never listen.**
>
> ERNEST HEMINGWAY 1899–1961, NOVELIST

Introduction

Communication and client care is one of the most important aspects of working in the hair and beauty sector. Professional stylists, therapists and technicians need to develop and build relationships with their clients and team members so that they understand and trust each other.

To become successful in the hair and beauty sector you will need to understand all the different forms of communication: verbal, non-verbal and physical communication. Understanding communication will help you to create an atmosphere where you can work harmoniously with your team members and to create a positive environment where clients will feel comfortable and special. When working with clients, it is critical to create a positive impression, so that each client gains confidence in their stylist, therapist or technician and feels comfortable to discuss openly their requirements and expectations.

The importance of creating a positive and lasting impression

First impressions count. How you look and behave that day will be the *image* and *impression* that you have created that someone will remember you by. So you need to consider that everyday is a new day and you will meet new people for the first time. How do you want them to view you? As some one that is fashionable?

Habia

Professional beauty therapist

What you are going to learn

This chapter will include:

- ★ The importance of creating a positive and lasting impression
- ★ Appearance, style and image
- ★ How to gain trust
- ★ Verbal and non-verbal communication
- ★ Physical communication
- ★ Understanding how people communicate differently
- ★ Communication with different client groups
- ★ Consulting with clients
- ★ Identifying your client's needs and wishes
- ★ Using open and closed questions
- ★ Using visual aids
- ★ Advice and after care

Well presented? Cares about how they look and behaves and respects others? Or do you want to be seen as scruffy, not interested or can't be bothered? What will employers think about the impression you will give clients, particularly in the hair and beauty sector where clients have come to professionals to improve their image or well-being? Employers do not always want their employees to dress the same. They want to create an image that reflects the type of company they are. Hairdressing salons often have trendy, fashionable images. The employer may wish their employees to have hairstyles that advertise the salon and to wear fashionable clothes that reflect their own personality as well as the salon image. However, they may put some *restrictions* on employees, such as the type of colour to wear or how much body flesh can be on show. An employer working in the nail, spa or beauty industry will probably want to portray a different image, one

Top tip Having good grooming habits and an image sense is pretty important socially, unless you have a great personality, people will find it hard to see past a sloppy appearance. Putting thought into your appearance sends out *positive* messages.

EXTEND YOUR LEARNING

How a person 'appears' or dresses can influence how we perceive them. In most Western societies wearing a suit reflects professionalism, however this is not necessarily the case in all societies. Research different societies and find out the different types of dress code that are used for different occasions.

of calm, relaxation and total uniformity, wanting staff to wear corporate uniforms of a certain colour with little of no jewellery.

What is a stereotype?

The *Oxford English Dictionary* defines the word stereotype as: A standardised image or idea of a type of person.

A good example of how we *stereotype* people is how we perceive that any one who wears a 'hoody' is a young person looking for trouble, when in many cases this is not the so.

Habia

Professional hairdresser

How does stereotyping work?

Stereotyping is a way of representing or *categorising* other people. This may revolve around a certain *characteristic* of a group of people and not looking at them as individuals. Stereotyping often makes assumptions about people in very narrow terms such as: nationality, disability and sexual orientation. This can often lead to preset ideas or prejudices.

Prejudices are a preset opinion, especially a dislike, for a person for a specific reason such as race, religion or social group; this can often be formed because of a lack of understanding or by influences determined by others. The hair and beauty sector is all about customer care. We are responsible for working closely will all our clients to improve appearance and well-being, we work with all types of people and must not *discriminate* against any. A professional needs to understand their clients, to ensure that they have identified their requirements and delivered a professional, high quality service. If they don't, their clients may not return and the business may fail, leaving everyone out of work.

Communication is essential to all *interpersonal* contact. This includes people from different *social* and *cultural* backgrounds. People are increasingly on the move; they **migrate** to different areas in the same country or move to new countries. Businesses and the way we work have become more and more influenced by this change and many businesses have become **global**. This has created a need for us all to learn more about other cultures and how to effectively communicate with people from different cultural backgrounds. This is no different for the hair and beauty sector where it has become more *critical* to understand different cultures and different communication methods to ensure that a wide variety of people are encouraged to visit our spas and salons to become part of the growth in the business clientele.

ACTIVITY  

Discuss in a group your thoughts of stereotyping, reflect on those discussions and decide if stereotyping people leads to prejudice; for example: do all 'blondes' have more fun?

How to gain trust

The *Oxford English Dictionary* defines the word *trust* as: A firm belief in the reliability or truth or strength of a person, a confident expectation.

When a client comes to a salon, they are putting their trust in a professional to carry out a treatment or service that meets their expectations. To keep that trust, professionals must make sure that they build a rapport with their client. *Rapport* is defined as a sympathetic relationship or understanding between two people. Rapport cannot be touched or measured, but you know when it is there. Building rapport with client starts the minute that you meet. How you communicate will determine how the client will perceive you. You can make a client feel special and comfortable during their visit or you can make them feel unwanted, uncomfortable and angry. You determine how a client will react by how you communicate through speaking, listening and using body language.

Basic communication

Communication is the exchange of *information*, *ideas* or *feelings*. How we do this and the way we do it will affect our relationship with other people. There are different methods of communication and it is important that we use all of them to make sure that when we are giving or receiving information that we have interpreted it and understood correctly.

Verbal, non-verbal and physical communication

There are many ways to communicate with people, this will be by either **verbal communication** – by using your voice – or by **non-verbal communication** – how you express information through body language. In addition to these types of communication, there is a third method that is used in the hair and beauty sector – that of **physical communication**. This type of communication is about touch, and how we use our skills to enter a person's **personal space.** To communicate effectively in the hair and beauty sector, you will need to use all forms correctly to ensure that you give the correct information to clients.

Verbal communication

One to one communication is an important skill that is needed within the hair and beauty sector. Your voice can reveal your attitude and your emotions. A client will quickly identify your interest in them by the way you speak through the tone of your voice. To communicate effectively you should:

- keep information straight forward and simple
- speak clearly
- vary voice tone, pitch and volume
- speak with courtesy and confidence

- use professional vocabulary and not slang
- never speak while you are eating or chewing gum

Non-verbal communication

There are many forms of non-verbal communication, the majority of which professionals will use every day whilst at work in the salon or spa. These may include such things as:

- making an appointment or writing down a message
- gestures and facial expressions
- eye contact
- clothes and accessories

When you are visually communicating with people, your message is delivered in three ways: **body language**, your *tone of voice*, and the *words* you say.

Your body language will account for approximately 50 per cent of the information a person will receive. Your tone of voice will be approximately 40 per cent of the information received and the words you use will make up the remaining 10 per cent.

As you can see from the chart, body language is a very important part of communication. The way you stand, make eye contact and use your facial expressions will all give a message to people about you, about your attitude and emotions for example:

- a genuine smile lights up your face and conveys happiness and interest
- eye contact lets people know you are listening and interested in them
- your head tilted to one side will indicate that you are interested

Whereas:

- standing with hands on your hips can give the interpretation of aggression
- crossing your arms can make you appear defensive

Usually in the hair and beauty sector, if a client's body frame is loose or more widely spread they are generally more relaxed or at ease. However, if a client holds their body in a stiffer, rigid or more uptight position, they are usually experiencing nervousness, tension or discomfort for example:

- a client touching their face usually indicates anxiety
- a client clenching their fist indicates tension or aggression

Being able to interpret these signals and act on them to reassure or relax a client will help to create a good relationship.

Clothing, jewellery and accessories are also part of non-verbal communication. The moment you look at the person, you take in information about their appearance, the clothes they are wearing, the type jewellery or accessories.

Top tip

Never use a *condescending* or *patronising* voice tone, as this will make people feel uncomfortable and annoyed.

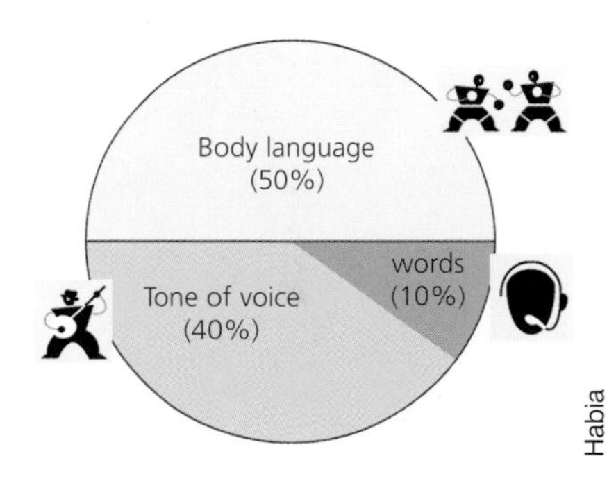

Habia

Using the images overleaf can you identify the signals that are being sent to other people. Discuss this with a partner.

Yawning

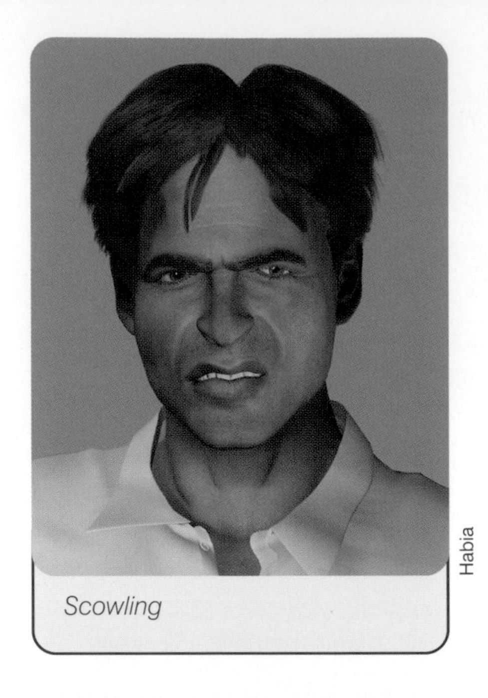
Scowling

Folded arms

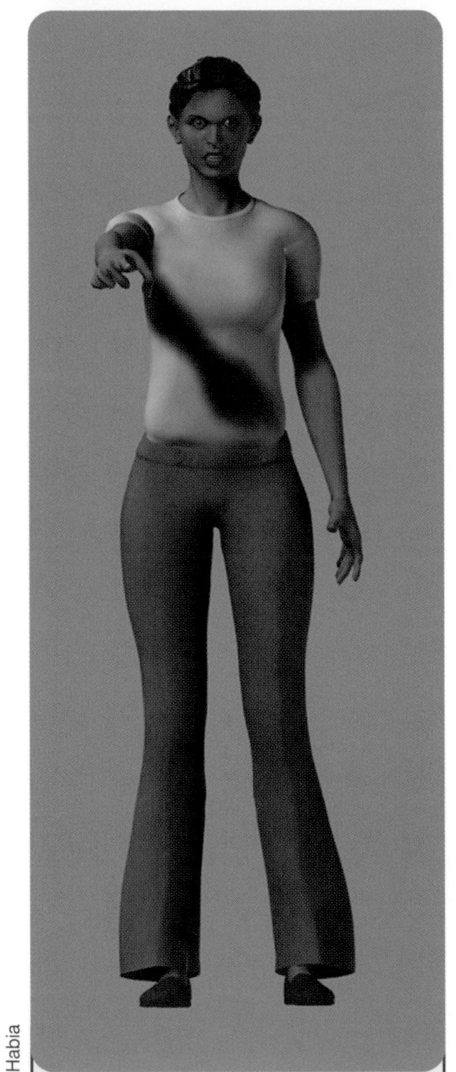
Pointing

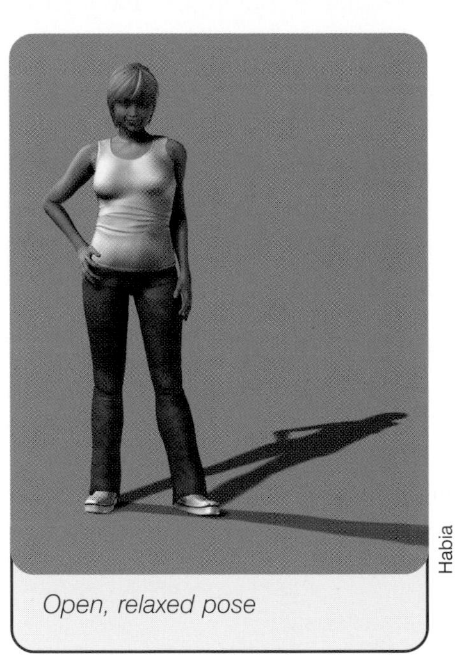
Open, relaxed pose

Smiling

Habia

Some accessories will be bold and vibrant, which may give you an indication that they are adventurous and outgoing. However, other people may wear discrete understated accessories and jewellery, which may give the impression that they would prefer a classic look rather than a contemporary look. A professional will use this information as part of their overall analysis during an initial consultation, to help build a picture. For example it will help a makeup artist to choose the types of colours and application techniques to use; it will help a hairdresser or barber to identify the types of styles that will suit and work well for the client; and help a nail technician identify the types of nail, nail colour or nail art that will work best for the client.

Physical communication

This type of communication is different and restricted to those who provide a service that requires them to have physical contact with their clients. In the hair and beauty sector physical communication is an important part of building up trust with clients. Clients know by the way they are touched by a person if that person is confident or unsure about what they are doing. At the beginning of your career in the hair and beauty sector this can be quite *intimidating*; you may not be used to touching strangers. It is important to learn how to enter a person's personal space without them feeling uncomfortable. The hair and beauty sector is a profession which requires you to work within a client's personal space.

Putting your hand on a client's shoulder or arm during a consultation will help break down *barriers*. This will help the client feel more relaxed so that you can then carry out *investigations* of the hair, skin or nails prior to carrying out a treatment or service. Identifying any problems at the consultation will enable discussions to take place on the need for any alterations to the treatment or service.

Non-verbal communication also includes two other important communication skills both of which are essential, they are *listening* skills and *reading* skills. You will have read about how you should talk to clients and how to use positive body language but, if professionals do not listen to what the client is saying, they will not provide the service or result that the client is looking for. They will miss vital parts of information such as sensitivity or dislike of certain products, the length of the fingernails during a manicure or that the client wants the stylist to disguise the length of the forehead with the fringe. Reading manufacturers' instructions and client record details and *extracting* the relevant information is vital to ensure safe working practice.

ACTIVITY  

Verbal and non-verbal communication – role play. Practise different methods of communication with a friend. Decide on a topic that you want to discuss. During the role play take turns in using different methods of communication. Can you identify when your partner is using positive and negative communication?

ACTIVITY 

Carry out a self assessment on your communication skills. What are your best communication skills? Which ones do you think you need to improve on? Discuss this with your teacher. Then develop an action plan to improve on your weakest skills and review your progress at different time intervals.

EXTEND YOUR LEARNING   

Neurolinguistic programming (NLP) examines different ways people think, feel and communicate with one another, and how this can build relationships. Research and then write a report on NLP. Do you think NLP could be used in a hair or beauty environment to help build relationships with clients or other people in the salon or spa?

Understanding how people communicate differently

Not everyone communicates in the same way. Some people are more expressive or *flamboyant* with their body language. Others may have a loud voice that booms or vibrates across a room. These *characteristics* could give you the impression that they are confident people. However, this is not always the case. Sometimes first impressions can be deceiving and it is not until you have had the opportunity to talk with them and review other forms of communication signals that you can truly make a judgement.

It is part of the role of a good therapist, technician or stylist to identify the best way to communicate with clients so that it builds a good relationship. For some clients this will be using visual aids such as style books or portfolios to draw out information to help explain what they want. For others the professional will listen carefully while the client gives detailed information about themselves and what they want.

Bring your learning to life

When you are on your work placement or in a salon environment, practise your communication skills with both clients and work colleagues. Keep a daily diary and note down how you have used different communication skills and what effect they had on other people. Discuss your findings with your teacher.

Communication with different client groups

The way you communicate with clients will often be determined by their age, *disability*, *gender* and *culture*.

If a client is a child it is important to treat them as individuals during the consultation. You will be gathering information not only from their parent or guardian but also from the child. It is important to make them feel comfortable and encourage two-way communication. It is also important to make eye contact and if possible talk to them at the same height level, which can be less threatening. Putting them at ease is important to encourage them to talk or respond to questions.

Some clients may have a disability that needs to be taken into consideration to ensure that communication is carried out effectively.

For people who are deaf or have a hearing impairment a professional stylist, therapist or technician will make sure they:

- have the person's attention before talking
- look at the person they are talking to
- don't mumble, or eat while talking
- use simple language and short sentences
- turn down any music or try to avoid background noise
- use style books or portfolios, visual clues and gestures to aid understanding
- write down questions or responses if necessary

For people with mobility limitations they will make sure they:

- sit at the same level
- make eye contact
- treat a wheelchair as the client's personal space
- talk naturally to the person in the wheelchair, not their companion

It's a fact! Did you know that the OK gesture may have different meanings in different cultures?

- In the United Kingdom and United States of America = OK
- In Japan = money
- In Russia = zero
- In Brazil = insult

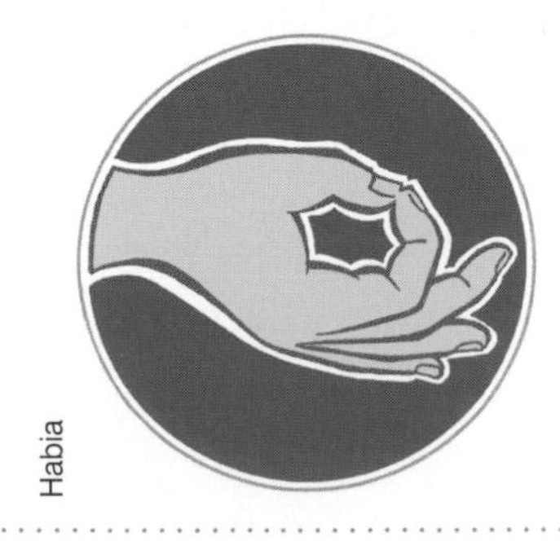

Habia

For people with sight impairments they will make sure they:

- touch them on the arm to indicate they are there and going to talk to them
- offer them an arm to lead them to the work area
- make sure the area is free of any obstacles which they may trip over
- make sure they use simple terminology that the client will understand when giving advice. Remember that the client may not be able to see hand gestures and images used help explain ideas or to confirm understanding
- if possible use touch to confirm information

Being aware of different cultures and not assuming that everyone is '*just like me*' will also give you a greater understanding of people and communication skills. Culture can refer to religion, social, political and family customs. To build a client relationship it is necessary to respect differences. Different cultures have different perceptions on many issues such as interpersonal distance or personal comfort zone. Some cultures use bowing as a form of greeting while others may shake hands, hug or kiss as a method of greeting.

Remember everyone communicates differently. Some people will talk in short sentences that are structured and to the point, while other people like to tell a story that combines different information. In the latter case you will need to listen carefully and extract the important facts needed to determine what the person is actually trying to tell you.

EXTEND YOUR LEARNING

Many different cultures use different gestures. Research the different gestures and the meanings that they may have in different cultures.

Top tip

When talking to people you do not know well, avoid conversations or stating an opinion on topics that are sensitive and could cause offence such as religion, racial remarks, sex and politics

How the hair and beauty sector communicates with the general public

The hair and beauty sector is made up of industries that work with individual clients on a one to one basis. The sector is mainly small businesses and they rely on their good reputation to maintain and increase their business, this is often done through *personal recommendation*. This is when clients pass on their comments and recommendations to friends and acquaintances. Salons will also use their local newspapers and magazines to promote the business and advertise special events that are taking place, such as an open day with special offers. Larger organisations or businesses that have **franchise** arrangements of salons/spas in different parts of the country will not only use local advertising but will also use national papers and magazines to promote the company as a whole, such as offering a discount for clients visiting any of the salons within the group. Salons and spas can also increase public awareness by getting involved in industry awards that increase the *status* of the business. Individuals can raise their own profile and that of their business by winning awards or appearing on local or national TV. There are a number of TV programmes that involve the guest appearance of stylists and makeup artists as part of make-over teams. Once recognised, these individuals are often used to promote skin and hair products and equipment to the general public. Manufactures such as L'Oréal will use large advertising campaigns in magazines and on TV to promote there products. They often use celebrities from popular TV programmes or film stars to sell a concept.

ACTIVITY 

Image you are a salon owner or manager. Working on you own or in a group, design an advertising campaign to promote a special offer or an event. The campaign could include an advert for the local paper, a poster or a form of display. Present your campaign to your teacher and classmates.

EXTEND YOUR LEARNING 

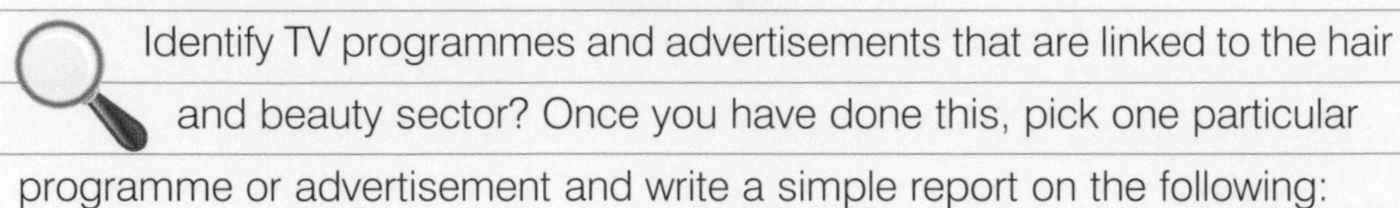

Identify TV programmes and advertisements that are linked to the hair and beauty sector? Once you have done this, pick one particular programme or advertisement and write a simple report on the following:

- What is the programme or advertisement about?
- Does it increase the profile of the hair and beauty sector as a whole, an individual industry within the sector or an individual person?

Top tip Professional hairdressers make their clients feel at ease by sitting next to their clients during the consultation process. For example in hairdressing, standing over the client can sometimes feel intimidating, as the stylist often ends up using eye to eye contact with the client and talking to the client through the mirror as they stand behind the chair.

Consulting with clients

The purpose of consulting with clients prior to the service or treatment is to find out exactly what their wishes are and if these can be achieved. To do this a professional stylist, therapist or technician will need to:

- examine the client's skin, nails or hair and scalp depending on the service or treatment
- decide on the most suitable service or treatment and the techniques to use to create the result
- decide on the most suitable tools and equipment needed to achieve the result
- decide what products will be needed and advise the client
- advise the client on the homecare maintenance procedures they will need to follow

The *consultation process* is an important part of any treatment or service, get it wrong and the business will have a dissatisfied and unhappy client. When practising your consultation skills, make sure you introduce yourself and show that you are interested in the client and their personal needs.

Using open and closed questions

As described above, there are many forms of communication that can be used to put a client at ease as well as to gather information. When practising your consultation technique, it is important that all forms of communication are used, firstly to make the client feel welcome and relaxed – especially if they are a new client.

During the consultation it is important that you use a variety of different questions to ensure you gather the correct information. Some clients will find it easy to respond to your questions and will give you clear guidance on their requirements and expectations, while other clients will find it difficult to explain and may feel a little intimidated by the salon or spa environment. The use of **open questions** will help clients to explain any difficulties they may have with their skin, nails or hair and what changes they would like.

Open questions

Open questions can start with any one of the following words:

- **who**
- **what**
- **where**
- **would**
- **when**
- **how**

Any question starting with these words will automatically encourage the client to give more information that a 'yes' or 'no' response. You will probably need to ask further additional open questions to build up a full picture of the client's requirements. Here are some examples of the types of open questions you can ask your client:

Hair and barbering questions:

- How would you like your hair today?
- When did you last have your hair cut?
- Would you like to change your current hair style?
- Can you tell me a little bit about your lifestyle? What type of job do you have?
- Would you like to look at a style book to help explain what your likes or dislikes are?

Beauty and spa questions:

- What is your skin care routine at home?
- What is your main concerns regarding your skin?
- Are you generally in good health?
- Do you have any known allergies or skin sensitivity?
- What are your main expectations?
- Would you like me to make some suggestions to the treatments we offer and the expected results we can achieve?

Nail service questions:

- What is your nail care routine at home?
- Are there any areas that cause you problems or concern?
- Do you have any known allergies or skin sensitivity?
- How would you like your nails to look, what shape do you prefer?

- What colour varnish would you like me to use?
- Would you like me to make some suggestions?

There are many types of questions you can ask. Once you start asking open questions the response from the client will lead you on to the next question. Do not be in a hurry and miss out questioning the client, as this could lead to an unhappy ending.

Closed questions

Closed questions are used to gain a limited amount of response, such as 'yes' or 'no'. They are useful to confirm your understanding of an earlier answer or to confirm the treatment or service with the client by repeating what has been agreed.

Here are some examples of closed questions you can ask a client:

- You are having a manicure today?
- Do you usually have your hair parting on the left?
- Do you want me to show you how to apply the products so that you can do it yourself at home between visits?
- Do you want your nails any shorter?

When you have asked the client questions and listened to the responses, make sure that you confirm the information that you have heard so that both you and the client have understood each other and are clear about the treatment or service agreed before starting.

Using visual aids

Top tip Hair and beauty professionals will always listen carefully to the client during a consultation and they will then confirm information with the client to show that they have understood. In hairdressing one of the main complaints from clients is that their hair stylist cut the hair too short and did not listen to them.

Using **visuals aids** during consultation can be another way of communicating with a client. Not all clients find it easy to explain how they would like their hair, makeup or nails. Style books and **portfolios** of your work are useful to help gather information. Use them to help to confirm your ideas such as:

- Do you want your makeup this bold for your event?
- In this picture, the image shows the eyes more dominant than the lips – which do you prefer?

However, when using visual aids to confirm the client's requirements, make sure the client is agreeing to *individual aspects* within the picture and not the *total image*. For example, you may be showing the client the effect of a fringe within a hairstyle but the client is seeing a stunning looking model, and has not fully focused just on the fringe detail – their mind may be agreeing to the total image in the picture and not their individual requirements.

Advice and after care

As part of the professional service a stylist, therapist or technician will always explain to the client how best to look after their hair, skin or nails at home and what types of products they should use to help them maintain the results of the treatment or service they have given. When talking about the product they will explain to the client how much to use and how to apply it to achieve the best results. They will explain the different techniques or routines they can use at home to maintain and prolong the condition and look of the hair, skin or nails. It is then up to the client to take and use the advice given, but if a professional has done their job well and gained the trust of their clients, the client is more likely to use the advice given and be happier with the whole service provided.

Top tip

Professionals in the hair and beauty sector will always record the details of the consultation process and actions taken along with the outcomes of any tests carried out. The records are always securely stored so that they can be used at the next visit.

ACTIVITY

Role play for consultation

With a friend practise carrying out a consultation service for either a skin treatment, hair or nail service. Don't forget to:

- speak clearly
- vary your voice tone
- speak with courtesy and confidence
- use professional vocabulary and not slang
- never speak while you are eating or chewing gum
- use positive body language
- use your listening skills

Swap over roles and at the end when you have both had a turn, discuss the outcome and give feedback on how well you each performed.

What you have learnt

Why it is importance to create a positive and lasting impression

- How we form opinions of people
- What is stereotyping and how it works
- How appearance, style and image has a impact on our working lives

What is trust

- The importance of building trust in a client relationship

The different types of communication

- Verbal and non-verbal communication
- Physical communication
- Understanding how people communicate differently
- How to communication with different client groups

How to consult with clients to find out your client's needs and wishes

- When and how to use open and closed questions
- What are visual aids and when to use them

The importance of giving your client advice and after care information

Assessment activities

Crossword

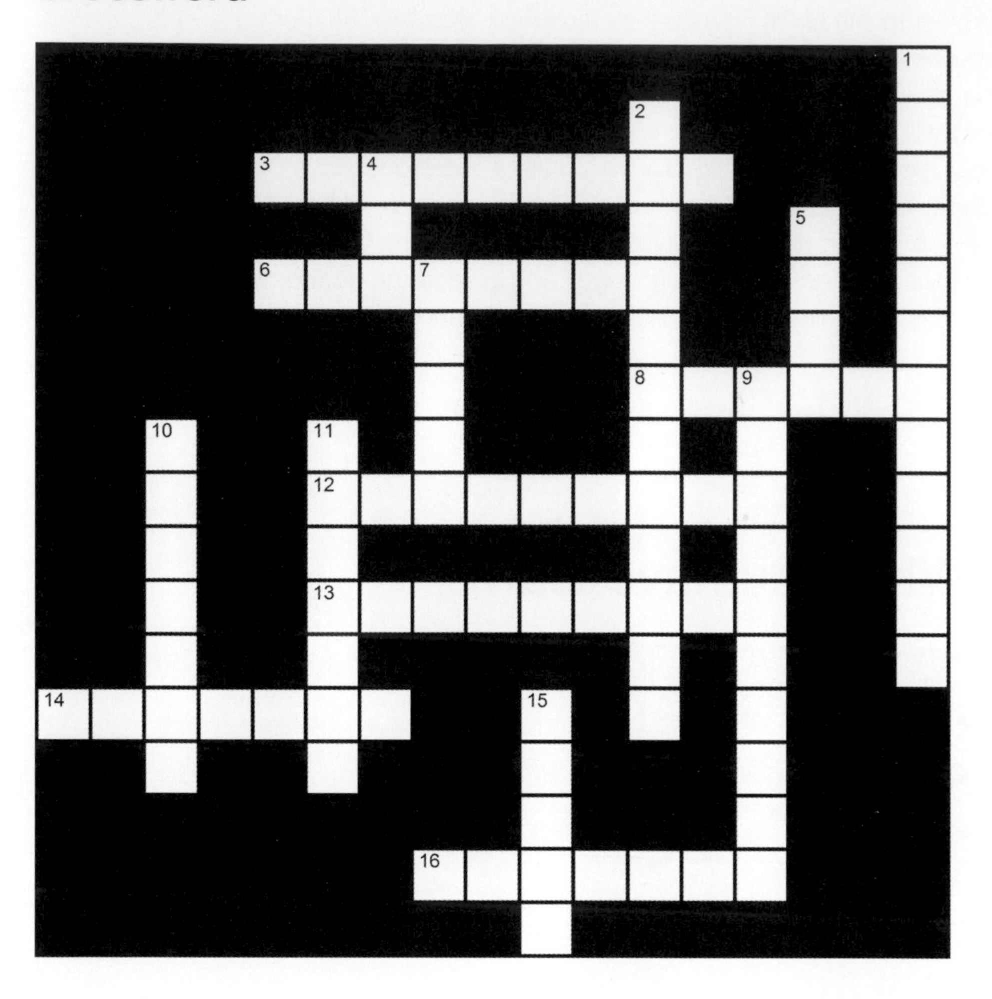

Across

3 Type of visual aid (5,4)

6 Non-verbal communication (8)

8 Some people hear but don't always ... (6)

12 Maintenance advice (9)

13 Predetermined opinion or dislike (9)

14 Make sure information is correct (7)

16 Religion, social, political or family customs (7)

Down

1 Tells people something about you (4,8)

2 Used to find out information prior to a service (12)

4 Response used for closed questions (3)

5 Word used in open questions (4)

7 A firm belief in a person (5)

9 An image or view of a type of person (10)

10 Verbal communication (7)

11 Understanding between two people (7)

15 Conveys happiness and interest (5)

Wordsearch

L	C	O	M	M	U	N	I	C	A	T	I	O	N	J	Q	P	E	H	E	M	Y	A
A	X	R	L	O	G	E	D	E	G	D	K	O	E	Q	A	O	L	K	V	Z	X	Y
N	G	S	E	H	P	L	B	E	F	K	F	B	S	O	X	C	T	R	U	S	T	D
O	H	F	W	S	T	I	K	J	E	C	N	E	D	I	F	N	O	C	Q	U	M	R
I	X	J	U	A	T	M	B	A	I	M	R	V	J	C	U	L	T	U	R	E	E	O
S	M	J	D	S	A	S	B	O	N	U	R	X	M	T	N	R	Z	X	Z	A	S	C
S	Q	S	R	S	L	J	D	L	T	B	J	S	L	A	N	G	U	A	G	E	S	E
E	G	H	Q	E	K	J	D	S	V	G	F	I	B	O	B	E	Y	L	H	M	A	R
F	N	O	W	S	I	N	E	L	A	C	I	S	Y	H	P	N	M	Y	T	E	G	S
O	O	U	G	S	N	G	C	K	Z	D	T	U	I	Z	S	Z	D	E	N	P	E	Y
R	I	T	A	M	G	Q	J	C	L	I	E	N	T	C	A	R	E	O	G	L	Z	Y
P	S	I	W	E	N	A	W	J	A	A	X	P	A	F	M	J	T	U	S	D	M	U
N	S	N	I	N	F	O	R	M	A	T	I	O	N	Y	Z	M	Y	K	X	Y	U	N
C	E	G	T	T	Q	E	I	Y	R	M	E	D	I	A	O	P	D	P	Z	E	B	J
C	R	P	T	N	E	M	E	S	I	T	R	E	V	D	A	B	K	J	O	M	X	N
G	P	Q	Y	P	Z	S	P	N	S	T	S	U	O	I	N	O	M	R	A	H	M	Y
I	M	C	W	T	D	H	I	O	D	E	Z	H	A	J	G	J	K	A	X	Y	D	C
Z	I	I	F	C	O	H	X	K	S	X	R	U	C	W	O	Y	F	Z	L	S	P	O
S	D	C	Q	E	V	E	V	H	U	I	A	P	E	U	J	R	X	X	S	F	O	N
N	X	S	T	P	P	A	R	V	A	G	T	A	X	Y	O	J	I	Q	X	Q	I	T
P	G	A	V	S	N	S	O	E	H	J	B	I	J	E	Y	T	K	W	L	F	N	A
X	H	T	F	E	C	O	X	T	T	Z	L	J	V	Q	H	A	X	N	O	X	T	C
J	N	A	R	R	H	K	E	C	S	S	G	X	L	E	A	W	Q	W	I	F	T	T

Advertisement
Assessment
Clientcare
Communication
Confidence
Contact
Culture
Expression
Flamboyant
Gestures

Harmonious
Impression
Information
Judgement
Language
Media
Message
Physical
Point
Positive

Professional
Record
Respect
Shouting
Smile
Stereotype
Talking
Tone
Touch
Trust

Assessment activity: Effective communication

Draw a table. In the first column list six essential attributes for effective communication. In the second column give an example of how you use them in the working environment.

Once you have completed the table, use your information in a group discussion to see if you all identified similar information and examples. Add any useful additional information you have gained from the group discussion to your table.

7

skin care and makeup

Adam Harris @ MG Martin Gold, Stanmore

Beauty is not in the face: beauty is a light in the heart.

KAHLIL GIBRAN 1883–1931, LEBANESE POET AND AUTHOR OF 'THE PROPHET'

Introduction

The world of skin care and makeup can be glamorous and exciting. It is a world full of thousands of different ranges of skin care and millions of makeup products. There are so many different looks and images you can explore, depending on whether you want to go for a natural look or be a glamorous glittering diva!

Looking after your skin is important when you want to look your best, and makeup can be used to enhance your features. How you wear makeup can say a lot about you. You can decide which image suits your personality or culture. You can have fun changing your look to suit different occasions and moods.

Your creative skills can be used when doing makeup and you'll have fun developing new ideas and looks. These techniques can be extended to help others to make the best of themselves – and it is so rewarding. Sometimes, if individuals think they look better, then they feel better and can have more confidence. The effect can be so profound that some people who have a 'make-over' can feel more positive and even try new things to improve their life.

In this chapter you will learn about the skills and knowledge that will help you care for your skin and apply makeup for different occasions. Then, you will learn how, if you develop these skills and study further, you can become a professional beauty therapist and care for the skin of others or, as a top makeup artist, work on a cruise ship or in an international spa resort. As the saying goes – the world is your oyster!

What you are going to learn

This chapter will include:

- ★ **How to identify the factors that affect skin care services**
- ★ **How to select skin care products and techniques for different skin types**
- ★ **How to carry out a basic skin care routine**
- ★ **How to choose and apply makeup products to achieve different looks**
- ★ **How to use products, tools and equipment for skin care and makeup**
- ★ **The terminology related to skin care and beauty services**

Skin care

Your lifestyle can be reflected in the appearance of your skin. You can't eat an unhealthy diet and stay out late every night, and still expect your skin to be clear and glowing. Your skin can be a good indicator of what is going on inside your body. Thinking about what is happening internally is vital, but it is also very important to look after the skin from the outside, making sure it is really clean and well nourished. Every day dirt, sweat, oil and makeup can build up on the surface of the skin, and can lead to skin problems if you don't follow a good skin care routine.

To be able to care for the skin and improve its appearance, you need to know about the structure of the skin and its function. You will learn all about the structure of the skin and its main characteristics in Chapter 4 'The science of hair and beauty'.

Clear and glowing skin is very attractive

Factors that affect skin care services

There are certain factors that affect skin care. These factors have to be taken into consideration before you begin any treatments. If you are aware of these factors, you will know that the skin care advice and treatment you provide is suitable for the client, and will enhance their appearance.

The factors you must consider are:

- **skin type (see Chapter 4)**
- **lifestyle**

- skin conditions that may affect skin care (see Chapter 4)
- skin allergies (see Chapter 4)

Lifestyle

Do you have a healthy lifestyle? How busy are you? Do you do everything you can to have healthy glowing skin?

When considering your skin care routine it is important to look at your lifestyle. How you live your life can show on your skin. Usually if you eat a healthy balanced diet, drink plenty of water, take regular exercise and get lots of fresh air, your skin will be clear and glowing with good health.

It's a fact!

Your skin can be affected by many factors, including

Poor nutrition	Smoking	Alcohol
Stress	Medication/drugs	Illness
Hormonal changes	Extreme weather	Poor skin care
Central heating	Sunburn	Lack of fresh air

You also need to think about how busy you are when it comes to how you will care for your skin. A complicated routine will not fit in with your life if you are juggling lots of activities such as studying, working part-time and hobbies or sport.

A simple but effective routine is best, so that it fits neatly into your everyday habits. And remember it only takes 30 days to start a habit. Your skin care routine should be as easy as brushing your teeth, done twice a day to get the best results … glowing skin!

iStockphoto.com/Vladimir Piskunov

Your lifestyle will affect your skin

EXTEND YOUR LEARNING

Research the effects of smoking on the skin. Design a leaflet to show the harmful effects on the skin, and to encourage young people not to smoke. Make your leaflet as hard hitting as necessary to get your point across. Look at **www.quitsmoking.about.com** to help you.

iStockphoto.com/Anna Bryukhanova

Healthy eating reflects in your skin

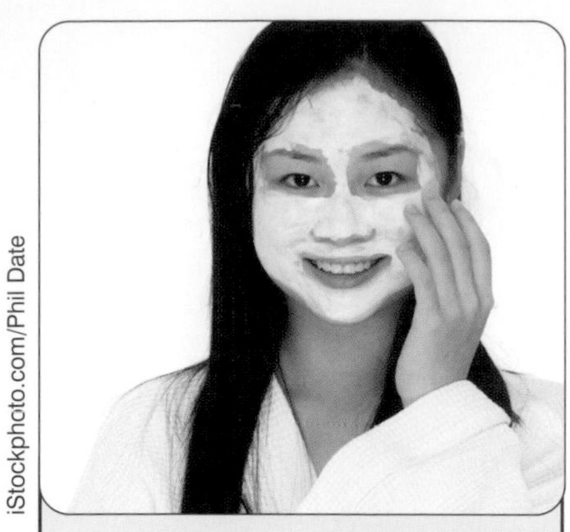
iStockphoto.com/Phil Date

Get into the habit of looking after your skin

Start when you are young, so you try and avoid many of the problems of teenage skin. You need to set the foundations for a lifetime of good skin care that will enhance your appearance and delay the signs of ageing. Get into the habit … you will soon see the results!

Skin conditions that may affect skin care

Contra-indications

A **contra-indication** is a condition that prevents a treatment from being carried out.

You must be aware of all the contra-indications to a facial and makeup, so that the treatment is carried out with full regard for the client's safety and well-being. Each individual is assessed so that the treatment can be adapted to meet their individual needs. If there is any concern about their health, you should advise them to seek medical advice.

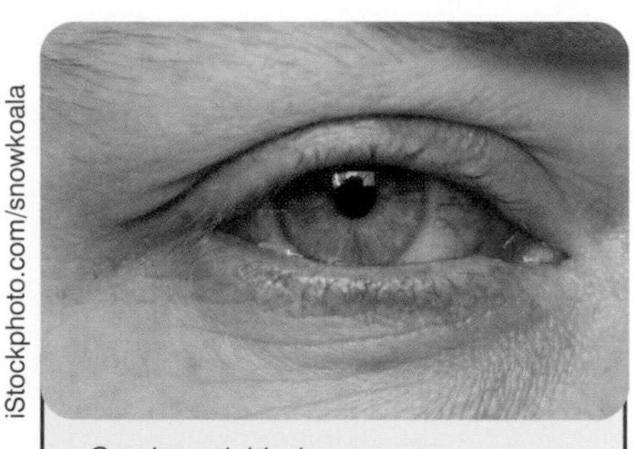
iStockphoto.com/snowkoala

Conjunctivitis is a contra-indication to a facial treatment

Contra-indications can be divided into three categories:

- **General** – contra-indications that affect the entire body. Treatment cannot be carried out whilst these conditions exist.
- **Local** – contra-indications that only involve a 'local' area of the face or body, a facial could be carried out as long as the area was avoided.
- **Temporary** – contra-indications that don't last very long, for example treatment is temporarily stopped, but can be carried out once the condition clears up.

There are many skin conditions that can affect skin care. You can find the details in Chapter 4 'The science of hair and beauty'.

It's a fact! Blemishes and spots can sometimes be the result of hormonal changes in the body.

Other factors that may affect the condition of the skin

Personality

The body must be at ease internally, as any 'unease' can be reflected in the external appearance. If someone is very nervous, shy, anxious or under pressure leading to stress, then it may show in their skin. Blemishes may appear on the skin, or spots may develop.

As well as a good skin care routine, it is vital that the cause of the stress is identified, so that the person can start to feel more relaxed, confident and can get their life in balance.

iStockphoto.com/Thomas Gordon

How we view beauty is influenced by our culture

Cultural influences

Cultural influences can impact on all aspects of our lives. For example, how beauty is perceived, what features are considered beautiful or how we enhance our appearance will vary from one culture to another. In addition, the use of skin products and makeup may or may not be totally acceptable or tolerated – they may even be discouraged. Certain cultures may frown on the use of skin care products, as they are seen as too superficial and frivolous and encouraging vanity. In other cultures, however, mothers pass skin care secrets and techniques down to their children as soon as they reach puberty, so they develop good skin hygiene and try to avoid teenage blemishes. You can read more about culture and identity in Chapter 1 'The history of hair and beauty'.

It's a fact!

The Javanese believe that a bride should be at her most clean, pampered and beautiful on her wedding day, so they have a **Lulur** treatment every day in the week leading up to the wedding. A 'Lulur' is a traditional treatment, ideally for younger skins and usually combines a massage, spice-wrap, yoghurt coated scrub and blossom-filled bath. After this treatment the skin is left soft, supple and shining with moisture.

A lulur treatment

It's a fact!

There are certain conditions that although they don't prevent facial treatments, they do restrict what you can offer – these include: dermatitis, eczema, psoriasis, acne rosacea and scar tissue.

Hereditary factors

We inherit many characteristics from our parents, which includes skin type. It may be that the family have a darker skin tone, tan easily and have a tendency to thicker, oilier skin. On the other hand, your family may have very fair, sensitive skin with freckles, that is prone to burning, and you need to protect your skin to avoid damage and premature ageing.

Gender

Men are becoming more aware of the benefits of looking after their skin, their body and general health. A huge industry is growing around male skin care and the specialist products developed to meet the needs of these clients. The media has helped change perceptions, and any previous sensitivity about not wanting to appear too vain has disappeared. A 'groomed' appearance has become an aspiration for many young men.

A man's skin can often appear much thicker, with a coarse texture. Very often, particularly in younger men, the skin may be oily, with blackheads and open pores. The skin may develop sensitivity due to shaving, and sporty men may

iStockphoto.com/Eva Serrabassa

Men are now more aware of the benefits of looking after their skin

iStockphoto.com/Mark Papas

We can learn a lot about our skin from our parents and grandparents

iStockphoto.com/Josh Webb

Regular exercise and fresh air is good for your skin

need to moisturise more because of the dehydrating effects of conditions when, for example, running, skiing, windsurfing, cycling or climbing.

Health

Your overall health is reflected in your skin, and if you are feeling under the weather or have been ill for some time, then your skin will suffer. The skin needs a good blood supply bringing oxygen and nutrients to every cell. Any condition that disrupts this nourishment will have a detrimental effect on the appearance and health of the skin.

It is vital that you eat healthily, drink plenty of water and get regular exercise and fresh air. A healthy balanced diet is essential, containing vitamins such as vitamin C which is said to improve skin healing, and vitamin E which has been used in creams for many years to improve skin condition.

EXTEND YOUR LEARNING  

In the media recently there have been details of experts who are 'face readers' and can analyse body health by studying the face. They then make recommendations about how to improve general health and restore balance to the body. Conduct research into this new technique, find out as much as you can, and then share your findings with your group/colleagues.

iStockphoto.com/Juanmonino

Skin can still glow well into your forties

Age

As we get older changes in the lower layers of the skin reduce its elasticity. The skin usually dries out and starts to show visible signs of ageing such as wrinkles, folds, thicker skin, lack of muscle tone, uneven **pigmentation** and often an increase in broken capillaries.

Skin care companies are continually trying to develop products that minimise the signs of ageing and will restore the skin to a more youthful condition, such as anti-wrinkle creams and anti-ageing serums. When you are young, if you do not care for your skin, it will age much quicker and you may appear much older than you really are.

Society generally encourages the pursuit of a youthful appearance, and so increasingly people are looking for 'miracle' creams that hold the answer to eternal youth.

EXTEND YOUR LEARNING   

Working in a small team, conduct research into four different ranges of skin care. Compare the ranges, including number of products, price, target customer and, if you get the opportunity, conduct some blind tests, finding out which range people prefer when asked to compare.

Skin allergies

Many people can be sensitive to the products used for skin care, facial treatments and makeup. Even if they have never been sensitive before, they can develop an allergy to a product and have a reaction. It may be that they have absorbed something into their body, or have applied a substance directly on to the skin. Substances known to have caused allergic reactions include:

- metal (containing nickel)
- lanolin (in many creams and lotions)
- hair dye
- lipsticks (can contain the dye eosin)
- gum, rubber, sticking plasters
- perfume
- foods e.g. shellfish, strawberries, peanuts
- eye makeup (can contain strong pigments or pearlised ingredients)

By law, any substance known to cause irritation has to be listed on the packaging, along with any recommended precautions.

It's a fact!

For no apparent reason you may start to be allergic to a product that you have used safely for many years. Likewise you may stop being allergic to a substance that you have always been sensitive to. Nothing is forever, the body is constantly changing.

It's a fact!

If a professional beauty therapist is at all concerned that someone may be sensitive to a product, then they carry out a 'sensitivity test'. Read Chapter 4 to see how to carry out a sensitivity test.

EXTEND YOUR LEARNING

Research 'Cobalt blue' to see which cosmetics contain this pigment?

Many people are sensitive to perfume in skin products

Preparing the treatment area

When preparing your treatment area for a facial treatment, you will need to ensure the environment is suitable. Do you have an individual room for the treatment? Or will you need to ensure there are screens/curtains for privacy? Is there a sink close to the treatment area, as you will need to wash your hands?

Make sure the temperature is nice and warm, but not too stuffy, or with any cold draughts. The lighting should be soft and not too harsh, as it would not be relaxing for the client having the facial. If possible a dimmer switch is ideal to dim the lights for a facial, then to brighten them for the makeup application. Fragranced candles can enhance the atmosphere, and make it a more relaxed setting, as can suitable background music.

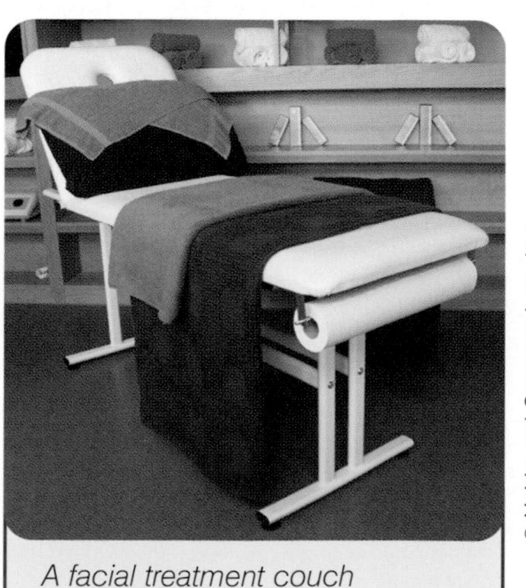

A facial treatment couch

Equipment and materials

It is good practice to make sure you have all the equipment you need ready and prepared before you start a treatment. You will then appear very organised, efficient and professional. For the facial treatment you need to have the following items ready for the client:

1. **Linen/duvet/blankets** – Clean bedding to keep the client protected and warm whilst having a facial.
2. **Towels** – Plenty of clean, soft, fluffy towels should be available, but do not use too many as it adds to the cost of the treatment.
3. **Clean gown/bathrobe** – For the client's modesty and comfort, a warm gown can be worn until they are under the duvet/sheet.
4. **Lined swing waste-bin** – Essential for hygienically disposing of waste.
5. **Steriliser** – Essential for ensuring equipment and tools are sterile, to prevent the spread of infection.

Set up the treatment area with the following specialised equipment:

EQUIPMENT	USE	BENEFITS	TIP	IMAGE
Treatment bed/couch/ beauty chair	A comfortable bed on which the treatment is carried out. It needs to be easy to clean	Can be adjusted to suit the comfort of the individual, so they totally relax during the treatment. A hydraulic bed is available that can be lowered to make it easier to get on	For extra comfort use a duvet under the body, it will feel like they are floating on a cloud!	© Habia and Cengage Learning
Equipment trolley	Specially designed trolley/table with shelves to hold all the tools and products. Should be easy to clean	Easy to move around the bed, so your tools and products are all in one place, and close at hand	Keep a spare pillow and extra towels on the bottom shelf so you don't need to interrupt your treatment. Have a fragranced candle on the trolley to help make the atmosphere more relaxing	© Habia and Cengage Learning

Beauty stool/chair	A special chair/stool designed for carrying out beauty treatments	Much easier to perform treatments, it is comfortable, with an adjustable height and has a back rest	Check out the stools that are designed to help your posture, some have knee supports and ensure your back is in the correct position	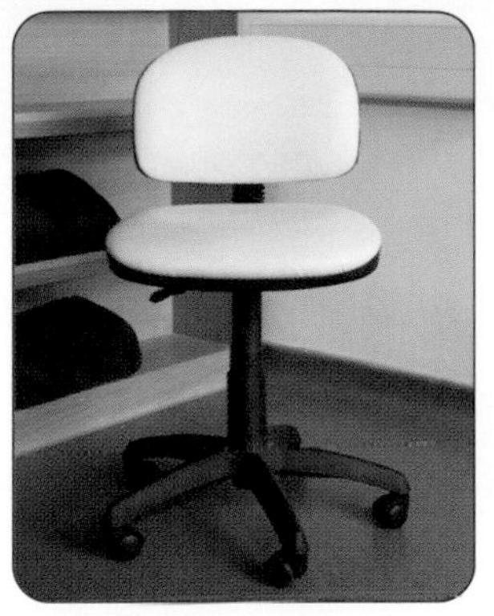 © Habia and Cengage Learning
Magnifying lamp	Special lamp used for 'skin analysis', as the skin features are enlarged and easier to analyse	Beneficial when doing a skin analysis, as the skin's features are enlarged and therefore easier to analyse	The light is very bright, so cover the person's eyes with cotton wool or tissues, to make the skin analysis more comfortable	 Sorisa

On the trolley make sure you have prepared the following:

1 **Spatulas** – clean spatulas to remove product from jars or containers
2 **Bowls** – selection of sizes, usually to hold jewellery, cotton wool and water for mask removal
3 **Headband** – protects and keeps hair secure, and out of the way of facial products
4 **Removal sponges** – sterilised sponges to remove the face mask
5 **Cotton wool (dry and damp)** – prepare plenty of cotton wool for the entire treatment
6 **Cotton buds** – necessary for removing any makeup close to the lashes.
7 **Tissues** – prepare plenty, to last the entire treatment. Double tissues can be split for economy
8 **Mask brush** – a specialised brush for applying mask to the face and neck
9 **Hand mirror** – essential for consulting with the client whilst analysing the skin type, during the treatment and at the end of the facial

In addition you need to make sure you have the following skincare products on the trolley:

1 **Eye makeup remover** – often a gel or oil-based solution that easily removes eye makeup
2 **Skin cleanser** – have a range available to suit all skin types

Have all the specialised products ready for the treatment

3 **Skin toner** – have a range available – astringent toners and more gentler freshners to suit all skin types

4 **Moisturiser** – a blend of oil and water, lighter ones suit younger and oilier skins. As the skin dries and ages, heavier, richer creams are used, or anti-wrinkle specialist creams

5 **Scrub** – have available scrubs that suit both normal to dry and normal to oily skins. Be careful the product isn't too harsh as it can cause sensitivity

6 **Face mask** – Prepared face masks are very effective, and usually available in a range to suit different skin types

Consultation

Consultation

Before you start any treatment you should carry out a consultation. This will ensure it is safe to perform the treatment, and that it can be tailored to the needs of the client. You will need to make sure you gather all the details at the initial consultation. It is so important that the client feels relaxed, and that you put them at ease during the consultation. This is the start of your relationship with them, so it is vital that you are warm, friendly, approachable and professional.

When carrying out a consultation, make sure that:

- the area is quiet and relaxing
- you have allocated plenty of time
- the person feels comfortable and at ease
- a thorough skin analysis is carried out
- the overall aims of the treatment and outcomes are discussed
- a treatment plan is developed
- the record card is filled in
- the record card is signed
- contra-indications are checked
- contra-actions have been explained
- there is an opportunity for any questions

ACTIVITY

Plan a list of questions you would ask during the initial consultation. Then, with a partner, take it in turns to ask and answer questions so that you become more confident in your manner.

Record card

A record card is completed at the initial consultation, and then up-dated after each visit. The record card is a very important document. It means there is a record of all the treatments provided, how the client reacted to the treatment and it records any adaptations made during the treatment. In Chapter 3, 'Salon Business Systems and Processes', you can read more about paper based record cards and those linked to a computer based reception management system.

BEAUTY RECORD CARD

Name: Age: Telephone Number:

Address:

PERSONAL DOCTOR

Name:

Address:

Tel. No:

DETAILS OF PRESCRIBED DRUGS

MEDICAL HISTORY

Height: Weight: Chest: Waist: Hips:

Heart Disease: Yes ☐ No ☐

Varicose Veins: Yes ☐ No ☐

Details of Operations:

Other Comments:

Example of a record card

Skin analysis

It is important to carry out a thorough skin analysis before deciding on what products to use, or which facial treatments would be beneficial. You will need to be looking at all the skin characteristics in each area of the face and neck, and then decide on the overall skin type.

Example of a Skin Analysis sheet:

SKIN ANALYSIS

Name:		**DOB:**	**Address:**		
Area of face/neck	Texture	Colour	Blemishes	Sensitivity	Type
Chin					
Nose					
Forehead					
Cheeks					
Eyes					
Neck					
General elasticity:			General colour:		
Overall skin type:			Cause/comments:		
Comments/notes					
Date of skin analysis:			Student:		

Note: *As the skin improves and changes over the coming weeks/ months, revisit this Analysis form, and if necessary fill a new one in and staple it to the record card (or input it on to the computer system if appropriate).*

The skin analysis will help you select all the products you need

Treatment plan

When planning to carry out a facial, the consultation is a very important stage, and involves you filling in a record card and carrying out the skin analysis. You then need to complete a treatment plan, so that you know exactly what you are going to concentrate on, what treatment is best, what products you will use and the expected outcome. A simple treatment plan that you could use when offering facial treatments is shown here:

TREATMENT PLAN

Priorities for treatment:	
Aim of treatment:	
What treatment is planned?	
What products to be used in the salon:	**Details of use:**
Makeup remover	
Cleanser	
Toner/moisturiser	
Scrub/exfoliant	
Mask	
Night cream	
Eye products	
Specialised products	
Suggested time between treatments?	
Course of treatments?	
Final result? (desired outcome achieved?)	
Advice given:	
Comments:	
Student signature:	**Date:**
Use prescription sheet for retail recommendations, and home care advice leaflet.	

Skin care products

From carrying out a skin analysis, you will have decided on the overall skin type. Then you need to select the best and most effective products for the skin type. Read Chapter 4 to find out all about the science behind the products you will use in a facial.

Cleansers

There are a variety of different type of cleansers, which are usually a mixture of oil and water with an emulsifier

- *Cleaning lotion* – a strong astringent type cleanser that is more effective for oily and congested skins
- *Cleaning milk* – a gentler, milky type that is effective on young skin types but may be too drying for older skins
- *Cleansing cream* – a heavier type of cleanser, more effective for dry and mature skins
- *Foaming cleanser* – becomes a mousse when mixed with water. Suitable for those who don't feel clean unless they have lathered up with a foam and water. Very cleansing and pleasant to use, effective on combination and oily skins

Cleanser

Courtesy of Guinot

Toners

Toners can vary in strength but all are designed to refresh the skin, remove any remains of cleanser and tighten pores.

- *Freshners* – Very mild, best for dry and mature skins, using ingredients such as rosewater, orange water and camomile
- *Toners* – slightly stronger than fresheners with a mild astringent effect, most effective on normal skin. May contain ingredients such as witch hazel
- *Astringent* – very strong as it contains alcohol, and sometimes antiseptic. Best for combination and oily skins, including those with blackheads and papules/pustules because of the drying effect

Toner

Moisturisers

A moisturiser is necessary to prevent the skin from drying out and becoming dehydrated. In addition, it is used to protect the skin from harsh elements such as strong winds, sun, central heating or air conditioning. There are many types of moisturisers, some work by attracting moisture to the cream (humectants) others by preventing moisture loss from the skin (occlusives).

- *Moisturising lotion* – a lighter product best suited to young and oily skins
- *Moisturising mousse* – a lighter 'whipped' cream consistency ideally suited for normal skin types
- *Moisturising cream* – heavier and richer, better for dry and mature skins.

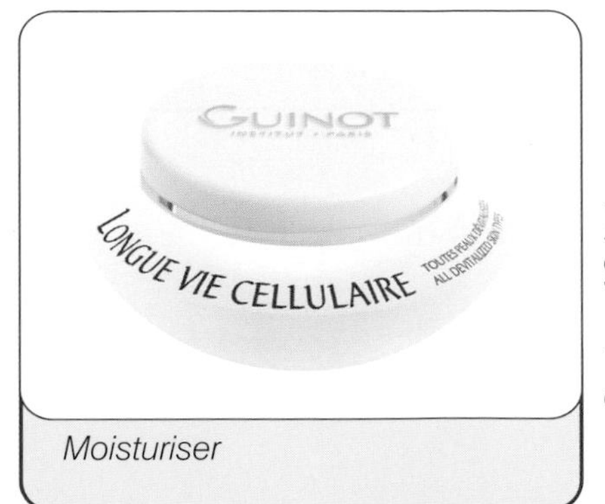

Moisturiser

Courtesy of Guinot

Specialised products

New ranges of specialised products are constantly being developed to treat different parts of the face, or that have special functions.

- *Eye gels/creams* – designed to suit the very thin and delicate skin around the eye, helping to minimise puffiness, bags, dark circles and crows feet

Courtesy of Priadara

Eye gel

- ***Neck creams*** – the neck is one of the first areas to show the signs of age, and is often very neglected. Neck creams help to improve the 'crepey' appearance and minimise lines and wrinkles.
- ***Night creams*** – active ingredients work on the skin during the night when skin cells are regenerated. Night creams are not normally used on young skins. However they are beneficial for those aged from around 30 years.
- ***Serums/ampoules*** – small phials of active ingredients that are applied as a course of treatments, to treat specific problems such as wrinkles, dull skin, acne, ageing.

Facial scrubs

This is a special product designed to remove dead skin cells (exfoliate) and to make the skin appear brighter, clearer and glowing. If the dead skin cells are removed, products can be absorbed more quickly into the skin.

Courtesy of Priadara

Facial scrub/exfoliant

ACTIVITY   

spa or by visiting a local department store. Choose two /spa or by visiting a local department store. Choose two different ranges of skin care products, one a reasonably priced range and one a very expensive product. Compare and contrast the two ranges, and write a report on your findings. Be sure to include:

- any promotions – leaflets, in magazines, TV, etc.
- type of model/role model used in campaigns
- who/what is the target market
- position in store/type of counter
- size of range, how many products
- products for male skin care
- only skin care, or makeup as well?
- concept of range – natural/organic, scientific/high-tech
- research undertaken by company
- price range
- treatments linked to the range
- samples available for you to try
- customers available for you to question about why they prefer the range

Present your report to your colleagues, sharing all your information with them. Find out which range they would choose to use after they have listened to all your research findings.

Most facial scrubs consist of a cream that contains fine particles that are abrasive and so 'slough' off the dead skin cells. Be careful to use a product with fine particles as some contain larger or rougher particles and can irritate the skin. Another type of scrub is one where the product is brushed on to the face, left to dry out, then massaged off. The product ends up as 'crumbs' and dead skin cells are once again sloughed off with the massaging technique.

Face masks

Face masks are a special treatment designed to give a more concentrated effect on certain skin types and conditions. They can reinforce the effects of cleansing, or enhance the moisture content of the skin; it all depends on the choice of mask.

There are two types of mask:

- *Setting masks* – usually applied thinly and then allowed to dry out, causing a tightening sensation. These can often be clay type masks that can be mixed in the salon from a variety of ingredients, for example, Fullers Earth.
- *Non-setting mask* – do not dry out or cause a tightening effect. They are the most popular type in the salon, and the type you will apply as part of your Diploma in Hair and Beauty Studies. There are many types of mask available, and almost every skin care range offers at least one mask. Some are for oily troubled skin, others for dehydrated and ageing skin, and even 'brightening' masks for dull sallow skin.

Face masks are a popular retail product in the salon

Courtesy of Guinot

Home care and treatment advice

At the end of the facial treatment, it is important that the client doesn't quickly get up and start getting dressed. Cover them up and keep them warm. Explain that they need to rest for at least 5 minutes, and then get up slowly. If they are too quick and rush, they may feel faint and dizzy, as the blood rushes from their head. After lying for an hour, the body needs to slowly get used to being in an upright position again. Whilst resting, it gives you an opportunity to go through the home care and treatment advice. Offer them a glass of water, and advise them to drink plenty of water generally.

A glass of water can be refreshing when offered at the end of the treatment

The skin analysis carried out during the initial consultation is essential as it informs the products and treatments to be used in the salon. In addition a home care recommendation form, or prescription, needs to be completed, so the client can keep a copy and know what retail products they need to buy to look after their skin at home.

SKIN CARE PRESCRIPTION

Name:	Address:
Overall skin type:	Areas for special attention/comments:

Homecare recommendations		
Type of product	Specific product	How often/special advice
Makeup remover		
Cleanser		
Toner		
Moisturiser		
Scrub/exfoliant		
Mask		
Night cream		
Eye products		
Specialised products		
Comments/notes		
Date of skin analysis:		Therapist:

Note: *As the skin improves and changes over the coming weeks/months, revisit this prescription form, and if necessary fill a new one in and staple it to the record card (or input it on to the computer system if appropriate).*

After you have completed the treatment, you may be asked questions related to the facial. Use the following checklist to make sure you cover all the different aspects:

HOME CARE AND TREATMENT ADVICE	
After-treatment advice	• Rest period • Reactions to treatment • Water/refreshment
Products used in the treatment	• Explain details of products • Home care recommendation • How to use the products • Written prescription • Retail opportunities – headband, sponges, candles, eye mask, etc.
Contra-actions	• Explain possible reactions • Advise on recommended action
Lifestyle pattern	• Healthy eating • Drinking water • Exercise habits • Sleep patterns • Hobbies/interests • Means of relaxation
Further facial treatment	• Benefits of continuing treatments • Courses/financial incentives
Linked treatments	• Benefits of combining with other treatments, e.g. manicures
Frequency of treatments	• Recommended frequency and time intervals

Contra-actions

If an individual has an abnormal reaction to the treatment it can be unpleasant and irritating. It needs immediate attention, to minimise the impact and discomfort for the client. Action taken to correct the unwanted reaction is called a 'contra-action'.

EXTEND YOUR LEARNING

Facial treatments

Research the list of possible contra-actions to a facial treatment and detail the action that should be taken:

Abnormal reaction	Possible cause	Recommended contra-action to be taken
Allergic rash	Reaction to a product or tool (plastic spatula)	
Burning sensation on skin	Reaction to a product	
Product in eye	Poor technique	
Bruising	Poor technique, or too much pressure	
Light headedness or fainting	Getting up too quickly after the facial	

Should someone suffer from an adverse reaction to a facial treatment, they must be allowed to relax before leaving the salon/spa. A professional therapist will:

- Provide a room for relaxation that is well ventilated
- Ensure that the client's gown or clothing isn't too tight, and they can breathe free and easily
- Provide a glass of water or other refreshment
- Apply a cold compress or soothing lotion to any irritated skin condition
- If symptoms persist, advise them to seek medical assistance at the earliest opportunity

On completion of the treatment, make a full note of any adverse reactions on the record card, so that future treatments can be adapted.

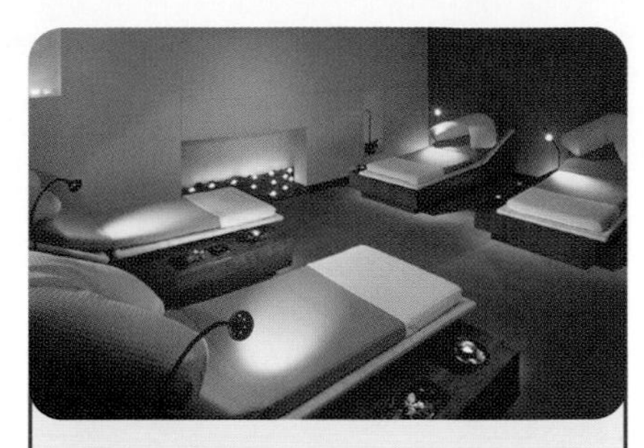

Relaxation room

Facial treatment procedure

Now that you are aware of all the factors that affect the appearance and condition of the skin, and you know how to select the right products and tools, and why you must carry out a consultation – you're now ready to put the theory into practice!

The five basic steps are:

1 cleansing
2 face scrub
3 face mask
4 toning
5 moisturising

Step 1: Cleansing

Cleansing is one of the most important stages in the skin care routine. Many people feel the key to great looking skin is how clean it is, and how it glows with health and vitality. Skin that isn't cleansed thoroughly can look dirty, dull, tired, with blemishes such as blackheads and spots. The skin needs to be very clean, as it is no good applying a mask, moisturiser or makeup to grubby skin as there will be a greasy barrier, products will not be as effective and it could cause a break-out of spots.

There are two parts to the cleansing routine:

1 **Superficial cleansing** – to remove makeup and surface grease and dirt
2 **Deep cleansing** – to give a deeper cleanse to the face, removing every trace of dirt to ensure the skin is squeaky clean

Top tip

Male skin care – don't use cotton wool pads to remove products as it gets caught in the strong facial hair, use dampened sponges instead.

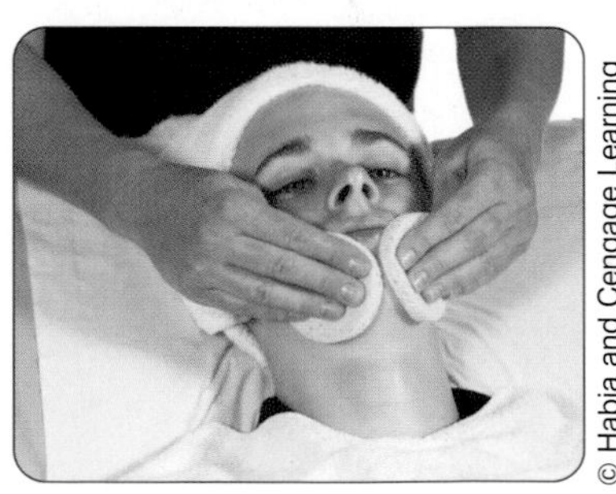

Superficial cleansing

The routine for the superficial cleanse is:

- eyes/lashes
- lips
- face and neck

Deep cleanse

The 'deep cleansing' procedure involves a routine of 10 massage movements, to help the cleansing product be absorbed deep into the pores and follicles to ensure the skin is cleaned thoroughly.

Superficial cleanse procedure

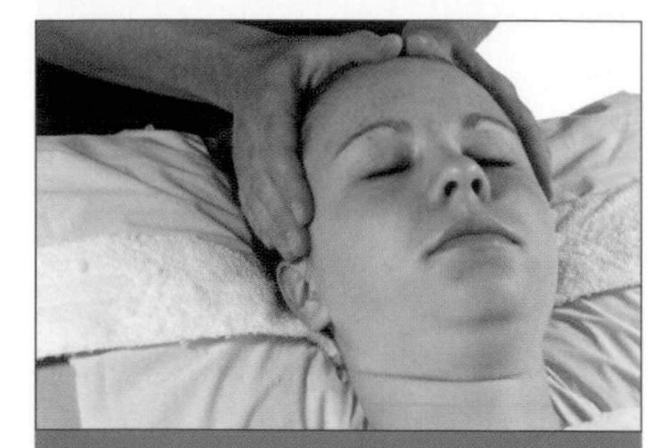

1 Wash your hands, and dry thoroughly. Apply pressure to the scalp, to start the relaxation process. Ensure the headband is firmly in place to protect the hair.

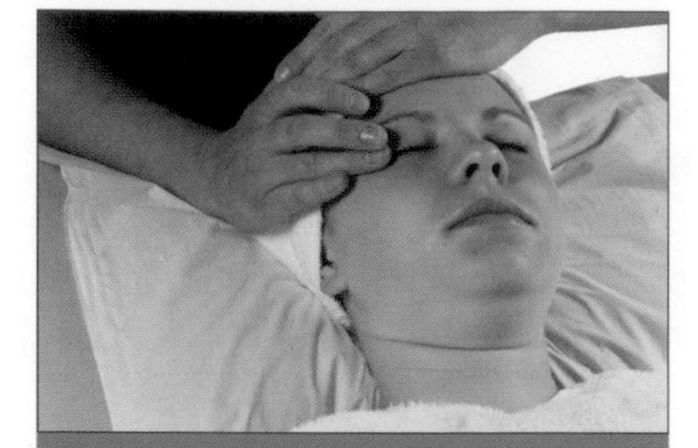

2 Cleanse each eye separately. Start with the right eye, apply eye makeup remover in small circular movements over the eye lid and lashes. Ensure the pressure is very light. Always support the eyebrow area with your free hand. Repeat on the left eye.

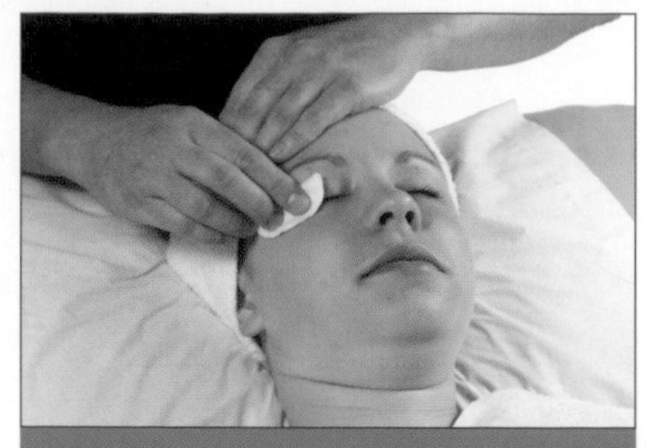

3 Take damp cotton wool pads and stroke the pads down over the lid and lashes, until all the eye makeup has been removed.

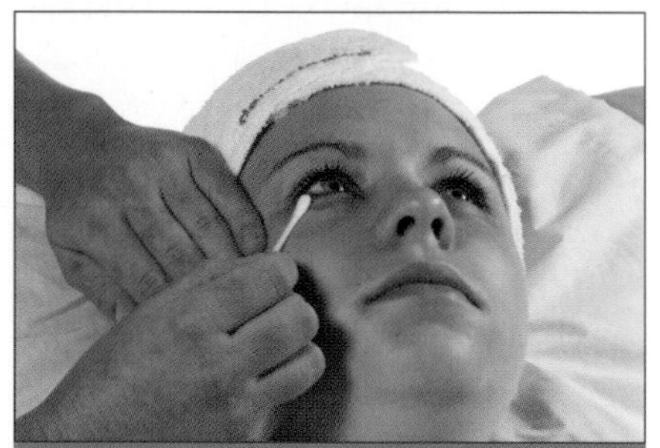

4 If necessary use a cotton bud to get the last traces of eye shadow and mascara off.

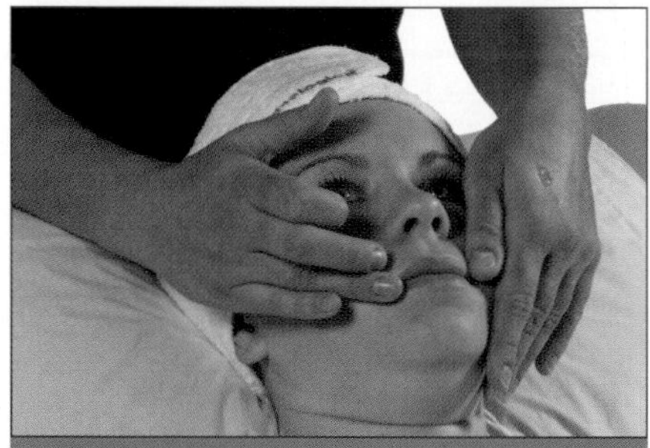

5 Cleanse each side of the lips separately. Apply a cleaning lotion or milk in small circles to the right side of the mouth, supporting the corner of the mouth with your free hand.

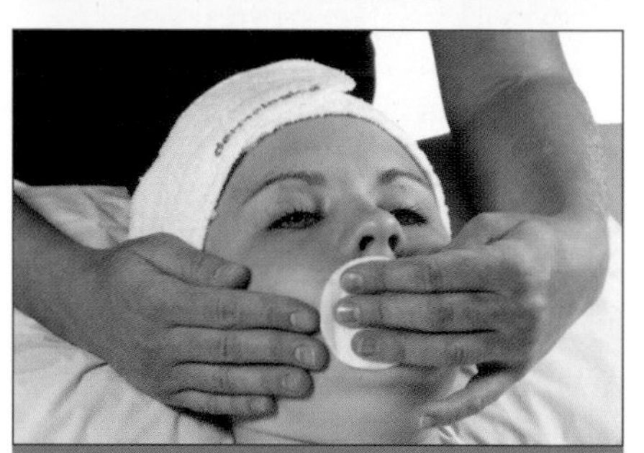

6 Take damp cotton wool pads, and stroke inwards across the lips to remove all lipstick, repeat until the lips are clean.

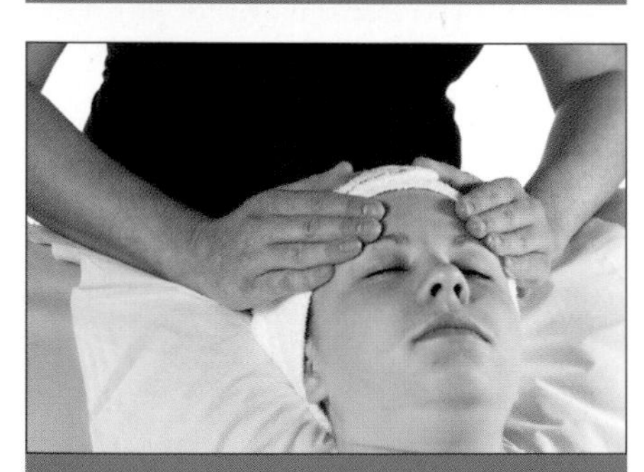

7 Apply the cleanser to the face and start at the forehead with light strokes.

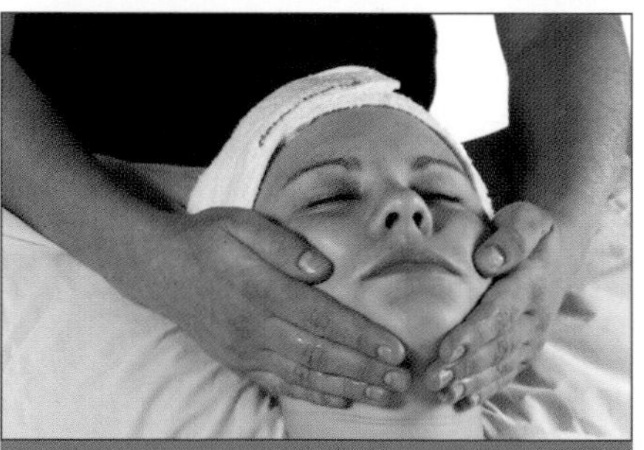

8 Work slowly onto the cheeks, with circular movements, finish on the neck area with sliding movements.

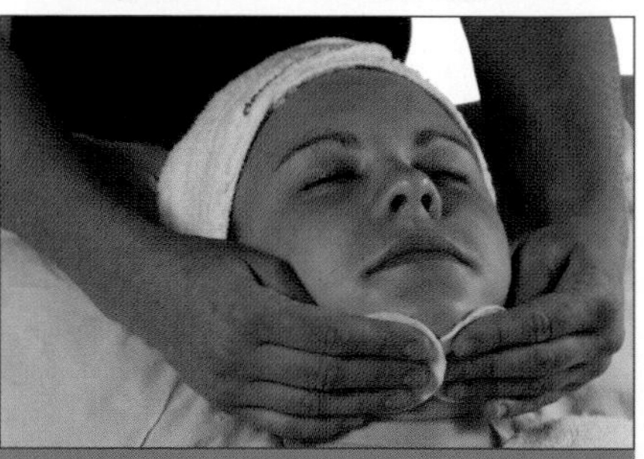

9 With damp cotton wool pads in each hand, remove the cleanser with light upward strokes. Facial sponges can also be used to remove the cleanser. Repeat until all the cleanser is removed.

Deep cleanse procedure

Choose a cleanser that is suitable for the skin type. Apply to both your hands evenly, and then apply to the face and neck in long flowing strokes. Then take 10 minutes to go through the following nine massage strokes:

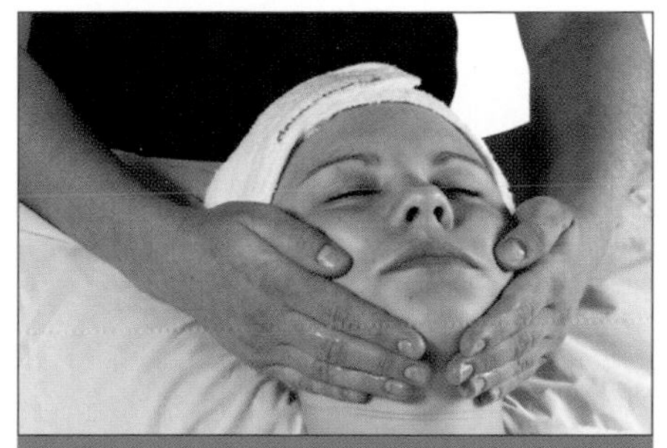

1 Stroking (neck area) – using your fingertips stroke up both sides of the neck, then outward under the jaw, and back down lightly to the starting position.

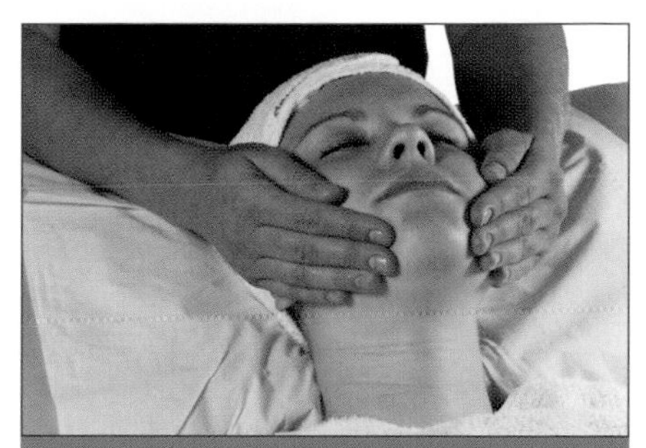

2 Finger kneading to the chin area.

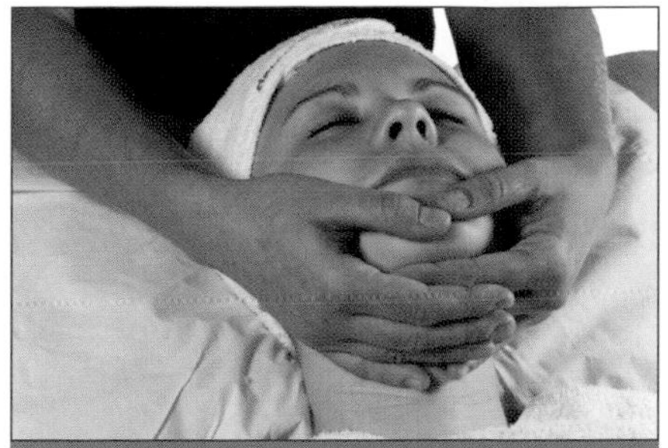

3 Thumb kneading to the entire chin area.

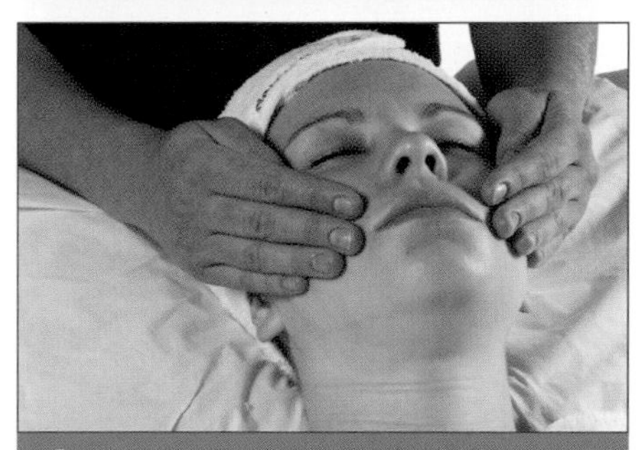

4 Circling (cheek area) – apply small circles with fingertips to entire cheek area, starting at the chin, working up around the nose, across the cheek bone and back along lower cheek to chin.

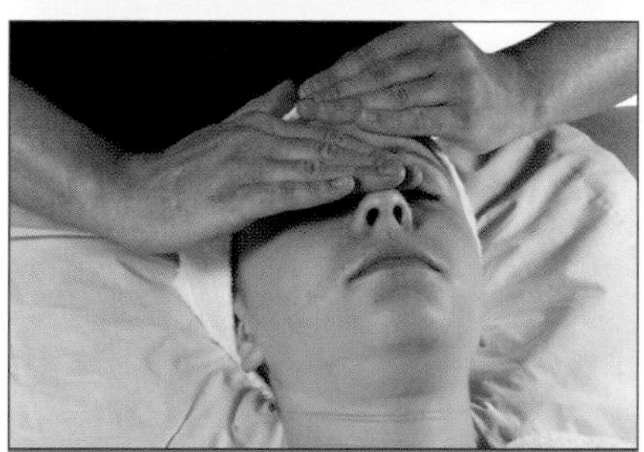

5 Gliding (nose) – with ring and middle fingers of right hand, start at base of nose and glide along the length of the nose and off the end, followed by the left hand.

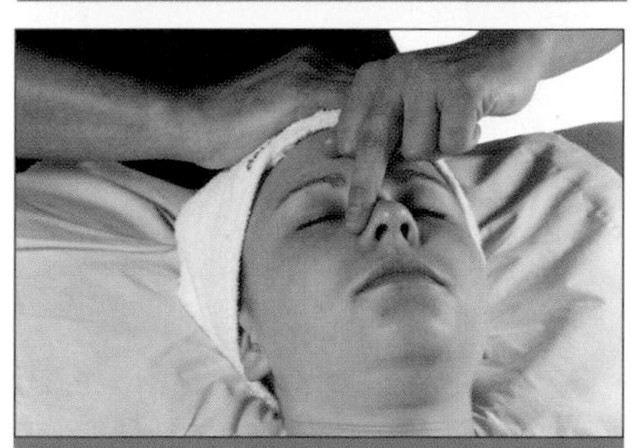

6 Circling (eye area) – with the middle finger circle around each eye. Start on the inner eyebrow, stroke out along brow bone and inwards under the eye. Adapt to form a 'figure 8' movement, with each hand working alternately.

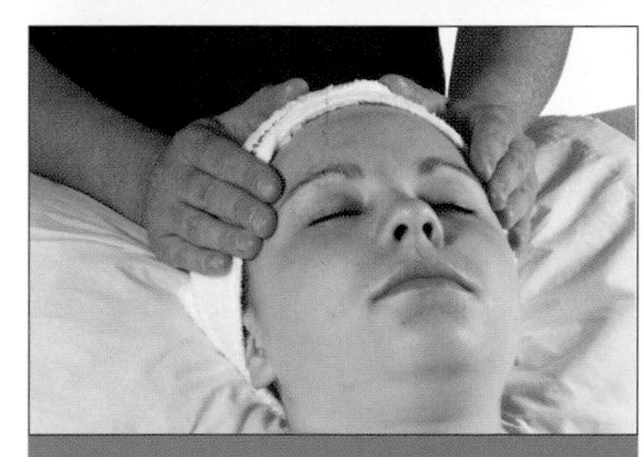

7 Circling (forehead) – with ring and middle fingers perform small circles across the forehead.

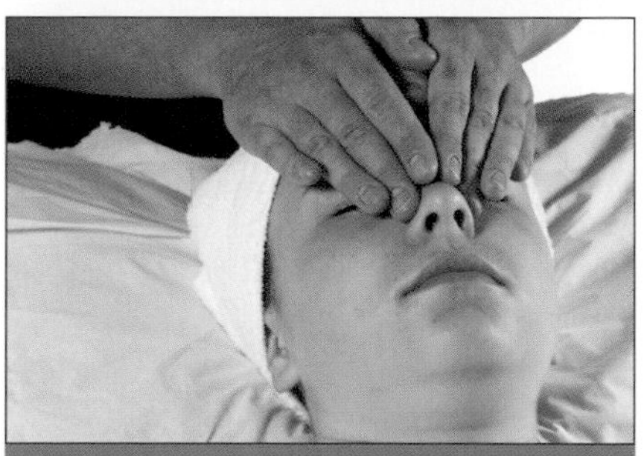

8 Sliding (eye area) – with index, middle and ring fingers, slide outwards around the brow bone and underneath the eye area. At the end of the stroke, lift and apply pressure with each individual finger on the brow bone.

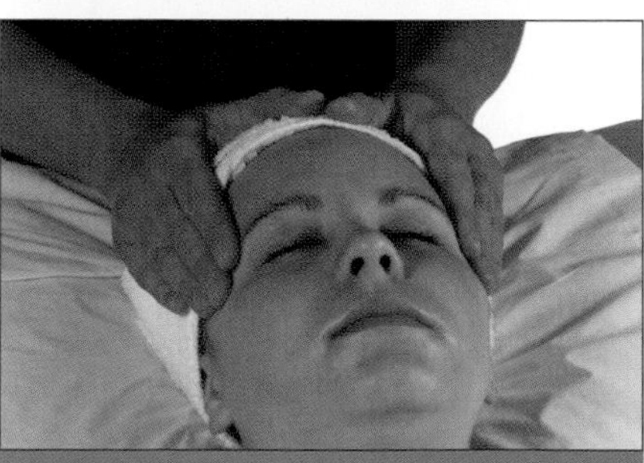

9 Circling (temple area) – with the index, middle and ring fingers circle on the temple area, applying slight pressure. Pause at the end, and hold for a count of 3.

Step 2: Facial Scrub

Application of scrub

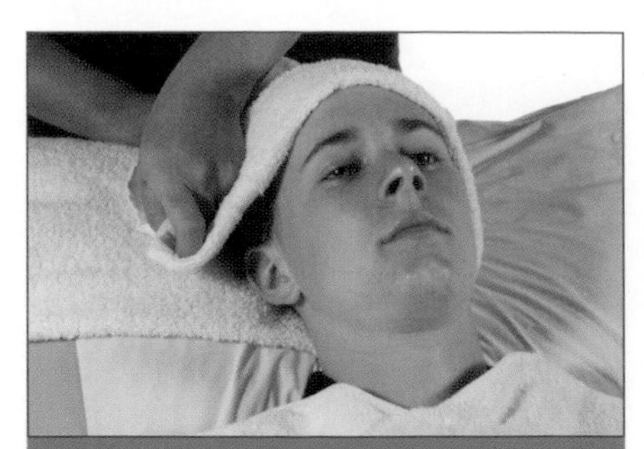

1 Place the clean towel on the pillow, and wrap the towel carefully over the head, protecting the hairline.

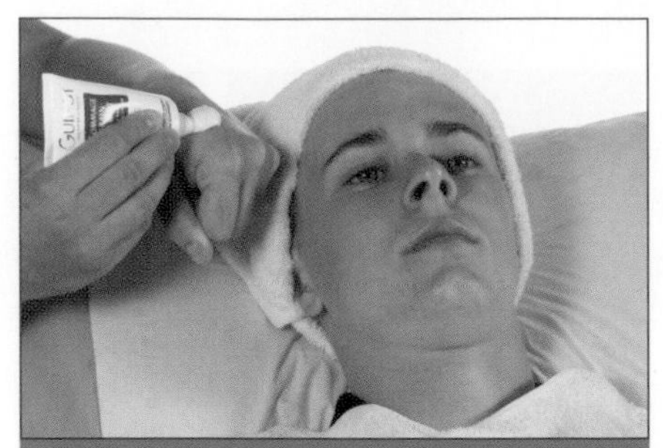

2 Choose the appropriate scrub for the skin type. Always read and follow carefully the manufacturer's instructions. Place a small amount of scrub on the back of your hand.

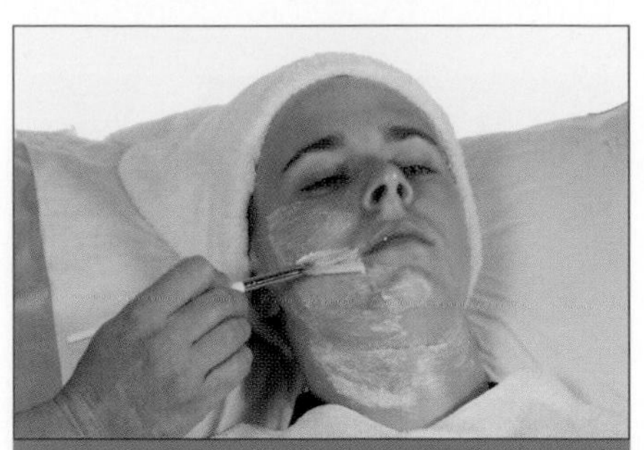

3 Apply the scrub to the face with a mask brush. Explain to the client the sensation they will feel.

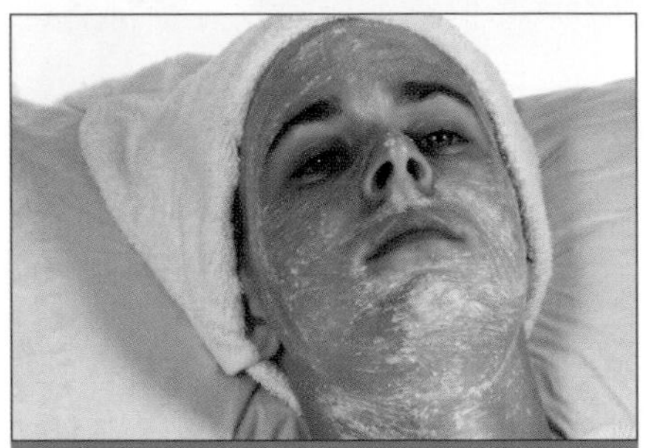

4 Make sure the scrub is applied evenly all over the neck, chin, cheeks, nose and forehead.

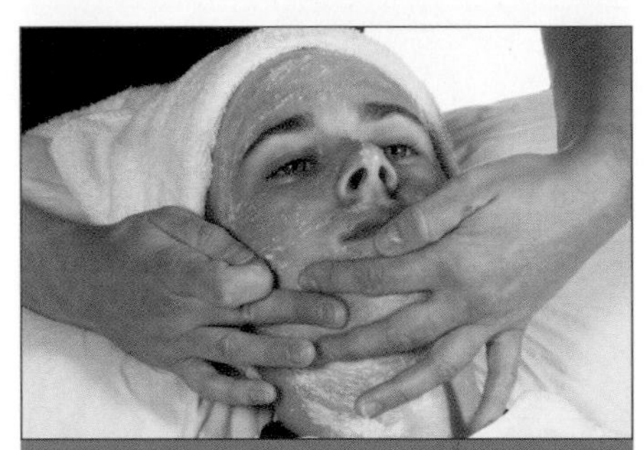

5 With small circular motions, lightly massage the entire face and neck in an upwards direction. Be careful on delicate areas such as the cheeks and avoid the eye area and lips. If the scrub dries out too much, and starts to drag, add water by dampening hands.

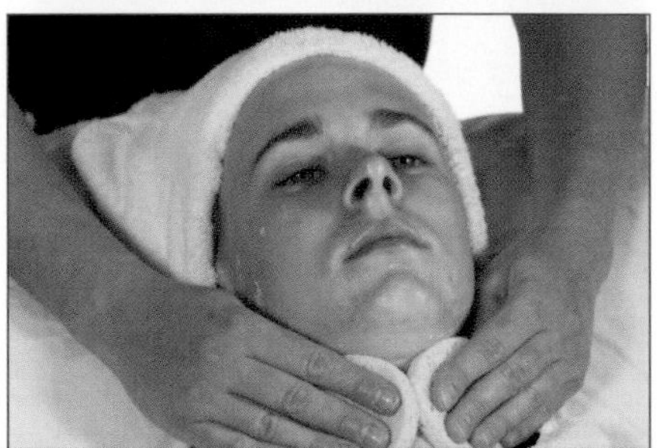

6 The scrub is left on the skin for the recommended time, according to the manufacturer's instructions. Use warm damp sponges to remove the scrub, start at the neck, make sure you check the hairline and around the nostrils. Do not have the sponges too wet or it will be uncomfortable for the client.

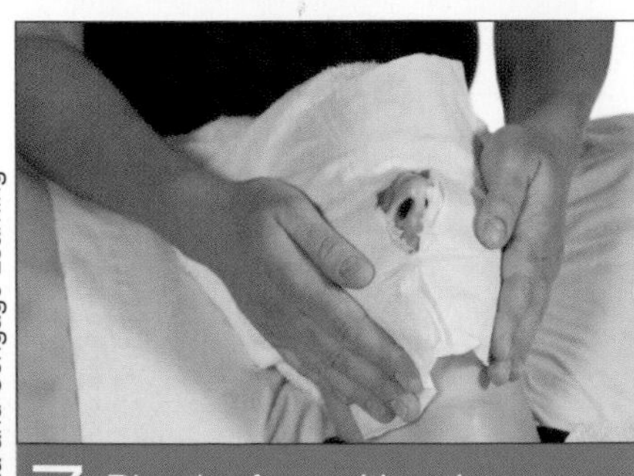

7 Blot the face with a tissue

Step 3: Face mask

Application of setting mask

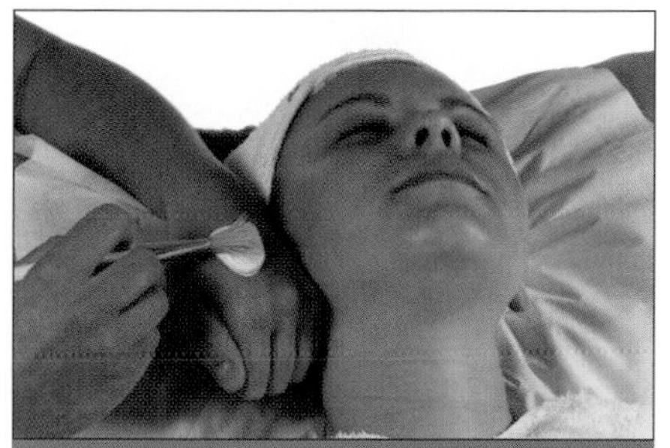

1 Choose the appropriate mask for the skin type. Always read and follow carefully the manufacturer's instructions. Apply a small amount of mask to the back of your hand.

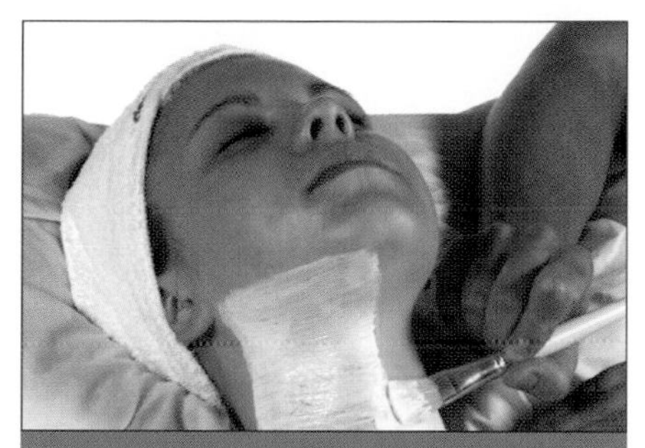

2 Using a clean mask brush, apply the mask quickly so the skin gets the maximum effect from the active ingredients in the mask. Start at the base of the neck.

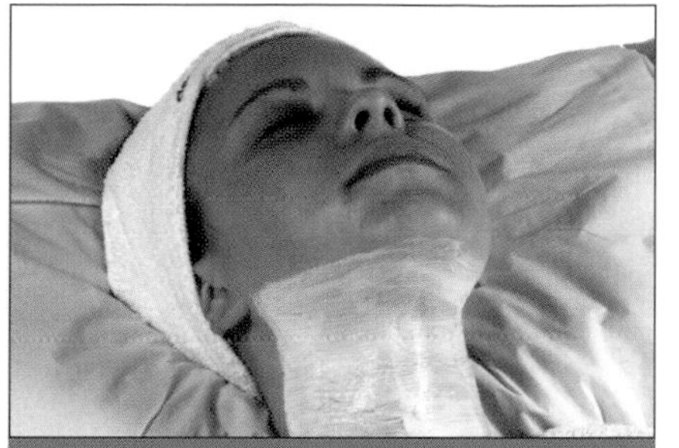

3 It is important to apply the mask quickly and evenly so it doesn't dry out sooner in some parts of the face or neck, as it could irritate the skin Explain to the client the sensation they will feel.

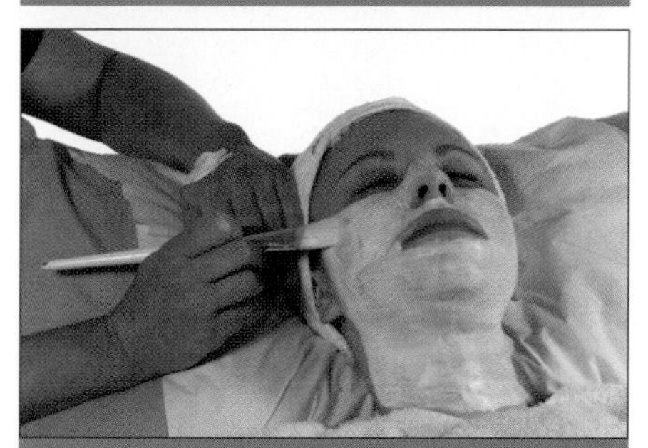

4 Work quickly and carefully upwards, avoid the lips, nostrils, eye area and eyebrows.

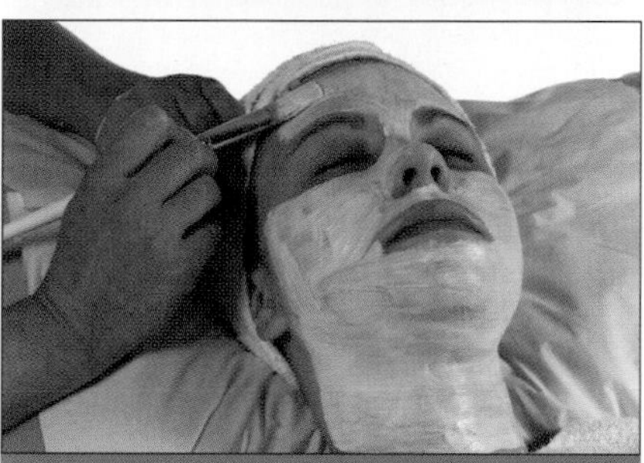

5 Finish on the forehead, being careful to avoid the hairline.

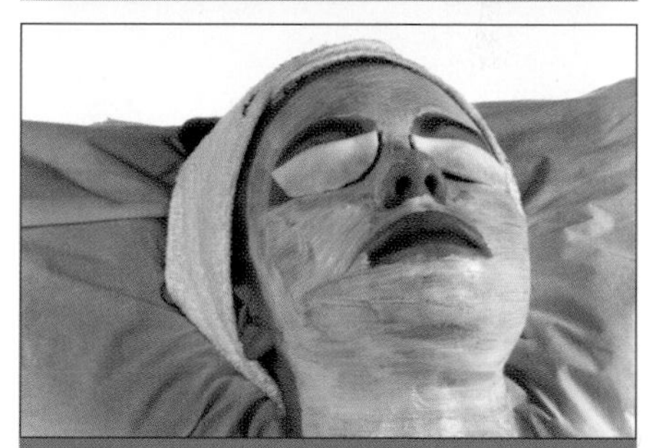

6 Dampened cotton wool pads are applied to the eyes, this helps to relax the client. The mask is left on the skin for the recommended time, according to the manufacturer's instructions.

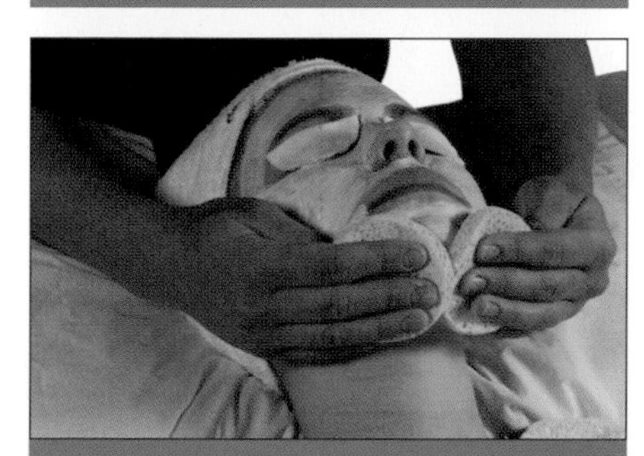

7 Use warm damp sponges to remove the mask, start on the neck area. Remove the eye pads and continue on to the cheek area. Do not have the sponges too wet or it will be uncomfortable for the client.

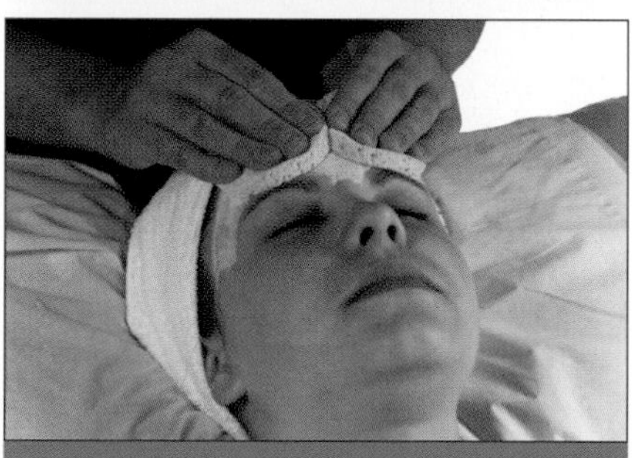

8 Be careful to remove every last trace of the mask, which can be a challenge with a 'setting' mask.

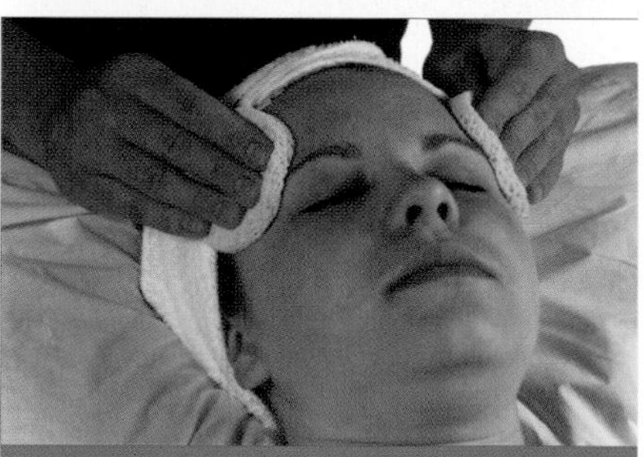

9 Check the hairline, around the nostrils and under the chin to ensure there are no traces of mask left on the skin.

Application of non-setting mask

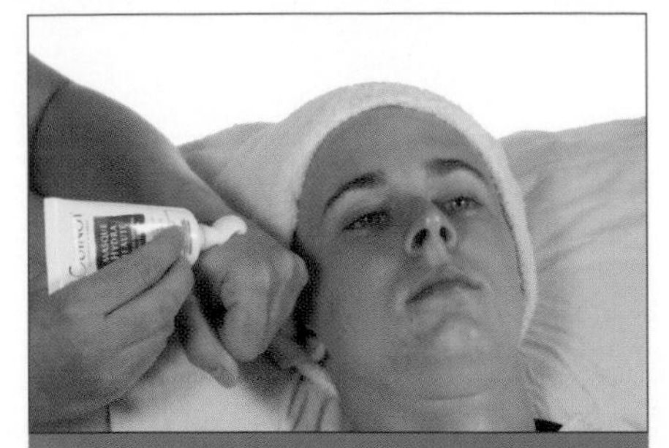

1 Choose the appropriate mask for the skin type. Always read and follow carefully the manufacturer's instructions. Apply a small amount of mask to the back of your hand.

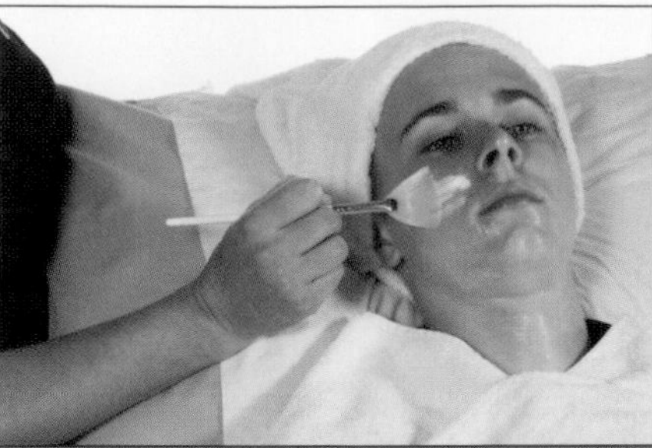

2 Using a clean mask brush, apply the mask quickly so the skin gets the maximum effect from the active ingredients in the mask. Start at the base of the neck and work carefully upwards, finishing on the forehead. Avoid the lips, nostrils, eye area, eyebrows and hairline. Apply the mask evenly so it doesn't dry out earlier in some parts of the face or neck. Explain to the client the sensation they will feel.

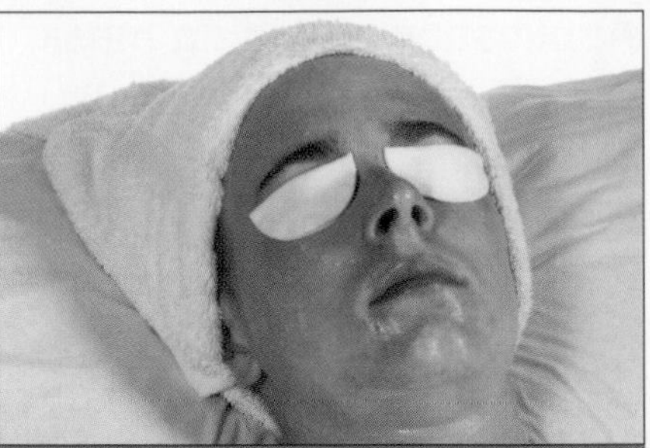

3 Dampened cotton wool pads are applied to the eyes, this helps to relax the client. The mask is left on the skin for the recommended time, according to the manufacturer's instructions.

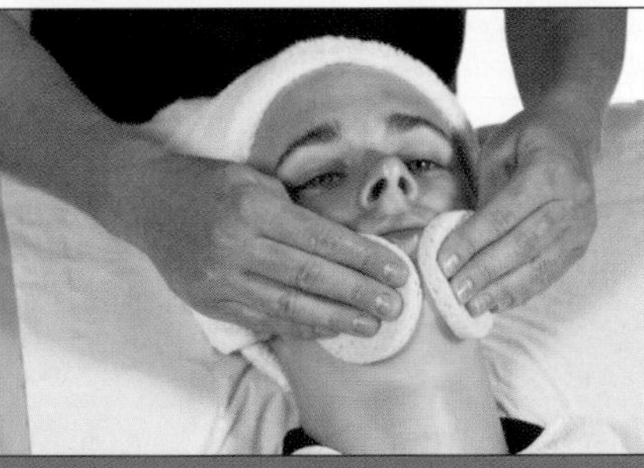

4 Remove the eye pads, and use warm damp sponges to remove the mask. Do not have the sponges too wet or it will be uncomfortable for the client. Be careful to remove every last trace of the mask, which can be a challenge, check the hairline, around the nostrils and under the chin.

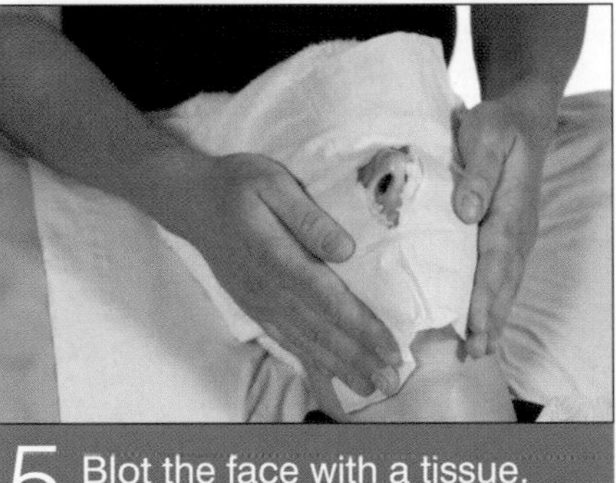

5 Blot the face with a tissue.

Top tip Some facial treatments use an individual mask for each area – eye, face and neck. These specialist masks have unique active ingredients that benefit specific areas, e.g. for crepey skin on the neck.

Top tip A specialised eye lotion can be applied to the eye pads, these lotions can soothe the eye area, decreasing puffiness and tired looking eyes.

Top tip Top salons and spas provide a relaxing hand massage when the mask is on, so the client gets the maximum benefit from their time with the therapist.

Step 4: Toning

Application of toner

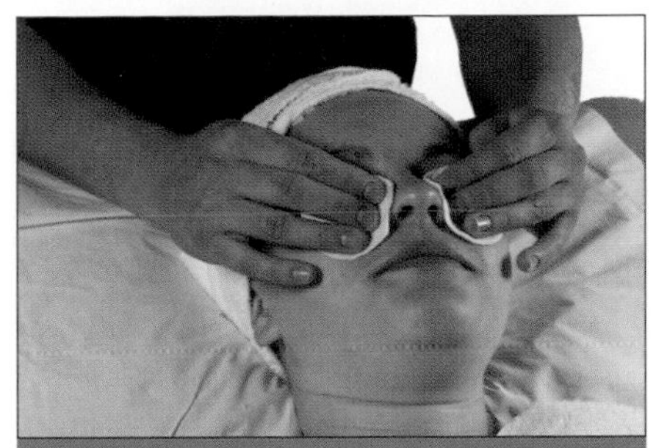

1 Choose the appropriate toner for the skin type. Apply the toner to two damp cotton wool pads. Starting at the base of the neck, wipe the pads gently over the neck and face using long sweeping, flowing strokes.

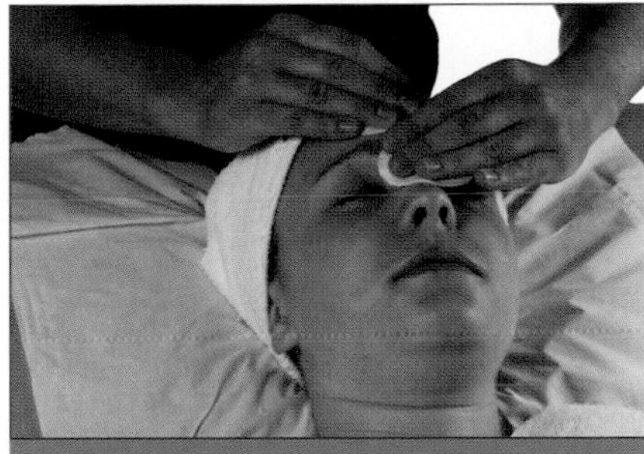

2 Continue over the entire face.

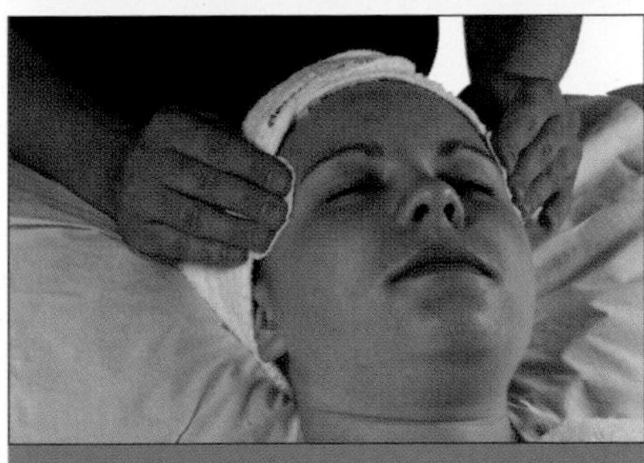

3 Repeat if necessary, until the skin is free of grease or product.

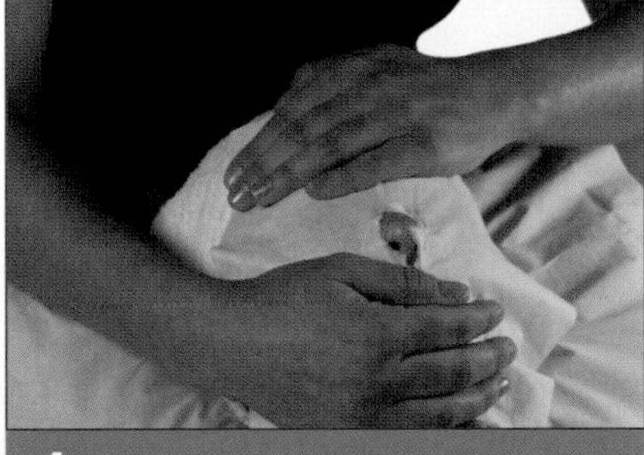

4 Blot the skin to remove any excess toner. Take a facial tissue, tear a small hole in the middle for the nose, apply to the face, and gently press all over to absorb any excess toner.

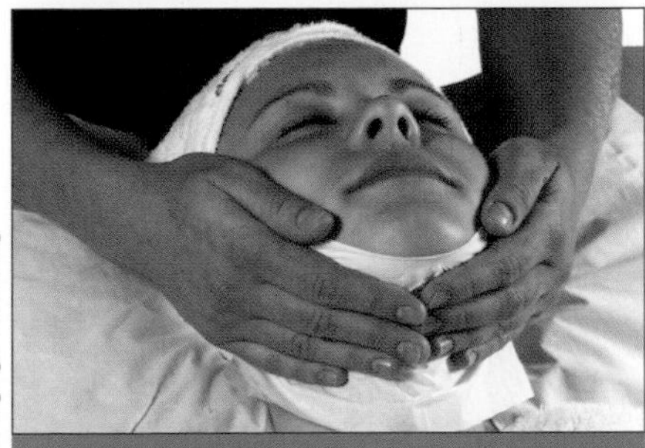

5 Remove the tissue, fold in half and apply to the neck area, and gently press.

Top tip

Toner can be applied as a 'mist' using a vaporiser, which can be both relaxing and refreshing for the client.

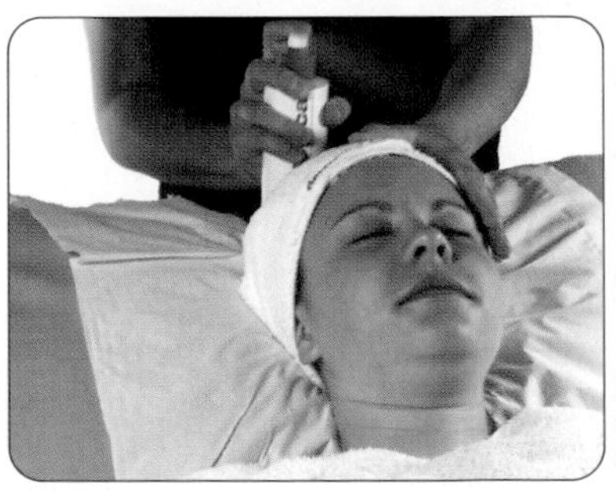

Step 5: Moisturising

Application of moisturiser

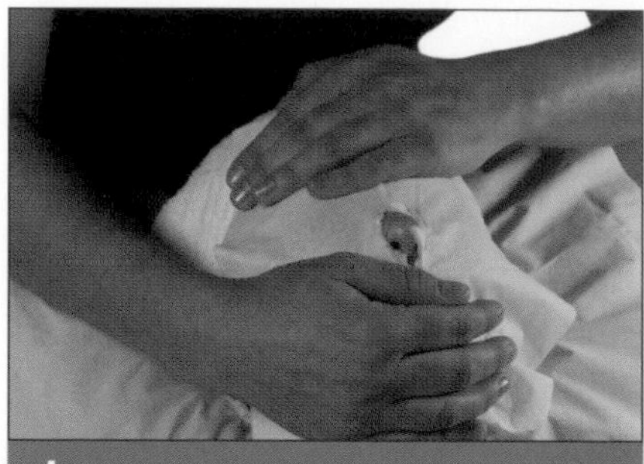

1 Ensure there is no excess toner on the skin, and that a tissue has been used to 'blot' the face and neck.

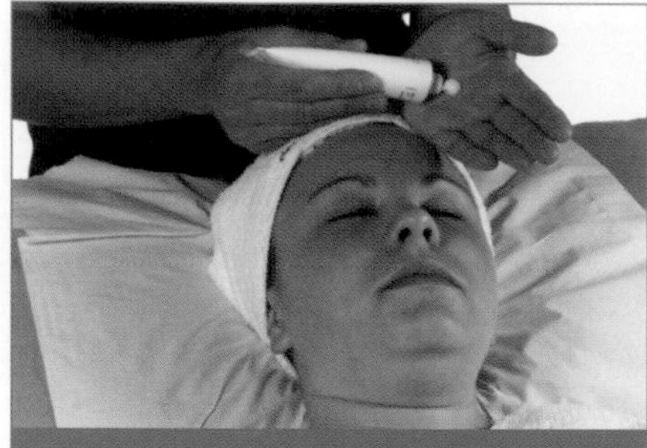

2 Choose the correct moisturiser for the skin type.

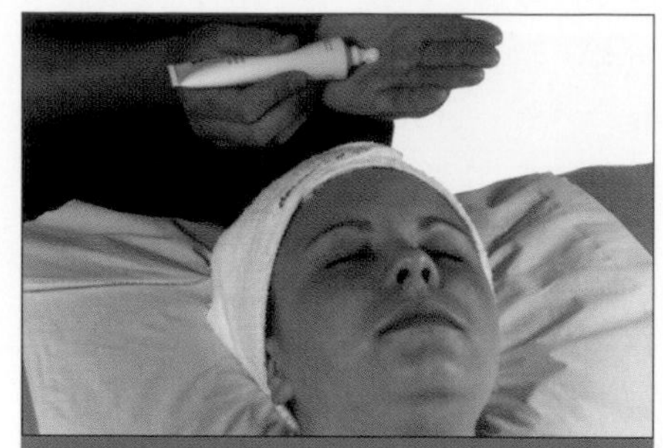

3 Place a small amount of moisturiser in the palm of your hand.

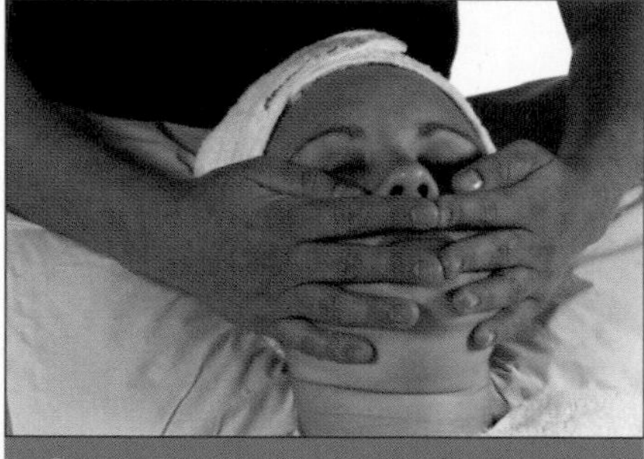

4 Apply the moisturiser sparingly to the neck, chin, cheeks, nose and forehead.

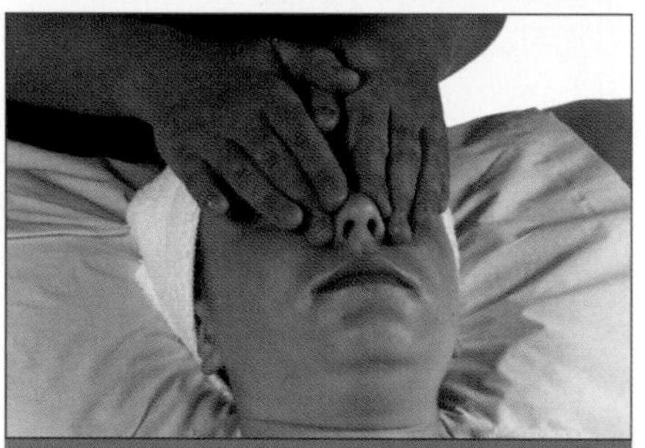

5 Lightly massage the moisturiser into the face and neck with upwards and outwards flowing strokes.

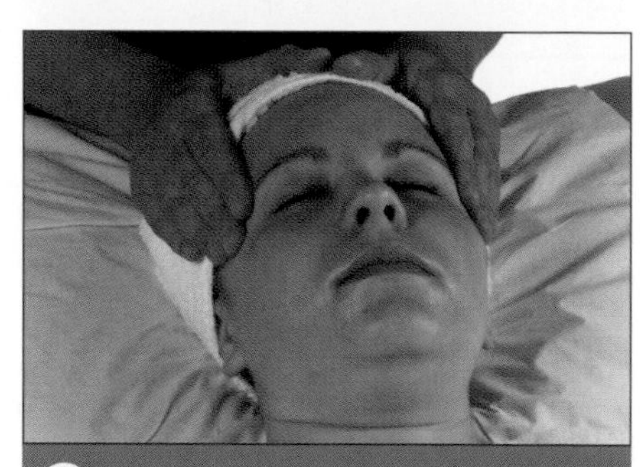

6 End with light pressure on the temples.

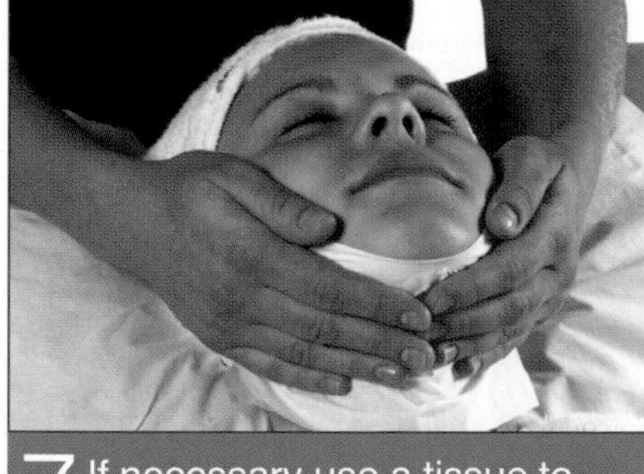

7 If necessary use a tissue to blot any excess moisturiser.

Top tip

Advanced facial treatments include a range of moisturisers or serums for the different parts of the face and neck, e.g. eye serum to help improve dark circles under the eyes.

Eye treatments

A professional beauty therapist will offer a range of eye treatments. They are extremely popular in salons and spas as they are quick and show immediate results.

Eyebrow shaping

The correct shaped eyebrows can appear to 'lift' a face and often take years off the person. The eyebrow shape has to suit the client's face shape, eye shape, their age and take into account lifestyle and current fashion trends. Makeup application is easier when the brows are shaped correctly and it can enhance the finished look.

The eyebrow shape frames the eye

iStockphoto.com/Valua Vitaly

Eyebrow tint

Many natural brows are very pale in colour. Eyebrow tinting helps to define the brows and help frame the eyes, and can be very effective. Care must be taken so the brows don't become too dark, as it can appear harsh.

Eyelash tint

This treatment creates dark luscious lashes, and can make them appear longer. It's a popular treatment just before a holiday or if the person does a lot of swimming or has very blonde lashes. A skin sensitivity test is essential to ensure there is no allergic reaction to the products in the tint.

Extension lashes are big business!

iStockphoto.com/Martin Carlsson

False lashes/lash extensions

For many years salons have offered a service to enhance the lashes, either with strip lashes or individual lashes. This treatment can often be linked to a makeup application to enhance the final look.

EXTEND YOUR LEARNING

New technology is fast transforming the world of extension lashes, and many beauty salons and spas are offering the new treatments. Research at least four companies offering the new technology, companies such as **Jinnylash.com**, **novalash.com**, **lavishlashes.co.uk** and **xtremelashes.com**. Find out all the details about the lashes and write a simple report comparing the differences.

Technological developments

Beauty is a very fast paced industry, there are new machines being developed weekly, and it only takes a walk around a beauty trade exhibition to realise how fast technology is developing. On one hand the beauty industry is about a highly skilled 'personal' service, that cannot be mechanised too much or the personal touch will disappear, but on the other hand we have to harness technology as it makes life so much easier, helping us to work 'smarter' as opposed to harder.

New equipment can do things such as digitally photograph the skin and magnify it on a laptop so we can do a much more in-depth skin analysis, or use lasers to remove unwanted hair or stimulate collagen to hold back the ageing process.

There are some new and exciting developments happening with eyelash extensions. New products are now available that make the eyelashes look thicker and longer, some effects are very dramatic. The technique is developing very fast in the USA, and many celebrities are endorsing certain products. New technology has enabled professional therapists to be able to apply individual synthetic eyelash extensions directly on to the natural lashes, with new bonding agents. These semi-permanent eyelash extensions are applied lash by lash and create a very natural look. They can last up to 8 weeks, some companies claim up to 3 months.

Advanced treatments

If you decide to do further training and become a professional beauty therapist, you will study a wide variety of advanced treatments, including specialised electrical treatments for the face and body.

Facial steaming

This is a popular treatment in a salon; it is incorporated into a facial treatment as it can benefit most skin types. There are floor standing steamers, but also smaller ones that can be attached to a trolley. A professional therapist has to be extremely careful when performing a steam treatment, and must follow the manufacturer's instructions at all times. Very sensitive skin and those people with acne rosacea and sunburn are contra-indicated to the treatment. The steam treatment is often used after the deep cleanse procedure, and can be as short as five minutes, depending on the skin type.

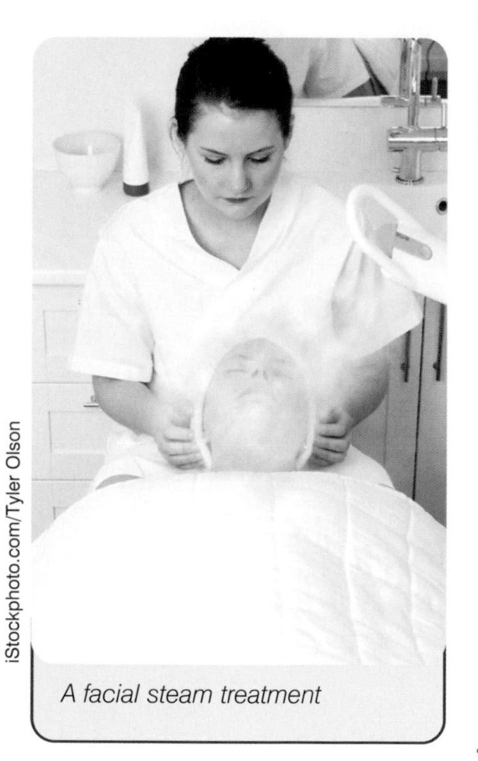
iStockphoto.com/Tyler Olson

A facial steam treatment

SKIN TYPE	BENEFIT OF A STEAM TREATMENT
Oily skin	Deep cleansing Skin colour is improved Unblock pores, helping the removal of comedones
Normal skin	Deep cleansing Improves skin colour Hydrates the skin
Dry skin	Deep cleansing Hydrates the skin Improves skin colour Helps 'desquamate' dead skin cells

High frequency

This is a specialised treatment used by qualified beauty therapists. The treatment uses an electric current to produce heat in the skin tissues.

There are two methods of high frequency:

- ***Direct high frequency*** – applied directly via a glass electrode to the skin. This method is more beneficial for oily and blemished skin as it dries it out and encourages healing. The treatment is also stimulating for poor circulation and sallow coloured skin. Ozone can be created under the electrode which has a germicidal effect on the skin.

It's a fact! Ozone(O_3) is a form of oxygen whose molecules consist of three oxygen atoms, it is present in the upper atmosphere and is known to be a powerful sanitizer.

- ***Indirect high frequency*** – this is applied at the same time as the facial massage. The therapist performs the massage whilst the client holds the electrode, which results in warmth and relaxation in the skin tissues, and increased absorption of the massage cream. This method is best for dry and mature skins, and those people who are tired and tense.

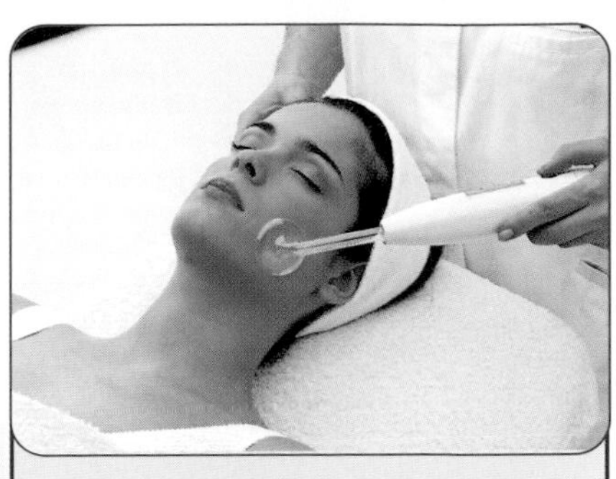

Direct high frequency treatment

Sorisa

EXTEND YOUR LEARNING  

Visit a Beauty trade exhibition, there is usually an annual one in each region of the country. Research new developments in beauty equipment and decide on two new machines:

- A facial steaming machine
- A facial high frequency unit/machine

Write a report on each of the pieces of equipment, including the following categories:

- Date launched to the market?
- What research is behind the equipment?
- Which country is it manufactured in?
- Price?
- What range of treatments does it offer?
- Equipment manual available?
- Training available? free?
- Warranty available?
- Repair service?
- Benefits over other machines on market?
- Associated product range available?
- National promotional campaign?
- Leaflets available for salon promotion.

Specialised masks

There are a wide range of specialised face masks available to suit all the different skin types and conditions.

- ***Oil masks*** – uses good quality natural oil. For example, almond, to treat dry, mature, dehydrated skin. Often heat is involved to help the absorption of the oil.
- ***Gel masks*** – these often involve active ingredients blended in a gel base. A wide range of active substances are available so the therapist can tailor make the mask to suit the individual. Very often the same ingredients can be blended into a massage cream to reinforce the treatment, and make it more effective.

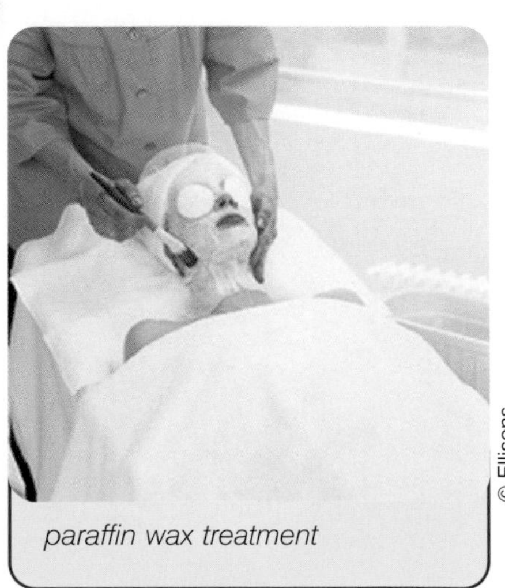

paraffin wax treatment

© Ellisons

- ***Wax masks*** – this is usually a combination of paraffin wax and beeswax, which is applied warm to the skin. The wax mask sets and then can be easily removed. This type of mask is best for dry dehydrated skins, and is a very relaxing treatment. Great care needs to be taken with the preparation and application of the wax.

Bring your learning to life   

When you are on your work placement or in a salon environment, speak to the manager/employer to see if you can carry out a survey of the most popular treatments on offer.

Conduct research into the main treatments available (e.g. facials, eyebrow shapes, lash tints, waxing, makeup) and over a period of time track the number of clients for each treatment. After you have spoken with the Manager to 'scope' your research, it may be that they would like you to include other information – such as when is the busiest time in the week for these treatments, do they bring friends, use gift vouchers, etc. Write a report on your findings, and if you get the opportunity present your results to the Manager.

iStockphoto.com/Kateryna Govorushchenko

Makeup

With makeup you can be who you want to be … a natural glowing Jennifer Aniston type? or a glamorous diva like Beyonce? … or something else? – you decide. Makeup can be artistic, creative, elegant, natural, fun, decorative, beautiful, funky … and unique to you.

Lots of different aspects of life can be expressed and visualized through makeup – such as personality, cultural influences, race, gender, age and fashion trends. Your personality is expressed by the makeup you wear. You may prefer to wear only a small amount of makeup to highlight your best features, not making a bold statement, as you don't want to attract too much interest. On the other hand you may be so confident that you want a lot of attention and use your makeup to make a statement.

Culture impacts on makeup as it influences how 'beauty' is viewed and what is acceptable in certain areas of society. The media will also be an influence as images are everywhere – on TV, cinema, websites and magazines.

iStockphoto.com/Nicole S. Young

Age must be considered when deciding on a makeup 'look'. Makeup can be used cleverly, to make the person appear to be younger. However, too much makeup can also make you look much older. People have to be careful not to get trapped in a certain 'look' that they have worn for years. Therefore, makeup needs constant updating, as it is closely related to fashion.

Each season, new makeup trends are launched. One season nude lips are on the catwalk and within weeks its nude lipstick that is all over the glossy magazines. You don't need to be a slave to fashion, you must decide what suits you, but keep an eye on new trends and techniques so you can incorporate bits of them into your 'look' so you are up to date.

iStockphoto.com/aldra

iStockphoto.com/Quavondo Nguyen

Male makeup is becoming more popular and some companies are now specialising in this area, such as Taxi cosmetics (London) who have developed 'Guyliner', an eyeliner for men, and 'Manscara', to enhance male eyelashes.

Guyliner by Taxi London

By kind permission of Taxi London

ACTIVITY     

Makeup for males is becoming more popular, with new ranges being developed alongside skin care products. With a partner, research the different ranges of makeup available for men. Find out the various reasons why men may wear makeup, and come up with some solutions as to how you can break down the stereotypical images associated with men and makeup. Present your findings to the rest of the group and discuss their views on the topic. Add these views to your final report.

Factors affecting makeup

There are certain factors that you need to take into account before applying makeup; these factors affect the final look. If you do this you will know that the image that you are planning will be achievable and suitable for the client you are making-up. If, when you have considered the factors, you find that it is not possible to achieve the makeup plan you have chosen, you may be able to make some adjustments or compromises to your original plan.

The factors you must consider are:

- **the occasion**
- **skin type**
- **shape of the face**
- **shape of the eyes**

Makeup is part of your self expression

iStockphoto.com/Alexander Hafemann

It's a fact! The worldwide annual expenditure on cosmetics is estimated at approx £9 billion.

It's a fact! The oldest and the largest cosmetic company is L'Oréal which was founded in 1909. The market was developed in the USA during the early 1900s by Elizabeth Arden, Helena Rubenstein and Max Factor, and then Revlon just before the First World War and Estee Lauder soon after.

iStockphoto.com/Quavondo Nguyen

Is it makeup for a prom…

- shape of the eyebrows
- shape of the nose
- shape of the lips
- any skin, eye or mouth conditions that may affect the makeup treatment

The occasion

If you don't carefully consider the occasion that the makeup is for, then you can end up looking very out of place and inappropriately presented. Imagine turning up for a job interview in the same makeup you would wear to go out to a night club – you may not get the job!

Most people usually think carefully about the occasion, and the lighting and what effect/image you want to portray. Other people don't care, they want to be themselves and perhaps go for shock tactics! A professional beauty therapist or makeup artist has to discuss the occasion at length with a client. Perhaps they are getting married, going to a prom, a 16th birthday party, having their photograph taken at a studio? If the makeup isn't planned carefully, the client may be very disappointed with the final effect.

Skin type

Skin type has to be considered when applying makeup as it will have an impact on the final effect. Be sure to take into account if the skin is oily, with blemishes or has spots, as a lot of corrective work will be needed. On the other hand if the skin is very dry and dehydrated, you have to be careful as it is easy for the skin to look flaky and aged. Characteristics such as birth marks, moles, fine lines, spots, facial hair – all need to be noted and the makeup adapted so that you minimise these imperfections and concentrate on the person's best features. Makeup should be about highlighting the best features, and camouflaging anything the person is not happy with.

Shape of the face

The face shape can be greatly enhanced by makeup, whether it be a square shaped face that needs the angles softening or if there is a wide forehead that needs minimising. Corrective makeup can work wonders, as is shown by the 'before and after' photos of celebrities in magazines – some are unrecognisable.

Shape of the eyes

Eyes are the focus of the face and makeup can enhance the shape, colour and look of the eye area. Corrective makeup can be very effective, making small eyes appear larger, and those that are close-set appear wider apart.

Shape of the eyebrows

Well groomed eyebrows that are the correct shape for the face help to enhance the makeup. It is more difficult to get the final look you were after if the eyebrows are very bushy and overgrown, or join together into a 'mono brow'. A good professional therapist will encourage the client to have an eyebrow shape regularly as it can change the whole look of the face and make them appear younger.

Shape of the nose
Many people have hang-ups about the shape of their nose – is it too wide, too long, too bumpy? Makeup can help minimise any imperfections and help someone be happier with their natural nose shape.

Shape of the lips
Lips come in all shapes and sizes, and it is personal preference as to what you find attractive – thin natural lips, or a fuller 'bee sting' pout ? Makeup can achieve different effects, be it helping to correct a droopy lip line or making lips appear fuller by using lighter colours and gloss.

Skin, eye and mouth conditions that may affect the makeup treatment
There are many skin, eye and mouth conditions that can affect a makeup treatment. You can find the detail in Chapter 4 'The science of hair and beauty'. Some conditions are not infectious, and this means your treatment can go ahead. However, if an infectious or contagious condition exists, then the services must not be carried out. These conditions are referred to as 'contra-indications' as they prevent you from performing the treatment.

..or for an interview?

iStockphoto.com/Justin Horrocks

It's a fact!
Conditions such as conjunctivitis, acne, impetigo and ringworm are all 'contra-indications' to a makeup treatment.

Makeup treatment
In a beauty salon makeup may be applied immediately after a facial treatment. However after some treatments it isn't recommended to have makeup immediately applied, as the skin needs to breathe and remain fresh and clean for at least 4–6 hrs. Some people prefer to keep their skin free from makeup so they get the best result from the facial.

Salons and spas offer makeup treatments for a wide range of occasions such as:

Weddings	Proms	Special party
Graduation	Photo shoot	Fashion show

To be able to offer a wide range of makeup services a professional beauty therapist or makeup artist must be able to offer different types of makeup such as:

- Day makeup
- Evening/glamour makeup
- Photographic makeup
- Camouflage makeup

ACTIVITY

Develop a treatment card for makeup so that you can conduct a consultation and agree on the makeup plan, including corrective work, colours and style. Use your template when working with a partner, record all their details and the makeup plan, so your treatment runs smoothly.

Preparing for the makeup treatment

Sterilisation/hygiene
As with all treatments it is essential that good hygiene practices are followed, so that the makeup is applied as safely and expertly as possible with no risk of cross-infection.

MAKEUP EQUIPMENT	HYGIENE PROCEDURE
Towels	Washed on high temperature to destroy harmful organisms
Makeup palette	Wash thoroughly and placed in an ultra-violet cabinet
Makeup sponge	Washed thoroughly and disinfected
Makeup brushes	Washed thoroughly then placed in ultra-violet cabinet. Advisable to have a few sets of brushes available so there is always a set ready to use
Disposable mascara wands	Use new each time and throw away after treatment
Disposable lip brushes	Use new each time and throw away after treatment
Disposable eye shadow sponges	Use new each time and throw away after treatment
Pencils	Sharpened before each client to expose a clean surface
Hands	Washed before and after treatment

Equipment

As well as the basic equipment needed for a facial treatment, you will need the following additional equipment:

TOOL/ EQUIPMENT	USE	BENEFITS	TIP	IMAGE
Makeup brushes	A range of good quality makeup brushes are essential to be able to correctly apply each cosmetic, e.g. blusher brush, lip brush	Makeup can be applied expertly, with a professional finish and can often last longer	Brushes made from natural hair are often the best, giving a great result and lasting a long time	Beauty Express

Makeup treatment plan card	A card that carries the details of the makeup: which products, colours, how applied, etc.	So the look can be repeated exactly if necessary, nothing is left to chance. The card should be attached to the record card	It is especially important when it is a trial run, as you need to repeat the makeup exactly on the big day!	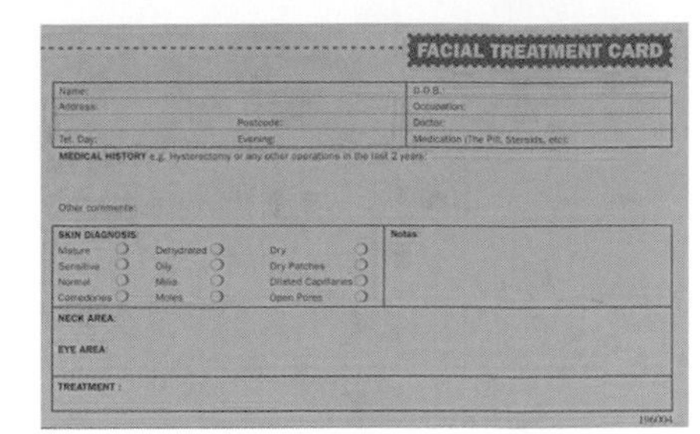 FACIAL TREATMENT CARD Name: / D.O.B.: Address: / Occupation: Postcode: / Doctor: Tel. Day: Evening: / Medication (The Pill, Steroids, etc): MEDICAL HISTORY e.g. Hysterectomy or any other operations in the last 2 years: Other comments: SKIN DIAGNOSIS: Mature, Dehydrated, Dry, Sensitive, Oily, Dry Patches, Normal, Milia, Dilated Capillaries, Comedones, Moles, Open Pores Notes: NECK AREA: EYE AREA: TREATMENT: Beauty Express
Cosmetic sponges	Small specialised sponges for applying foundation			Beauty Express
Makeup palette	Usually a plastic or glass palette that allows mixing of makeup.	Small amounts of makeup are placed on the palette, and then you work directly from the palette. Much more hygienic, there is no risk of cross infection	Use the palette to mix and blend 'prescription' colours to suit the person exactly, e.g. lipsticks	 Beauty Express
Disposable mascara wands	Mascara wand that is used only once and then thrown away	Enables mascara to be applied hygienically, without the need for sterilising brushes, etc.	Can be used to apply colour to the eyebrows, for better definition	 Beauty Express

Disposable lip brushes	Lip brush that is used only once and then thrown away	Enables lipstick to be applied hygienically, without the need for sterilising brushes, etc.	Also useful for applying eye shadow or eyeliner close to the eye	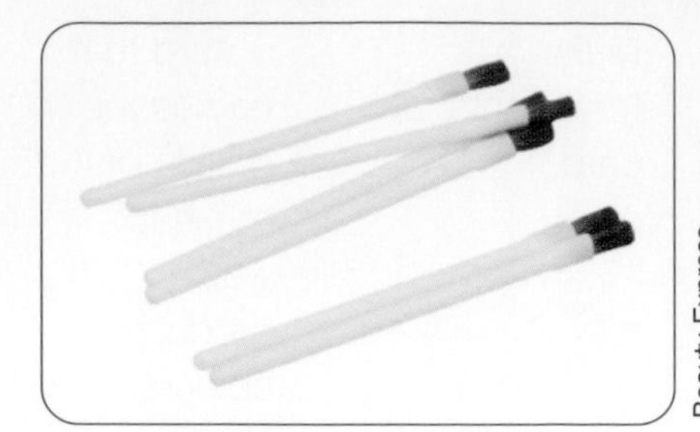 Beauty Express

TYPES OF MAKEUP BRUSHES	
TYPE	**DESCRIPTION**
Concealer brush	Small flat brush used to blend concealer over blemishes, spots, dark circles under eyes, areas of pigmentation, etc.
Foundation brush	Some therapists prefer to apply foundation with a brush rather than a makeup sponge. Half the size of a powder brush, with a flatter end, so it can easily blend the foundation without showing any brush strokes
Face powder brush	Large brush, full and round. Used for blending loose powder into the skin, and removing any excess
Contour brush	Smaller than a blusher brush, with shorter hairs. It is used to blend shader and highlighter onto the face to enhance the face shape
Blusher brush	Similar to the powder brush but roughly half the size and slightly flatter. Applies blusher to the cheek bones
Eyeshadow brush	Small short-haired brush used for general shading
Angled eyeshadow brush	Small short-haired brush with an angled edge, which is important for blending in the socket area
Sponge applicator	Some prefer to apply and blend eyeshadow with a sponge: loose powder eyeshadow doesn't tend to flick onto the surrounding skin as much

Eyebrow brush	Short bristles arranged like a thin tooth brush. It is used to brush the eyebrows into shape and remove any powder. It may have a comb on the opposite side of the bristles for separating lashes
Eyeliner brush	Small very thin pointed brush, used to apply eyeliner or to blend kohl or eye pencils
Lip brush	A lip brush needs to be small, flat and fairly stiff so that the lips can have a clean edge

Makeup products

PRODUCT	USE	DIFFERENT TYPES
Foundation	Provides the complexion with an even colour and texture, enhancing the skin's natural colour tone	• Cream • Liquid • Mousse • Gel • Pressed powder/block
Face powder	Sets the foundation, making it last all day and provides a smooth dry base for other powders such as blusher	• Pressed/block/cake • Loose
Shaders	Minimises areas, useful for corrective work	• Powder • Cream • Gel • Stick
Highlighters	Draws attention to areas, helping to enhance features	• Powder • Cream • Gel • Stick
Blushers	Adds warmth and colour to the cheeks, giving a healthy glow	• Pressed powder/block • Loose powder • Cream • Gel • Liquid

© iStockphoto.com/Kris Hanke

Eyeshadow	Enhance the eyes	• Pressed powder/block • Loose powder • Cream • Pencils/crayons • Gel • Water colours
Eyebrow makeup	Defines the eyebrow	• Pencil • Block/powder
Eyeliner	Defines the eye, and can help make lashes appear longer	• Pencil • Liquid • Block/cake
Mascara	Length, thicken, curl and colour the eyelashes	• Wand/liquid • Block
Lipstick	Adds colour to the lips to balance the face	• Stick • Tube • Pot/container • Pencils/crayons
Lip gloss	To add gloss and shine to the lips	• Wand • Tube • Pot/container

Basic principles of makeup application

When applying makeup you need to be organised, fully prepared and to avoid wasting time it is best to follow a detailed plan. Makeup is usually applied in the following sequence:

1. Colour correction or primer e.g. green tinted cream
2. Foundation
3. Concealer
4. (Cream/gel shaders and highlighters)
5. Face powder
6. Powder shaders and highlighters
7. Eyebrow pencil/colour
8. Eye-shadow

9 Eye-pencil or Kohl pencil
10 Eyeliner
11 Mascara
12 Blusher
13 Lip liner
14 Lipstick and gloss

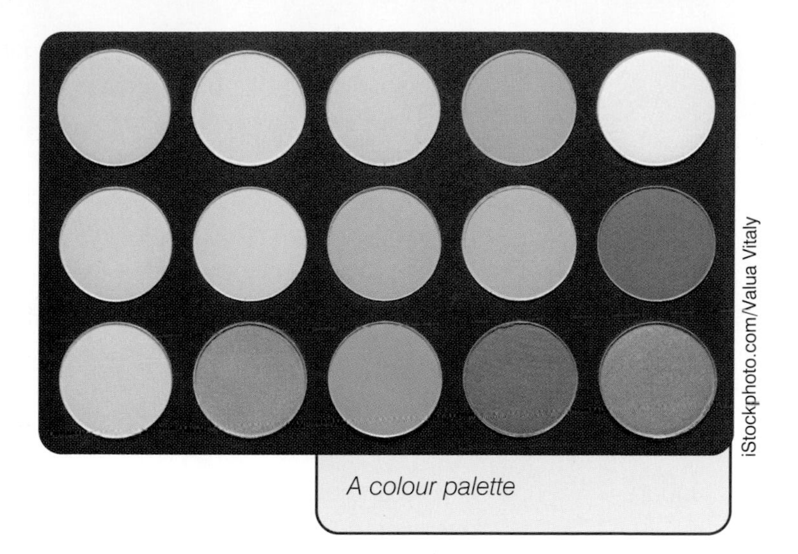
iStockphoto.com/Valua Vitaly

A colour palette

Face shapes – corrective makeup techniques

FACE SHAPE	CORRECTIVE MAKEUP	IMAGE
Oval	Thought to be an ideal, balanced face shape. Apply blusher along the cheekbone, highlighter above it and shader below to enhance the bone structure	
Oblong/long	Length needs reducing, and extra width creating. Apply shader to the top of the forehead and tip of the chin. Blend highlighter over the temple area and lower jaw to create width	

Round	Full and rounded cheeks need slimming down, so a subtle highlighter could accentuate the tip of the chin and down the centre of the face to give the illusion of length. Blusher is applied along the cheekbone extending up to the temple. In addition shader should be blended over the lower cheek area and angle of the jaw, and temple area	
Square	The angles of the face need softening to create a more oval effect. Blend shader over the angles of the lower jaw and both corners of the forehead. Blusher is applied to the cheek bones toward the temple area, and highlighter just above to create a rounded effect	
Heart shape	The forehead needs to look narrower and the lower face wider to achieve a more balanced look. Shader is applied to the sides of the forehead and temples. Apply blusher to the cheek bone and highlighter to the lower cheek and angles of the lower jaw	
Diamond shape	Needs to be more balanced to create a more oval effect. To reduce the length apply shader to the chin and top of the forehead. To widen the narrowest parts, apply highlighter to the temple area and angle of the lower jaw. Apply blusher along the cheek bone to create fullness	

Pear shaped	The opposite of the heart shape – forehead needs widening and lower part of the face slimming down. Apply highlighter to the sides of the forehead and temples. Apply blusher along the cheek bone and shader to the sides of the cheek and angle of the lower jaw	

General characteristics – corrective makeup techniques

PROBLEM	CORRECTIVE MAKEUP
Sallow skin	A lilac tinted moisturiser or primer is applied before the foundation, which then gives a brighter effect
High colour/florid	A green tinted moisturiser or primer can be applied before the foundation, which should not be pink-toned, its better if it is beige
Dark circles under eyes	A concealer/specialist product can be applied, or a foundation a shade lighter than for the rest of the face
Puffiness around eyes	Apply a darker shade of foundation over the swollen area to minimise the puffiness
Excess 'down' hair on face	Don't apply loose face powder, avoid it as it makes the hairs more obvious and can be caught in the 'downy' hair
Double chin	Apply shader or a darker shade of foundation to the double chin area to minimise the appearance
Receding chin	Apply highlighter or a lighter shade of foundation to emphasise the chin.

Nose shapes – corrective makeup techniques

NOSE SHAPE	CORRECTIVE MAKEUP
Long	To make the nose appear shorter, apply shader to the tip and highlighter to the sides
Wide	To narrow the nose, apply shader on the sides
Short	The nose will appear longer if you apply highlighter down the centre of the nose to the tip

Eye shapes – corrective makeup techniques

EYE SHAPE	CORRECTIVE MAKEUP	IMAGE
Wide-set	The eyes will appear closer together if you extend the eye shadow to the inner corner of the eye towards the bridge of the nose. Darker colours on the inner eye area and lighter on the outer draws the eyes together. Eyebrows can be shaped to start slightly further inwards than normal	
Close-set	Eyes will appear wider-set if you keep darker colours to the outer eye area, and lighter on the inner area. Ensure eyebrows are shaped to widen the area between the brows, as this helps draw the eyes outwards	
Deep-set	Eye lids need to appear to be larger and more forward, so apply lighter or frosted colours all over the eyelid. Blend a darker shade in the socket to add definition to the eye area. Eyeliner can be applied on the outer lower lash line to balance the eye	
Round	These eyes may appear more attractive if they are slightly elongated. Apply darker shadow to the outer eye area in a v-shape. Add soft eye liner on the outer part of the top and bottom lids extending slightly beyond where the lashes finish, smudge for a more subtle effect	

Small	Light colours on the lid can make the eye appear larger, as will highlighting under the brow area. White pencil on the inner rim of the lower lid can open up the eye, and soft eye liner can be used on the outer part of the lower lash line, smudged so it is subtle
Prominent/protruding	The eyelid needs minimising, so apply a darker colour matt shadow. On top apply a slightly darker matt shade to the outer lid area blending it towards the socket. Balance the brow area by applying a highlighter under the brow

Lip shapes – corrective makeup techniques

MOUTH/LIP SHAPE	CORRECTIVE MAKEUP
Very thin lips	Draw a line slightly outside of the natural lip shape, fill with a light shade of lipstick and gloss if appropriate
Large full lips	Darker colours make the lips appear smaller, and a lip liner can be used to draw a line slightly inside the natural lip shape
Drooping mouth	On the top lip don't extend the lip liner into the very corners of the mouth. On the lower lip, extend to the outer corner but build up the corners in an upward direction to give a subtle lift
Straight upper lip	Create a 'bow' by using a lip liner to draw a natural subtle bow shape. Highlighter can be applied to the outer side of the lip liner to give a fuller look, more of a 'pout'
Asymmetric/ unbalanced	Whether it be the top or bottom lip, or one side that is out of symmetry, simply use the lip pencil to draw the desired shape that will create a balanced effect

Corrective makeup for very thin lips

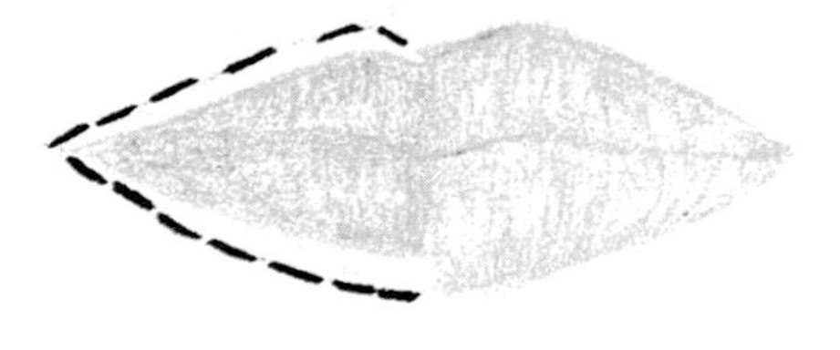

Corrective makeup for large full lips

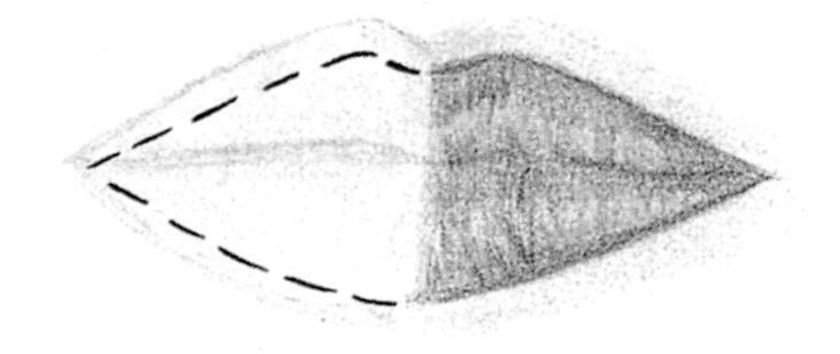

Corrective makeup for asymetric lips

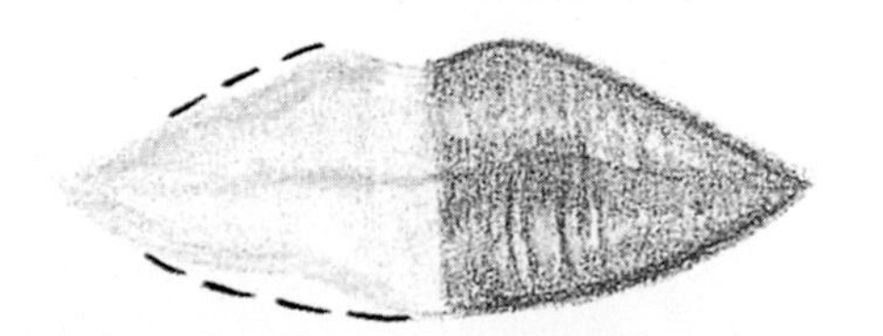

Top tip

Always have good lighting when you apply makeup. Daylight is best or a warm white fluorescent light. However if the makeup is for evening, the stage or a photographic studio, you need to try and create the same lighting effect so you can ensure the makeup will be ideally suited for the occasion.

Make sure you have all the makeup products laid out before the treatment

© Habia and Cengage Learning

Makeup application

Use hair clips to keep the hair secured off the face and ensure skin has been thoroughly cleansed, toned and moisturised, and there is no excess grease on the skin. Blot if necessary.

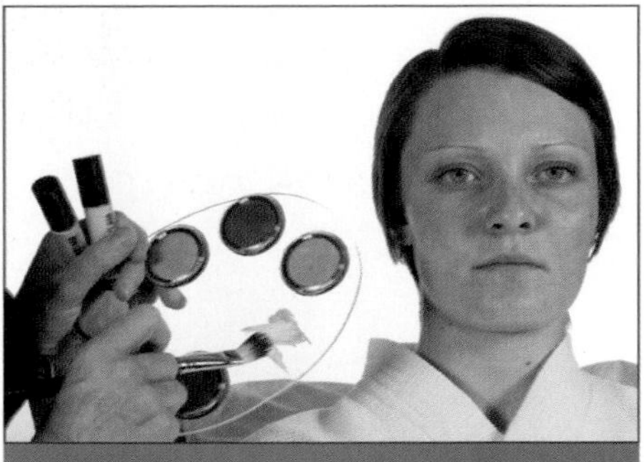

1 If appropriate, apply a colour corrective cream e.g. green tinted for high colour. If using cream shader and highlighter, apply a small amount to enhance the features.

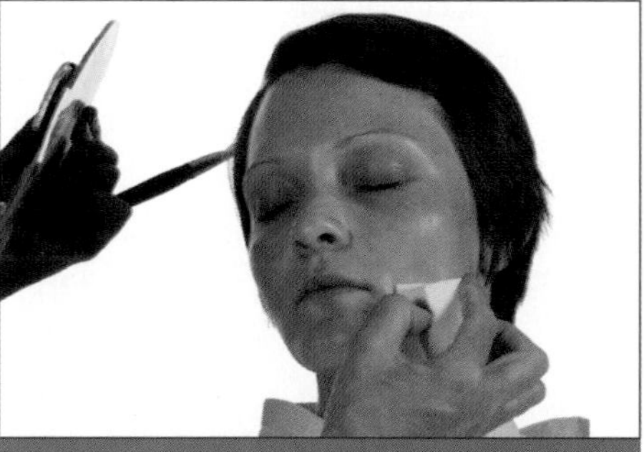

2 Select the correct type and colour of foundation, test the colour on the lower cheek area. Apply the foundation with a special brush or makeup sponge to get an even professional finish. Apply and blend the foundation from the centre of the face outwards, taking care to blend carefully around the jaw and nose.

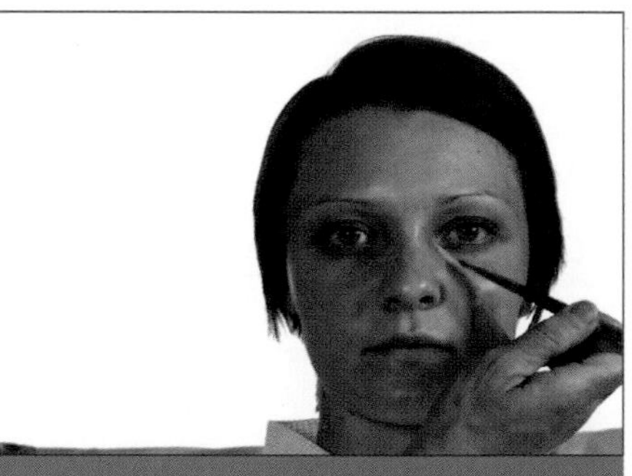

3 Place a small amount of concealer/corrector onto a makeup palette, and using a small brush apply to the under eye area, blend well to cover any darkness under the eye. Apply concealer to any blemishes.

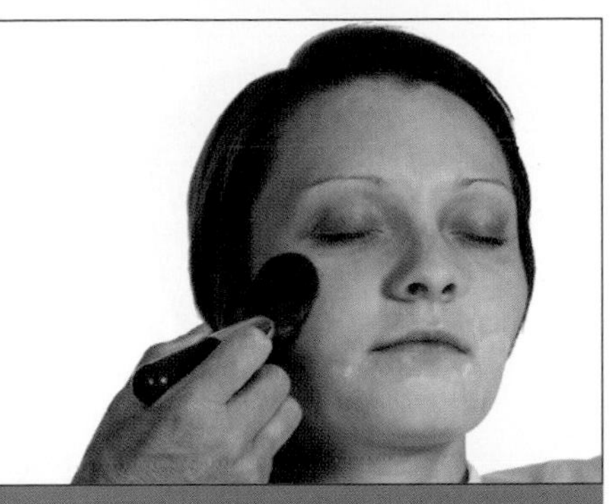

4 Select the correct colour of face powder. Apply a small amount in the palm of your hand, and with a small pad of dry cotton wool lightly press the powder into the skin all over the face and neck, including eyes and lips. Take a large clean powder brush and remove any excess powder, finish with downward strokes. Apply extra face powder under the eye area, so that it protects the skin from any excess eye-shadow that is 'flicked' from the brush.

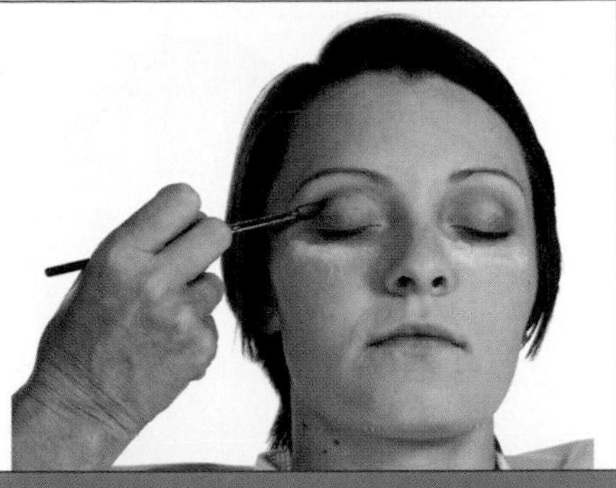

5 Using a disposable eye shadow applicator or clean brush, apply the eye shadow, following the plan agreed during the consultation. Start with a base shade over the entire eye area. Build the eye colour up slowly to define the socket and enhance the eyes.

6 Using a disposable mascara wand, apply two coats of mascara carefully. First ask the client to look down, and apply the mascara to the top of the upper lashes. Finally apply to the under side of the upper lashes in an upwards direction. The lower lashes can be included if appropriate.

If possible a professional beauty therapist will always do a 'trial' makeup before the big occasion, this helps the client feel confident, with no worries, and helps the therapist plan her time and application. This is vital for bridal makeup, but is recommended for all important occasions.

Top tip

Using an eyebrow brush/comb, brush the eyebrows to ensure they are neat and all the hairs are lying flat (you can use a little hairspray on your finger, stroke along the brow to encourage them to stay in place!)

Top tip

Measure from the nostril up past the inner edge of the eye, to decide where the eyebrows should begin. To decide where the eyebrows should end, measure from the nostril past the outer corner of the eye.

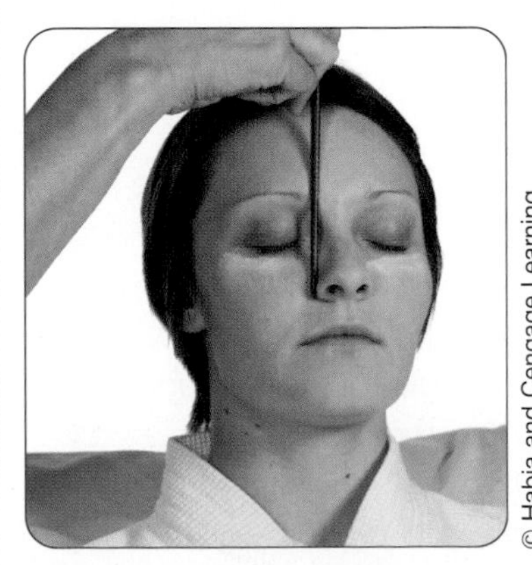

7 With a clean brush apply blusher along the cheek bone, apply a little at a time, outwards and upwards, building the colour up slowly.

8 Blot the lips, and using a sharp lip pencil outline the lips with a colour matched to the chosen lipstick. Apply a small amount of lipstick to a spatula or pallet, and with a disposable lip brush carefully apply the lipstick, blot and repeat.

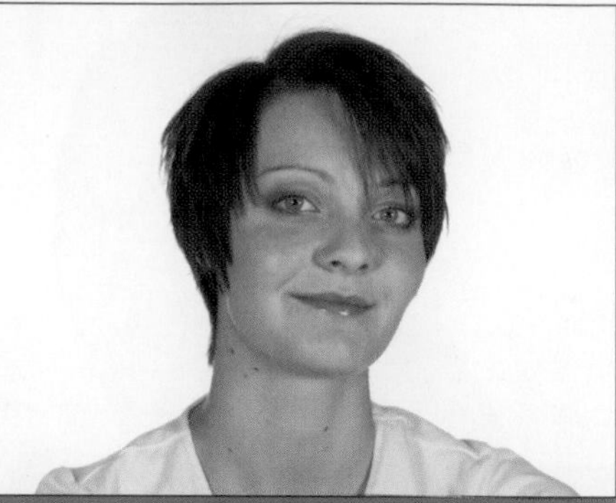

9 Remove hair clips, show the client the finished result in a hand mirror. Be sure to make any small adjustments the client wants, so that she is very happy with the final effect.

Top tip **Make sure there is natural light available when applying a day** time makeup, as artificial lighting may distort the colours and the result could be a look that is much too heavy for the day time.

Top tip **Shader and highlighter can be applied to enhance the face** shape and general features. Fantastic results can be achieved, highlighting all the good points and minimising any imperfections. Just look at some 'before and after' shots of celebrities, and you'll see why they won't go anywhere without their makeup artist!

Top tip **Eyes and lips can be** included when applying foundation, as it acts as a good base for the makeup to follow and will help it last longer – till dawn if necessary!

Top tip **If appropriate apply a colour corrective cream e.g. green tinted for** high colour. Some makeup companies offer a primer that goes under foundation to make the skin glow, which looks effective in the evening.

Top tip **Apply extra face** powder under the eye area, so that it protects the skin from any excess eye-shadow that is 'flicked' from the brush – this is very hard to remove and can ruin the makeup.

Makeup for special occasions

The same application procedure is followed, but you would adapt the style and colours to suit the occasion, lighting, outfit, etc.

Prom makeup

Don't use a headband, use a few grips/clips instead so you don't flatten the hair completely. Ensure skin has been thoroughly cleansed, toned and moisturised, and there is no excess grease on the skin. Blot if necessary.

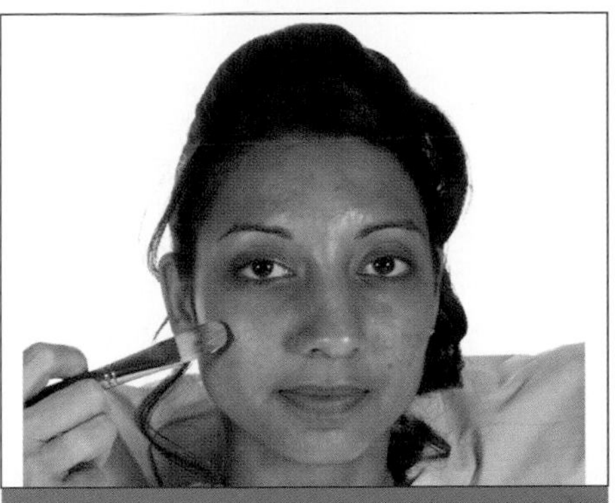

1 In the evening you can use a foundation a shade darker than in the day, as the light isn't as harsh. Apply with a special brush or makeup sponge to get an even professional finish. Cream shader and high lighter can be applied at this stage to enhance the features. Apply and blend the foundation from the centre of the face outwards, taking care to blend carefully around the jaw, nose and hairline.

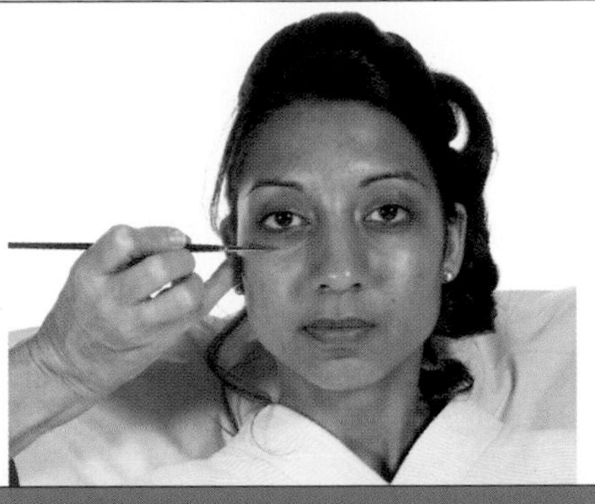

2 Cover blemishes with concealer: make sure you have covered any spots, uneven pigmentation and under-eye shadows so that it will provide a great base for the foundation. Time spent at this stage will pay off later as you want to achieve a flawless, glamorous final look.

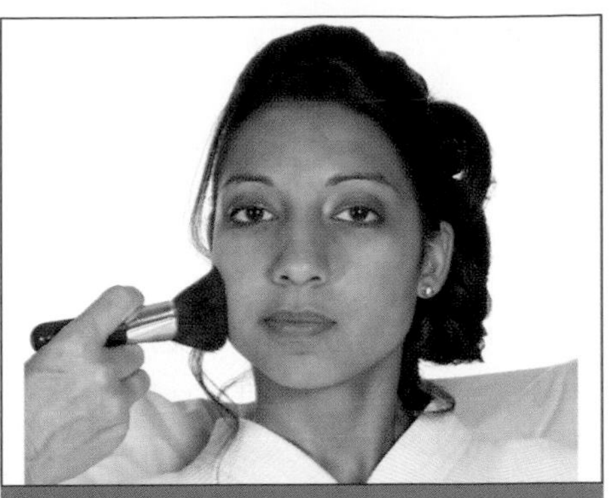

3 Select the correct colour of face powder – in the evening you can apply a powder with a subtle shimmer or shine, as it can look very glamorous. Be careful that it isn't too glittery. Apply a small amount in the palm of your hand, and with a small pad of dry cotton wool or a special applicator, lightly press the powder into the skin all over the face and neck, including eyes and lips.Take a large clean powder brush and remove any excess powder, finish with downward strokes.

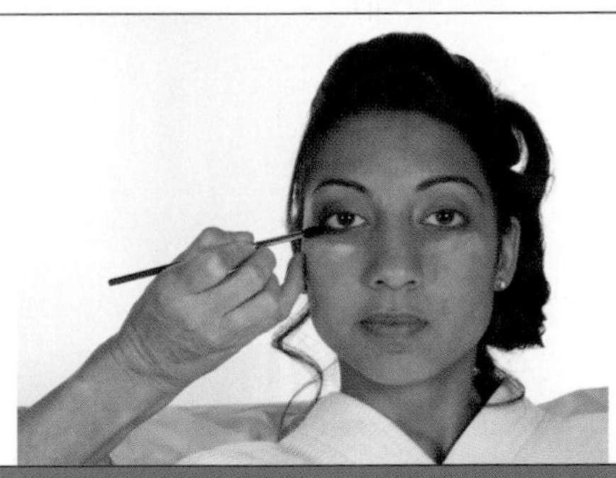

4 Apply the eye shadow, following the plan agreed with the client. Start with a base shade over the entire eye area. Build the colour up slowly to define the socket and enhance the eyes. Make the eyes a strong feature, so that they are the focus of the makeup.

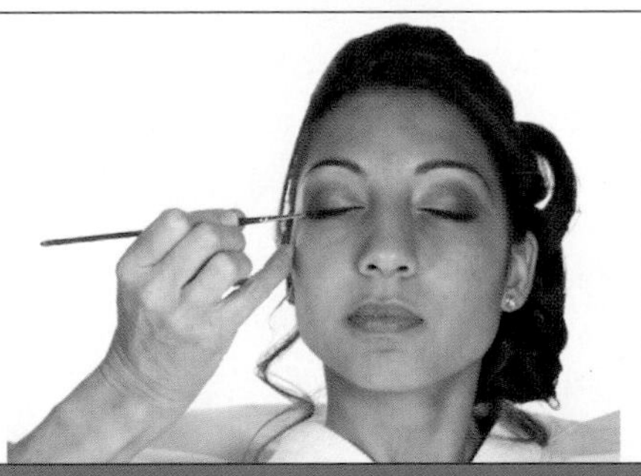

5 Apply eye shadow carefully under the eye, just below the lower lash line, and blend well, if appropriate apply eyeliner to the lash line.

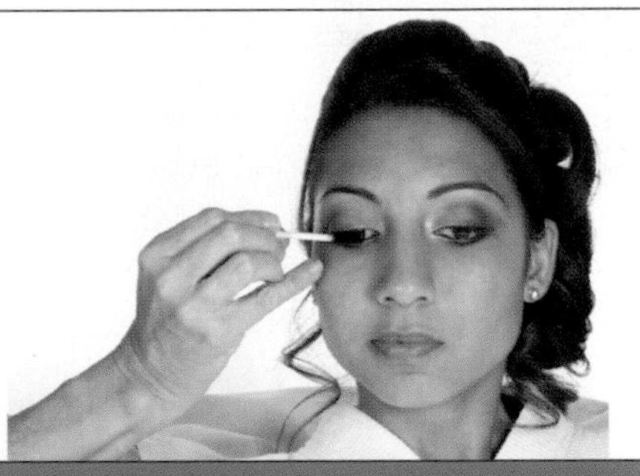

6 Using a disposable mascara wand, apply two coats of mascara carefully. First ask the client to look down , and apply the mascara to the top of the upper lashes. Finally apply to the under side of the upper lashes in an upwards direction. The lower lashes can be included if appropriate. A very steady hand is needed, so as not to irritate the client and make the eyes water.

Top tip Using an eyebrow brush, apply eyebrow colour to the brows to enhance the natural shape. Many eyebrows have 'gaps' or need extending at the outer edge.

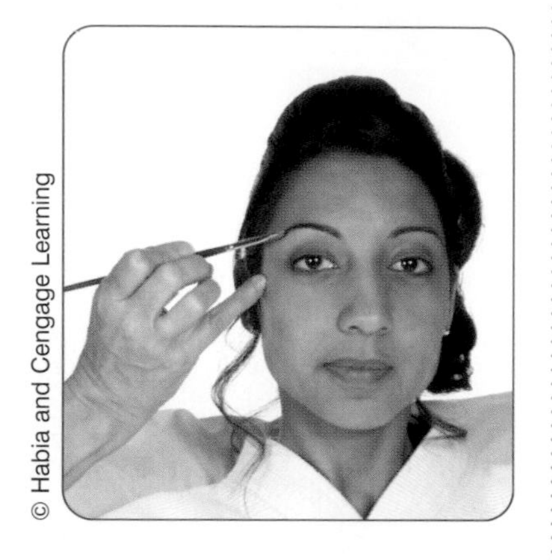

ACTIVITY

'Proms' are now very popular and an exciting event for many young people. Conduct some research into the 'total look' including information on hair, beauty, makeup, dresses and shoes for Proms. Present your findings and share with your group/colleagues (websites such as prettyforprom.com may be useful).

Top tip Decant the chosen eye shadow onto the makeup palette – in the evening you can use bolder, sparkling, shimmery colours, that enhance the eyes, hair and outfit. Consider the 'total look' so that it all works together well and looks a knockout!

Top tip There are some exciting mascara colours for special occasions, plus an increasing range of false strip lashes, some with glitter or diamante on the tips.

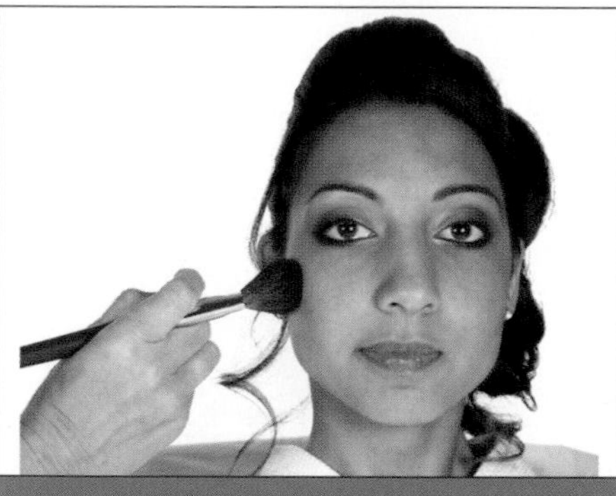

7 Apply blusher along the cheek bone, apply a little at a time, outwards and upwards – in the evening you can be more adventurous and use a shimmery blusher if appropriate.

8 Blot the lips, and using a sharp lip pencil outline the lips with a colour matched to the chosen lipstick. Once again you can be much bolder with evening makeup, using a darker shade, or a shimmery/glittery colour. Apply a small amount of lipstick to a spatula or pallet, and with a disposable lip brush carefully apply the lipstick, blot and repeat. Apply lots of gloss to bring the lips alive.

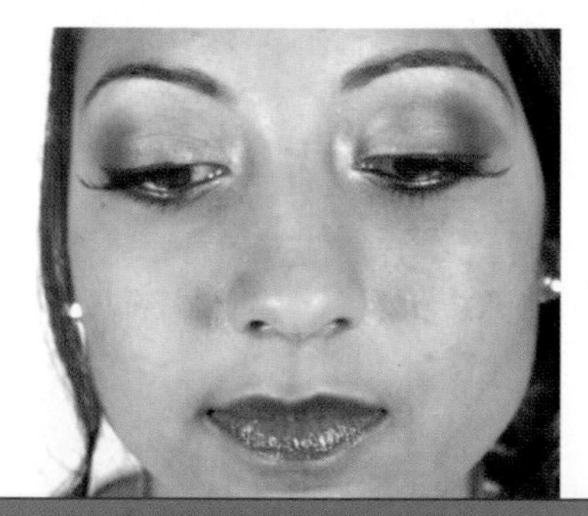

9 Show the finished result in a hand mirror. Be sure to make any small adjustments that they want.

© Habia and Cengage Learning

Prom makeup

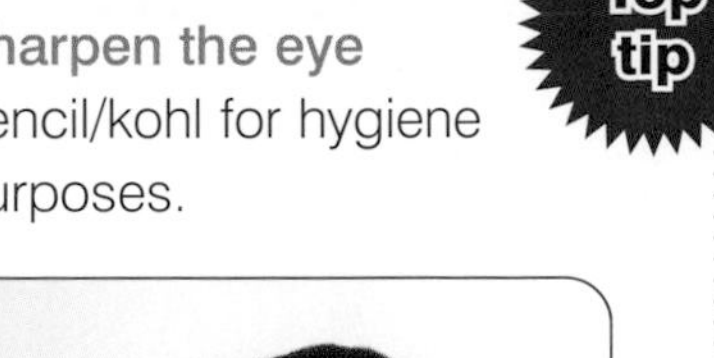

Sharpen the eye pencil/kohl for hygiene purposes.

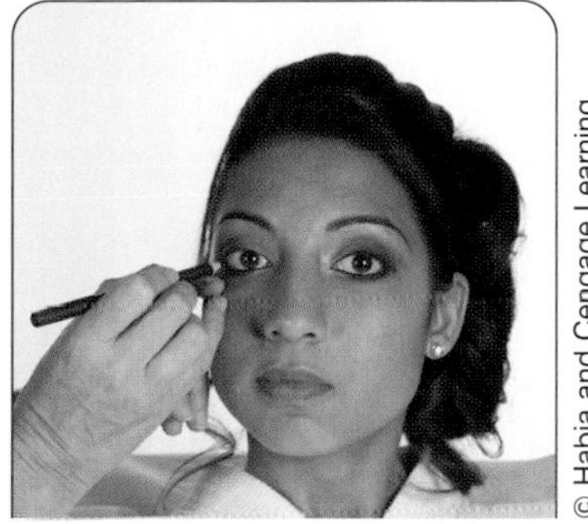
© Habia and Cengage Learning

Top tip

Special occasion makeup can usually take a slightly heavier application of eye pencil or kohl pencil, as in the evening it needs a stronger line to define the eyes. Apply carefully to the lash line, or on the inner rim of the lower lid if appropriate.

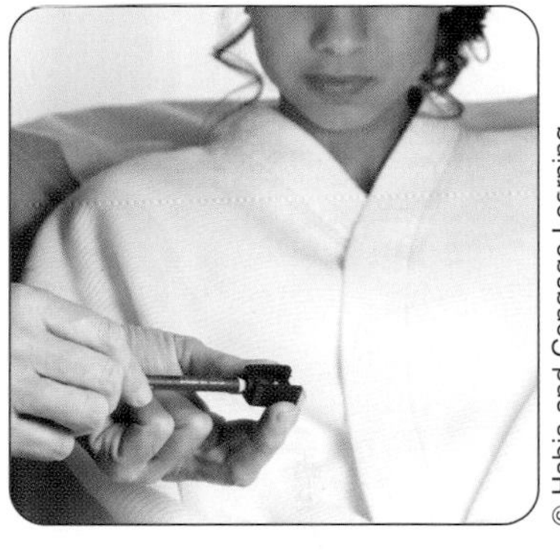
© Habia and Cengage Learning

EXTEND YOUR LEARNING

Makeup project

Find out if your college or school is holding an event such as:

- Theatre Play
- Musical
- Concert
- Prom

Ask if you can be involved in doing the makeup for the event or for an individual person. Maybe if it is a large event you will need to work as a team. Consider:

- planning
- equipment/tools
- makeup products
- audience
- lighting
- number of performers
- can you do a 'trial' makeup before the event?
- reflect on results/feedback/review

Present your project professionally in an attractive booklet, detailing the preparation you undertook, any research necessary, team work, where possible showing photographs of before and after images. If there is the opportunity, do a presentation to the rest of your group so they can share your experience and learn from it.

iStockphoto.com/Amanda Rohde

Make sure all the makeup you use is for sale in the salon

What you have learnt

How to identify the factors that affect skin care services

Lifestyle, personality and different cultural influences.

- How health can effect the skin

How to select skin care products and techniques for different skin types

- How skin allergies can effect the choice of products
- Different types of specialist skin care products available

How to carry out a basic skin care routine

- Superficial cleansing
- Deep cleansing
- Application of a facial scrub
- Application of a face mask

What is a consultation and how to carry one out

- The importance of completing documentation as part of a consultation
- How to carry out a skin analysis

How to choose and apply makeup products to achieve different looks

- Understanding the different products, how they work and when to use them

How to use products, tools and equipment for skin care and makeup

- How to prepare products, tools and equipment ready for the treatments

The terminology related to skin care and beauty services

Assessment activities

Crossword

Across

5 On a nose that appears very wide, what corrective product should be applied along each side? (6)

6 A type of face mask (7)

8 A strong type of toner (10)

12 A substance that causes an allergic reaction on the skin (8)

13 Temporary removal of unwanted body hair (10)

Down

1 A lighter type of toner (8)

2 This can be reflected in your skin (6)

3 These conditions prevent a treatment from being carried out (16)

4 If skin is lacking in moisture (10)

7 Certain people are allergic to this in skin care products (7)

9 A facial scrub does this to the dead skin cells (9)

10 The facial product that is applied after cleansing but before moisturising (5)

11 If a skin has high colour, what colour cream can be applied under the foundation to tone it down (5)

Wordsearch

A P R O D U C T S S G E J F O F W U P
R L U H W H N L P K N Y F B C M S N K
E Y L C A Q W X S I I T X S H A D E R
T E N E A C Z L T N T I M Z L T W S S
H J C O R M K U W C H L F P L L F P P
G I V E U G O H T A G A K U I H W A O
I D A T J R Y F Y R I N K F K T O T N
L M N L J G I T C E L O E Z S L R U G
H N C A I F U S Z D I S P O S A B L E
G O O E B A W U H L T R M C Q E E A N
I Y N I E D G P V Y T E K A G H Y V H
H E S B T S A V L T C P S U K Y E F A
E T T E L A P E M A S C A R A E S H N
O K F E A P D U H C C R M K N C U A C
O T D O K V Z N O E A O U J C U H P E
N O I H S A F W U T D G L H S E A V C
A N Z G L A M O R O U S E O F Y T P J
R E L A E C N O C L F E I S U N P V N
Q R S T E A M I N G K X O V D R N P C

Spatula
Headband
Beauty
Nourish
Fashion
Palette
Allergy
Colour

Eyebrow
Toner
Steaming
Mask
Personality
Products
Health
Skill

Cheek
Foundation
Lifestyle
Enhance
Skincare
Shader
Glamorous
Sponge

Routine
Lighting
Mascara
Hygiene
Concealer
Disposable
Highlighter
Makeup

Assessment question: Skin analysis

Choose a partner and conduct a simple skin analysis. In each of the following areas of the face write down what you can see. Then analyse all the characteristics and come to a conclusion on the overall skin type. You may need to recap skin types in Chapter 4 'The science of hair and beauty'.

AREA	CHARACTERISTICS
Forehead	
Cheeks	
Chin	
Nose	
Eye area	
Neck	
Overall muscle tone/firmness	
Overall skin colour, circulation and pigmentation	
Overall skin type is:	
Normal ☐	
Dry ☐	
Oily ☐	
Combination ☐	
Additional characteristics:	
Sensitive ☐	
Dehydrated ☐	
Moist ☐	
Oedematous/puffy ☐	
Comments:	
Signature:	Date:

Assessment question: Skin products

On the table below, next to each product, add the type of skin that it is most suitable for.

PRODUCT TYPE	BEST FOR WHICH TYPE OF SKIN?
Cleansers	
Cleansing milk	
Cleansing cream	
Cleansing lotion	
Foaming cleanser	
Cleansing bar	
Toners/freshners	
Skin bracer/freshner	
Skin tonic	
Astringent	
Moisturisers	
Moisturising lotion	
Moisturising cream	
Specialist creams/serums	
Night cream	
Neck cream	
Eye cream	
Eye gel	
Serums/ampoules	

Assessment question: Corrective makeup

You will need four blank templates of the outline of the face. On each template you have to design and plan a makeup, and colour in the template. The four designs need to reflect the application you feel is appropriate for the following occasions and individuals:

1. Day makeup for someone with a square jaw and very close-set eyes.
2. Wedding makeup for a person with a very long shaped face.
3. Makeup for an interview; the person has a very long shaped nose and wide-set eyes.
4. Prom makeup; the individual has a triangular shaped face (widest point across the forehead) and dark circles under the eyes.

Present your work as neatly and professionally as possible.

Project: Different concepts of beauty

Choose two countries that are geographically far apart and appear to have very different cultures, e.g. India and Iceland. Research, then compare and contrast each country's concept of beauty, including:

- Brief background history of the country
- History of their concept of beauty
- Any significant developments?
- Is there a beauty industry established?
- Popular treatments?
- Popular products?
- Linked to hair or health sector?
- Beauty in the media?
- International influences?
- 'Beauty' stereotypes – male and female

Present your project professionally in an attractive booklet, detailing all the information you discovered, showing images where appropriate. If there is the opportunity, make someone up or draw images in the style considered beautiful for each of the two countries, including dress, hair, makeup, etc. Deliver a presentation to the rest of your group so they can share your research and learn from it.

8

hair care and styling

Arena: Leonardo Rizzo @ Sanrizz

I am surprised I have so much hair after all the things I have done with it.

DAVID BECKHAM 1975–, FOOTBALLER

Introduction

Have you noticed how many hairstyling magazines you can buy today? When you look through them you will see the possibilities for styling hair are endless. Hairstyles designed for long or short hair, straight or curly hair. Hairstyles that are simple or elaborate – there is always something new you can try. It is great fun experimenting and finding out the different looks you can create for yourself and for others. Experimenting with hairstyles is a good way to develop your creative skills. One of the great things about experimenting with different hairstyles is that the look is not permanent – if you don't like the result, you can just wash it out and start again.

The way you style your hair is very important and can say a great deal about you and the image you want to reveal. Hair can reflect your personality, identity and even your culture. Some hairstyles are easy to achieve because you happen to have the right hair type. Sometimes you may find that you cannot create a certain look for yourself because your hair just won't do want you would like it to. This is because when styling your hair you may not have taken certain factors into consideration.

In this chapter you will explore what those factors are, and the skills and knowledge that will help you style your own hair. Then, you will learn how developing those skills can, if you want to, lead to skills that will enable you to style the hair of others in commercial hairdressing salons and barbershops.

What you will learn

Throughout this chapter you will learn about:

★ The main factors that affect hair care and styling

★ How to take account of the differences in hair types

★ The diverse hairstyles that can be created

★ How to use products, tools and equipment for hair care and styling

★ How to style your own hair and that of others

★ The key historic hair trends that influence the hairstyles you wear today

★ The technological advances which aid hair care and styling

★ The terminology related to hair care and styling

Hair care

Factors affecting hair care and styling

There are certain factors that affect hair care and styling that have to be taken into consideration before you begin. If you do this, you will know that the style you are planning will be achievable and suitable for you, or the person it is intended for. If, when you have considered the factors, you find that it is not possible to achieve the hairstyle you have chosen, you may be able to make some adjustments or compromises to your original plan.

The factors you must consider are:

- the shape of the head
- the shape of the face
- the shape of the body
- lifestyle
- the direction of hair growth
- the amount of natural curl in the hair – hair type
- the texture of the hair
- the strength, or elasticity of the hair
- the amount, or density of the hair
- any skin, hair or scalp conditions that may affect hair care and styling

Once you have considered and analysed these factors you can begin to successfully style hair.

Head shape

In Chapter 4 'The science of hair and beauty' you can see and read about the bones that make up the **cranium**. It is the cranium that gives the head its overall shape. The most prominent and visual bones that affect the shape of the head are the **frontal** bone that forms the forehead and the **occipital** bone. The occipital bone is at the back of the head. You are more likely to see the shape of this bone if the hair is very short, or when the head is shaved.

It's a fact!

The skull is made up of two main parts – the cranium (bones that protect the brain) and the face.

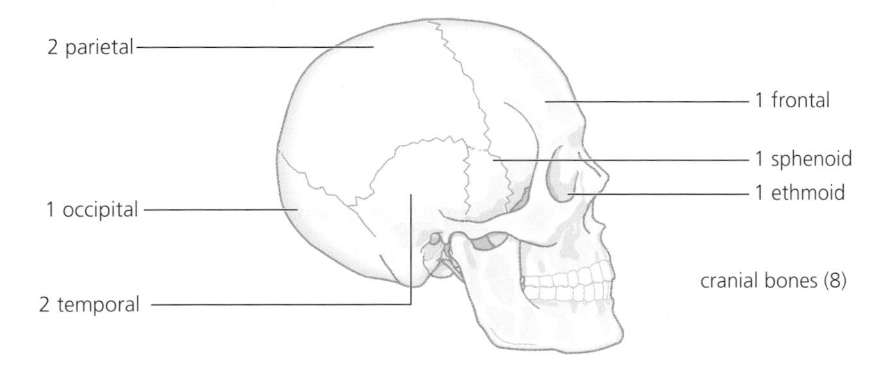

The bones of the skull

ACTIVITY

Work with a partner, or use a mirror, and check the size and shape of your frontal and occipital bones. Is your frontal bone large or small? What is the shape of your head at the back? Depending on the size and shape of your occipital bone, the back of your head may be very full and round. Or, it could be very flat.

The top of the head can also vary in shape. The bones that form this area of the head are the **parietal** bones. Sometimes the top of the head can look quite pointed, sometimes, quite flat.

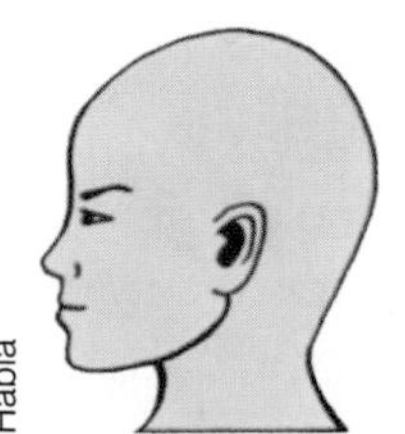
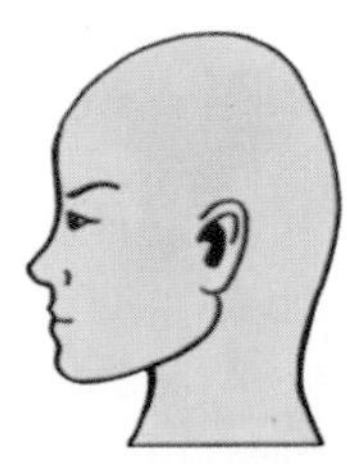
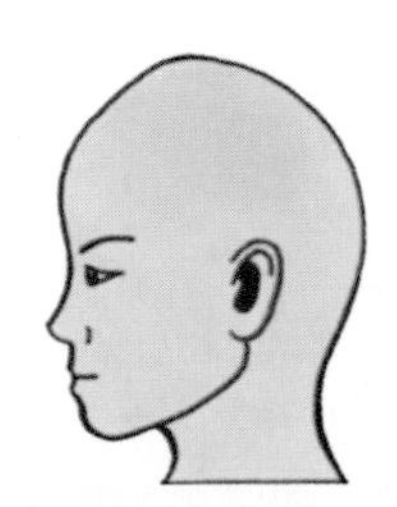
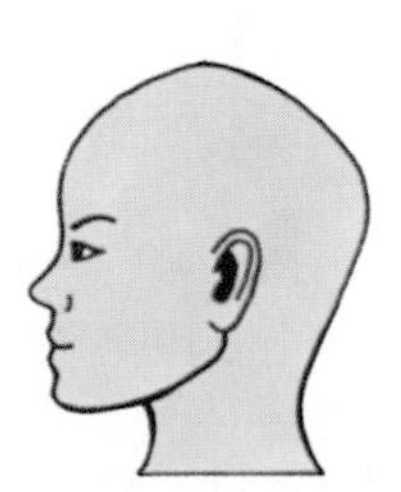
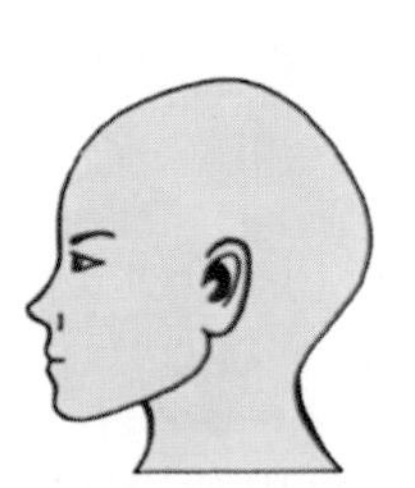

Habia

The different shapes of the head

When professional hairdressers and barbers style hair they ensure that the finished result gives an overall look that is as balanced as possible. So, if the client has a flat occipital bone, this can be disguised by styling the hair so that it stands away from the head at the back. If the client has a very large frontal bone, it can be softened with a fringe. If the parietal bones lie very flat, a hairstyle with a little height can be created to make the top of the head appear rounder.

Face shape

Facial shape with guide lines for analysis

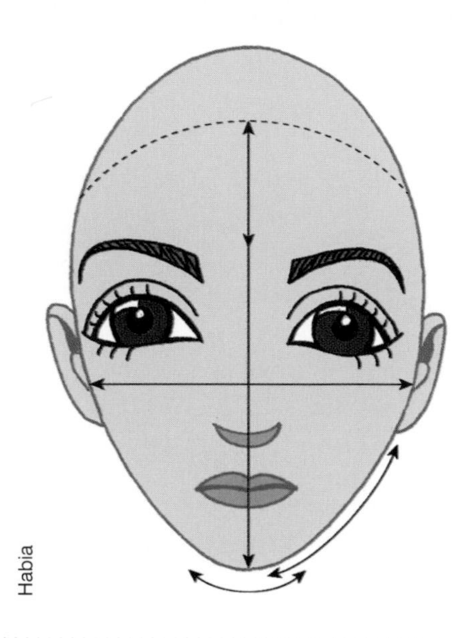

Habia

Everyone has a facial shape that is unique to them – unless you are an identical twin. The bones of the face determine the overall shape and you can read about them in Chapter 4 'The science of hair and beauty'.

The shapes of the face can be categorised as follows:

- **oval**
- **round**
- **square**
- **rectangular**
- **long**
- **heart or triangular**
- **pear**
- **diamond**

You can identify the shape of your face by looking at the:

- length of the face from the top of the forehead to the chin
- the width across the face from ear to ear
- the shape of the jaw line
- the height and shape of the forehead
- the shape of the chin

The length and width of the face will give an indication of the overall shape. If the length is slightly longer than the width, it is likely to be oval. However, if the width and length are equal in length, it is likely to be round or square. A face that is much longer than it is wide is likely to be long or rectangular.

The shape of the forehead and jaw line also influences the facial shape. An angular jaw line will be linked to a square, rectangular or pear shaped face, whereas a curved jaw line will be related to a round, oval, long or pear shaped face.

A pointed chin can indicate a triangular, diamond or heart shaped face.

ACTIVITY   

Take all the hair away from your face, then work with a partner (or look in a mirror), and identify the shape of your face. Use the guidance in the table below to help you make a decision. But – remember this is just a guide and you need to make visual checks for the slight differences between the facial shapes.

		NOTES
Facial length		
the length is much longer than the width	A	
the length is the same as the width	B	
the length is slightly longer than the width	C	
Jaw line		
the jaw line is angular	A	
the jaw line is curved	B	
The jaw line is wider than the forehead	C	
Chin		
the chin is pointed	A	
the chin is curved	B	
Forehead		
the hairline is angular	A	
the hairline is round	B	
the hairline is narrower than the jaw line	C	

Answers (use this for guidance, but remember there will be slight differences that determine the actual shape of the face)

ABBB = oblong

AABA = rectangular

ABAC = diamond

BABA = square

BBBB = round

CBBB = oval

CAAA = triangular

CCBB = pear

The perfect shaped faces

Who can say what the perfect shaped face is? Different people, different cultures, different races, different genders all have their own ideal.

As an individual you should choose a hairstyle that you feel most comfortable with, that reflects your identity, personality and culture. When a professional hairdresser or barber recommends a hairstyle that will suit their clients, they use the head and facial shape as a starting point. Hairstyles will be recommended that flatter and enhance the appearance of the client.

ACTIVITY

Find a range of hairstyles that you think will suit the shape of your face – and state why.

Different body shapes

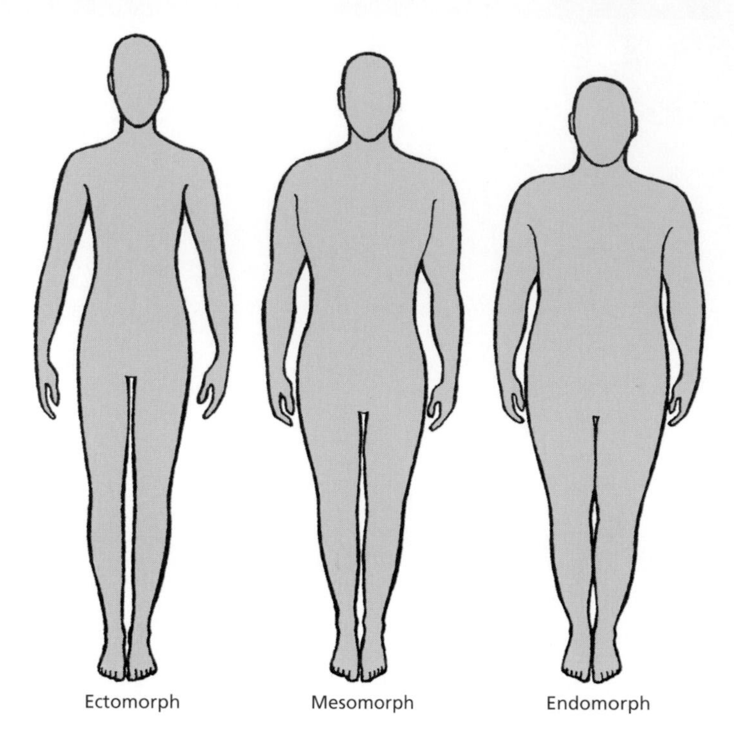

Body shape

When you look at the people around you, you will see that everyone has a different body shape. Some people are naturally tall and slim, others, small and round. The three main body shapes are:

- **Ectomorph** – If you have this body shape you will be tall and slim with long limbs
- **Mesomorph** – If you have this body shape you will have an athletic build with wide shoulders and a narrow waist
- **Endomorph** – If you have this body shape you will have a rounded shape with short limbs and neck

When styling hair, the body shape must be taken into consideration. For example, a tall and slim person may not want a hairstyle that is tall and high – as this will make the body look even longer. However, for someone who has a short, rounded body shape, a hairstyle with height will add length to the body. Likewise, for a person with a very large body, a very short, flat hairstyle may not be in proportion with the rest of their body shape. The reverse can be said for very thin people who wear a very large, full hairstyle – this look is sometimes referred to a *lollipop effect* as the large head is out of proportion to the rest of the body.

Lifestyles

EXTEND YOUR LEARNING  

There are lots of self analysis quizzes that you can complete to find your body shape. Explore the Internet to find out what your body shape is.

Lifestyle

How busy are you? Do you have lots of time to spend on your appearance? Do you play a lot of sport, or do you enjoy swimming, where your hair will be constantly wet? Do you have a job where you have to wear your hair off your shoulders, or perhaps covered up?

Lifestyle will determine how hair is styled. Those who have to wash their hair every day might prefer to have a hairstyle that is easy to maintain – that can be washed and quickly styled or perhaps left to dry naturally. Some people have a lifestyle that requires them to have a change of hairstyles. For example, some people who have long hair may have to tie it back during the day time while they are at work, school or college, but, in their free time, they like to style it in a different way.

Hair growth

The hair grows in distinct patterns all over the head. There are three main areas where you can see individual hair growth patterns. They can be seen at the crown, the nape and the front hairline.

Areas of different hair growth patterns

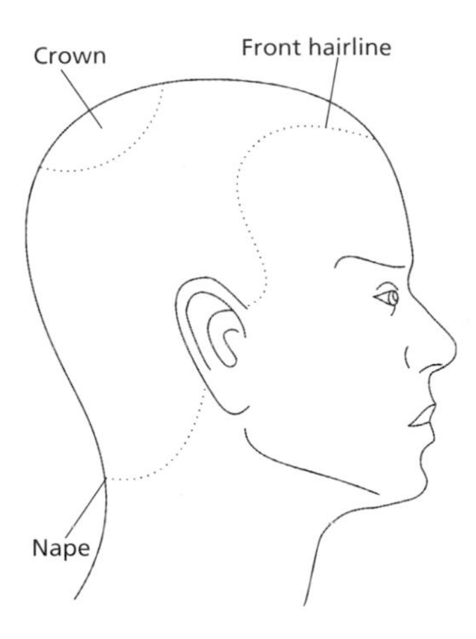

Hair growth patterns at the crown

The **crown** is the area generally found at the top of the head. At this point you can quite plainly see the circular growth pattern of the hair. The vast majority of people only have one crown, but some have a double crown. If there is a double crown, you will be able to see two clear areas of circular growth.

It's a fact!

Sometimes the 'crown' or circular area of hair growth is not at the top of the head in the place you may expect it, but is found on the side of the head, or lower down towards the occipital bone.

It's a fact!

Have you ever noticed that when styling hair, one side goes into the style much easier than the other? The reason for this is due to the direction of hair growth. Hair grows in a circular pattern, going round the head in one direction. The circular pattern begins at the crown. This means that one side of the hairstyle will easily turn under and the other side will turn out. You can clearly see the direction of the hair growth on the head of a baby when the hair first begins to grow.

Double crown

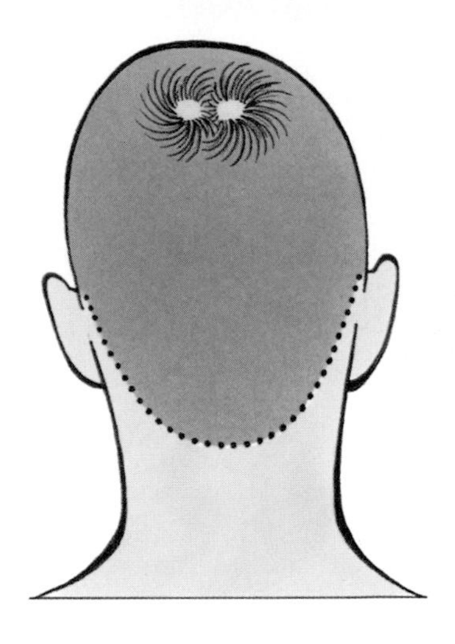

Hair growth patterns at the nape

For some people, the hair at the nape of the neck lies flat and neat – even when it is cut very short. However, most have hair that grows in one, two or even more different directions at the nape of the neck.

These swirling patterns of hair are known as **nape whorls** and they can be seen on one or both sides of the neck. Sometimes the nape whorls grow in the same direction. For example, the hair may grow from the left side of the nape to the right. Or, you may see the hair growing from the right to the left. However, sometimes, the hair grows in opposite directions on either side of the centre of the nape area. When this happens the hair can grow towards the centre, from both sides, creating a tail of hair at the centre.

Hair growth patterns at the front hairline

Some people have hair that grows flat and straight at the front hairline, which means that if they wear a fringe, the fringe also lies flat and straight. However, many people have a hair growth pattern that causes the hair to lift at the roots in one direction or another. The two most common patterns of hair growth at the front hair line are known as a **cowlick** and a **widows peak**.

Cowlick A cowlick is frequently found on one or both sides of the forehead hairline. The hair generally grows back from the hairline meaning that the hair will stick up if you have a short fringe. However, having a cowlick can be an advantage if you wish to create a fringe that is spiky and requires lift in the fringe area. Some cowlicks vary in extreme to others. Some just have a slight change in direction of hair growth, while in others the hair grows straight back, away from the face, across the entire front hairline.

Widows peak With this type of hair growth pattern, the hair initially grows back from a deep point at the centre of the forehead. Alternatively, the hair on both sides of the centre of the forehead can grow into the middle to form a point. The growth pattern is usually symmetrical, at the centre of the forehead and because of this it is very difficult to cut a fringe into the hairstyle.

Nape hair growth patterns

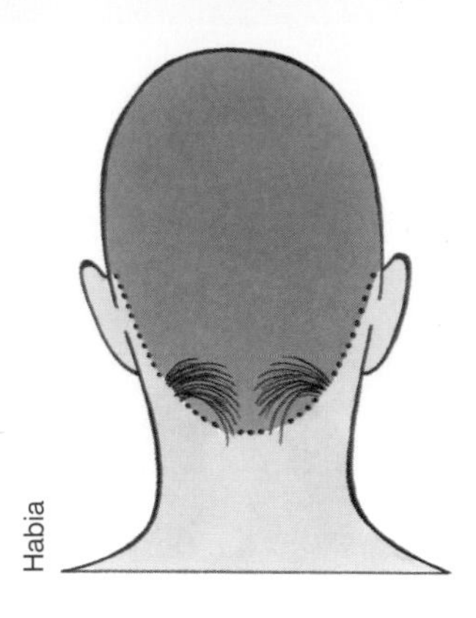

Habia

Cowlick

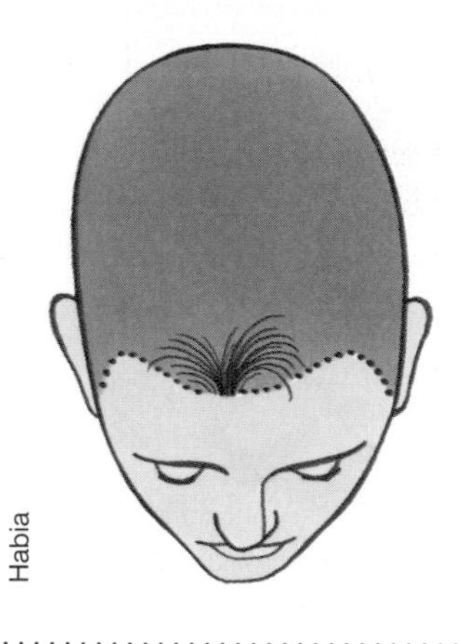

Habia

Widows peak

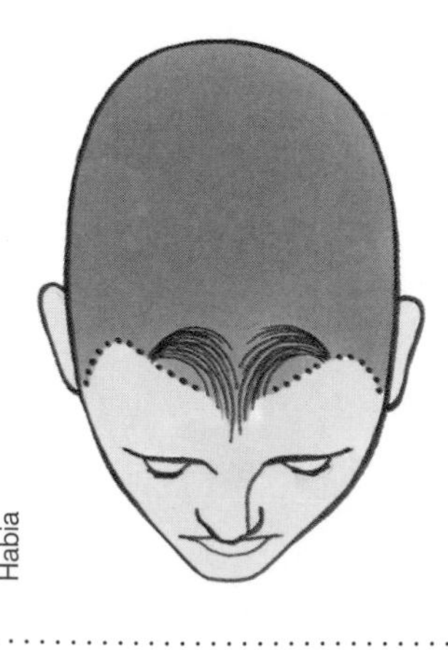

Habia

Hair growth cycle

When choosing a hairstyle, the existing length of the hair must be considered. In Chapter 4 'The science of hair and beauty' you can read all about the hair growth cycle. Hair constantly grows, falls out after a certain length of time and then replaces itself.

Hair type

Some hair is curly, some is straight and some is wavy. The amount of natural curl in the hair is referred to as *hair type*. You can read all about the different hair types in Chapter 4 'The science of hair and beauty'. It is important for you to identify the type of hair so that a hairstyle can be created that is suitable. For very curly hair, it may not be practical to have a hairstyle that requires it to be constantly straightened. Likewise, very straight hair that is curled may need a great deal of time to maintain the look. Therefore, it is generally best to have a hairstyle that matches the existing hair type.

Hair texture

Have you noticed how some hair feels really fine and other hair feels quite coarse? How fine or how coarse your hair feels is known as *hair texture*. Hair texture is measured by the diameter of a single strand of hair. The larger the diameter, the coarser the hair is. Hair texture is important when styling hair, as some hairstyles are easier to achieve with coarse hair – and vice versa.

Hair elasticity

In Chapter 4 you can read all about hair structure and how to carry out the test to check the elasticity of your hair. The more elasticity that is present in the hair, the more you can temporarily change the structure of it when creating hairstyles. Hair that is damaged has less elasticity than hair that is in good condition. This means that if you try to curl hair that is in poor condition, the curl will not last very long, as the bonds in the internal structure which hold the curls in place, are damaged, or lost. Hair with a lack of elasticity can easily be damaged further, or even broken with the excessive use of heated styling equipment such as straighteners or curling tongs.

Hair density

Hair density refers to the amount of hair that is present on the head. If the hair texture is coarse, the number of actual hairs on the scalp is likely to be less than if the hair is fine. The two extremes of hair density are described as *sparse* – not much hair – or *abundant* – lots of hair. As a general rule, if you can see the scalp through the hair, the hair is sparse. Some hairstyles are difficult to create if you have very sparse hair.

Hair skin and scalp conditions

There are many hair, skin and scalp conditions that can affect hair styling. You can find the details in Chapter 4. Some conditions are not infectious, and this means your hairstyling services can be carried out. However, if an infectious or contagious condition exists, then the services must not be carried out.

Hair and scalp analysis

Once all the factors that affect hair care and styling have been identified, you can begin to find and create a hairstyle that is suitable and appropriate.

ACTIVITY 

Consultation Sheet for Hair Styling

Part 1 Complete parts a–k on the consultation sheet for hair styling, first for yourself, and then for another person.

Part 2 Look in a hairstyle magazine and first, choose a new hairstyle for yourself. Then work with a partner to choose another hairstyle for them. When you have chosen your hairstyles, complete parts 1–11 on the consultation sheet. Check if the hairstyles chosen will be suitable for you, and possible to achieve. If necessary, refer to Chapter 4 for further information about analysing your hair.

ACTIVITY 

Look in a style magazine, choose some images and make a collage of hairstyles that would be suitable for curly hair, straight hair and/or wavy hair. Choose a hairstyle that would be most suitable for your own hair type.

ACTIVITY 

You can see the different diameters of hair quite easily. Compare the diameter of one of your hairs to that of one of your friends.

It's a fact!

It is possible to have very sparse, coarse hair and very abundant, fine hair and vice-versa.

ACTIVITY 

Complete the consultation sheet, first to identify the factors about your own hair that affect your hairstyling choices. Then complete the consultation sheet about another person.

Head shape

Tick the box that best represents the head shape:

(a)

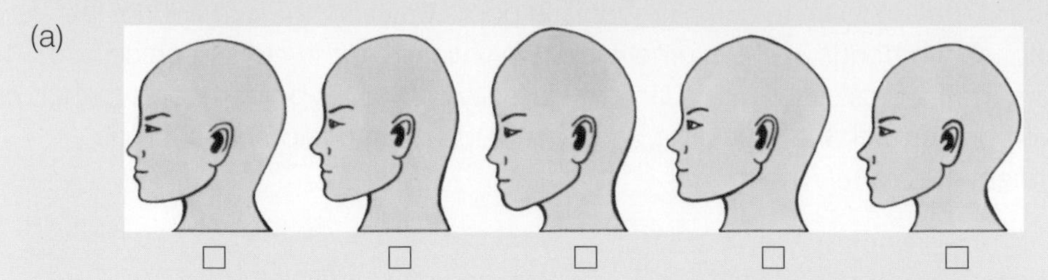

☐ ☐ ☐ ☐ ☐

1. Will the hairstyle suit the head shape and make it appear evenly shaped?
Yes ☐ No ☐

Face shape

Tick the box that best represents the face shape:

(b)

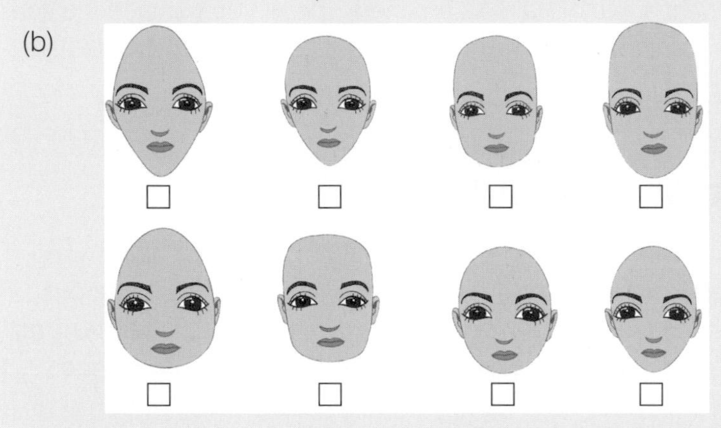

2. Will the hairstyle suit the face shape? Yes ☐ No ☐

Body shape

Tick the box that best represents the body shape:

(c)

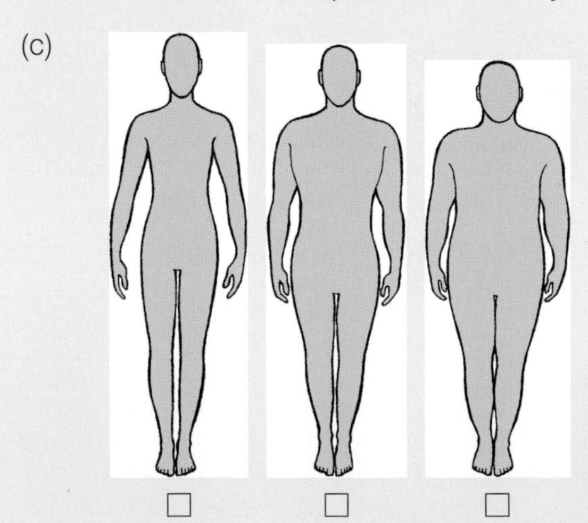

☐ ☐ ☐

3. Will the hairstyle be in proportion with the body shape? Yes ☐ No ☐

Lifestyle

Tick the box(es) which most match the lifestyle:

(d) ☐ busy ☐ quiet ☐ sporty ☐ sedentary ☐ school/college ☐ work

4. Will maintaining the hairstyle fit in with the lifestyle? Yes ☐ No ☐

Hair growth

Tick the boxes that match the hair growth patterns:

(e) ☐ Cow lick ☐ widows peak ☐ nape whorl ☐ single crown
☐ double crown

5. Is the hairstyle possible to achieve with the hair growth patterns?
Yes ☐ No ☐

Hair length

Tick the box(es) that match the hair length:

(f) ☐ Short ☐ shoulder length ☐ long ☐ very long ☐ layered ☐ not layered

6. Is the hair the right length for the chosen hairstyle? Yes ☐ No ☐

Hair type

Tick the box that matches the hair type

(g) ☐ Frizzy ☐ very curly ☐ curly ☐ very wavy ☐ wavy ☐ straight

7. Is the hair the correct type to achieve the hairstyle? Yes ☐ No ☐

Hair texture

Tick the box that matches the hair texture

(h) ☐ Very coarse ☐ coarse ☐ medium ☐ fine ☐ very fine

8. Is the hair the correct texture to achieve the hairstyle? Yes ☐ No ☐

Hair elasticity

Tick the box that matches the elasticity of the hair (you will need to do an elasticity test)

(i) ☐ Very good elasticity ☐ good elasticity ☐ poor elasticity

9. Is there sufficient elasticity in the hair to achieve and maintain the hairstyle? Yes ☐ No ☐

Hair density

Tick the box that matches the density of the hair

(j) ☐ Very abundant ☐ abundant ☐ medium ☐ spare ☐ very sparse

10. Is the density suitable to achieve the chosen hairstyle? Yes ☐ No ☐

Hair, skin and scalp condition

Tick the box that matches the condition of the hair, skin and scalp

(k) ☐ The hair, skin and scalp are in good condition
☐ The hair, skin and scalp are in poor condition

11. Is the hair, skin and scalp in good enough condition to achieve the hairstyle? Yes ☐ No ☐

Generic hair types

Hair type refers to the amount of natural curl that is present in hair. Hair can be curly, wavy or straight. As a very general rule, the amount of curl is directly related to three, broad generic hair types:

- **African type hair**
- **Asian type hair**
- **European/Caucasian type hair**

African type hair is generally very tightly curled and often frizzy. Asian hair is often very straight, or has a very slight, loose wave. European hair varies a great deal from very curly to very straight. In Chapter 4, 'The science of hair and beauty', you will see that because the British Isles were invaded by many different races over hundreds of years, there are numerous different hair types that are classed as European hair.

In addition to the historic mix of racial hair types, which gives European hair curls, waves and straight hair, it is increasingly common to find *mixed race hair* types. Mixed race hair can be any combination of races. For example, it can be mixed race African and Asian type, Asian and European type or African and European type.

Whatever the hair type, there will be a hairstyle that is suitable for the characteristics of the hair. Recognising the characteristics of your hair ensures that the hairstyle you choose emphasises its best features.

Hairstyles for different hair types

There are certain hairstyles that are perfect for the characteristics of the different hair types. It is technically possible to create virtually any hairstyle on most hair types. However, by using the natural curl, wave or straightness, you can find a hairstyle that is easy to achieve and maintain.

Hairstyles for very frizzy, curly hair

Some people with very frizzy, curly hair choose to have it chemically **relaxed**. This is a process that should only be carried out by a professional hairdresser or barber as it can be damaging for the hair. Frizzy, curly hair often looks strong and tough, but in fact it can be very weak and fine.

It's a fact! The word 'perm' is short for permanent wave, which is the service that is used to create a permanent change in the structure of the hair which results in curls and waves.

Hairstyles suitable for frizzy or very curly hair

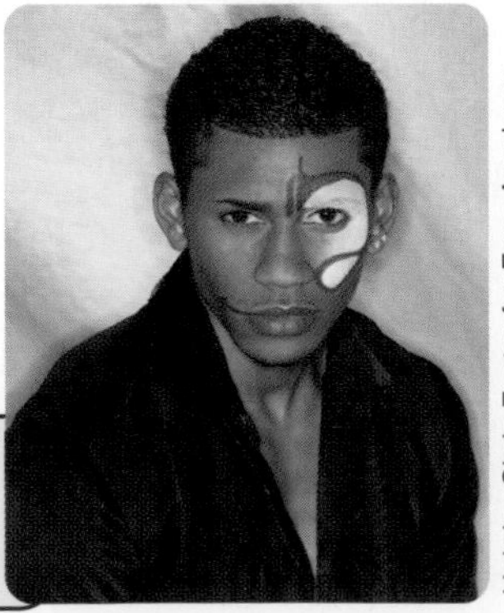

Hair by Chris Foster for Foss Academy, Photography: Andy Kruczek

Hair by Louise smith. Photography: Mark Bond. Salon: Essensuals

Marcus King, Hooker and Young. Products: Matrix. Photography: Malcolm Willison

Other people with frizzy, curly hair like to emphasise the natural beauty of the very tight curls. In Chapter 1, 'The history of hair and beauty in society', you can read about black identity and the revival of traditional and fashionable West African hairstyles.

Hairstyles for very straight hair

Some people with very straight hair have it chemically **permed** to create curl and movement.

The professional perms that are carried out today are very soft and can be used to give extra body to fine, straight hair. Hair that is permed can be styled into a chosen hairstyle, or can be left to dry naturally, leaving soft, natural looking curls.

Hairstyles for curly hair

People with curly hair are able to wear a range of hairstyles that accentuate the natural characteristics of their curls. Some curls are open and loose, other curls

It's a fact!

Some people with very curly or wavy hair chemically straighten it.

It's a fact!

The 1960s–inspired geometrical hairstyles are perfect for very straight hair. The haircuts used to create these looks rely on the straightness of the hair to give a clean, blunt, finish to the look.

Kay McIntyre, McIntyre's Salons

Hair by Reds Hair & Beauty, Sunderland. Photography by John Rawson @TRP

Katrina Rees & Jayne Beecroft: Academy

Hair by Faruk Mohammed @ Hair by JFK, Edinburgh

Michelle Thompson for Francesco Group

Hairstyles suitable for straight hair

Top tip

Be very careful when using straightners as, if used too frequently, they can cause damage to the hair that can lead to breakage.

can be small and tight. Therefore the hairstyle should be chosen to match the amount of natural curl in the hair.

It's a fact! **Natural curls can also be temporarily loosened by setting the hair** on large rollers or blow drying. Or they can be straightened by the use of electrical straighteners.

Jayne Beacroft and Katrina Rees

Hairstyles suitable for curly hair

Hair: Rainbow Room International Artistic Team, Glasgow

Hair: Terri Kay, Eastern hairdresser of the Year, Mark Leeson Hair, Body & Mind, Mansfield

Hairstyles for wavy hair

Wavy hair is neither straight nor curly. The amount of wave can vary from soft, gentle waves where hair is almost, but not quite straight, to very tight waves that are almost curls. The hairstyle should be chosen that accentuates the waves and movement in the hair.

Beverley Rosser and Bett Sawyer, Bobbers Hairdressing, Liverpool

Hairstyles suitable for wavy hair

Susan Hall, Reds Hair and Beauty

ACTIVITY     

Make a style book that could be used to show to clients when choosing a hairstyle. Remember that you will have clients will all types, textures, density and lengths of hair, so your book should reflect this.

Influences on hairstyling

The way you wear your hair is one of the most distinctive things about your whole appearance. When you describe one person to another, you probably describe their hair and hairstyle before you would talk about the features of their face, such as the colour of their eyes.

When you decide to style the hair, what influences you most? Is it your friends, movie stars, people in bands, in magazines or those you see on the television? If you read Chapter 1, 'The history of hair and beauty in society', you will see that many of the hairstyles we see today have been influenced by those that were created hundreds of years ago, from almost every culture and country in the world.

Occasions

Hairstyles are also influenced by the occasion for which they are going to be worn. For example, hair may be worn very simply for work or school, but may be styled to look different when attending a wedding, or a very special evening occasion.

Personality

Personality will also determine how hair is worn. For example, if you have a very outgoing personality, you may want to reflect this trait in your hairstyle. With your hair you can make statements about yourself. You can say – 'I am outrageous'. Alternatively, you may be introverted, in which case, your hairstyle may say, 'I am shy and reserved'. You can style your hair to look very professional, or you can choose to look untidy. You can have a hairstyle that looks fashionable or you can have a look that is timeless and classic.

ACTIVITY    

On an A4 sized card, make up a collage. Begin with a photograph of yourself in the centre of the card wearing your every day hairstyle. Then, arranged around your photograph, add hairstyles that would suitable for your own culture, hair length, type and texture that you could wear for different occasions. For example, a hairstyle that you would wear to a friend's party, one that you would wear as a guest at a wedding.

ACTIVITY  

Try to describe a mutual friend or family member to another without mentioning the colour, length or shape of their hairstyle – how difficult is it?

ACTIVITY  

Find a range of images which could represent different personalities. For example, a hairstyle that someone would wear if they wanted to attract attention. Another that would be worn by someone who has to show that they are very serious. You could also find examples of hairstyles that say, 'I am funny', 'I am fashion conscious', 'I am quiet' or 'I am loud'.

It's a fact!

Hairstyles have been used as an outward sign of social identity. For example, the sub-culture known as 'Emos' like to wear their hair in a style that typically has a long fringe partially covering the face.

iStockphoto.com/Chris Schmidt

A range of different hair types

It's a fact! Marcus Mosiah Garvey, National Hero in Jamaica, who died in London in 1940 said, of African type hair *'Don't remove the kinks from your hair. Remove them from your brain!'*

Identity

The term identity used in a **sociological** way relates to the way individuals *label* themselves as members of a particular group. Being a member of a particular group can sometimes determine how hair is styled. In Chapter 1, 'The history of hair and beauty in society', you can read about the **sub-cultures** that were formed in recent history from the 1950s to the 1980s.

Hair, the way you style it, or the length you wear it, will provide a visual sign to others to show that you belong to a particular group or sub-culture.

Hair and culture

The word *culture* has a variety of meanings. One meaning can be related to *patterns of human activity* and the importance of such activities. If you extend this meaning to the importance of hair, you will find that hair and hairstyling is important in a number of cultures, and determines how hair is styled or presented. In Chapter 1, 'The history of hair and beauty in society', you can read how hair was, and still is, a major aspect of life in many cultures and civilisations.

In black culture the natural appearance of hair is very much seen as a way of representing identity.

Hair and religion

Culture is also directly related to religion. In some religious cultures, such as Hindu and Buddhism, it is necessary to shave the head to indicate that fashion and personal appearance are no longer important. In other religions, such as Sikhism, shaving and the cutting of hair is forbidden. It is culturally appropriate for Muslim women to wear a *hijab*, which covers their head as their religion does not allow them to expose their hair in public. The covering of hair was also evident in the Christian religion when, until recent times, women were required to wear hats or head scarves whenever they were in a church.

Shampooing and conditioning the hair and scalp

Hair that is clean and in good condition is necessary for successful hairstyling. If the hair is excessively oily, dirty or has a build up of hair products, you will not be able to create a hairstyle. Hair that is very dry or in poor condition will not shine or be easy to manage.

Shampoo and conditioning products

The range of shampooing and conditioning products that you can buy, or are available in hairdressing salons and barbershops, can be confusing. However, if you look at each product you will see that products are categorised so you can choose one that is suitable.

Before you choose a product, you should know:

- the hair type
- the hair texture
- the condition of your hair and scalp

Frequency of shampooing

a I have to shampoo my hair every day

b I have to shampoo my hair every 3–5 days

c I only need to shampoo my hair once each week

Appearance of hair

a my hair looks lifeless if I do not shampoo it every day

b my hair is shiny

c my hair looks dull

Appearance of the scalp

a I have sticky scales on my scalp

b I have no scales on my scalp

c I have flaky skin on my scalp

Answers

Mainly **a** you have oily hair

Mainly **b** you have normal hair

Mainly **c** you have dry hair

Shampoos and conditioning products for different hair types

Hair type refers to the amount of curl in the hair. Some shampoos and conditioners are designed for use on very curly or frizzy hair. These shampoos will have additives which smooth and coat the **cuticle** layer to make the hair easier to comb and allow it to shine. Shampoos and conditioners for very straight hair are designed to emphasise the glossy appearance that is possible to achieve with flat, straight hair.

Shampoos and conditioning products for different hair textures

Hair texture refers to the diameter of a single strand of hair. Very fine hair can be made to look and feel thicker by the additives in some shampoos and conditioners. The additives will coat the hair shaft and make the hair feel fuller. Shampoos for very coarse hair will have additional conditioning properties to make the coarse hair feel silkier.

Shampoos and conditioning products for different hair and scalp conditions

You need to know if your hair is dry, oily or normal, and, if your scalp is dry, oily or dandruff affected before you can choose a suitable shampoo or conditioner.

ACTIVITY 

Analyse your own hair and scalp by completing the following analysis questionnaire. When you have done this, try it out again by asking another person the same questions.

CONDITION OF HAIR AND SCALP	SHAMPOO
Normal hair	Use herbal shampoos such as those that contain rosemary or soya and frequent wash mild shampoos
Dry hair	Use shampoos with additional oily additives, such as those that contain jojoba, coconut or almond
Dry scalp	Use products with additives such as juniper or oil based shampoos containing almond, coconut or olive oil
Greasy hair/scalp	Use camomile shampoos that contain citric acid (lemon, lime, etc.) or mild, frequent use shampoos
Dandruff affected scalp	Use treatment shampoos containing zinc pyrithione or selenium sulphide

Conditioners

There are two different types of conditioners:

- **surface conditioners**
- **penetrating conditioners**

Surface conditioners

Surface conditioners work by coating the outside layer of the hair, the cuticle. Following the application of conditioner, hair is easier to comb, and once dry the cuticle scales lie flat which makes the hair appear shinier. Surface conditioners also maintain the natural pH of the hair. You can read about pH in Chapter 4, 'The science of hair and beauty'.

You should use a surface conditioner on the following hair conditions:

- dry
- normal
- chemically treated
- oily hair (apply to the ends, or points of the hair only)

Penetrating conditioners

Penetrating conditioners are often used on hair that is in very poor condition. It may be naturally very dry because the **sebaceous glands** that produce the natural oil, **sebum**, are under productive. Or, the hair may have been damaged.

Hair can be damaged by:

- chemical damage such as perming, relaxing, chemical straightening, colouring and bleaching
- physical damage, such as over use of heated styling equipment, for example straighteners or thermal irons
- environmental damage, such as over exposure to the wind and sun

The penetration of a conditioner is achieved by applying the product to the hair and then adding heat. The added heat opens the cuticle layer, allowing the conditioner to enter the hair shaft. Professional hairdressers and barbers use a variety of electrical equipment to add heat during a conditioning treatment.

The electrical equipment used for penetrating conditioners includes:

- **steamer**
- **accelerator**
- **infrared heater**

Top tip

You can apply heat yourself by covering the hair with something that will retain the body heat from your head. A good way to do this is by using a plastic shower cap.

It's a fact!

Some conditioners are designed to be applied and are not rinsed from the hair. These are known as *leave in conditioners*.

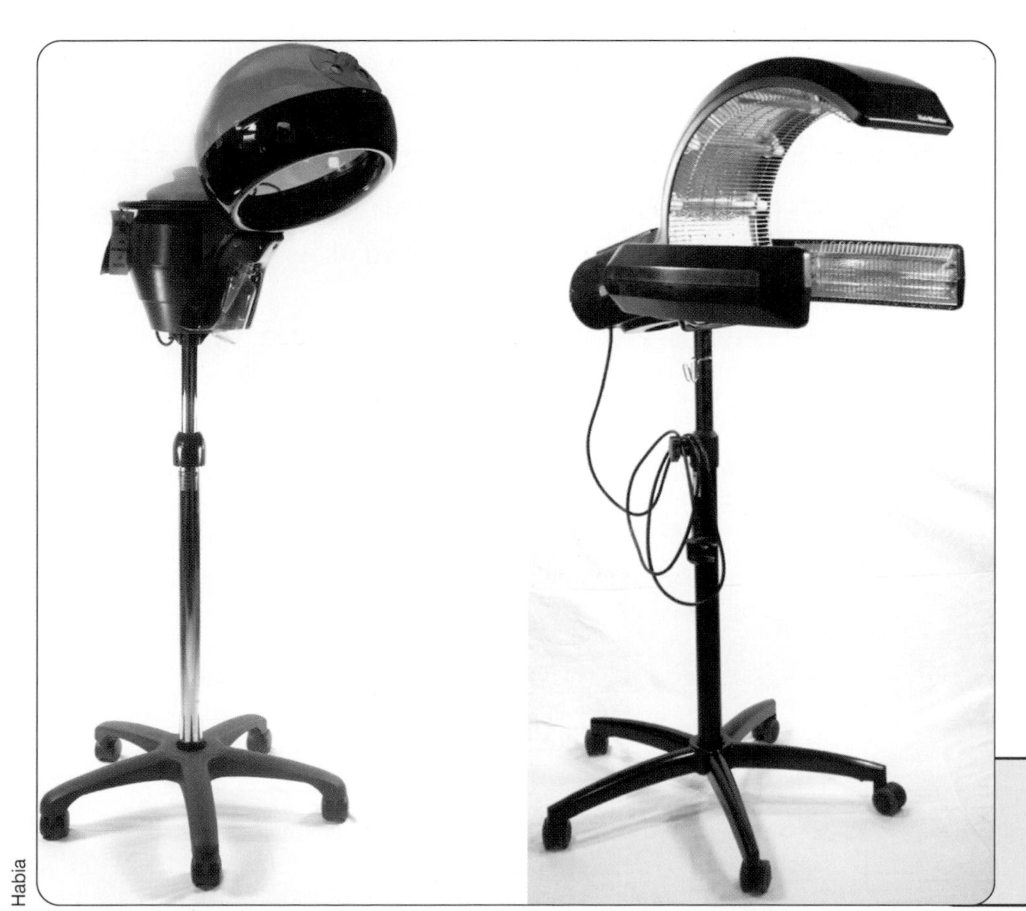

Habia

Steamers and accelerators are used to open the cuticle during a penetrating conditioning treatment

The added heat is applied for approximately 10–15 minutes before the conditioner is rinsed from the hair. When the hair is rinsed, the cuticle layer closes, leaving some of the conditioner trapped in the hair shaft.

Shampoo and conditioning products for African type hair by Avlon

HAIR AND SCALP	CONDITIONER
Dry hair and scalp	Use conditioners that contain moisturisers, lanolin, or vegetable oils
Damaged hair	Use a penetrating conditioner that contains moisturisers, or proteins which will temporarily repair internal damage to the cortex
Dandruff affected hair and scalp	Use conditioners that contain **coal tar** or **zinc pyrithione**.

Shampooing products

All product manufacturers will make a range of shampoo and conditioning products for different hair types.

EXTEND YOUR LEARNING 

Investigate the features and benefits of the shampooing and conditioning products by looking on the manufacturers' websites. Useful inks are **www.clynol.com**, **www.loreal.co.uk**, **www2.wella.co.uk** and **www.avlon.com**.

Shampoo and conditioning products by Wella

Shampoo and conditioning products by Clynol

Bring your learning to life   

When you are in your salon placement or the training salon, try the different professional products for shampooing and conditioning hair.

Complete the table and make comparisons about the products – what you liked and the results achieved.

PRODUCT	WHY I LIKED THIS PRODUCT	RESULTS
State manufacturer's name and the brand name of the product	State why you liked the product – e.g. texture, consistency, smell, appearance of packaging	State the results by using the product e.g. left the hair in good condition, lathered well, left the hair tangle free, easy to rinse

Compare the findings of your research with your friends – did they like the same products as you, if not, why not?

Scalp massage used for shampooing and conditioning

There are different massage movements that are used during the shampooing and conditioning process. You need to consider the length and density of hair when using the massage techniques. Head massage should be a pleasurable, relaxing experience, but, if you use the wrong technique, it can be quite uncomfortable.

The massage movements that are used for shampooing are:

- effleurage
- rotary
- friction

Top tip

When carrying out scalp massage techniques, use the pads of your fingers and not the tips. This is particularly important if you are doing the massage on a client, as long nails on the scalp can be painful.

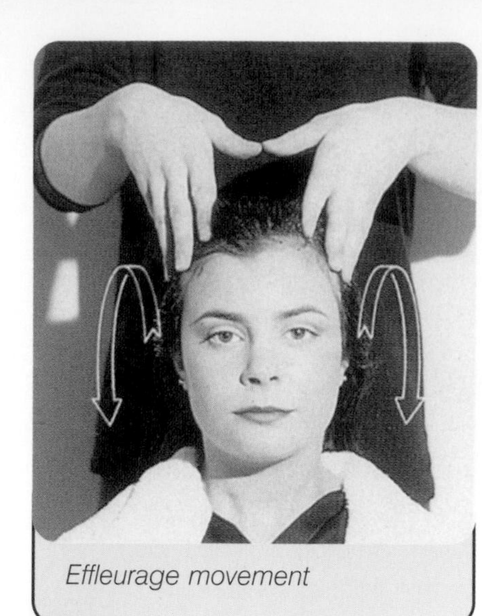
Effleurage movement

The massage movements that are used for conditioning treatments are:

- effleurage
- petrissage

Effleurage

Effleurage massage is used for shampooing and conditioning. It is a smooth, flowing, stroking movement which is soothing and relaxing for the client.

It is used for the following purposes:

- Spreads the shampooing and conditioning products through the hair lengths
- Cleanses the lengths of long hair during the shampoo process. The stoking movement ensures that the long hair does not tangle
- Ensures that conditioner is spread to the lengths and ends of long hair.

Some clients may have oily scalps that do not need conditioner, but even if the scalp and roots of the hair are oily, most people need to condition the ends of their hair. Therefore, the effleurage movement would only be used on the ends of the hair.

Top tip Special conditioning treatments applied to the scalp can be used to improve the symptoms of oily hair and scalps.

Rotary

Rotary massage movement is used for shampooing only. The massage name is as it sounds – a rotating, round, revolving action. To carry out this massage you must use the pads of your fingers with the hands held in a claw like position and move them across the scalp in small circular movements.

Rotary is used for the following purpose:

- To cleanse the scalp during shampooing

Top tip You must be very careful if you use this massage on long hair, as tangling could occur.

Top tip Practice the movements on your arm so you can see the different amount of pressure that is required.

Position of hands for rotary movement

Habia

Friction

Friction massage movement is used for shampooing only. It is a fast, short rubbing action and carried out by using the pads of the fingers on the scalp. You must be very careful if the hair is long as tangling could occur.

Friction is used for the following purposes:

- To stimulate the blood supply on the scalp. This causes the scalp to tingle and feel clean
- To increase the blood flow to the muscle of the scalp, which covers the cranium

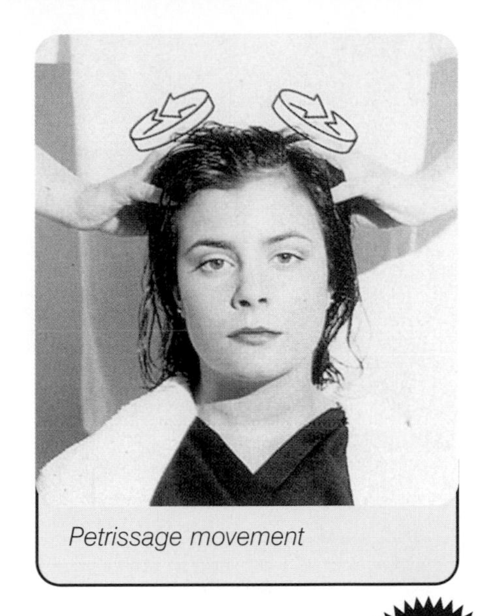
Petrissage movement

Petrissage

Petrissage is used on the scalp during the conditioning process. It is a very relaxing massage movement. It is carried out by using the pads of the fingers, with the hand held in a claw like position. The movement is similar to rotary, with very subtle difference. During the rotary movement, the fingers move *across* the surface of the scalp. Whereas, during the petrissage movement, the fingers move the scalp *over* the cranium, so a little more pressure is required. The movement is much slower than the massages used for shampooing.

Top tip

You must ensure that you remove all products that have been used for shampooing and conditioning. If you do not, the hair will look lank and dull.

Petrissage is used for the following purposes:

- To stimulate the blood supply on the scalp. An increased blood supply will provide the nutrients to the new hair cells that are developing in the **papilla**. For more details read Chapter 4, 'The science of hair and beauty'
- To increase the production of **sebum** from the **sebaceous glands**
- To relax the client

At the end of shampooing and conditioning the hair and scalp, the hair should be gently towel dried to remove excess moisture prior to hairstyling.

Protecting yourself and others when shampooing, conditioning and hairstyling

One job role that a hairdresser or barber carries out while they are training is shampooing and conditioning hair. Therefore, their hands are wet for much of the day and they also come into contact with products that can irritate the skin. In Chapter 5, 'Safe working practices' you can read about the dangers of this and how to prevent **contact dermatitis**.

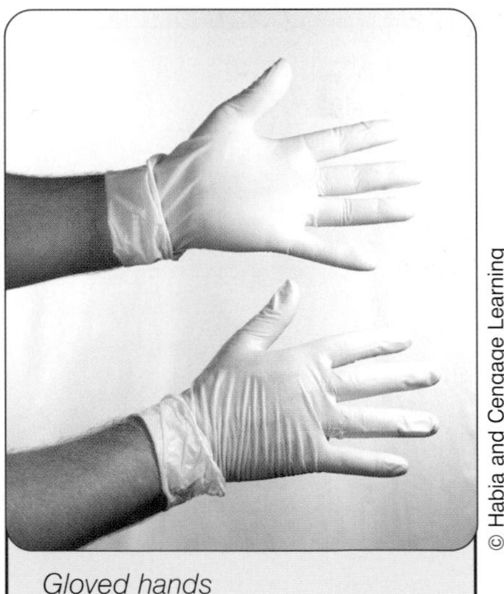
Gloved hands

It's a fact!

Hairdressers and barbers who shampoo and condition hair every day must protect their hands and skin with gloves. You can see how to use the gloves in Chapter 5, 'Safe working practices'.

Step by step methods for shampooing hair

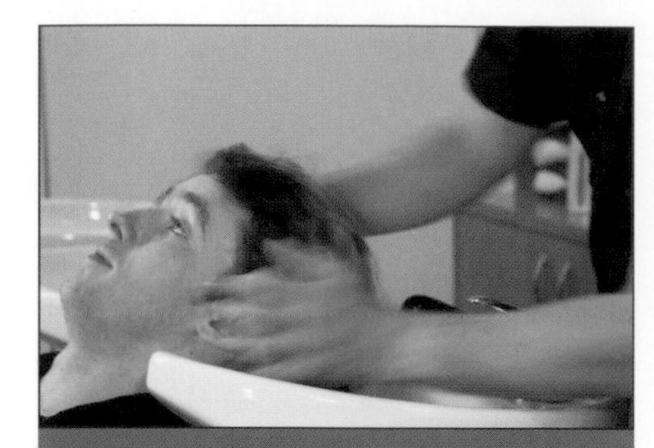

1 The client is gowned for a shampoo and the head is positioned for client comfort and to ensure a water tight seal at the basin.

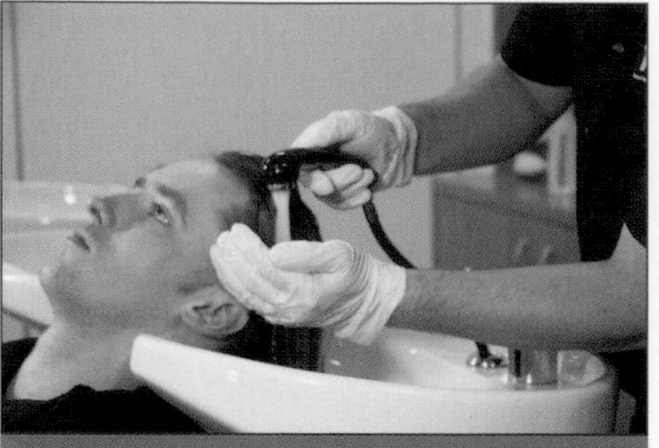

2 Protective gloves are worn and the temperature of the water is tested to ensure client comfort. The hair is evenly wet prior to the application of the shampoo.Note how the hand is cupped near the ear to prevent water running onto the client face.

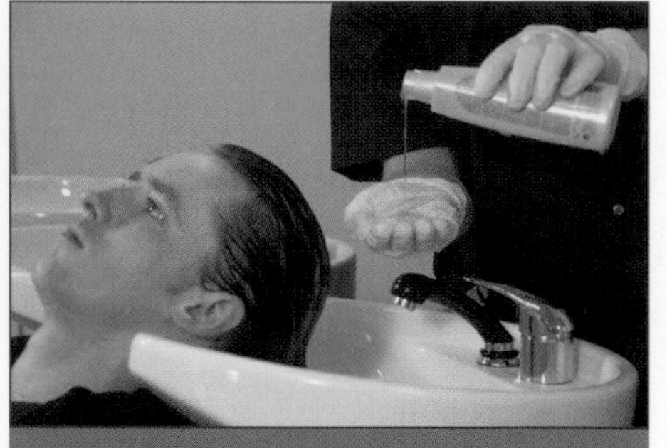

3 Shampoo is poured into the palm of the hand prior to applying to the scalp.

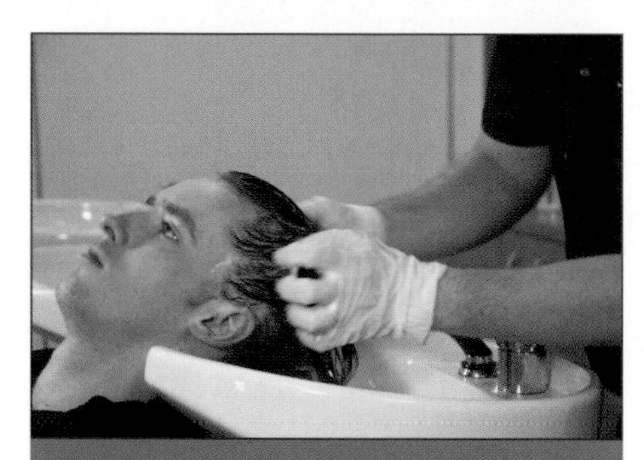

4 *Effleurage* is used to spread the shampoo evenly through the hair and then the scalp is cleansed using *rotary* and *friction* techniques.The hair is shampooed twice.

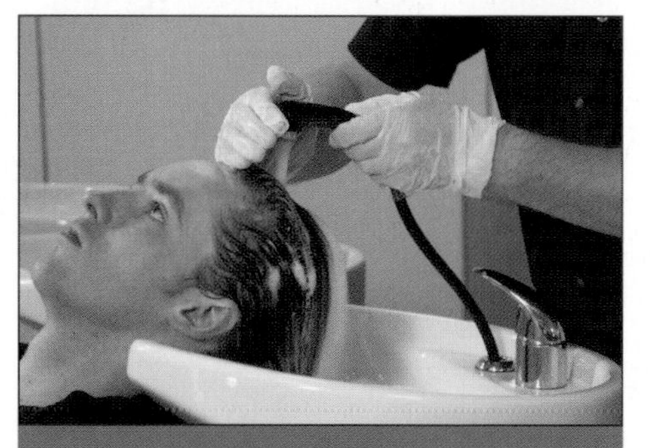

5 Shampoo is rinsed from the hair ensuring the scalp and hair are free from product.

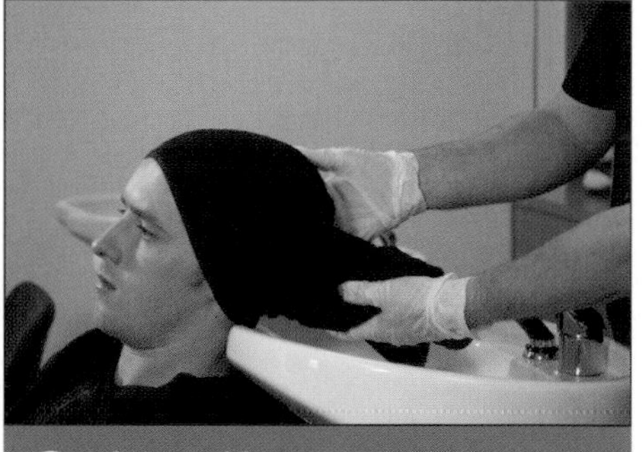

6 A towel is wrapped around the head at the end of the shampoo treatment.

Step by step methods for conditioning hair

Conditioning the hair with a penetrating conditioner

1 The conditioning product is placed into a small bowl.

2 The product is applied to the hair using a tinting brush.

3 An *effleurage* massage technique is used to spread the conditioning product evenly through the lengths of the hair.

4 The hair is lifted to ensure the finger tips can touch the scalp. The massage is carried out using a *petrissage* massage.

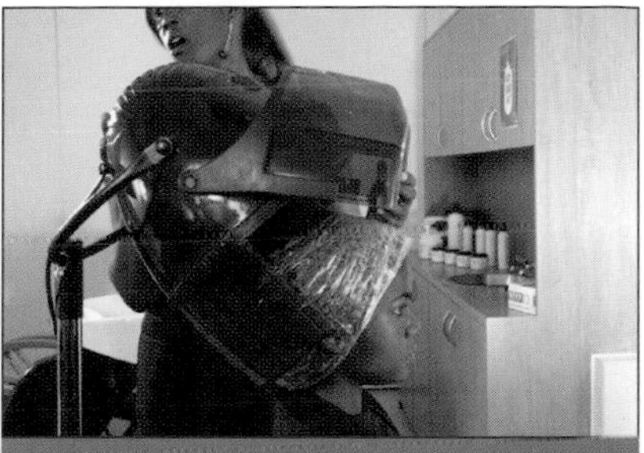

5 To retain the body heat, a plastic head cap is placed over the scalp. A hair dryer is used to add additional heat which allows the cuticle scale to lift, and the product to enter under the cuticle scales. At the end of the treatment, the conditioner is rinsed from the hair ensuring the product is removed from the scalp and hair.

Conditioning the hair using a leave in conditioner

1 Following the shampoo, leave in conditioner is applied to the hair.

2 The conditioner is combed through and not rinsed away.

Tools and equipment for hairstyling

There is a wide range of tools and equipment that you can use for styling hair. Some is available for personal use. There are other tools and equipment that are used by professional hairdressers and barbers which is used for styling the hair of others.

Bring your learning to life

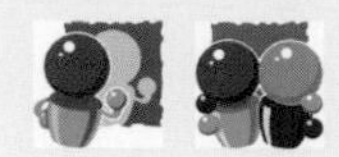

When you are in the training salon or in your work placement, work with a partner to shampoo and condition each other's hair.

When you do this for the first time, you should ask your partner for feedback about the pressure you are using for the massage techniques. Check that the pressure is comfortable and relaxing.

When you have finished the service, write down your experiences in your *Diploma file*.

You should record:

- The condition of the hair before the shampoo and conditioning service. Was the hair dry, oily or normal? Did the hair have a build up of hairdressing products, such as wax or styling cream?
- The condition of the scalp before the shampoo and conditioning service. Was the scalp clear of dry skin and scale? Was the scalp oily? Were there any signs of infection or infestation?
- The products used for the service. Why did you choose them?
- The method used for the shampoo and conditioner. Which massage movements did you use?
- The condition of the hair after the shampoo and conditioning service. Is the hair more manageable? Does the condition feel better?

Then ask your partner to write in your Diploma file. They should write about their experience during the shampoo and conditioning service. How did the massage feel? What was the pressure like? Did they enjoy it? Did they get wet!

Finally ask your partner what you could do to improve the shampoo and conditioning service next time. Note their answer. Then, when you shampoo your partner's hair again, refer back to your notes to see how you can improve.

Health and safety

You can read more about health and safety in Chapter 5, 'Safe working practices'. You need to use tools and equipment that are suitable for use and maintained for safety purposes. You must ensure that tools and equipment are clean and sterilised so that any infections, diseases and disorders are not passed from one person to another. When you are applying products for shampooing, conditioning and styling, you need to ensure that you read the manufacturer's instructions to and ensure that the products you are using are suitable for the type of hair they are to be used on. You must also ensure that the application of the product does not lead to damage of hair, skin or clothes.

Tools

The tools you need to carry out hairstyling will vary according to the hairstyle you wish to create.

Combs

You will need a variety of combs to carry out combing techniques on different *types* and *textures* of hair. The combs should be made from materials that prevent damage to the hair structure and reduce static electricity. Professional combs are

COMBS	IMAGE	USE	BENEFIT	TIP
Wide tooth combs	© Habia and Cengage Learning	For combing hair to remove tangles for styling	The wide teeth are good for coarse, dense hair, or very curly hair	Always comb hair from the points to the roots to prevent damage
Wide and narrow tooth combs	© Habia and Cengage Learning	For combing a variety of hair types and textures	The wide teeth are good for coarse, dense hair, or very curly hair. The fine teeth are good for combing very short hair and backcombing	Do not use the fine teeth on coarse, curly or frizzy hair
Tail combs	Image courtesy of Denman	For making sections when setting and styling hair	The tail of the comb enables you to make clean, neat sections. This means that you will be able to work methodically and efficiently when styling and dressing hair	Use the point of the tail to make the sections
Afro Pick	© Habia and Cengage Learning	For use on very tight, curly or frizzy hair	The wide teeth enable the combing of this hair type	Comb from the outside edges of the hair, into the centre

made from **tourmaline** and **carbon**, which are minerals which will not damage the structure of hair. And, because the minerals that are used to make the combs have properties that reduce **static electricity**, hair will appear shinier as the cuticle layer will lay flat.

Your own combs should be kept clean with hot soapy water and only used for one person. Professional combs must be sterilised between uses.

Hair brushes

Top tip Avoid the use of hair brushes that are made from damaging man-made materials or have inflexible, hard bristles.

Professional hairdressers and barbers need a variety of hair brushes that are suitable for different hair *types* and *textures*. The bristles of professional hair brushes are made from materials that are designed to prevent damage to the cuticle and reduce static electricity. Some bristles are made from boar bristle, which is good for the hair as boar bristle and human hair are made from the same protein, **keratin**.

Your own hair brushes should be kept clean with hot soapy water and only used for one person. Professional hair brushes must be sterilised between uses.

HAIR BRUSH	IMAGES	USE	BENEFIT	TIP
Flat back brushes		For brushing hair during drying and styling	Removes sectioning marks after setting. Prepares hair for styling. Removes tangles from hair	Do not use brushes on wet hair as this would cause the hair to stretch
Paddle brushes		For brushing hair during drying and styling	Removes sectioning marks after setting. Prepares hair for styling. Removes tangles from hair. Massages the scalp	The cushioned base and gentle bristles means this type of hair brush is good for massaging and stimulating the scalp of dry hair. Do not over use on hair that is naturally oily, as stimulating the scalp will produce more sebum
Radial brushes	© Habia and Cengage Learning	For creating curls in hair when blow drying, or for smoothing and straightening curly hair	Lifts the hair at the roots to create volume	Use a small radial brush to create tighter curls and a large radial brush for large curls

Vent brushes	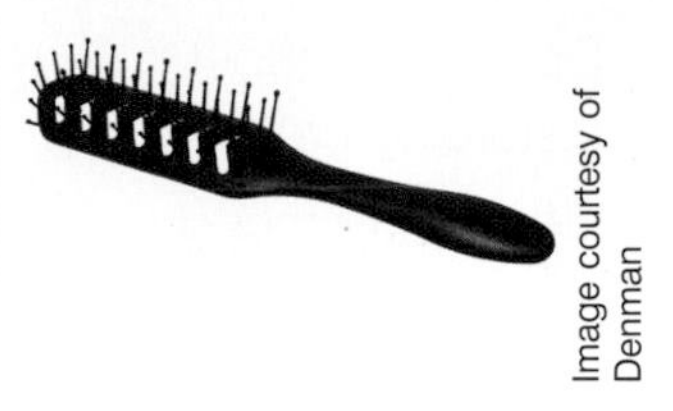 Image courtesy of Denman	For styling during blow drying	The open back of the brush allows the air to pass through to quicken the drying time	Use on straight hair to create texture

Equipment

If you want to create a wide range of hairstyles, you will need a variety of setting and styling equipment. Some equipment it designed to be used on wet hair, others just for dry hair. All equipment should be made from materials that will not damage the hair.

Your own equipment should be kept clean with hot soapy water and only used for one person. Professional equipment must be sterilised between uses.

EQUIPMENT	IMAGES	USE	BENEFIT	TIP
Velcro™ rollers	© Habia and Cengage Learning	For creating soft curls and movement in hair	Soft, natural looking curls. Adds volume to hair	Only use Velcro™ rollers on dry hair. The small teeth on the rollers attach themselves to the hair shaft and will not work on wet hair
Rollers	© Habia and Cengage Learning	For creating curls and movement in hair	Different size curls can be produced using different sized rollers	Use large rollers to create big, open curls and small ones for tight curls
Pin curl clips	© Habia and Cengage Learning	For making pin curls in hair	Curls the hair without lifting from the roots	Use small sections when creating the pin curl
Hair bands, pins and grips	© Habia and Cengage Learning	For holding long hair in place	Keeps a long hairstyle neatly in place	Use dark coloured pins on dark hair and pale coloured pins on light hair to help to disguise them

Diffuser	© Habia and Cengage Learning	Attached to a hand held dryer	Dries hair without disturbing natural curl	Use the dryer speed on a low setting to prevent 'frizzing' curly hair
Afro pick attachment	© Habia and Cengage Learning	Attached to a hand held dryer	Straightens hair as it dries	Keep the dryer on a medium heat to prevent burning the scalp and damaging the hair
Back mirror	© Habia and Cengage Learning	To enable the client to see the back of the hairstyle	Ensures the client is happy with the finished result	Hold the mirror to one side so the image is reflected back into the main mirror
Sectioning clips	© Habia and Cengage Learning	To clip hair into sections	Enables you to work in a logical and methodical way	When inserting the sectioning clips, open them fully to prevent pulling the hair
Trolley	© Habia and Cengage Learning	To store tools and equipment	Keeps tools and equipment safe and tidy	So you don't have to bend over to reach the trolley, keep it on your right hand side if you are right handed and vice versa. This will prevent back strain and injury

Electrical equipment

The range of electrical equipment to style hair is vast. Hair can be dried, curled, straightened, pressed and crimped with specialised equipment. Professional electrical equipment is designed for prolonged use.

Electrical equipment should be used following the manufacturer's instructions and for the purpose for which it is intended. Check equipment before you use it. Look at the plug and ensure there are no loose or exposed wires. Check the cable for fraying or damage. Professional electrical equipment must be checked for safety once each year by a qualified person. More information about the safe use of electrical equipment can be found in Chapter 5, 'Safe working practices'.

EQUIPMENT	IMAGES	USE	BENEFIT	TIP
Hand held hair dryer	© Habia and Cengage Learning	For drying, and styling hair	Portable and easy to use	Use the different adjustable temperatures and speeds to suit your hair texture and density. Fine hair will need a cooler, slower setting than dense, coarse hair
Straighteners	© Habia and Cengage Learning	For straightening and curling hair	Can be used to create a variety of effects	Use moisturising products to protect the hair from heat damage
Tongs	© Habia and Cengage Learning	For curling hair	Can be used to create a variety of different sized curls	Use small barrel tongs to create tight curls and large barrel tongs for soft curls
Pressing comb	© Habia and Cengage Learning	For smoothing very curly and frizzy hair	Can be used to smooth and blend unevenly relaxed hair	Use on the hair line straighten where straighteners cannot reach
Crimpers	© Habia and Cengage Learning	For creating a zigzag or waved appearance to hair	Can be used to create a variety of looks	Crimp longer, one length hair for the best effects
Thermal irons	© Habia and Cengage Learning	For smooth curls and movement in the hair	Can be used to create a variety curl sizes – even on very short hair. Heated in an oven	Use thermal irons to straighten the regrowth of chemically straightened hair
Heated rollers	© Habia and Cengage Learning	For creating waves, curl and movement	Can be used on long and short hair to produce a quick result	Only use on dry hair

Hood dryer	© Habia and Cengage Learning	For drying hair	The whole head can be dried at the same time	Check the temperature to ensure client comfort
Steamer	© Habia and Cengage Learning	For creating moist heat	Steam opens the cuticle to allow conditioner and some chemicals to enter the cuticle	Only use distilled water to prevent lime scale
Accelerator	© Habia and Cengage Learning	To create dry heat	Can be used to dry hair and to speed up the process of chemical treatments	Place the equipment to ensure even distribution of heat over the whole head

Top tip Always keep yourself up to date with your product knowledge. Read manufacturer's instructions on how and when to use a styling product to achieve the best results.

Products for styling hair

Technology in hair products is always advancing. This is true both for products that you purchase for use on your own hair and for those used by professional hairdressers and barbers.

Today, there are a wide variety of products available to protect, strengthen, reduce or maximise curl, add moisture to dry hair or even to create shine on dull, dry hair. No matter what condition hair is in, there will be a product available to help achieve the result you are after.

Understanding the different types of styling products will help you to select the right one for the styling result you are after. When professional hairdressers and barbers use styling products, they always explain how they use them to the client, so that the client can re-create the hairstyle at home, between salon visits.

Different types of styling and finishing products

All product manufacturers will make a range of shampoo and conditioning products for different hair types. Many products can be used in combination with each other to help you provide the result you and your client want to achieve the total look.

Styling and finishing products for men by L'Oréal

Styling and finishing products for African type hair by Namaste

Styling and finishing products by Goldwell

Styling and finishing products by L'Oréal

Styling hair

Styling hair requires creativity and imagination, as well as technical skills. Changing your hairstyle can completely change your whole appearance. Hair is one of the things that people first notice about others – often, even before they notice the clothes that they are wearing. In addition to this, your hair is more permanent than the clothes you wear, so it is important in terms of personal presentation and making a good, first impression.

ACTIVITY  

Review a styling and finishing product range. Identify the products that are best used to achieve:

- either soft, medium and strong styling support
- moisture retention
- additional strength to the hair
- added shine to the hair
- environmental protection, for example, from the sun or from swimming
- heat protection, for example, from styling equipment
- definition to finished styles

It's a fact! **If lift and volume are** required, hair is set *on base*, if you want to decrease the amount of volume in the hairstyle, you position the rollers *off base*.

To be successful with hairstyling, you must carry out an analysis of the hair, ensure that the hair is clean and in good condition and have all the necessary and correct tools, products and equipment available.

To create hairstyles, you can only use three main hairstyling techniques. However, the number of hairstyles that can be produced are only limited by your imagination and the restrictions found during hair analysis.

The three hairstyling techniques are:

- make hair look curly and/or wavy
- make hair look straight
- plait or braid hair

Step by step methods for making hair curly and wavy

Creating curls and waves by setting hair in rollers

This technique is used to create longer lasting curls, waves, volume and movement.

1 Styling product is applied to wet hair.

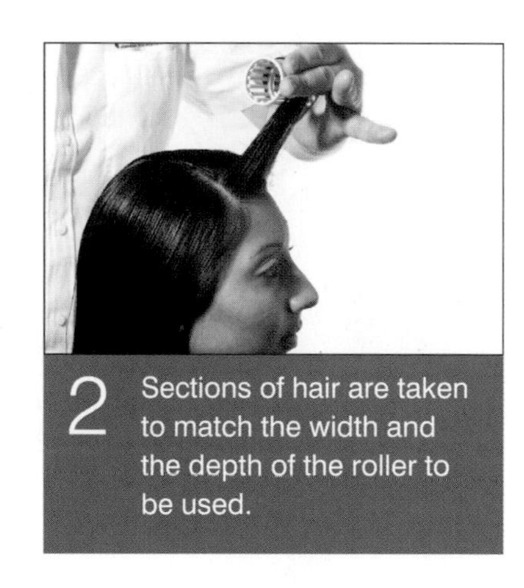

2 Sections of hair are taken to match the width and the depth of the roller to be used.

3 The first roller is in place.

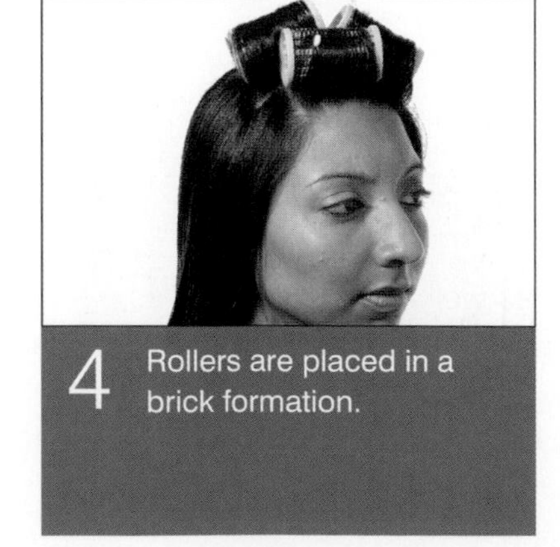

4 Rollers are placed in a brick formation.

5 The roller set complete.

6 The hair is dried under a hood dryer.

7 The finished result dressed down.

8 The hair is styled up by twisting and pinning into position.

9 The finished hair up result.

10 A second finished hair up result.

It's a fact!

A roller with a small diameter will produce a tighter curl than a roller with a large diameter.

Creating curls and waves by setting hair in pin curls

This technique is used to create a soft curl in short hair.

1 The client before styling.

2 Hair is sectioned, curled into position and held in place with a pin curl clip.

Top tip To prevent burning the client, keep the air from the dryer pointed away from the scalp.

Top tip To prevent burning the hair, keep the dryer at least 5 cms away

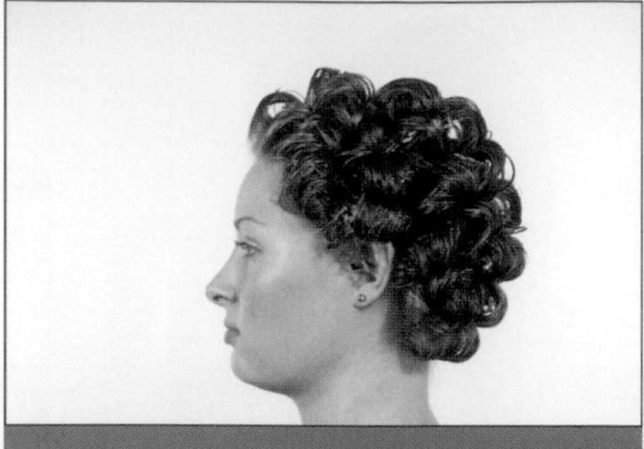

3 On completion of the pin curls, the hair is dried under a hood dryer.

4 The finished result. The hair is dressed by using the fingers to break up the curls.

Creating curls and waves by blow drying

A radial brush can be used to create curls, waves, body and movement in hair

1 Styling product is applied to the hair.

2 The hair is sectioned, and a radial brush is used to create curl and movement.

3 The sides of the hair are wound into the radial brush and dried with the hair dryer.

4 The finished result.

Top tip To prevent the curls from dropping, place the dried sections into a pin curl clip

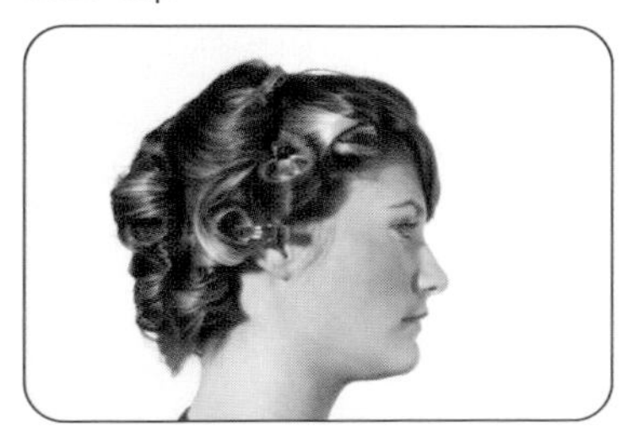

Top tip Once the section is dry, blast it with a shot of cold air from the dryer to help the newly curled hair to stay in place

Creating curls and waves by setting hair on heated rollers

1 Heated rollers are placed into the hair in a brick formation.

2 Finished result.

Other methods for creating curls and waves in hair

Curling tongs of different sizes will create different sized curls.

Curls can be created by turning straighteners as they are moved down the hair shaft.

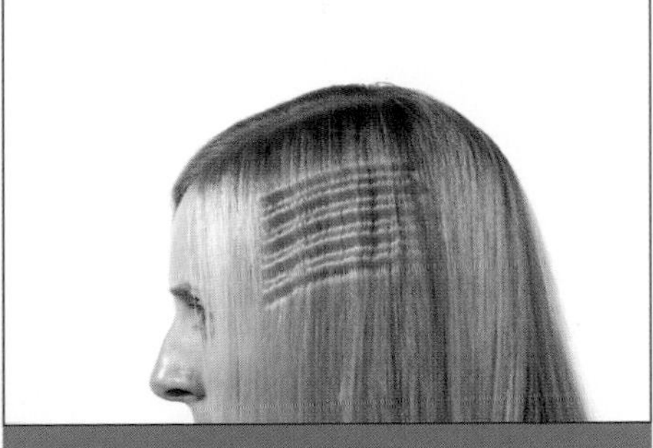

Tight waves can be created by using crimpers.

The natural curl in hair can be increased by using a diffuser attachment on a hand held hair dryer.

Velcro rollers can be used to create soft curls, wave and volume.

Step by step methods for making hair straight

With technological developments in heated electrical equipment and the improvement in products to maintain the condition of hair, it is possible to temporarily straighten most hair types.

The prolonged use of straighteners is not recommended as this can lead to hair damage and breakage.

Making hair straight by using a wrapping technique

The wrapping technique is used to smooth hair and uses the shape of the head to create movement.

1 The client before styling.

2 A styling product is applied and a large roller is wound into a section at the crown area.

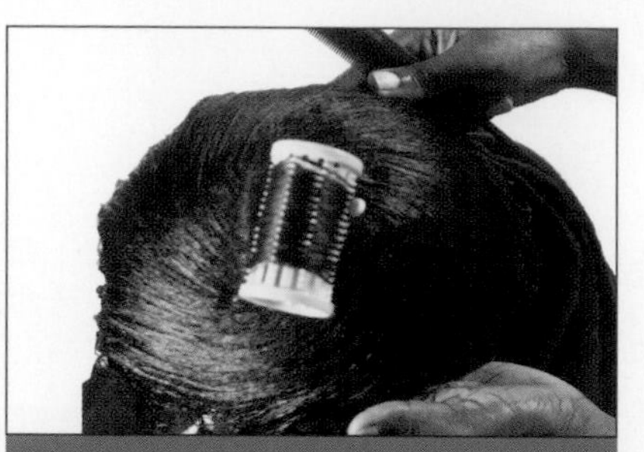

3 A parting is made and the wrap is started by combing and directing away from the parting. At the same time, the other hand is used to smooth and blend the hair around the roller.

4 The finished wrap.

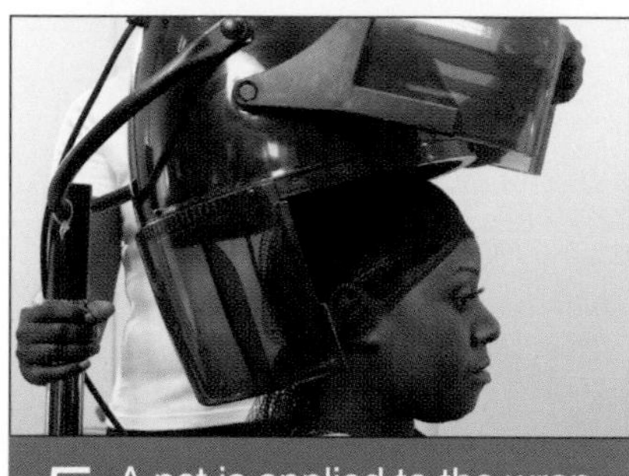

5 A net is applied to the wrap and the client is placed under the hood hair dryer.

6 The finished result.

Making hair straight by blow drying (radial brush)

By using a large diameter radial brush, hair can be smoothed and straightened.

1 The client before styling.

2 The hair is sectioned and gently stretched by placing the radial brush on top of the hair.

3 The process is repeated at the sides of the head.

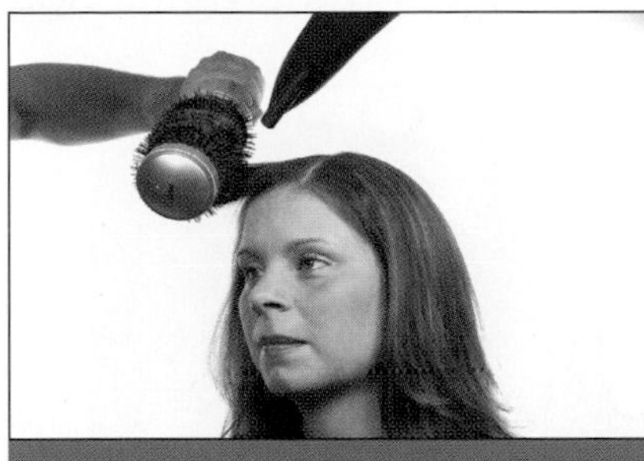

4 The process is completed at the front of the head. Note how smooth and straight the hair is.

5 To create texture and movement, the client tips their head back and cool air is blown into the hair from the dryer.

6 The finished result.

Making hair straight by blow drying and electrical equipment (paddle brush and straighteners)

1 The client before styling.

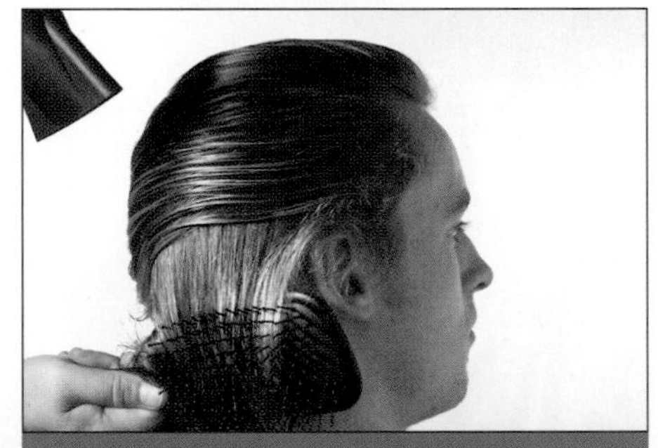

2 A styling product is applied and a paddle bush is used to smooth the hair.

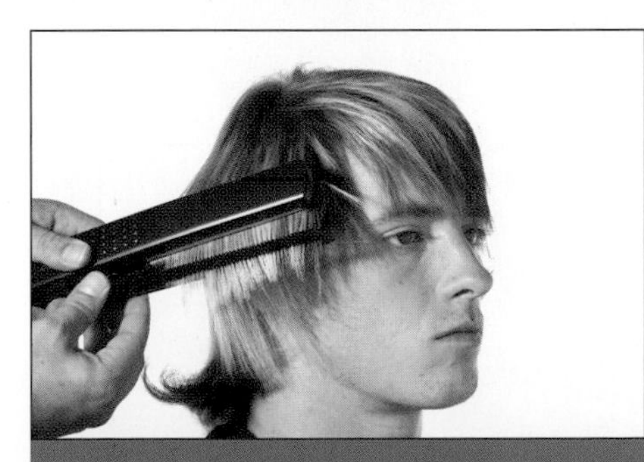

3 A heat protective product is applied and straighteners are used to smooth straighten the hair.

4 Finished result.

Making hair straight by using a rake attachment and thermal tongs

1 The client before styling.

2 A rake attachment is used with a hand held dryer. The rake is combed slowly through the hair, working from the ends to the roots.

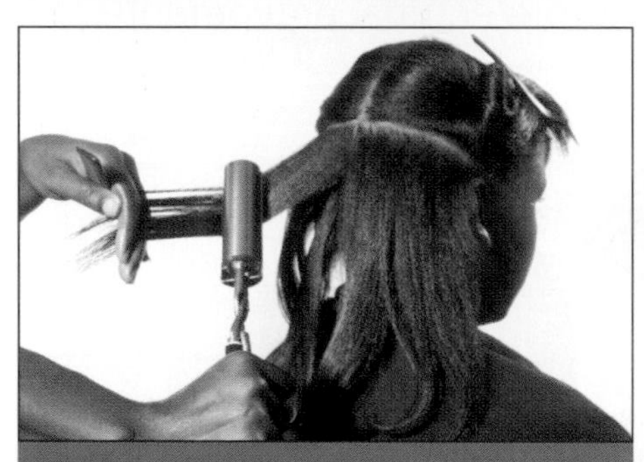

3 When dry, the hair is re-sectioned and thermal tongs are used to smooth and straighten the hair.

4 The finished result.

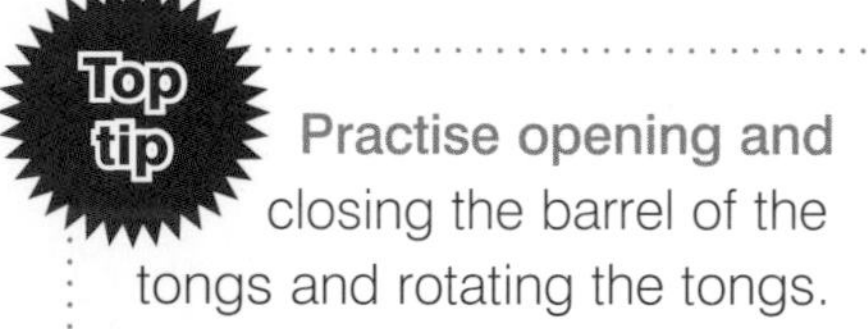

Practise opening and closing the barrel of the tongs and rotating the tongs.

Top tip

As pressing combs get very hot, you must check the temperature before applying it to the hair. To test, place the heated pressing comb on tissue. If the tissue becomes scorched, or burns, the comb is too hot and must be cooled by placing on a prepared cooling pad. The cooling pad is a pre-dampened, folded towel.

Other methods for making hair straight

Hair can be smoothed using a flat back brush

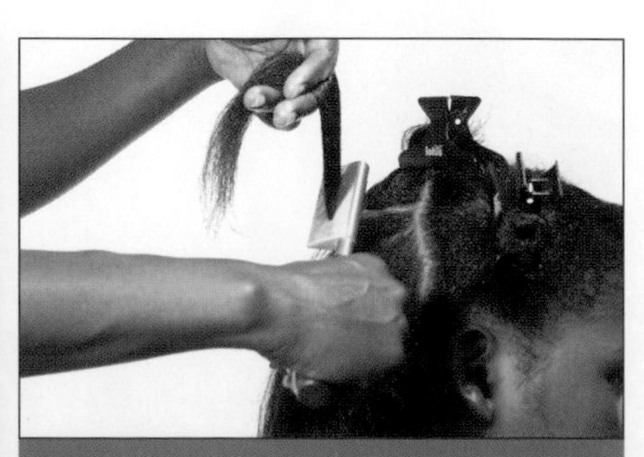

Hair can be straightened using a pressing comb

Bring your learning to life

Work in a pair and complete a consultation for hairstyling. Take a 'before' photograph of each other before you begin. Style each other's hair to make your hair wavy, curly or straight in at least two different ways using any of the techniques you can see in the step by steps. Take an 'after' photograph.

Record the results in your *Diploma file*. Identify what you did well and what you would do better next time.

Top tip

Ask the client to bend their head forward to enable you to keep the plait close to the head when braiding under the occipital bone at the back of the head.

Step by step methods for creating plaits

Once you know how to braid hair, the results you can produce are endless.

Braiding hair to create one scalp plait

1 The first section is evenly divided into three strands.

2 The strand on the right hand side is passed over the centre strand.

3 The strand on the left hand side is passed over the centre strand.

4 The process is repeated. Each time the outside strand is passed over the centre, hair is added to the strand from the hairline.

5 The braiding continues down the back of the head.

6 Finished result.

Braiding hair to create multiple scalp plaits

The same technique to create one scalp plait is used to create multiple scalp plaits.

1 The client before styling.

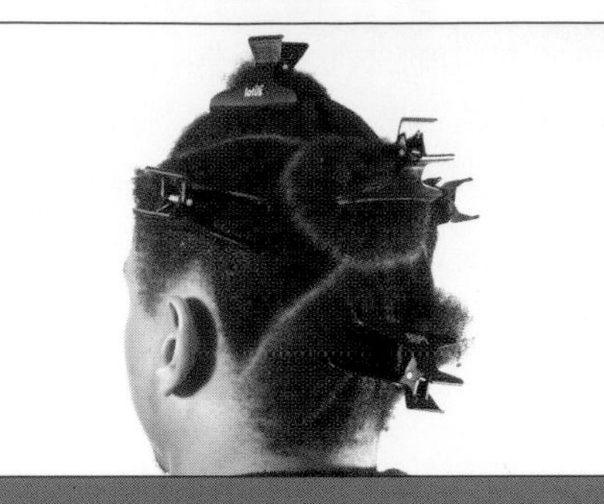

2 The hair is divided into neat sections.

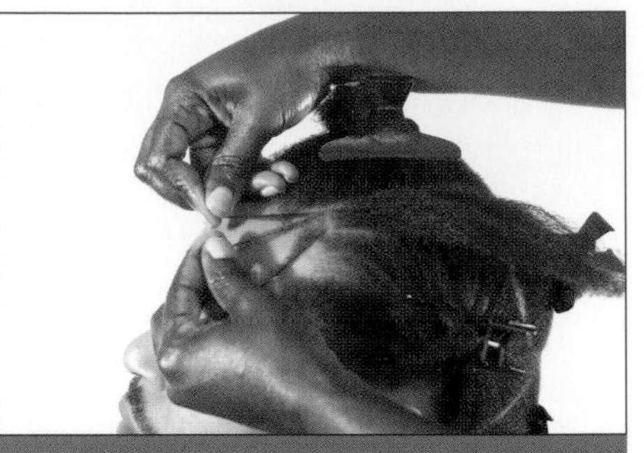

3 A neat subsection is made and divided into three strands. The right had strand is passed over the centre strand, then the left hand strand is passed over the centre strand.

4 The process is repeated. Each time the outside strand is passed over the centre, hair is added to the strand from the outside of the section.

5 When the corn row is completed, make the three strands into two.

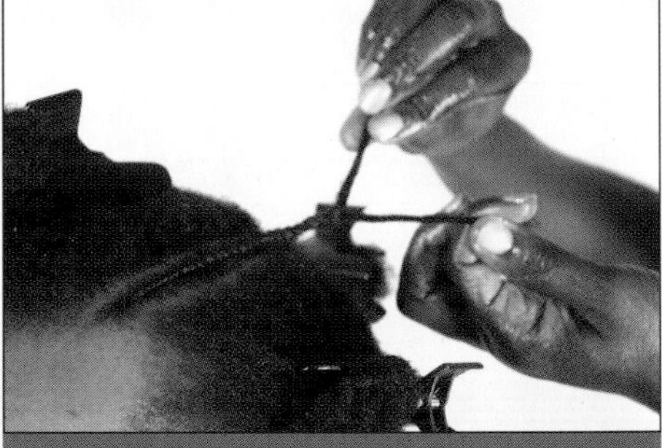

6 Finish the corn row by twisting. This is achieved by twisting a strand in each hand, while at the same time twisting the two strands around each other.

7 The process is repeated in all the sections.

8 A hair band is used to keep the twists together.

9 The finished result.

Bring your learning to life   

Work in a pair or on a head block and create a look using plaits. Take a 'before' photograph and when you have competed your look, take an 'after' photograph.

Record the results in your *Diploma file*. Identify what you did well and what you would do better next time.

Technological developments

Hairstyling today is much easier than it was even a decade ago, and certainly easier than a century ago. This is because of the technological developments in tools and equipment. For example, combs and hairdryers have improved dramatically over the last two centuries. (Combs, made out of tourmaline and carbon today, were made out of bone in the seventeenth century and horn in the eighteenth century.)

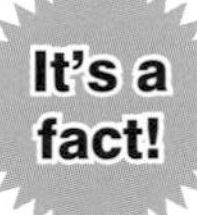

It's a fact!

Multiple scalp plaits are called **corn rows** or **cane rows**.

EXTEND YOUR LEARNING

Choose a product, tool or equipment used for styling hair and research its history. Make a time line.

What you have learnt

The main factors that affect hair care and styling

- You must always consider the factors that affect hairstyling
- The factors include head and face shape, hair type and texture, hair density, hair growth patterns

How to take account of the differences in hair types

- There are three generic hair types, African, Asian and Caucasian
- Mixed race hair is a mixture of the different generic hair types
- Hairstyles should be chosen to suit the characteristics of the hair type

The diverse hairstyles that can be created

- Hair can be made curly or wavy, or hair can be straightened to produce a range of different hairstyles

How to use products, tools and equipment for hair care and styling

- Always read the manufacturer's instructions before using and applying products
- Check electrical equipment before use

How to style your own hair and that of and others

- Carry out a consultation to ensure that the hairstyle chosen is suitable
- Style hair using the correct products, tools and equipment for the intended hairstyle

The key historic hair trends that influence the hairstyles you wear today

- Hairstyles worn today are influenced by those worn over many centuries in different civilisations
- Culture, identity and religion may determine the way hair is worn

The technological advances which aid hair care and styling

- The tools, products and equipment we use to today ensure safer and easier hairstyling

The terminology related to hair care and styling

- There are many terms and words used to describe hairstyling techniques. The new words appear in bold and an explanation can be found in the glossary.

Assessment activities

Crossword

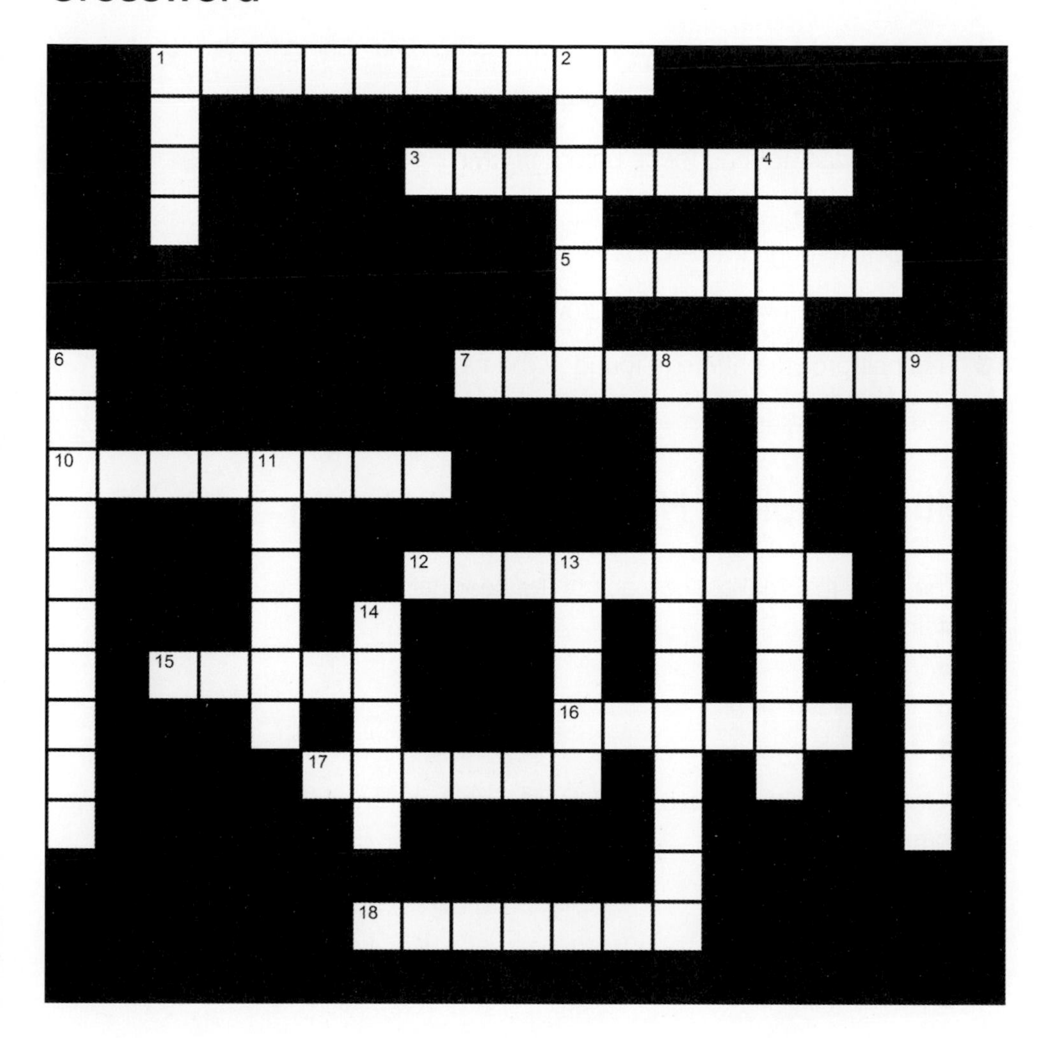

Across

1 This hair pattern is found at the front hairline (6,4)

3 When working on a client you must do this to tools after each use (9)

5 A method of plaiting hair (4,3)

7 This type of product can be used on very dry hair (11)

10 This comb is good for making sections in hair (4,4)

12 This hand held equipment is used for drying hair (4,5)

15 You can create a curl in hair using this electrically heated equipment (5)

16 This massage technique is used to cleanse the scalp (6)

17 This type of hair brush is used to create curls when blow drying (6)

18 Place these in wet hair to create curls (7)

Down

1 This hair type is neither straight nor curly (4)

2 A hair type that is often very curly (7)

4 You can remove natural curls and waves from hair using these (13)

6 This massage technique is very relaxing for the client (10)

8 It is important to read these before applying products to hair (12)

9 This massage technique is good for spreading shampoo and conditioning products through the lengths of hair (10)

11 You can have two of this hair growth pattern (6)

13 This hair growth pattern is found at the nape of the neck (5)

14 A hair type that is often very straight (5)

Multiple choice: Hair care and styling

1 The bone that makes the back of the head fat or round is:
- **a** occipital
- **b** frontal
- **c** parietal
- **d** mandible

2 A facial shape that has an angular jawline, with length that is much longer than the width is
- **a** oblong
- **b** square
- **c** round
- **d** rectangular

3 An ectomorph will have a body that is
- **a** small and slim
- **b** tall and slim
- **c** small and round
- **d** tall and round

4 A hair growth pattern known as a whorl can be found
- **a** at the crown
- **b** behind the ears
- **c** at the nape
- **d** at the front hairline

5 A hair type can be
- **a** fine
- **b** abundant
- **c** long
- **d** curly

6 In relation to temporarily changing the shape of the hair structure when hairstyling, hair with good elasticity will
- **a** curl well
- **b** lay flay
- **c** not curl well
- **d** will dry more quickly

7 Shampoos with added oils are good for
- **a** oily hair
- **b** normal hair
- **c** dry hair
- **d** coloured hair

8 Effleurage is a
- **a** smoothing massage movement
- **b** cleansing massage movement
- **c** stimulating massage movement
- **d** hard massage movement

9 The massage movement used to cleanse the scalp is
- **a** petrissage
- **b** effleurage
- **c** rotary
- **d** vibration

10 Coarse is a description of
- **a** hair texture
- **b** hair type
- **c** hair density
- **d** hair strength

Short questions: Hairstyling

1 Describe three different facial shapes.

2 State the main characteristics of the three different hair types.

3 Describe a mesomorphic body shape.

4 Why do you need to consider lifestyle when recommending hairstyles?

5 Where would you find a widows peak?

6 What is the average rate of growth for hair?

7 Name two different types of conditioners.

8 When would you use a radial brush?

9 When would you use a tail comb?

10 State three ways to make hair curly or wavy.

9

hand care and nail art

Viva: Sharon Cox @ Sanrizz

I am passionate about nails and know how vital it is they look groomed in today's society.

LEIGHTON DENNY, WINNER BRITISH NAIL TECHNICIAN OF THE YEAR 2001–04 AND VOTED INTO THE HALL OF FAME.

Introduction

The world of nails is growing. Even though it's so closely linked to the beauty industry it has become an industry in itself. Over the last ten years there has been an explosion in the demand for nail services; it's come out of the shadows and is now centre-stage.

A new career route has developed to support the expanding nail industry. No longer do you have to study beauty therapy and offer a wide range of treatments. If you love nails, and that's what you want to specialise in, then you can study and become qualified in a wide range of nail services. It's a highly rewarding career and can involve working as a nail technician in nail salons, owning your own business, working in the media through magazine work, working on a cruise ship or in an international resort. The opportunities are amazing.

In this chapter you will learn about the skills and knowledge that will help you care for hands and nails, and how to apply nail art. If you develop these skills and study further, you can become a professional nail technician and care for the nails of clients in commercial nail salons and spas.

What you are going to learn

This chapter will include:

- ★ Basic hand care and nail treatments
- ★ The main factors affecting nail care services
- ★ How to choose hand and nail care products, tools and techniques to achieve different looks
- ★ Basic factors that affect the appearance and condition of hands and nails
- ★ How to carry out a basic hand and nail treatment
- ★ How to carry out basic nail art techniques
- ★ The terminology related to hand and nail care services

© iStockphoto.com/Miranda Salia

Having well cared for hands and nails gives a good first impression.

Nail care

People often say they can tell a lot about a person by their hands. This can be quite worrying if you don't really care for them, and they look rough and unloved!

Lifestyle is often reflected in the hands and nails. A person may look as though they do a lot of physical work with their hands. For example, like a builder or a mechanic. Some people may nervously chew their nails; others have perfectly manicured and polished nails.

© iStockphoto.com/Knape

Nails can reflect your personality and lifestyle

ACTIVITY

You can tell a lot about a person from their hands. Look at the two photographs on p.333 and, working with a partner, discuss the 'personality' behind each of the images.

Put together a profile of each person, let your imagination run wild – what's their name, age, what do they do? Where do they work or study? Where do they live? What clothes do they like? What music, holidays, hobbies and sports do they enjoy?

Find some pictures from magazines and create a **story board** for each image to illustrate the aspects of this person's life.

Finally, present your work to the rest of your group, and share your imaginative thoughts.

Looking at the condition of the hands and nails does not give you the full story of someone's life, but it's a start. Hands are very visual, always on show, whether you are using a computer, working in a shop or holding someone else's hand. Many people use their hands when speaking, as it helps them to communicate and therefore they need to be confident about the look of their hands and nails.

Your nails can be a good indicator of what's going on inside your body. If you eat an unhealthy diet, you can't expect your hands to be soft and smooth, or your nails to be strong. Your nails are more likely to be flaky, split, broken and ridged.

What is happening inside your body is vital, but it's also very important to look after the hands and nails from the outside. You need to ensure that they are kept clean, nourished and cared for. To be able to care for the hands and nails and improve their appearance, you need to know about the structure of the nail and its function. You can read all about the structure and function of nails in Chapter 4 'The science of hair and beauty'.

You can tell a lot about a person from their hands

Nail care for men

Men are enjoying the benefits of nail care. More and more are having regular manicures and wearing nail enamel. Professional men often choose to follow a manicure or pedicure with clear enamel or buffing. However, black and other dark colours are becoming increasingly popular.

Rock bands probably popularised the wearing of nail enamel. The colours were usually very dark, or black. In 1997 the cosmetic company Hard Candy developed 'Candy Man' a nail enamel brand aimed at men. It offered colours called testosterone (Gunmetal grey), Gigolo (Silver-specked black), Superman (Dark blue) and Dog (Deep purple).

EXTEND YOUR LEARNING   

Research the treatments and services provided by your local nail salons to find out about male hand and nail care. Investigate the treatments available, the packages and prices. If you live in the London area, look out for the Martyn Maxey salon and find out about the New York fashion for 'Grooming Friday'. This service is popular with men for making sure their hands and feet look good for the weekend. If you don't live in London look at the website **www.martynmaxey.co.uk/men.php**.

Hands can indicate a person's personality

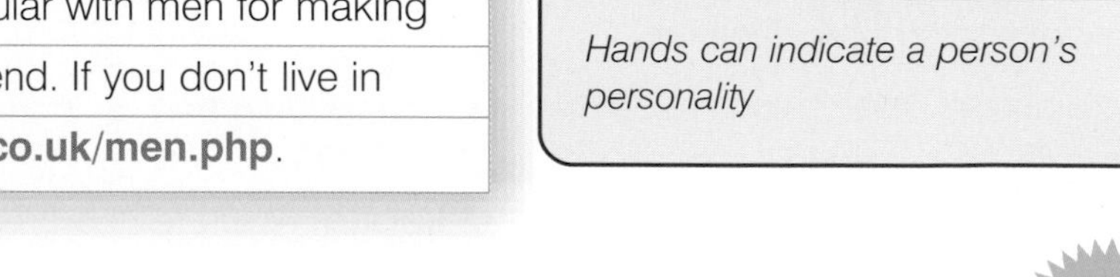

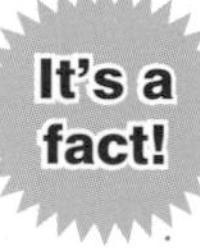

A manicure involves the care of the hands and fingernails.

Nails and fashion

Every season nail companies bring out the new *collection* of colours, which become the hot colours for the coming months.

© iStockphoto.com/Slava Gutsko

Dark colours are popular with men

© iStockphoto.com/Famke Backx

Dark nail enamel can be very dramatic

EXTEND YOUR LEARNING

Mehndi is widely used to create temporary tattoos, not just for traditional celebrations such as weddings, but as a fashion statement. Draw around the outside of your hands and fingers to make a template. Then create a mehndi design.

Fashion and trends will dictate the nail length and shape as well as the nail enamel colour. Some seasons the must-have look is very natural pale colours (even white) on short nails. Then, later its longer, square shaped, dark, hot chocolate coloured nails. Films have been known to start trends, for example, when the actress Uma Thurman wore Chanel's Rouge Noir nail enamel in the film *Pulp Fiction*. The stores were sold out for months and it became a cult colour.

Nails and personality

Your personality can all be expressed through the hands, feet and nail art.

If someone has a very quiet and shy personality, they may prefer to have short natural nails, avoiding bright **nail enamel** so they don't attract attention. On the other hand a person with a very confident, bubbly extrovert personality may want to express themselves through the appearance of their nails. For example, they may choose to have long nails, painted dark blue with silver stars.

Anything is possible, as long as you feel comfortable with the style you have chosen.

The good thing is, unlike haircuts or some hair colours, nail painting is temporary. Therefore, you can be sensible with short unpolished nails in the week when you are at school or college, and then at the weekend you can live your dream with long talons covered in bling!

Nails, culture and religion

Different cultures and countries decorate the hands to express their beliefs and at times of celebration.

Mehndi is the application of **henna** to the hands, feet and nails. It is used to stain the hands, feet and nails, leaving beautiful, intricate designs in shades of red, orange and brown. This temporary form of skin decoration is commonly used in Southern Asia, the Middle East, North Africa and Somalia. In Kerala in Southern India, henna is known as *mylanchi* and is widely used by the Muslim community.

The pattern for the designs reflects the traditions and cultures of the country. For example, in ancient India it was the tradition to apply the henna in fine lines to produce a beautiful pattern that resembled lace and paisley.

Henna is absorbed best on dry skin, which is why the soles of the feet and the palms of the hands are decorated. The skin in these areas contains higher levels of **keratin** which temporarily binds to the main colourant in henna.

The process of application was and still is very time consuming. Therefore, the application of henna becomes a very special and social time, when brides meet with their women friends and family who share the application event as well as exchange advice for a happy marriage. Traditions in India, Bangladesh and Sudan mean that sometimes bridegrooms have henna applied as well.

In Arabic and Persian speaking countries such as Morocco and other countries in central Asia, a henna application is completed for other special occasions. For example, during the seventh month of pregnancy, after having the baby, for engagements, family get-togethers or simply to celebrate an event.

Henna design on a Bride's hands

Mehndi decorations became fashionable in the UK in the late 1990s, where they are usually called *henna tattoos*. The henna paste is applied on the skin using a plastic cone or a paint brush. Sometimes a small metal-tipped bottle used for silk painting is used. The painted area is then wrapped with tissue, plastic or medical tape to lock in body heat, creating a more intense colour on the skin. The wrap is worn overnight and then removed. The final colour is reddish brown and can last from two weeks to several months depending on the type of the paste.

Application of a temporary henna tattoo

Factors affecting nail care services

There are certain factors that affect nail care and should be taken into consideration before nail and hand care treatments can take place. Professional nail technicians ensure that they are aware of these factors, so that the advice and treatment given are suitable for the client and will enhance the appearance of the hands and nails. The factors are:

- occasion
- lifestyle
- skin condition/type
- allergies
- nail shape
- skin and nail conditions that may affect hand care services

© iStockphoto.com/Rich Legg

Nail treatments are very popular for brides

Occasion

The look of the nails must be appropriate for the occasion. A professional nail technician will ask their clients questions to find out if they are having a treatment for a particular occasion. Their clients may be having a nail treatment because they are attending an interview; they will want to look very smart and groomed and their nails to look neat, in good condition and well cared for.

Some may be getting married and want their hands and nails to look their best but in a natural, understated way. Others may be going to a fancy dress party – perhaps as a Thai dancer with long intricate jewelled nails.

Whatever the event, agreement needs to be reached on the look that is needed before the colour for the enamel is chosen.

Lifestyle

The client's lifestyle is a factor that must be considered. Their job, college course, hobbies or home activities may mean that long nails with pale enamel would be unsuitable – especially if they have a horse and are clearing our stables every night.

Working in certain professions mean that some people are not allowed to wear nail enamel at all. For example, those who work in a sterile environment, surgeons, nurses or chefs. However, such clients can be offered an attractive, groomed effect by buffing the nail to a shine.

It's a fact! The word manicure derives from two Latin words: *manus* for hand, *cura* for care.

Skin condition

The condition of the skin must be taken into consideration. For example, if the skin is dry and dehydrated, this will affect the nail and cuticles. The cuticles will be very dry, flaky and could split, which may lead to infection. Dehydrated nails would be very flaky and may start to peel in layers. The client would have to be advised to take more care of their hands and nails to ensure they stay in good condition. For example gloves may need to be worn when washing up, and a good quality hand cream or oil massaged into the hands and nails every night. Regular manicures would help the dehydration, as would ensuring enough water is drunk each day.

© iStockphoto.com/Eva Serrabassa

The nail shape should flatter the hand

Allergies

Some people may have an allergic reaction to the products that are used for hand and nail care treatments. For example there could be a reaction to lanolin, enamel remover, acetone and the perfume in hand lotion or to the nail enamel. Such allergies should be discussed during the consultation.

Nail shape

Many different nail shapes can be achieved. The natural shape of the nail should be considered when deciding on the final look. It will be impossible to achieve long sleek pointed nails, if the natural shape of the nail is very wide and square. To avoid disappointing the client, a professional nail technician will keep the expectations of the client realistic, and provide a full explanation of what can be achieved.

Skin and nail conditions that may affect hand care services

Contra-indications

A **contra-indication** is a condition that prevents a treatment from being carried out. You must be aware of all the contra-indications to a hand and nail treatments to ensure the client's safety and well-being. Each individual is assessed so that the treatment can be adapted to meet their individual needs. If there is any concern about their health, the client would be advised to seek medical guidance.

Contra-indications can be divided into three categories:

- *General* – contra-indications that affect the entire body
- *Local* – contra-indications that only involve a *local* area of the hand or nail, for example, scar tissue. A manicure could be carried out providing the area is avoided
- *Temporary* – contra-indications that are not permanent. Treatment is temporarily stopped, but can be carried out once the condition clears up, for example, the client may have a cut or swelling

There are many skin conditions that can affect hand and nail care. You can read about them in Chapter 4 'The science of hair and beauty'. Some conditions are not infectious. This means nail care treatments can be carried out. However, if an infectious or contagious condition exists, then the treatments must not be carried out.

There are certain conditions that, although they don't prevent treatment, they do restrict what can be offered. The nail treatment routine may have to be adapted. The conditions are:

- *Onychopagy* (nail biting) – be extra careful as the free edge is often very tender, and the cuticles may also be bitten. A bitter tasting product can be applied to the nails to discourage biting.
- *Pterygium* (overgrown cuticles) – needs lots of gentle cuticle work to loosen the cuticle, may take two or three manicures to see good results. Need to apply cuticle cream or oil each night.
- *Hangnail* (cuticle cracked) – massage lots of cuticle cream/oil into the cuticles to add moisture and regain flexibility. Hangnails can be very sore, they should never be bitten as this can look very unsightly and can lead to infection. Need to apply cuticle cream or oil each night.
- *Leuconychia* (white spots on nail plate) – avoid pressure over these areas, as it can be as a result of an injury. The white spots can be disguised by a coloured nail enamel.

EXTEND YOUR LEARNING

Research international nail bars, salons and spas to see what nail and hand care services are available for improving the condition of the skin of the hands, and the nails.

Try looking at the websites for Bliss Spa **www.blisslondon.co.uk** and Nails Inc. **www.nailsinc.com**.

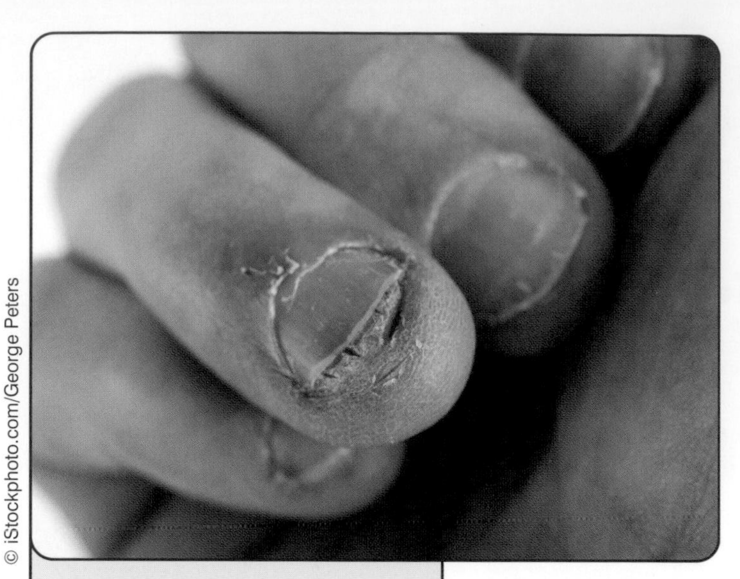

© iStockphoto.com/George Peters

Nail biting can be unsightly and may mean the manicure has to be adapted.

- ***Bruised nail*** – with mild bruising, avoid this part of the nail, and don't apply pressure. If the whole nail is bruised it could be very painful. Don't treat the nail until it has healed.
- ***Ridges in the nail plate*** – depending on the severity, treat the nail gently and avoid too much pressure, as some nails may also be fragile if it is caused by illness or old age. Buffing can help reduce ridges, as can applying a ridge-filling base coat.
- ***Onychorrhexis*** (split/flaking nails) – use plenty of cuticle cream/oil in the manicure and encourage clients to apply this at home, daily. File gently to avoid any further splitting of the nail, and use a special base coat for this nail type.
- ***Non-severe psoriasis of the skin and nail*** – be careful over this area (often around the elbow), and use a good quality nourishing, but soothing massage cream. Avoid any areas of broken skin. If the nail is involved, treat gently and keep the nails short.
- ***Non-severe eczema of the skin*** – If the skin is broken avoid the area, use a soothing massage cream, and find out what makes the condition worse. For example, perfume may cause irritation. If nails have eczema, keep them short and treat gently.

It's a fact! A bruised nail appears deep purple or black. In extreme cases the injury can result in the loss of the nail. A new nail will usually grow back again unless there is severe damage to the matrix.

Contra-actions

Action taken to correct an unwanted reaction that may have occurred during a treatment is called a **contra-action**. If an individual has an abnormal reaction to the treatment it can be unpleasant and irritating. The reaction needs immediate attention, to minimise the impact and discomfort for the client.

Should someone suffer from an adverse reaction to a hand treatment, a professional nail technician will ensure that they:

- provide a room for relaxation, that is well ventilated
- ensure the client's clothing isn't too tight, so they can breathe freely and easily
- provide a glass of water or other refreshment
- apply a cold compress or soothing lotion to any irritated skin condition
- If symptoms persist, the client will be advised to seek medical assistance at the earliest opportunity

On completion of the treatment, the nail technician will make a note of any adverse reactions on the record card, so that future treatments can be adapted.

EXTEND YOUR LEARNING 

Research the list of possible contra-actions to a hand treatment and detail the action that should be taken.

Abnormal reaction	Possible cause	Recommended contra-action to be taken
Allergic rash	Reaction to a product (e.g. Lanolin) or tool	
Burning sensation on skin	Reaction to a product	
Product in eye	Poor technique, splash of product	
Bruising	Poor technique, or too much pressure when massaging	
Cuticles bleeding	Poor technique, cuticle has been cut	

Basic hand and nail treatment

A basic manicure treatment is carried out with the aim of improving the condition and appearance of the:

- lower arm
- hands
- cuticles
- nails

The lower arm

Sometimes, the skin of the lower arm can dry out due to neglect, sunburn or ageing. A body scrub can be used to **exfoliate** dead skin cells. Then the area needs lots of attention during the massage – concentrate on the area, making sure you really massage the cream or oil deep into the skin, especially around the elbow, which can be very dry.

The hands

The hands are one of the first areas of the body to show the signs of ageing. So it is important to look after them. Hands are used constantly and suffer a lot of wear and tear – and it shows. The skin on the back of the hand can become very dry, rough, chapped, crepey and aged. The palms can become rough with **calluses**. The fingers can become cracked, which can be very sore.

A manicure will help to restore moisture to the skin of the hands, helping to keep them healthy, smooth and soft. Miracles may not happen overnight and it can take three or four manicure treatments to really show results, but there is usually some immediate improvement.

It's a fact! Nails grow quicker when the body is active and the blood circulation is increased.

Nails grow more quickly:

- on hands rather than feet
- in summer rather than in winter
- in younger people rather than in older
- in pregnancy

The cuticles

This is the area of skin around the base of the nail, which should be smooth, flexible and soft, with no breaks. However if this area is neglected or there is a lack of care, the cuticle can dry out and become rough, tight and, sometimes, spilt open. The aim of a manicure treatment is to restore moisture to the cuticle, so that the cuticle, once again, becomes soft and supple.

The nails

Nails should be a healthy beige or pale pink colour. They should be flexible and have a smooth surface. The edge of the nail, known as the **free edge**, should be even and smooth. If nails are neglected, they can become dry, flaky, brittle, bruised, pitted, ridged and the free edge can split, flake or break. A manicure treatment will help to restore the nail back to its former glory – clean, smooth and supple.

It's a fact! Fingernails grow on average 0.5–1.2 mm per week. It can take approximately 5–6 months for a new nail to grow from the matrix to the free edge. Toenails grow more slowly. It may be up to a year to grow a new nail. However, there is an advantage to this – nail enamel worn on the toes can often last a lot longer than that worn on fingernails.

Nail shapes

Nails and hands come in all shapes and sizes. During the consultation, it is important to carefully consider which nail shape would best suit the shape and length of the hands. Factors such as lifestyle and occupation must be taken into consideration when deciding on the shape and length of the nail.

The advantages and disadvantages of different nail shapes.

NAIL SHAPE	ADVANTAGES	DISADVANTAGES
Round	Ideal for short nails, and for men. Can suit square shaped hands as it can soften the angular lines	Will not suit large round hands, as it will make them appear much bigger
Square	Suitable for people who do a lot of work with their hands, e.g. manual workers, computer/key boarding. The shape can be flattering for long thin fingers	Will not suit square shaped hands as it highlights the angular lines
Oval	Flattering for small hands, and short stubby fingers as the shape can appear to lengthen the fingers	Can accentuate long thin bony fingers and hands
Pointed	May be suitable for special occasions – for dramatic effect	Can make long thin bony fingers look aggressive. Can be more prone to break as the nail is weakened at the sides
Squoval	A square shape with curved corners can be very flattering on long slim fingers, can appear more attractive than a regular oval shape	Will not suit square shaped hands as it can emphasise the angular lines

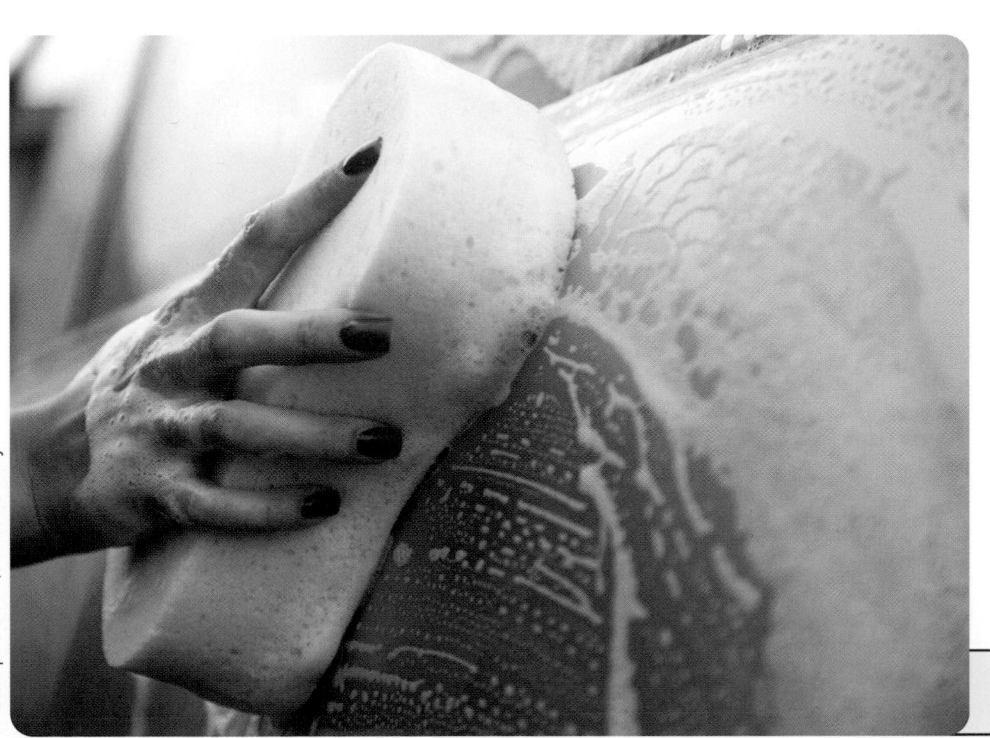

Nail shape should suit your lifestyle

It's a fact!

Square shaped nails can often be very angular, so to make them more attractive file them with a slight curve at the corners – this is what is know as a **squoval** shape, and it's very popular in nail bars and spas.

Preparing the treatment area

When preparing your treatment area for a nail treatment you will need the following:

1 manicure table or work station, with chair
2 towels
3 comfortable chair
4 washbasin

It's a fact! A *pedicure* involves the care of the feet and toenails

You will also need to consider the environment in which the manicure treatment is taking place. You should ensure that the temperature of the room is comfortable. The room should not be stuffy, or have cold draughts. The lighting should be bright enough for you to clearly see what you are doing, but not too harsh as it would not be relaxing for the client. To make a more relaxed atmosphere, you could use fragranced candles and suitable background music.

Equipment and materials

In order to be organised, efficient and professional, it is good practice to make sure you have all the equipment you need ready and prepared before you start a treatment.

A prepared manicure table/workstation

Tools and equipment for the manicure station or table

TOOL/ EQUIPMENT	USE	BENEFITS	TIP	IMAGE
Nail files	For shaping the free edge of the nail	Some files have a variety of surfaces, always end with the finest abrasive side to smooth the edge of the nail	The direction of filing should always be from the side to the centre, never in a sawing action across the free edge	
Hoof stick	To gently ease back the cuticle	As they are made from wood or plastic with a rubber end, they are better than using metal tools to loosen the cuticles	Use the rubber end and gently work in circles, to ease the skin at the base of the nail	Ellisons
Orange stick	Pointed end can clean under the free edge at the end of the treatment, to remove cream, etc. Can remove small amount of product from a pot	The angled end can be covered with cotton wool and used like a hoof stick on the cuticle area	Use to clean up stray nail enamel, either 'dry' or dipped in enamel remover	Ellisons
Nail scissors	To reduce the length of longer nails, prior to filing	Can reduce nail length quickly, saving valuable time during the manicure. Scissors need to be large and strong enough to cut though thick nails	Never cut straight across, always angle the scissors, to avoid damaging the nail	Ellisons

Nail buffer	Promotes blood circulation to the nail and produces a shine on the nail surface	Improves health of the nail and smoothes the surface. Men often prefer a buffed 'natural shine' than the effect of clear enamel	Use fast strokes over the nail surface to produce a smooth surface and a sheen and shine	Ellisons
High shine or three way buffer	To smooth the nail and produce a sheen and shine	A three surface flexible buffer is much easier to use than a traditional buffer, often with better results	Always end with the finest abrasive side to get the best shine	Ellisons

Top tip 'Bevel' is a slanting edge, and if you file directly downwards over the free edge of the nail (bevelling) it can help to avoid the nail plate splitting and separating.

Plan a list of questions you would ask during the initial consultation for a manicure, use these with a partner so you get used to asking questions and become more confident.

Consultation

Before you start any treatment you should carry out a consultation. This will ensure it is safe to perform the treatment, and that you can tailor the treatment to the needs of the individual client.

The consultation is the start of your relationship with a client, so it is vital that you are warm, friendly, approachable and professional. It is important that the client feels relaxed and at ease during the consultation process.

In the consultation you need to gather important information, such as:

- name
- address
- telephone number/Mobile
- date of birth
- occupation
- name of Doctor
- medical history (Allergies, Epilepsy, Diabetes)
- previous nail treatments
- analysis of the condition of the hands, cuticles and nails

When carrying out a consultation, ensure:

- The area is quiet and relaxing

The manicure consultation

- You have allocated sufficient time for the treatment
- The client feels comfortable and at ease
- A thorough hand and nail analysis is carried out
- The overall aims of the treatment and outcomes are discussed
- A treatment plan is developed
- Contra-indications are checked
- Contra-actions have been explained
- There is an opportunity for any questions
- The record card is filled in
- The record card is signed

Top tip

A professional nail technician would show the client how to file their nails correctly, in case they needed to trim the free edge in between treatments.

Record card

The **record card** is a very important document. One is completed at the initial consultation, and then up-dated after each visit. It means there is a record of all the treatments provided, and how the client reacted to the treatment. Records can also be made for any adaptations that have to be made during the treatment. In Chapter 3, 'Salon business systems and processes', you can read more about paper based record cards and those linked to a computer based reception management system.

ACTIVITY    

Design and develop a record card that you would want to use if you were offering nail treatments in a nail salon or spa. Use your record card with a partner to test. Find out if the record card needs improving.

Top tip As the skin and nails change or improve through the manicure treatments it is a good idea to revisit the analysis form, and if necessary fill in a new one. The new one would be kept with the client record card or input to the reception management system.

Hand and nail analysis

It is important to carry out a thorough hand and nail analysis before deciding on which nail treatments would be beneficial and what products to use. You will need to look at all the characteristics in each area of the hands, cuticles and nails. Only when you have completed the consultation can you decide on the best treatment to carry out. The hand and nail analysis is recorded and the results are normally attached to a record card.

Example of a hand and nail analysis record.

Hand and Nail Analysis		
Name:	**Date of Birth:**	**Address:**
Area of hands/nails	**Texture/colour/dryness**	**Blemishes/conditions/ problems**
Forearm		
Back of hands		
Skin on fingers		

<table>
<tr><td>Palm of hands</td><td></td><td></td></tr>
<tr><td>Cuticles</td><td></td><td></td></tr>
<tr><td>Nails</td><td></td><td></td></tr>
<tr><td colspan="2">General skin tone and elasticity:</td><td>General appearance:</td></tr>
<tr><td colspan="2">Overall hand and nail condition:</td><td>Priorities for treatment:</td></tr>
<tr><td colspan="3">SALON TREATMENT RECOMMENDATIONS</td></tr>
<tr><td>Skin cleanser/sanitiser</td><td colspan="2"></td></tr>
<tr><td>Enamel remover</td><td colspan="2"></td></tr>
<tr><td>Nail file</td><td colspan="2"></td></tr>
<tr><td>Buffing cream</td><td colspan="2"></td></tr>
<tr><td>3 way buffer</td><td colspan="2"></td></tr>
<tr><td>Hand scrub/exfoliant</td><td colspan="2"></td></tr>
<tr><td>Hand mask</td><td colspan="2"></td></tr>
<tr><td>Massage/hand cream</td><td colspan="2"></td></tr>
<tr><td>Cuticle oil/ cream</td><td colspan="2"></td></tr>
<tr><td>Base coat</td><td colspan="2"></td></tr>
<tr><td>Nail enamel</td><td colspan="2"></td></tr>
<tr><td>Top coat/sealer</td><td colspan="2"></td></tr>
<tr><td>Nail art materials</td><td colspan="2"></td></tr>
<tr><td>Comments and notes</td><td colspan="2"></td></tr>
<tr><td>Date of skin analysis:</td><td colspan="2">Therapist:</td></tr>
</table>

It's a fact! White spots on the nail is not caused by a lack of calcium, it is usually the result of an injury, and the layers of the nail plate have separated in a small area.

Treatment plan

As part of the consultation, after completing the analysis and client record card, you then need to do a **treatment plan**. A treatment plan will enable you to focus on exactly what treatment is best, what products you will use and what the expected outcome will be.

A simple treatment plan that you could use when offering nail treatments is shown below:

Treatment Plan	
Priorities for treatment	
Aim of treatment	
What treatment is planned?	
What products to be used	**Details of use**
Skin cleanser/sanitiser	
Enamel remover	
Nail file	
Buffing cream	
3 way buffer	
Hand scrub/exfoliant	
Hand mask /type	
Massage/hand cream	
Cuticle oil/ cream	
Base coat	
Nail enamel	

Top coat/sealer	
Nail art materials	
Suggested time between treatments	
Course of treatments	
Final result **Was the desired outcome achieved?**	
Advice given	
Comments	
Manicurist:	**Date:**
Use Prescription sheet for retail recommendations, and home care advice leaflet.	

To avoid causing any harm when performing a manicure or spreading any infection it is very important to make sure you work hygienically and safely at all times. To ensure hand treatments are carried out in a hygienic manner, you will need to ensure:

- The manicure station or trolley is cleaned with hot soapy water, and wiped with disinfectant
- You use clean, fresh towels
- The chair is wiped with disinfectant
- Tools are sanitised in an **autoclave** or **ultra-violet cabinet**. You can read about methods of sterilisation in Chapter 5 'Safe working practices'.

Top tip

Always plan the treatment carefully, it looks professional, avoids wasting time and maximises the effectiveness of your hand treatment.

Hand and nail care products

Once the condition of the hand and nails are known, products can be chosen.

The following list details the main hand and nail products used in manicures.

PRODUCT	APPLICATION	BENEFIT
Skin cleanser/ sanitiser	Use to clean the hands before the hand treatment	Removes harmful micro-organisms that could cause infection
Skin exfoliant	Product designed to remove dead skin cells (exfoliate) A cream containing fine particles that are abrasive and so 'slough' off the dead skin cells Used at the beginning of the manicure	Removes dead skin cells Prepares the skin for massage cream, which will be absorbed better Leaves the skin smooth, soft and brighter
Nail enamel remover	Usually contains acetone, and oil such as glycerol Can dry the nail plate if used excessively Applied on cotton wool pads	Dissolves nail enamel and grease from the nail plate
Buffing paste	Coarse texture, contains powdered pumice or silica Very small amount needed Used with a traditional buffer	Smoothes the nail plate and gives a shine to the nail
Cuticle cream/oil	Contains a mixture of fats, waxes and oil, e.g. beeswax, cocoa butter	Replaces moisture Softens and nourishes the cuticle, so it can be easily pushed back and loosened
Cuticle remover	Contains potassium hydroxide, which is an alkaline and can be very drying on the nail After cuticle work has been done ensure any excess is removed by gently using a nail brush	Applied to the cuticles to help loosen it from the nail plate

Nail enamel remover can be available to retail

ACTIVITY

Choose five manicure products and find out what you can about the COSHH regulations for the products.

Massage cream/oil	Contains waxes, oils and perfumes Used as a medium for the hand massage Apply with hands, apply sufficient so the massage flows smoothly	Replaces moisture, and leaves the hand soft and smooth
Base coat	Apply one coat to a clean, grease-free nail plate	Smooth base for the nail enamel Prevents dark colours from staining the nail
Nail enamel	Plain/cream nail enamel – apply 2 coats Pearlised nail enamel – apply 3 coats (don't use a top coat)	
Top coat	One coat applied on top of the nail enamel Don't apply over pearlised nail enamel	Adds extra gloss Prolong life of the manicure/nail enamel Protect nail enamel from chipping
Quick dry oil/ spray	Oil is drizzled over the top coat A spray can be applied evenly	Speeds up the drying process

Top tip

Pearlised or chrystalline nail enamel is not recommended for dry nails

Nail enamel peels if

- it is applied too thickly
- poor quality or thickened nail enamel is used
- oil or grease is left on the nail plate

Nail enamel chips if

- there are ridges on nail plate
- there is a flaking nail condition
- the nail enamel is dried too quickly
- the nail enamel has been thinned too much

Massage techniques

Massage strokes are classified into three main groups. Within each group there are a range of strokes. The table lists the main movements in each of the three groups.

CLASSIFICATION/GROUP	INDIVIDUAL MOVEMENTS
Effleurage (Stroking)	Superficial effleurage Deep effleurage Stimulating stroking Soothing stroking

Petrissage (Compression)	Kneading
	Knuckling
	Skin rolling
	Pinching
	Wringing
Tapotement (Percussion)	Beating
	Pounding
	Hacking
	Clapping/cupping

The effects of massage

Massage has many uses and effects on the body.

MASSAGE GROUP/ CLASSIFICATION	MAIN USES AND EFFECTS
Effleurage (Stroking) 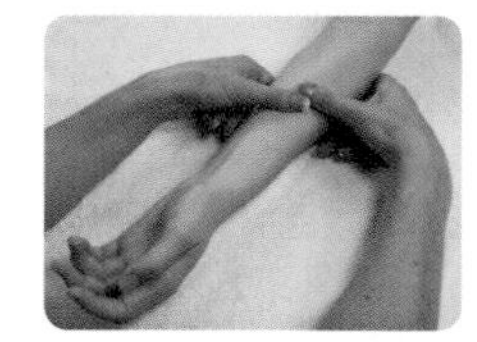	Increase blood circulation Increases **lymphatic** circulation Relieves tension Helps reduce **non-medical oedema** Aids **desquamation** Help with relaxation
Petrissage (Compression) 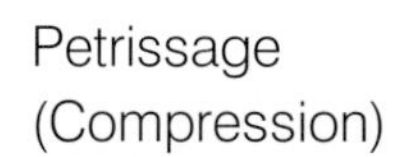 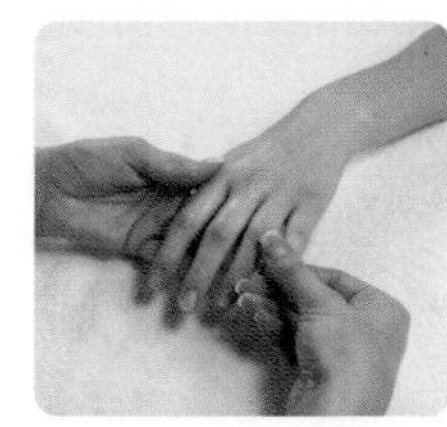	Increase blood circulation Increases lymphatic circulation Breaks down tight **nodules** in the muscles Aids removal of waste products from the tissues Promotes relaxation in the client Increases sluggish circulation

Top tip When massaging the palm of the hand, give extra attention to the muscles at the base of the thumb. Hands do a lot of work and can be very tense and tight, and kneading to the palm and base of the thumb feels so good!

Top tip Some people think that the massage is by far the best part of the manicure, it is so incredibly relaxing. So don't miss it out or rush it, as it may be disappointing for the client. They may feel like you have not given a full manicure treatment.

Tapotement (Percussion) 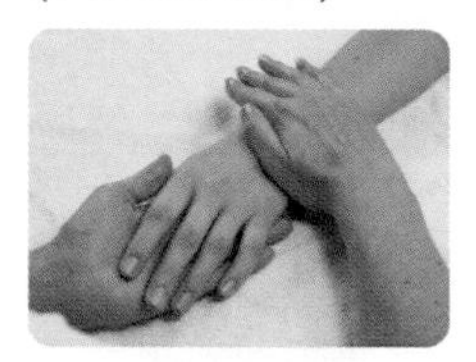	Stimulates the sensory nerve endings Improves muscle tone and response Stimulates a **lethargic** client

ACTIVITY    

Whilst you are working in your training salon or on work placement in a nail salon, carry out some research into nail treatments. Investigate the barriers for clients booking in for nail treatments

You will need to decide where to conduct this research. You can do this by talking to people in the salon who don't have nail treatments. Or, talk to people who do not go the salon at all, so therefore, do not have any of the services. Use your research to find out what is a barrier – is it time? Price? Lack of awareness of benefits of the hand and nail treatments?

Write up your research findings and suggest ways in which the salon could overcome the barriers and increase the number of clients booking for nail treatments. Present your findings to the rest of your group.

If you are very lucky you may have the opportunity to combine your research with one of the salon's promotional activities.

© iStockphoto.com/Nathalie Beauvois

EXTEND YOUR LEARNING   

Research the international nail experts Marian Newman and Leighton Denny. Find out where they are based, what competitions they have won, about their own range of nail products and which celebrities are their clients … and learn just how far you can go in the nail industry.

Practical nail treatment procedures

Now that you are aware of all the factors that affect the appearance and condition of the hands and nails, and you know how to select the right products and tools, and why you must carry out a consultation – you are now ready to put the theory into practice!

Top tip

Be careful not to use a 'sawing' action when filing the nails as this can cause the layers of the nail plate to split and separate.

Step by step method for a manicure procedure

Carry out a consultation and fill in the record card. Analyse the hand and nails, and discuss the treatment plan.

1 Cleanse the hands with an antiseptic spray to remove dirt and micro-organisms and remove nail enamel from both hands.

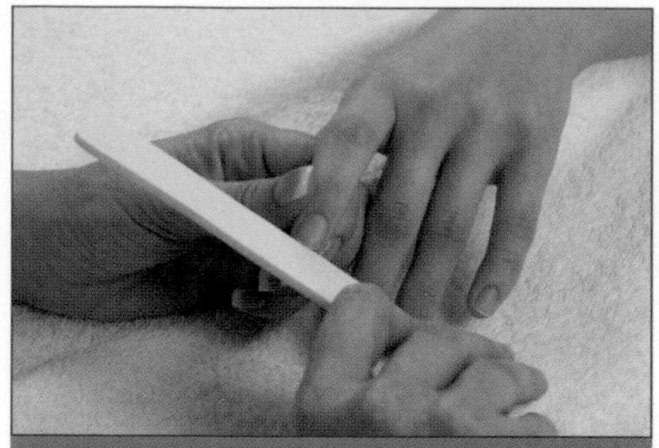

2 Start on the first hand, file the nails into a flattering shape.

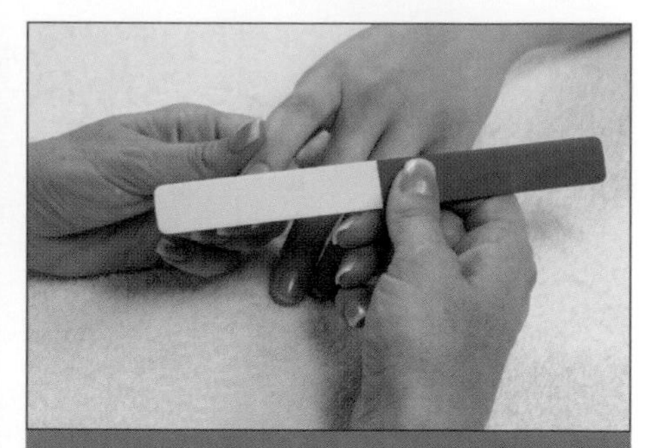

3 Buff the nails lightly using the three-way buffer.

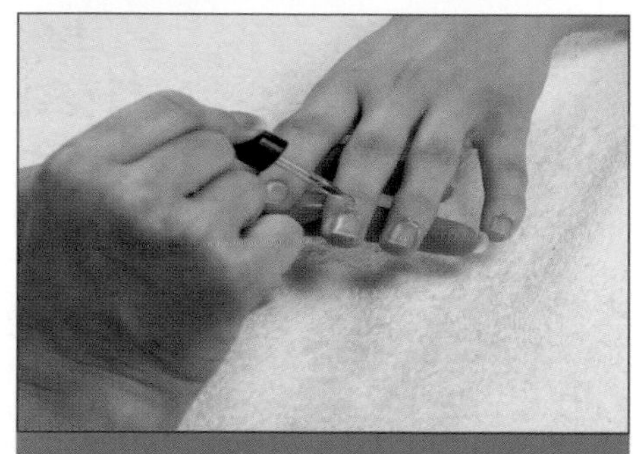

4 Apply cuticle oil to the cuticle area.

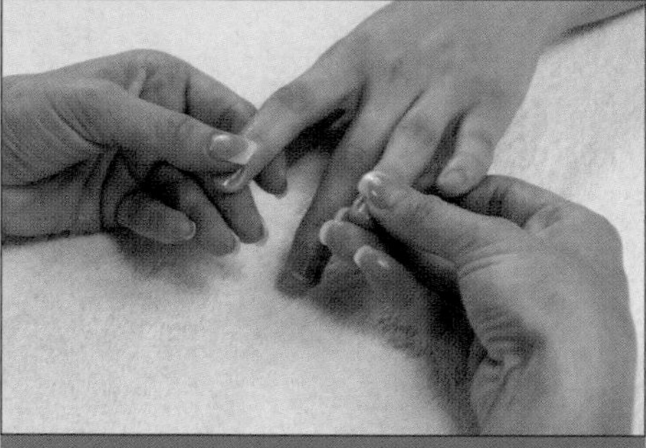

5 Massage cream/oil in gently.

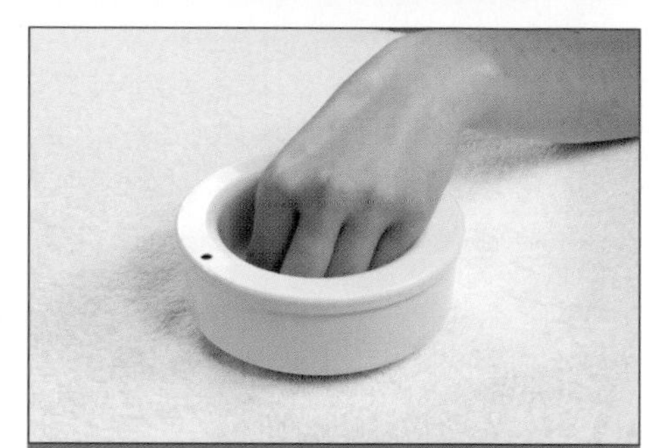

6 Place hand in a bowl of warm water to soak. Meanwhile file nails on second hand, buff gently and apply cuticle cream.

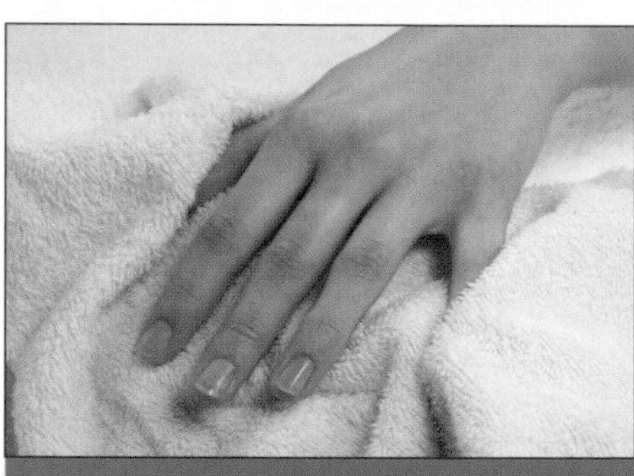

7 Remove first hand from bowl and dry with a towel, and place second hand in the warm water to soak.

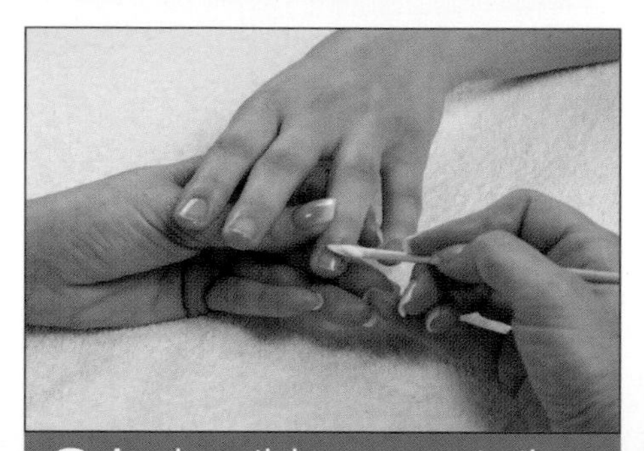

8 Apply cuticle remover to the cuticles and with a 'tipped' orange stick, carefully push back the cuticles. Remove second hand from the bowl and thoroughly dry. Apply cuticle remover and carefully push back the cuticles with the orange stick.

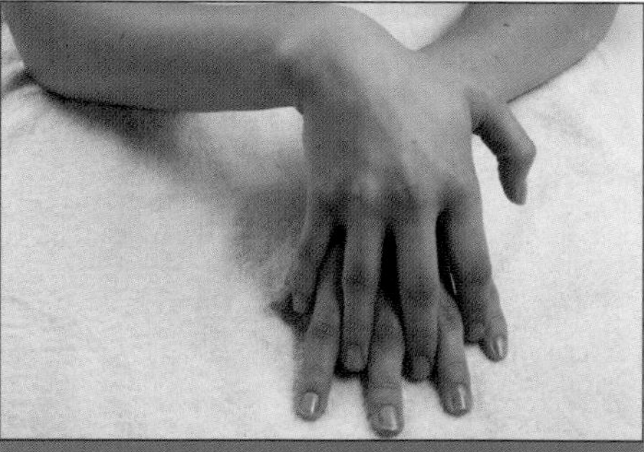

9 Remove any excess cuticle remover with a damp nail brush and dry. Perform hand massage (see separate procedure). Hands are ready for the application of nail enamel, if appropriate (see different techniques).

Step by step method for a hand massage

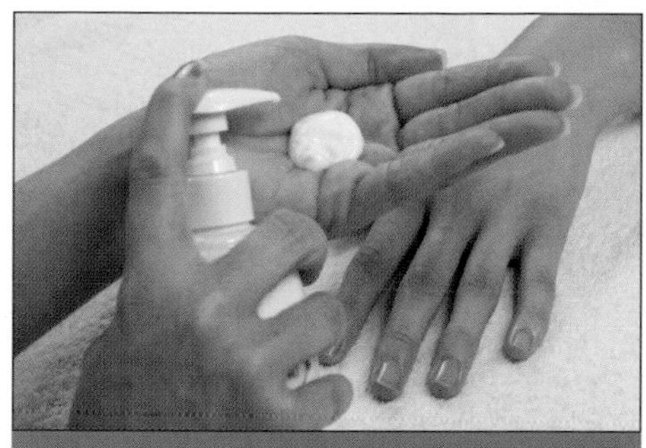

1 Apply sufficient massage cream/lotion in your palm and rub both hands together to evenly spread the product.

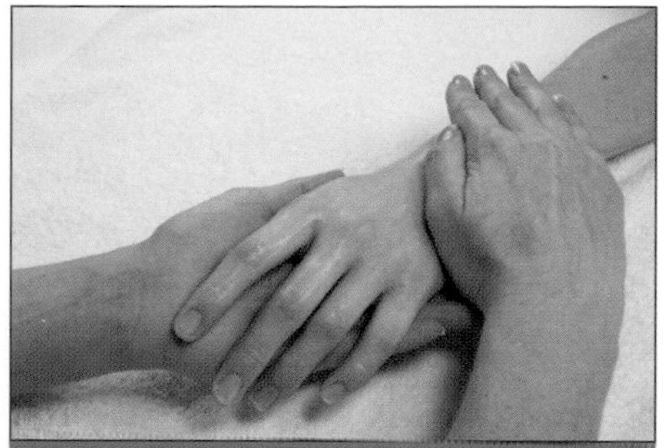

2 Using the palm apply 3 effleurage strokes to the outer part of the lower arm and hand, and then repeat to the inner part.

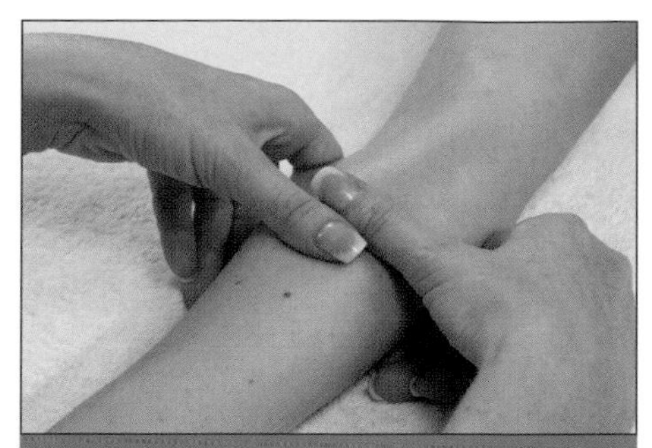

3 Use both thumbs in circular movements, work slowly from the elbow towards the wrist.

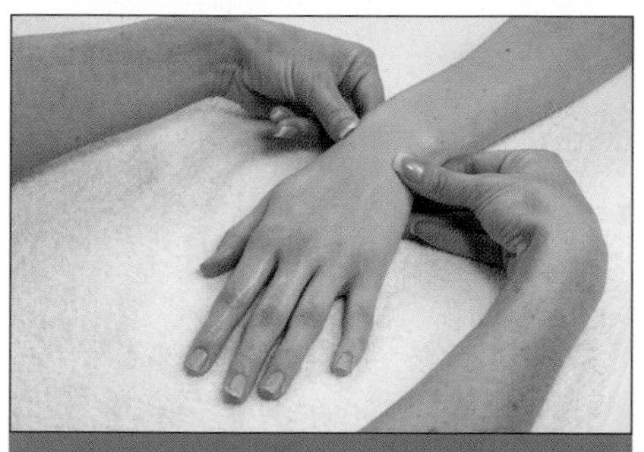

4 Carry out thumb kneading to the wrist area.

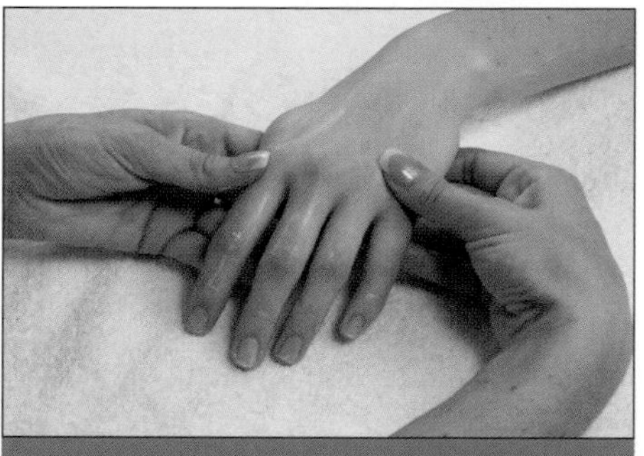

5 Carry out thumb kneading across the back of hands towards the fingers.

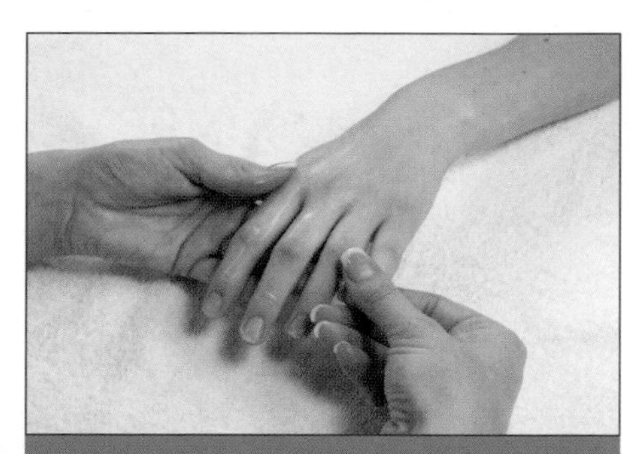

6 Apply thumb kneading to each finger.

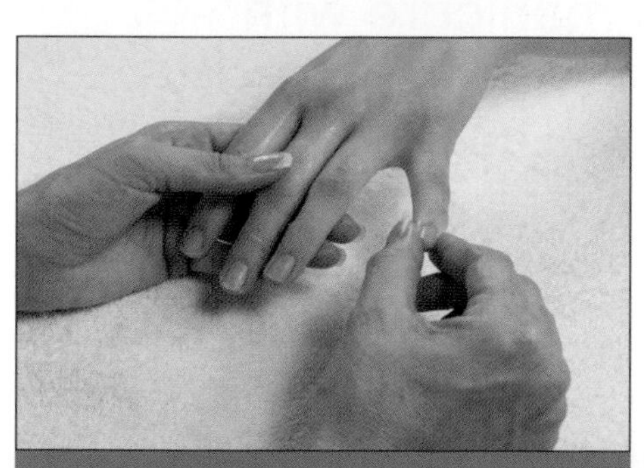

7 Support the hand, start with the smallest finger and gently rotate each finger twice in each direction. Finish with a slight pull, and a sliding motion off the end of the finger.

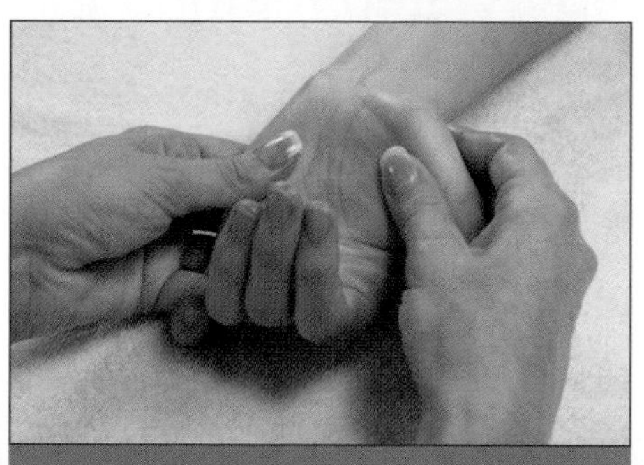

8 Turn the hand over; use your thumbs to apply deep circular kneading movements across the whole palm area, paying particular attention to the base of the thumb.

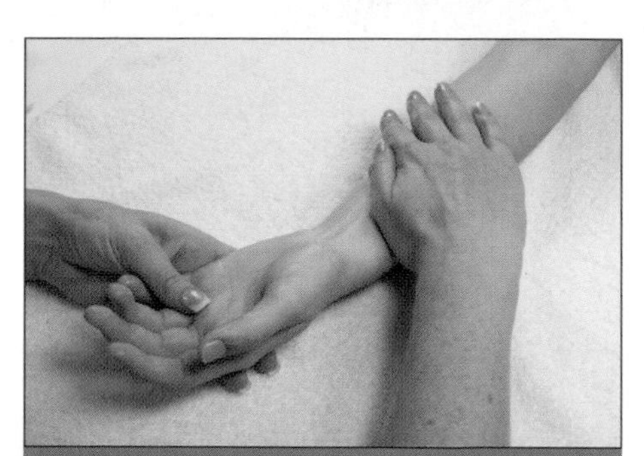

9 Finish with 3 effleurage strokes to each aspect of the lower arm and hand.

Bring your learning to life 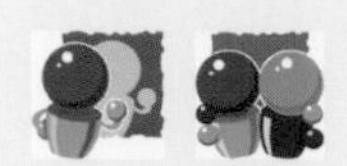

When you are in the training salon or in your work placement, work with a partner and carry out a manicure treatment.

When you do this, you should ask your partner for feedback about the treatment.

When you have finished the service, write down your experiences in your *Diploma file*.

You should record:

- The condition of the hands and nails before the treatment
- The products used for the treatment. Why did you choose them?
- The result – did it match the results identified in the treatment plan?

Then ask your partner to write in your *Diploma file*. They should write about their experience during the manicure treatment. How did the massage feel? What was the pressure like? Did they enjoy it?

Finally ask your partner what you could do to improve the manicure treatment next time. Note their answer. Then, when you carry out another manicure, refer back to your notes to see how you can improve.

Top tip **Dark colours can** draw attention to nails, so they are best avoided if the nails are very short, bitten or in a poor condition.

It's a fact! **A professional manicure with enamel should take no more** than 30 or 40 minutes. However a file and enamel application can take as little as 10 minutes.

Step by step method for a manicure with transfer

Carry out the full manicure (see previous procedure) and discuss the desired final look and decide on the nail enamel colour.

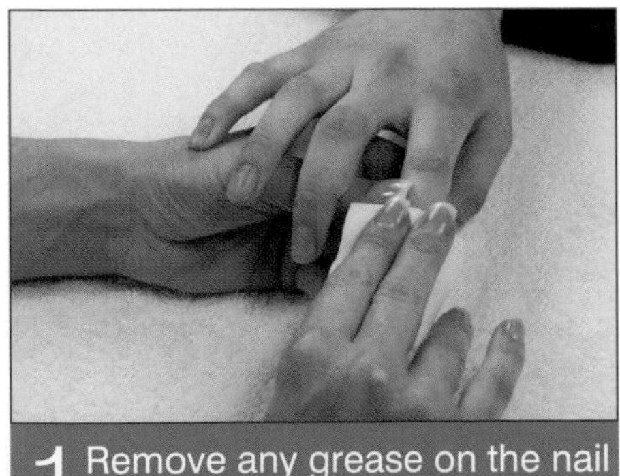

1 Remove any grease on the nail plate with the nail enamel remover.

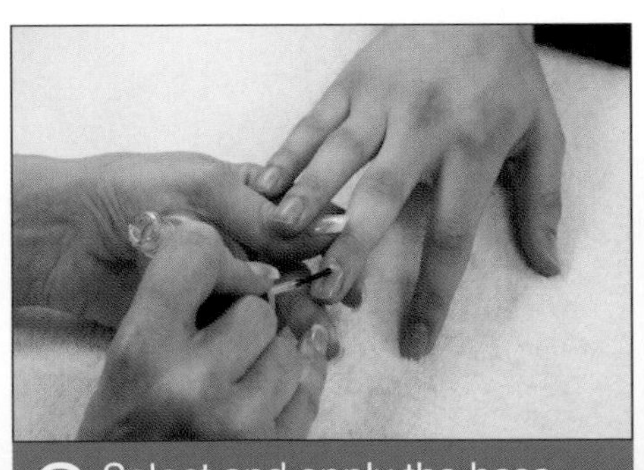

2 Select and apply the base coat.

3 Apply the first and second coat of enamel.

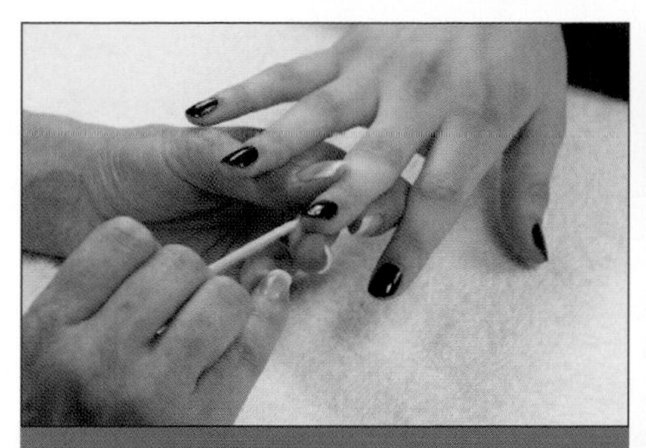

4 Tip an orange stick with cotton wool, wrap the cotton wool tightly around the orange stick, dip the tipped orange stick in enamel remover and remove any smudges of enamel, to ensure a perfect finish.

5 Select a nail transfer and soak it in water.

6 Use tweezers to slide the transfer from the backing paper.

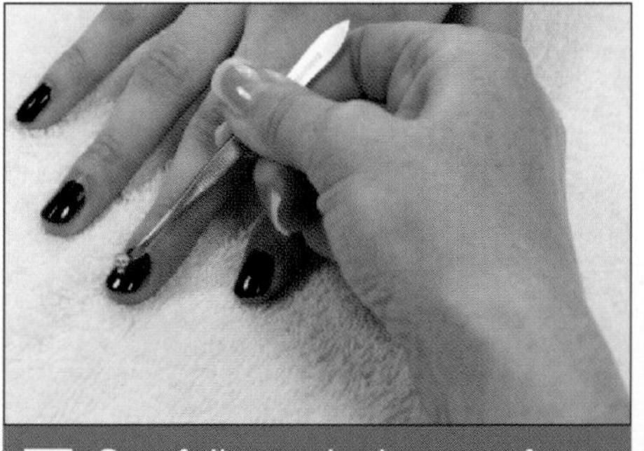

7 Carefully apply the transfer to the nail, and ensure the transfer is positioned carefully on the nail.

8 Apply a coat of top coat/sealer to protect the enamel, transfer and prolong the life of the manicure.

9 The final result can be very effective.

French manicure

The **French manicure** technique is designed to resemble a natural nail. The tips of the nail are painted white while the rest of the nail is enamelled in a pink, beige or other suitable shade. The style is chosen because it is very simple and gives a natural and clean look. French manicures are very popular with brides. The look has developed to be part of a pedicure, as the clean natural look is ideal for toes.

French manicures are thought to have originated in eighteenth-century Paris and were popular in the 1920s and 1930s.

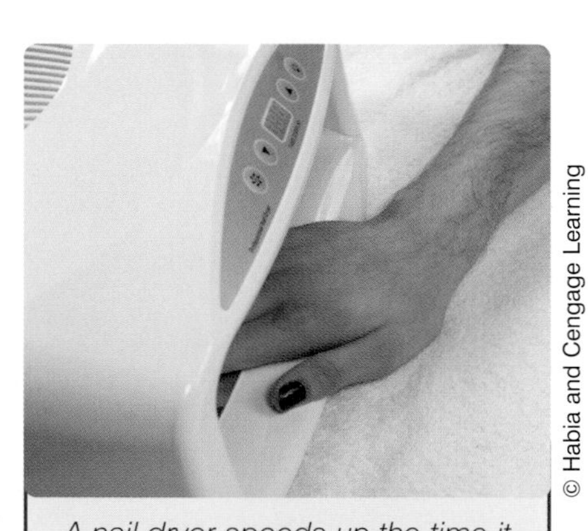

A nail dryer speeds up the time it takes for the nail enamel to dry which reduces smudges

Correct nail enamel application

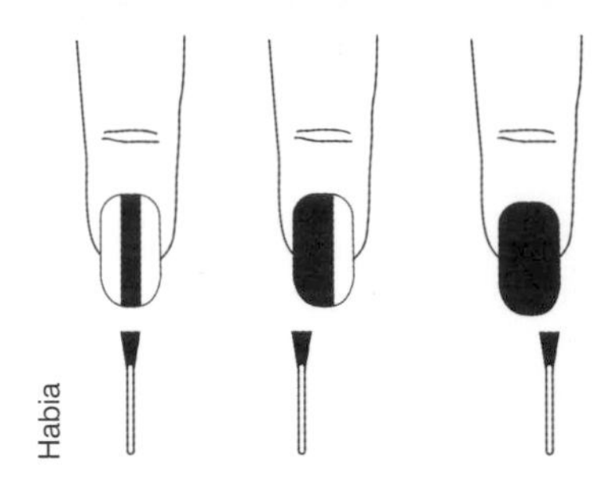

Top tip To achieve a good final effect it is important that the nails and cuticles are in good condition, or it will spoil the French manicure technique

Step by step method for a French manicure procedure

Carry out the full manicure (see previous procedure) and discuss the desired final look, and decide on the two colours to be used.

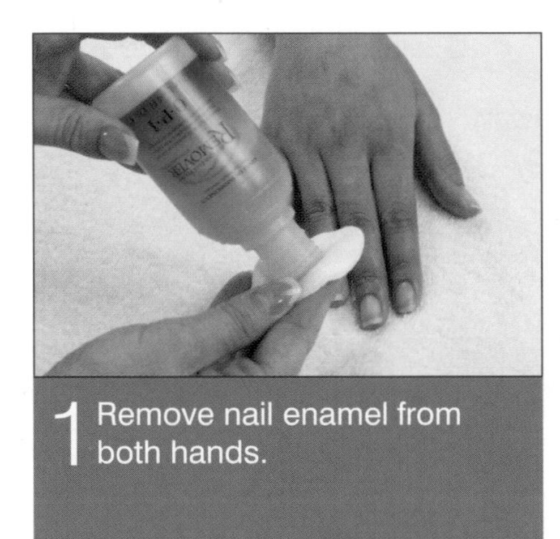

1 Remove nail enamel from both hands.

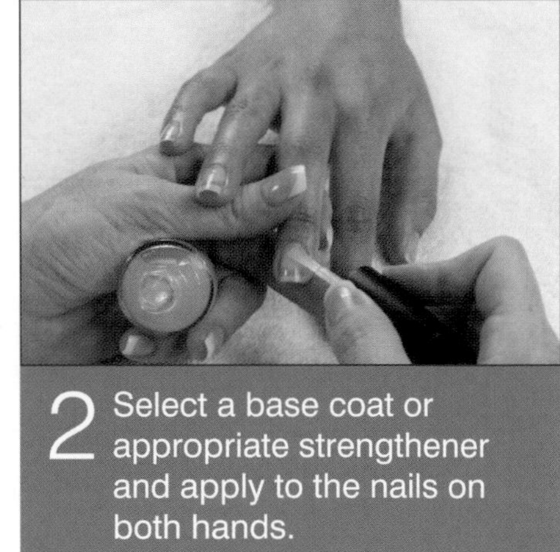

2 Select a base coat or appropriate strengthener and apply to the nails on both hands.

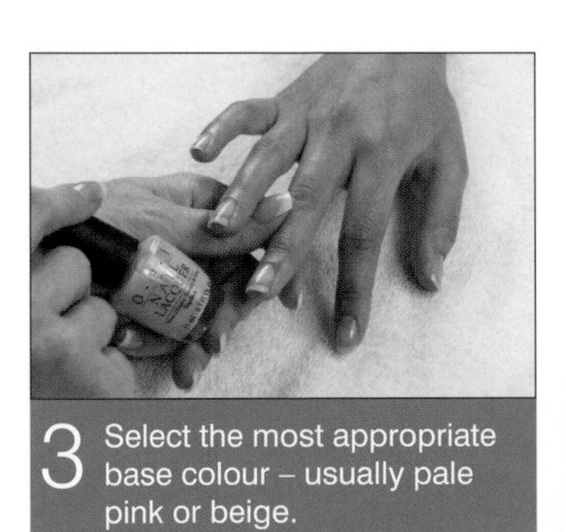

3 Select the most appropriate base colour – usually pale pink or beige.

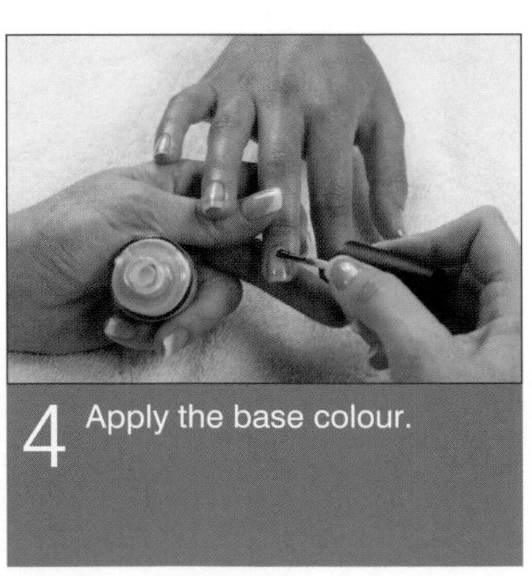

4 Apply the base colour.

5 Apply the white tip to the free edge of the nails.

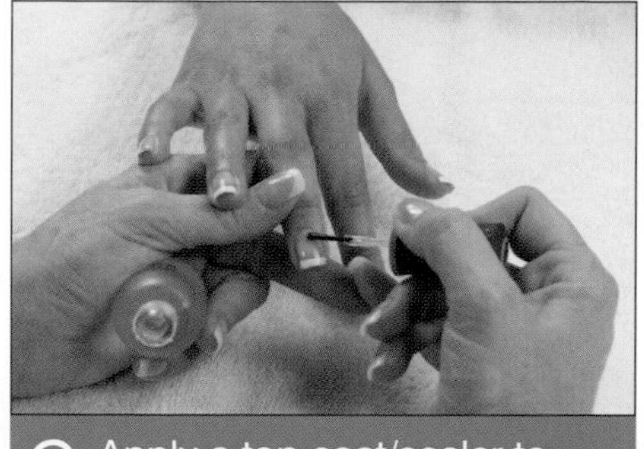

6 Apply a top coat/sealer to protect the nail enamel.

7 The final effect – groomed, natural looking nails.

Step by step method for an extra glamorous French manicure

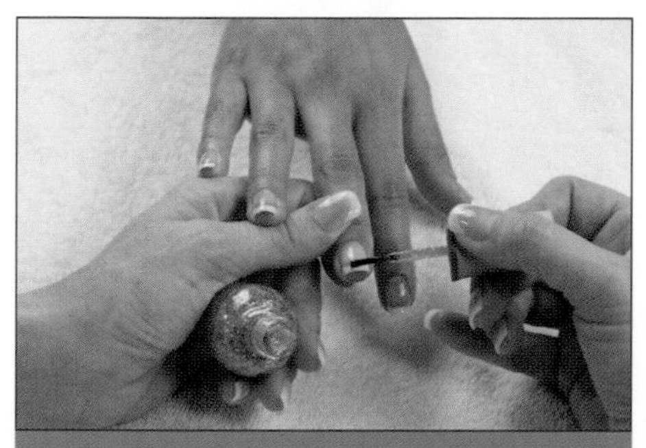

1 To add extra glamour to the French manicure, select a silver glitter polish and paint over the white free edge.

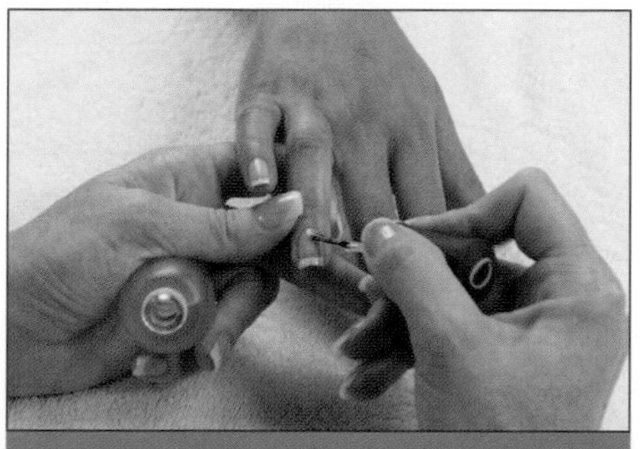

2 Apply top coat/sealer to the nail.

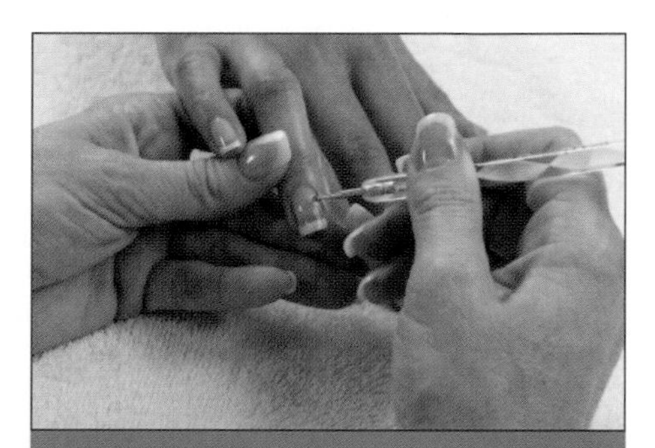

3 Using some 'star' shaped enamel secures, place carefully on one nail on each hand.

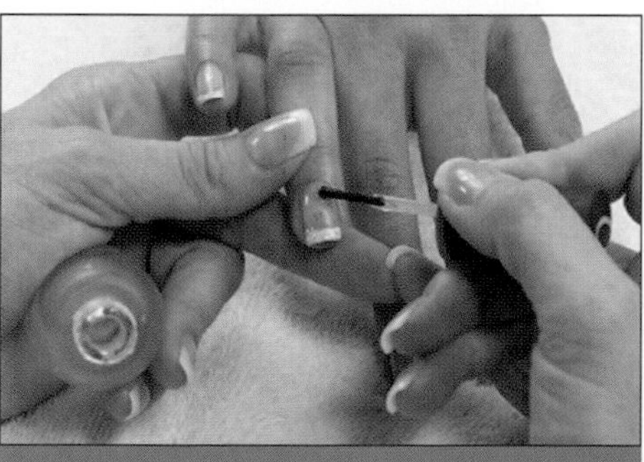

4 Apply a top coat/sealer to protect the glitter enamel and the 'stars'.

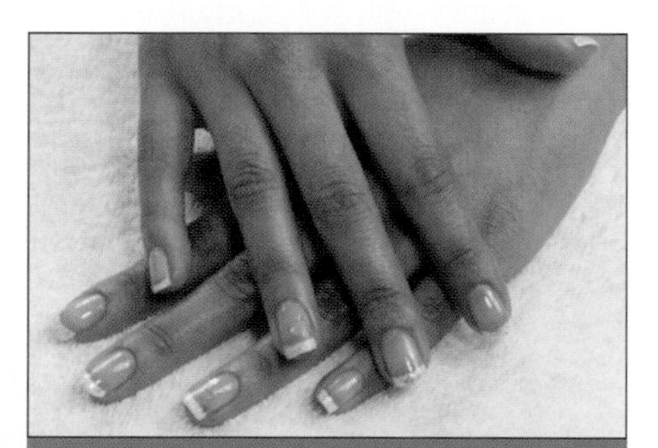

5 The final effect is a more glamorous, unique look.

French manicure

EXTEND YOUR LEARNING

Research the different websites to find at least 10 different variations of French manicure. For example, look on the website **www.prom.net/nails** to find out different styles.

Bring your learning to life   

Creating the perfect 'smile line' on a French manicure is not easy – you need to have lots of practice. Record the improvements you make by taking photographs of your work. Take a photograph of your first attempt – even if it is not as good as you would have liked. Then, take another each time you have the opportunity to practise.

Arrange the photographs in a timeline to show the improvements you are making.

Here are some tips to help you:

- Don't paint the tip straight across the nail – create a 'smile'
- Ensure the whole of the nail tip is coloured and blended evenly
- Don't apply it too thick, as it will make a ridge and is more prone to chipping off
- Very 'opaque' white can tend to be thicker and harder to apply expertly
- Make sure you take the white colour to the outer edges of the nail, in a sharp line, not rounded

Hand treatments

If you decide to do further training and become a professional beauty therapist or nail technician, you will study a wide variety of treatments, including specialised treatments for the hand and nails.

Salt scrub or rub

Using salt as an exfoliant, dead skin cells are removed (desquamation) and circulation is increased and improved. The treatment can improve the skin colour, and even out a fading suntan. After the treatment, the salt needs to be removed thoroughly and followed by a relaxing hand massage with a nourishing cream.

Warm oil treatment

The effects of a warm oil treatment are to soothe and moisturise the skin and nails, helping dry flaky conditions. Depending on the effect required, either the whole hand or just the nails are soaked in a bowl of warm oil. After 10 minutes the residue oil can be used as the lubricant for the hand massage.

Thermal mitts

Thermal mitts use electricity to provide an insulated heated 'mitt'. A rich cream or oil is applied to the hands; they are then individually wrapped in cling film and placed in the mitt. The client can relax for approximately 15 minutes. Then the mitts and cling film are removed, followed by a hand massage. The heat is really beneficial for stiff joints, and also helps the absorption of the cream, which improves dry and flaky skin.

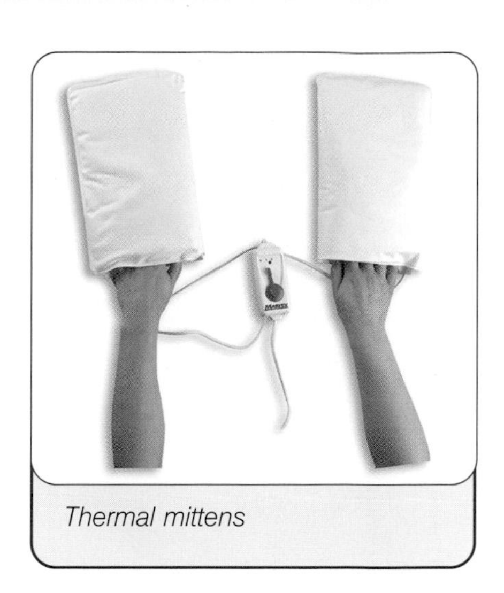

Thermal mittens

Paraffin wax treatment

The hands are thickly coated in melted paraffin wax, and then wrapped to maintain the heat for approximately 20 minutes. The combined effect of the heat and the

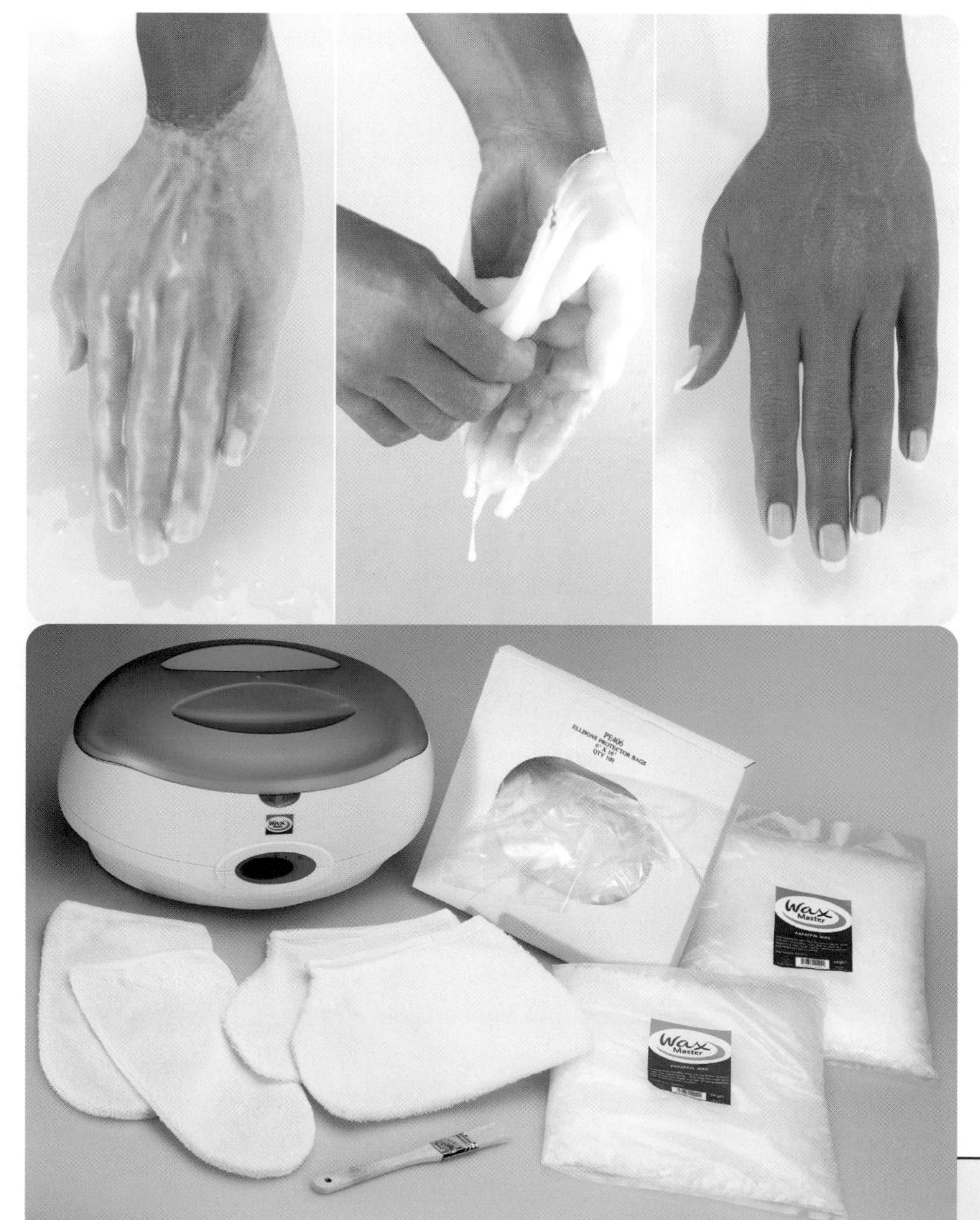

Paraffin wax

softening wax is very beneficial, helping joint mobility, improving circulation and skin colour, cleansing and moisturising dry and flaky hand and nail conditions.

Simple designs can look very striking

Nail art

To be successful at nail art, the nail technician needs to be very skilled at painting nails. To be an expert at nail painting takes a lot of practice, a steady hand, patience and great skill. Once regular enamelling has been mastered, progression can be onto a French manicure and this is where the *art* needs to develop alongside the skill and experience.
You don't have to be wildly creative to be a good nail artist, as there are templates and ways of producing excellent finished effects with limited artistic talent. However, those with natural artistic talents can let their true potential flourish; they will really love this area of the industry, and take advantage of the huge opportunities both nationally and internationally.

Nail art has become very popular in recent years and has become a regular service for clients. The increase in popularity has been fuelled by the media, and high-profile celebrities wearing increasingly detailed nail art.

In the USA it has developed into a huge industry, with nail bars on every corner – in shopping malls, in gyms, even at Wal Mart supermarkets. The UK nail industry is rapidly catching up, no longer is nail art a luxury treatment for special occasions; it has become the norm – what many people wear to work!

Start to collect plenty of nail colours for your nail art designs

Have fun with nail art

Basic nail art techniques

Nail painting

It is essential to have a good set of quality nail art brushes.

You will need:

- Flat brush – small flat head so that it is versatile and can create shading, smudging and swirls.
- Striping brush – it is good to have 2 or 3 of these, of different lengths and thicknesses so you can produce a variety of stripes, lines and flicks.
- Detail brush – small brush used for detailed work such as small dots.

Specialised water-based acrylic paints are used, as you can mix these well, get lots of detail with a good strong colour. A base colour is applied to the nail, then using a variety of nail art brushes and a marbling tool, lots of different effects can be achieved:

- dots of colour – random or more formal
- marbling – blending 2 or 3 colours
- stripes – across the corners, or fanning out from one side
- stencils – applied to the nail and then painted over, great for those who are less creative
- abstract patterns
- pictures – better if you are creative, or can copy a design.

Glitter enamel can be used in a variety of ways

© iStockphoto.com/Dmitriy Norov

Glitter enamel and dusts

Glitter nail enamel can be used in a variety of ways, over the whole nail, on the free edge or on a specific part of the nail. It is a simple way to get a more exciting look, and can be used quite creatively.

Glitter dust is equally as versatile and comes in lots of different shades. It can be applied to the entire nail or to highlight a pattern or design.

Dip your brush in sealer, then pick up the glitter dust on the end of the brush and apply to the nail. This will give a much denser appearance than glitter polish. An easy but effective method can be to apply sealer to the tip of the nail, then the tip is dipped in the glitter pot, and the dust will only stick to where the sealer was applied. The design will have to be secured with sealer, which must be painted on carefully in a thick coat to protect the glitter dust.

Glitter enamel and dust

© Habia and Cengage Learning

Transfers and tapes

Transfers produce a professional effect for minimal creative input. The transfers and tapes are ready made nail art. Some transfers peel off a backing, and are stuck straight onto the nail, others need soaking first, then slide onto the nail.

Tapes can be used in lots of designs, and come in a variety of widths, colours and patterns. Like transfers, they are sticky-backed and can be trimmed once they are in place on the nail. A thick coat of sealer must be applied to protect the design.

Enamel/polish secures

An **enamel/polish secure** is the name for a range of items that have a flat back and can be placed carefully onto wet nail enamel, then sealed for protection. An increasing range of secures are available. They include:

- pearls
- beads (coloured)
- stone shapes, e.g. flowers
- rhinestones/diamante
- foil shapes, e.g. stars, palm trees.
- metal studs

Once the nail enamel is applied, apply the top coat. While wet, use an orange stick to pick up the secures, and place them on the nail. Once the design is complete, apply a thick coat of sealer or top coat, be careful not to dislodge the secures.

A simple stripe design can be achieved using tape or painted on

© iStockphoto.com/Ewelina Kadyla

Top tip The top coat or sealer can be reapplied every few days to protect the design.

Nail 'secures' can look very effective

Star 'secures' can be fun for parties

Nail art procedures

To achieve a good final effect it is important that the nails and cuticles are in good condition; if not, the nail art won't look as effective and may not last very long.

Nail art (striping, blending, marbling)

To achieve a good final effect it is important that the nails and cuticles are in good condition.

Step by step method for blending

Carry out the full manicure (see previous procedure) and discuss the desired final look, and decide on the colours to be used.

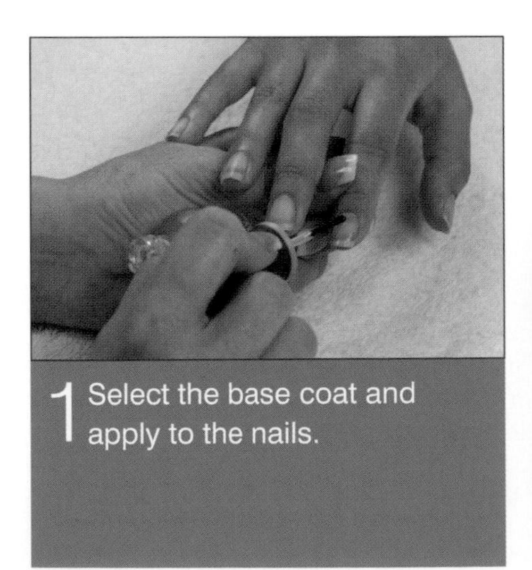

1 Select the base coat and apply to the nails.

2 First apply the lightest colour all over the nail, make sure the colour is applied evenly.

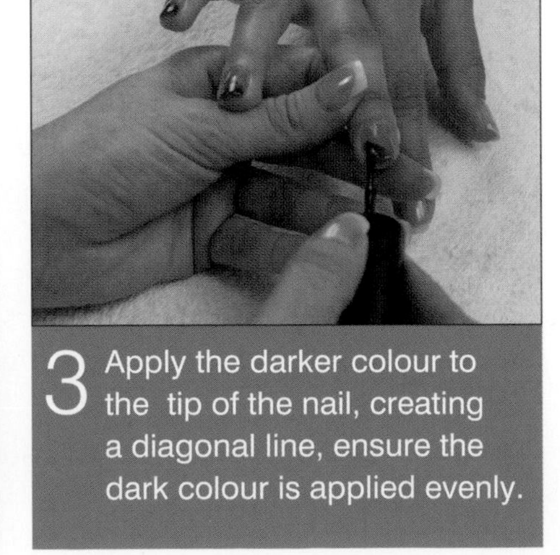

3 Apply the darker colour to the tip of the nail, creating a diagonal line, ensure the dark colour is applied evenly.

4 Use a special blending brush to blend the line between the two colours. Work quickly to ensure the colours blend easily.

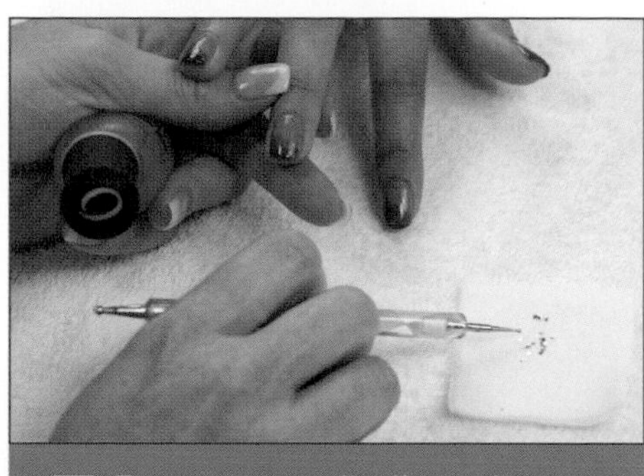

5 Prepare small glitter dots, place some on a tissue, ensure you have the correct tool ready.

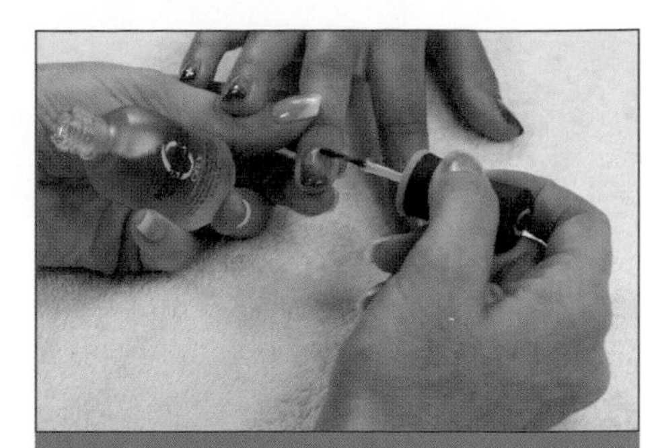

6 Choose a top coat/sealer and apply to the nail.

7 Place the glitter dots carefully on the enamel, apply in a row along the blended line.

8 A sealer is applied to protect the nail art.

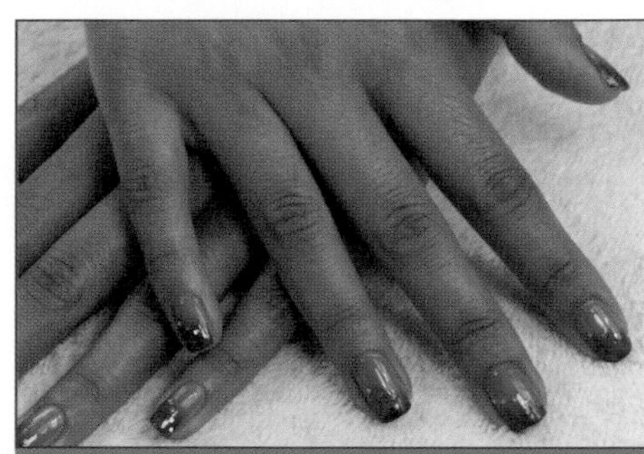

9 The finished effect.

Step by step method for striping

If appropriate, carry out the full manicure (see previous procedure) and discuss the desired final look, and decide on the colours to be used.

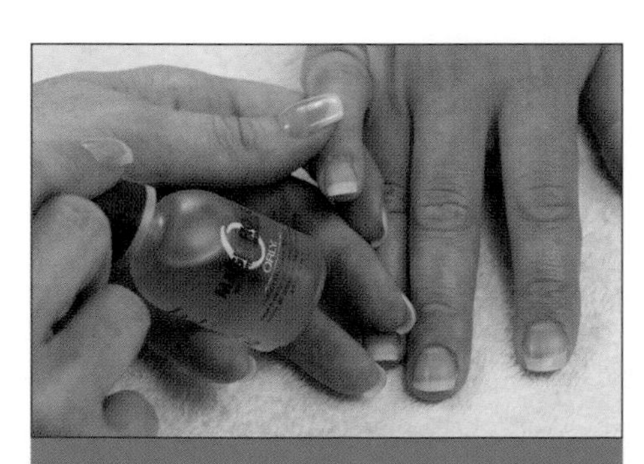

1 Remove any grease from the nail plate with enamel remover and apply the base coat.

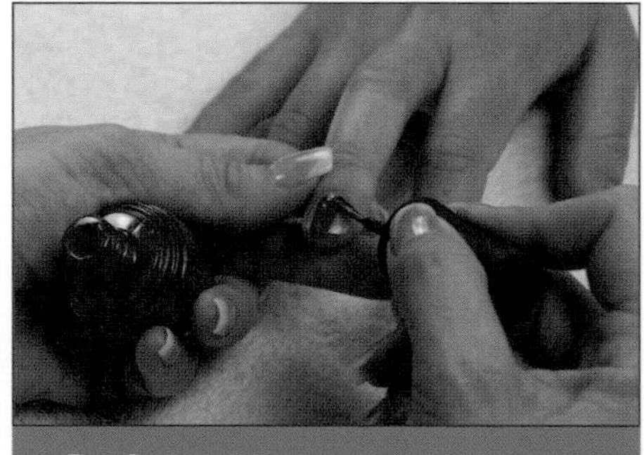

2 Select the appropriate nail enamel colour and apply.

3 Apply the base colour to all the nails, let dry.

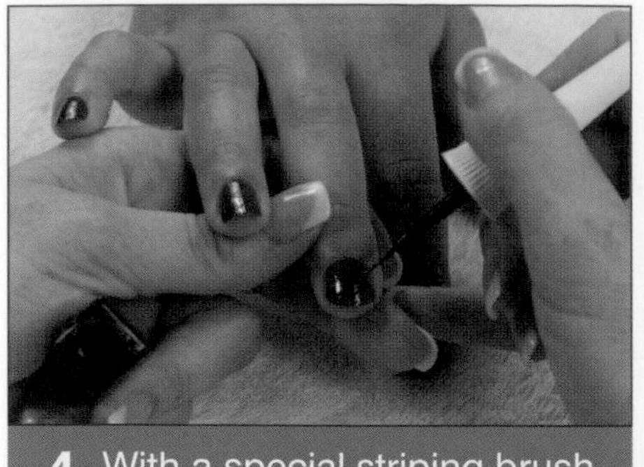

4 With a special striping brush apply the black lines.

5 Apply 3 black lines in a 'flare' design.

6 Next apply white lines alongside the black lines.

7 Finally add 3 silver lines to accentuate the design.

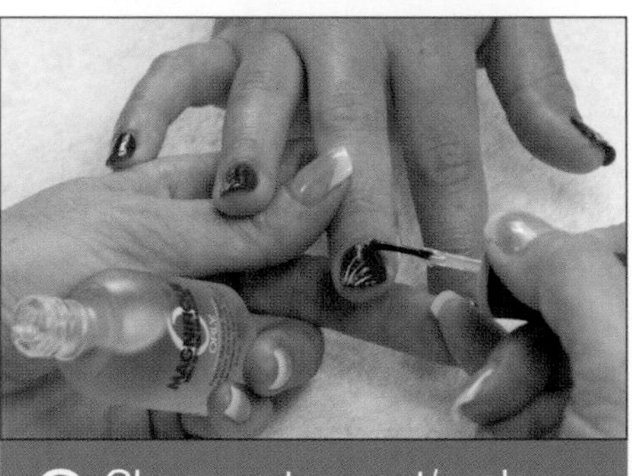

8 Choose a top coat/sealer and apply over the design.

9 The finished effect.

Top tip Ensure the coats of nail enamel are *touch* dry before you start the nail art.

Top tip Apply the nail art paints to a palette, so they can be mixed easily. Have a cotton bud available to help remove any small mistakes.

Step by step method for transfers or tapes

1. Agree final effect with the client.
2. Apply base coat.
3. Apply 2 coats of nail enamel.
4. Select transfer/tape and decide on position on the nail plate.
5. Apply the transfer/tape in the agreed/final position. With tape, small sharp scissors are needed to trim the tape once it is secured on the nail plate.
6. Apply sealer/top coat.
7. Recommend that top coat is reapplied every 2–3 days to protect the nail art.

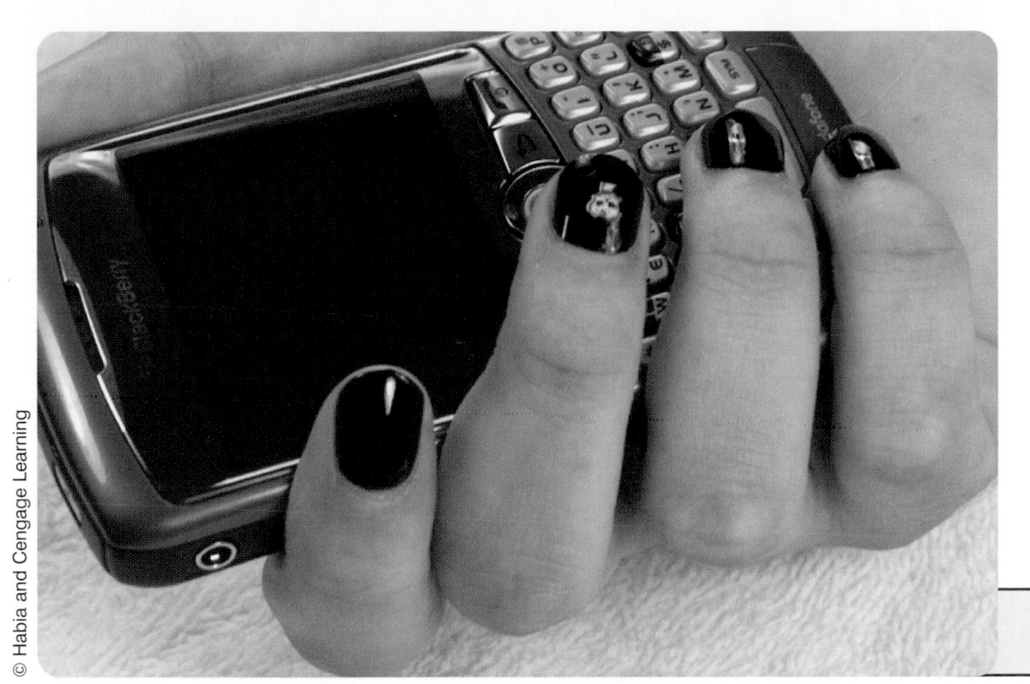

Transfers can look very effective

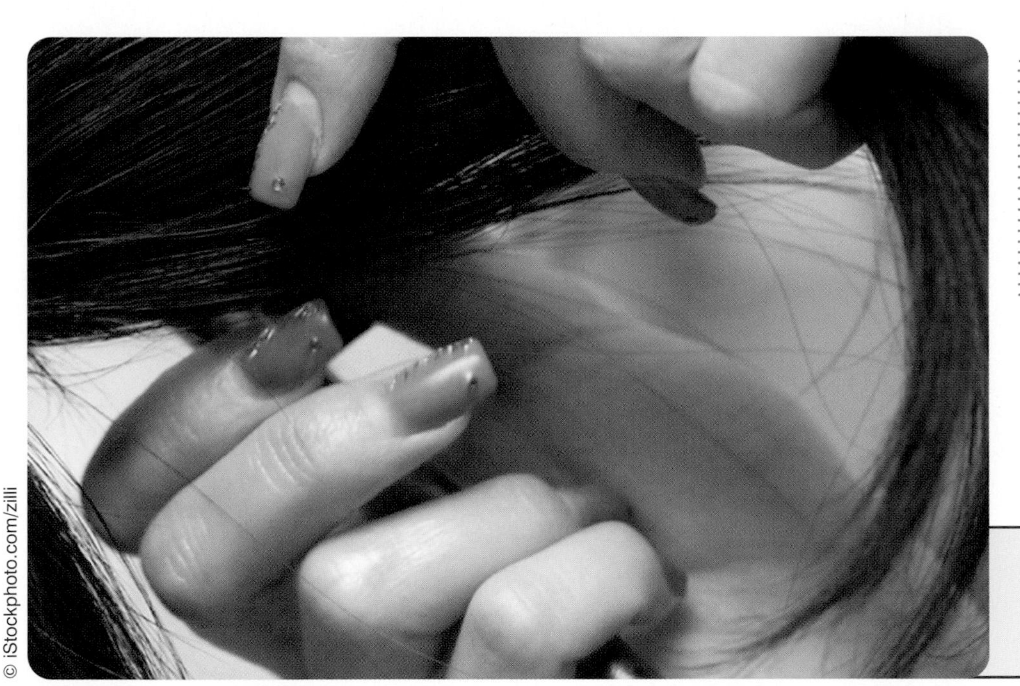

A simple design using 'secures' can be very eye catching, yet not too dramatic for work.

Top tip

Be careful to always use the top coat or sealer recommended by the manufacturer of the nail art paints.

Step by step method for nail art (enamel/polish secures)

To achieve a good final effect it's important that the nails and cuticles are in good condition.

1. Agree final effect/design with the client and select the 'secures' (stones, jewels, studs, pearls).
2. Apply base coat.

3 Apply 2 coats of nail enamel (or nail art design), this should be touch dry before you start the nail art.

4 Apply sealer/top coat – whilst wet the 'secures' are placed on the nail following the agreed design. Secures can be placed using delicate tweezers, or a wet orange stick.

5 Apply a thick layer of sealer/top coat.

6 Recommend that top coat is reapplied every 2–3 days to protect the design and to avoid losing any of the 'secures'.

Advanced nail art can look very effective

Advanced nail art techniques

Nail art is developing all the time, in professional nail salons you will find a range of advanced techniques available including:

- foiling
- airbrushing (including French manicure and layering)
- nail jewellery
- embedding
- colour overlays
- semi-permanent polish
- 3D designs

Home care

While they are relaxing at the end of a hand and nail treatment, there is an opportunity to go through the home care and treatment advice with the client.

Treatment advice

Some clients may only visit a nail salon monthly, so it is important that the professional nail technician recommends products for them to use at home, to continue the effects of the treatment.

The majority of professional products used in a nail salon are the same as those that are available for retail. It is a professional nail technician's responsibility to make sure the client knows that the products sold in the salon are the same as those used in the nail treatment, and if used regularly at home, will prolong the effectiveness of the treatment.

A homecare recommendation form, or prescription, needs to be completed for the client. The client will then have a record of the retail products they need to buy in order to look after their hands and nails at home.

It's a fact! There may be a small number of products that are only manufactured for use in a professional nail treatment procedure, and are not available to be bought and used at home.

© Habia and Cengage Learning

Make sure all the products are available to buy for use at home

Top tip

Promote makeup when selling nail enamel, especially a lipstick or gloss to match the nail colour.

HAND/NAIL CARE PRESCRIPTION	
Name:	**Address:**
Overall hand and nail condition :	**Areas for special attention/Priorities:**

HOME CARE RECOMMENDATIONS

Type of product	Specific product	How often/special advice
Skin cleanser		
Enamel remover		
Nail File		
Buffing cream		
3 way buffer		
Hand scrub/exfoliant		

Hand mask		
Massage/hand cream		
Cuticle oil/ cream		
Base coat		
Enamel		
Top coat/sealer		
Nail art materials		
Comments/Notes		
Date of hand/nail analysis:		**Therapist:**
Notes:		

Retail products. After a hand treatment, people enjoy using the same products at home. Ensure the full range of products are available to buy after the treatment

HOME CARE AND TREATMENT ADVICE SUMMARY

After-treatment advice	Relaxation time Reactions to treatment Water/refreshment
Products used in the treatment	Explain details of products Home care recommendation How to use the products Written prescription Additions – files, buffers, candles
Contra-actions	Explain possible reactions Advise on recommended action
Lifestyle pattern/advice	Dietary and fluid intake Hobbies/interests Wear gloves for washing up Wear gloves when gardening Apply hand cream daily Avoid hard detergents and chemicals
Further hand treatment	Benefits of continuing treatments Courses/financial incentives
Linked treatments	Benefits of combining with other treatments, e.g. pedicures
Frequency of treatments	Recommended frequency and time intervals

ACTIVITY    

When you are in the training salon or on your work placement, investigate which hand and nail treatments are available. For example, manicure, pedicure, file/enamel, artificial nails. Then find out which are the most popular treatments.

You could also investigate what is the busiest time in the week for hand and nail treatments or which enamel colours are the most popular.

When you have finished your research, write a report about what you have found out and present your results to your group.

Technological developments

The nail sector is a fast paced industry, and technology is constantly developing to support the needs of clients. Although many developments have been made in basic manicure treatments, it is with artificial nails that the most changes have been made over the past ten years.

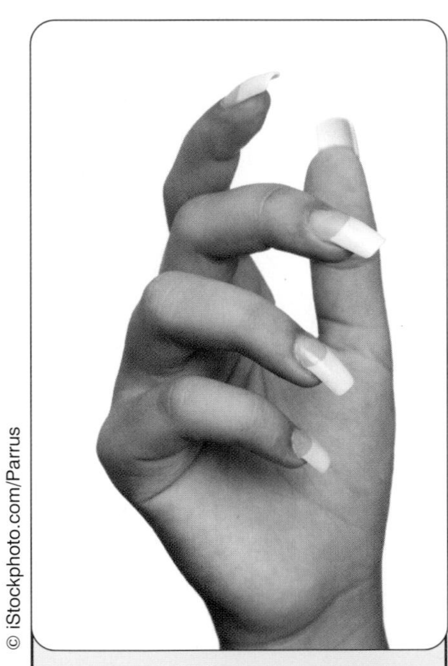

Artificial nail systems can appear very natural

Many different types of artificial nail products are available, but they are usually grouped into three systems – acrylic, UV gel and fibreglass. They all can produce excellent results as long as the nail technician is skilled and experienced.

The acrylic system was the first system to be developed commercially and was derived from the dental industry, even using similar colours; pink and white shades. The acrylic system is very popular in the UK and USA and involves mixing a liquid and a powder to form strong but flexible nails. The UV gel system has also been developed from dental technology and involves a ready-mixed product that needs to be cured by ultra-violet light. As dental technology becomes more and more advanced, it appears to transfer very rapidly into the nail industry, producing more and more impressive, natural looking nails.

The demand for artificial nails has increased greatly over the last few years, and new technology is helping to fuel the growth. The results are more natural, longer lasting and much more impressive.

The technology is constantly adapting, such as the use of the UV gel system to offer a 'permanent' nail enamel effect. A variety of colours and effects are available, including French manicure. People love the fact that their nail enamel lasts for weeks and weeks and never chips.

Technology in both nail systems and nail art is constantly pushing the boundaries, and this, coupled with the strong link with the fashion industry, makes this one of the most exciting sectors to be part of.

EXTEND YOUR LEARNING 

Artificial nail systems have had an enormous impact on the nail service industry. The technology of the products that are used has improved over time and the nails can look so natural, that you can hardly tell the difference. Although some people wear the extended nails so long, it is obvious that they are false – but that may be the wearers' intention!

There are now many different types of nail systems:

- acrylic liquid and powder
- UV gel
- nail tips
- fibre

Investigate the different systems. Make a leaflet that would be available to clients explaining the benefits of each system.

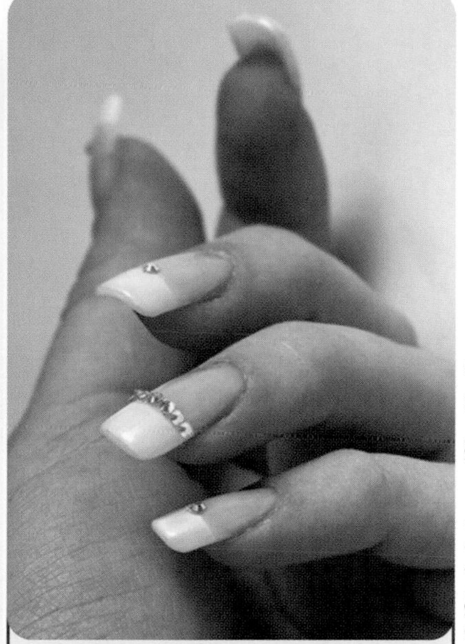

Artificial nail systems produce fantastic results

What you have learnt

Basic hand care and nail treatments

- The importance of completing documentation as part of a consultation

The main factors affecting nail care services

- Lifestyle
- Allergies
- Hand/nail conditions
- How health can affect the nails

How to choose hand and nail care products, tools and techniques to achieve different looks

- Hand and nail analysis
- How to prepare products, tools and equipment ready for the treatments
- Understanding the different products, how they work and when to use them

Basic factors that affect the appearance and condition of hands and nails

How to carry out basic hand and nail treatments

- Shaping of the nails
- Cuticle work
- Massage
- Enamelling

How to carry out basic nail art techniques

- French manicure
- Transfers
- Blending
- Striping
- Nail 'secures'

The terminology related to hand and nail care services

Assessment activities

Crossword

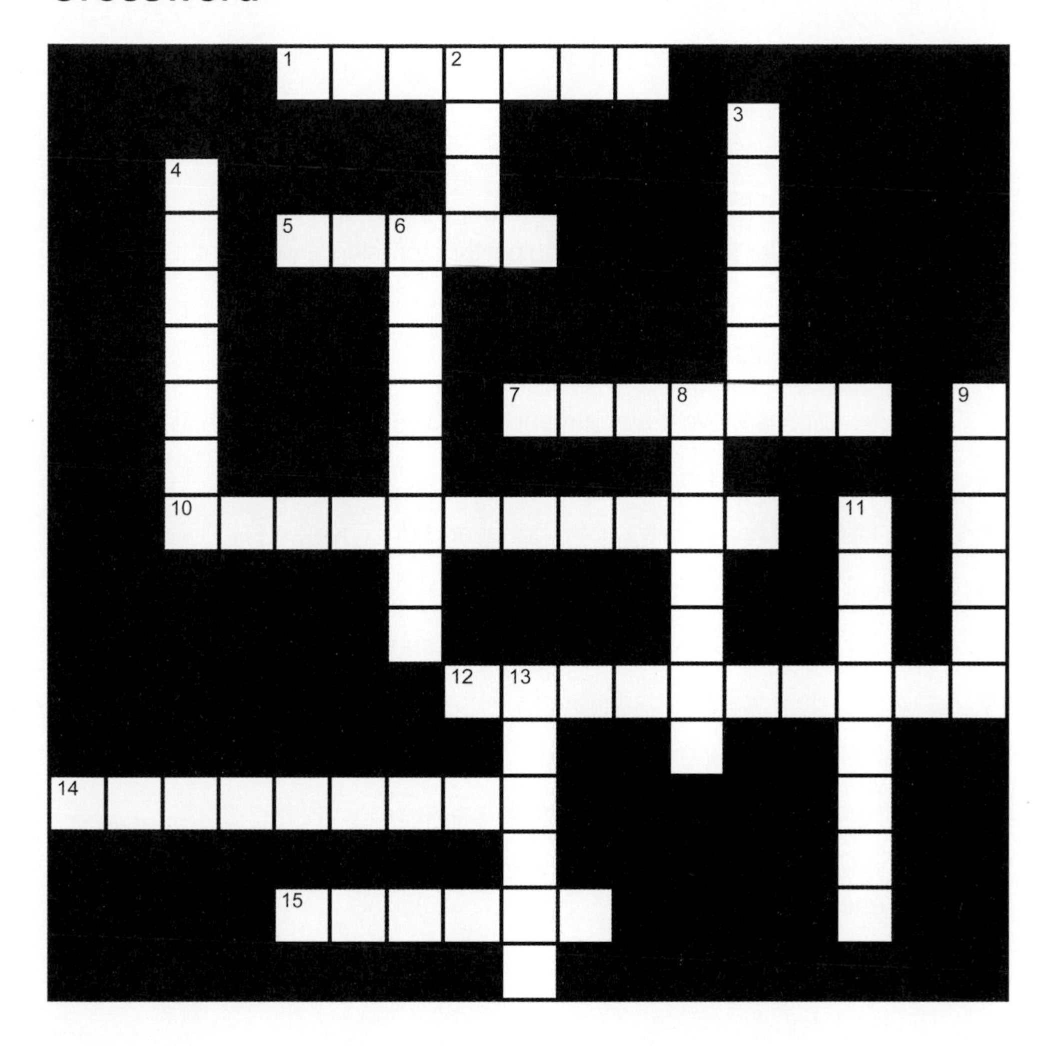

Across

3 A substance that causes an allergic reaction on the skin (8)

5 Ringworm is caused by this (6)

8 If skin is lacking in moisture (10)

9 Technical name for a blackhead (8)

12 Substance produced in sebaceous glands (5)

13 A function of the skin (10)

15 If a skin has high colour, what colour cream can be applied under the foundation to tone it down (5)

17 Cold sores are caused by this (5)

18 Condition with red patches with silvery scales (9)

22 Temporary removal of unwanted body hair (10)

23 The facial product that is applied after cleansing but before moisturising (5)

24 A strong type of toner (10)

25 Technical name for a blind spot (6)

Down

1 A skin type that is quite rare (6)

2 A machine similar to a pressure cooker for sterilising equipment (9)

4 The outer layer of the skin (9)

6 A lighter type of toner (8)

7 These conditions prevent a treatment from being carried out (6–10)

10 This can be reflected in your skin (6)

11 A skin type that has an oily centre panel and dry cheeks (11)

13 Technical name for an infected spot (7)

14 A discolouration of the skin after an injury, can be swollen and painful (6)

16 A facial scrub does this to the dead skin cells (9)

19 A type of face mask (7)

20 Certain people are allergic to this in skin care products (7)

21 On a nose that appears very wide, what corrective product should be applied along each side (6)

Wordsearch

E P I D E R M I S R Y J R K W O Q W V
C Z S Y S S Z R U H L J S Q L E J M Z
C E U H X K A H H T I W L I D Q P T S
I X N O I I C B M L O C M I V U C S E
T L B A U N Z O F L S J S O S S O G Z
E B U R A C R P L O I V X T K E M B P
C K R R A A Y A H A X F U D G U E V E
O D N X J R S T Y B S L E X K H D J R
M B F I X E L I T E E Q O S G S O W S
B B B H K A B Y B V M H W P T L N U O
I C J Z E L H U L N D K C J Q Y E K N
N H H H S L M T E I A F G Z U D L S A
A S G K W E F Z M P R M B W S O N E L
T I O C X R U T I J B V E P A L J I I
I R G G M G F O S S J O A Z D A J E T
O U O A N Y P N H S Z T U W C C W D Y
N O C Q C X U E O J U S T M K E D Z U
E N E I G Y H R P L Q G Y Y M A S K K
E E X U T Q G K A R O U T I N E T Z V

File
Buffer
Pedicure
Manicure
Bruise
Nail
Glamour
Talon
Culture

Ridge
Flake
Marbling
Wrist
Template
Foiling
Carpal
Grow
Enamel

Massage
Stencil
Transfer
Exfoliant
Stripes
Hangnail
Cuticle
Technician
Airbrushing

Tape
Onychopagy
Psoriasis
Sealer
Hygiene
Overlay

Short questions: Health and Safety for manicure treatments

1. Describe three symptoms of an allergic reaction to a manicure product.
2. What does 'contra-indication' mean?
3. List three contraindications to a manicure treatment.
4. State two methods of sterilising metal manicure tools.
5. Why should the manicurist wash their hands before starting the manicure treatment?
6. Why should the cuticle knife always be used wet and flat?
7. List three manicure tools that should be thrown away (disposed of) after each manicure.
8. Why is the orange stick always tipped with cotton wool before use in a manicure?

Assessment questions: Nail art service

Imagine because you are so good at nail art, your manager asks you to develop a 'nail art' service and promote it to existing clients.

1. Inform the staff about the new service, the designs available, features/benefits, cost, time, etc. Write a notice about the new service that could go on the staff room wall.
2. Make a 'display board' with at least 10 nail designs (painted on false nails) so people can see the designs you offer in the salon.
3. Design a leaflet to promote this new treatment to individuals who currently have manicure treatments.

The leaflet could include

- Features of the new treatment
- Benefits over regular nail enamelling
- Encouragement to book an appointment
- Images of designs available
- length of treatment
- Price
- Name/Logo of salon

Where possible, design the notice and leaflet on a computer, making sure it appears professional and ready to use in a salon situation.

10

selling skills

Tracey Devine @ Sanrizz

> **Everyone lives by selling something.**
>
> ROBERT LOUIS STEVENSON 1850–94, NOVELIST

Introduction

To become a professional in the hair and beauty sector you will need to learn that as part of your role you do not just have to be good at providing services and treatments for your clients. You will also have to learn how to look after them and provide a complete professional service. Part of the service will be to provide advice and recommendations to the client on how best to achieve the result the client is after and how to maintain that result for as long as possible after they have left the salon or spa. This may include the use of additional products at home or the need for additional treatments or services to maintain or enhance the end result. In this chapter you are going to explore basic selling skills and how to sell by professional recommendation and why this is important to the success of the business.

Basic selling skills

Within the hair and beauty sector, selling is all part of the professional service we provide to our clients. The way the salon environment looks and the way individual staff present themselves and behave is all part of the selling process. We are *selling* an image that we want the client to buy into. Once we have got the client through the door to book an appointment, we still need to sell the whole service. This will involve a number of different things, such as the way we look after the client during their visit and the professional way that the treatment or technical service is carried out. Part of that professional service is in the way we offer our expert advice as part of the consultation process and aftercare advice. During these periods we are giving advice to ensure the client achieves the best possible

What you are going to learn

This chapter will include

- ★ Basic selling skills
- ★ The principles of best practice
- ★ Sales legislation
- ★ The difference between promoting and selling products in a retail environment and by professional recommendation
- ★ The importance of selling by professional recommendation

Top tip

Remember, selling is about the overall image and complete service that we provide to the client

results. This could be by suggesting additional services such as a colour that will *enhance* a haircut or a series of treatments that will be needed to achieve the result the client is seeking. As part of that advice we are selling to the client. This type of selling is not the same as the selling that is used in a retail shop where you can pick up any product from the shelf and just buy it, it is selling by **professional recommendation**. Whatever type of selling process we use there are a number of basic roles that you can learn.

Basic selling rules

Dos:

- *Focus* on the reason the client has visited the salon or spa
- Use all types of *communication*. This will help you to build a good relationship with the client; you must listen to the client and ask open and closed questions to find out information
- Know and understand the products, equipment or services that you are using and selling
- Be *realistic* about what a product, service or treatment can do
- Be able to recognise a *genuine* need for what you are selling so that the client is confident and comfortable with you and will return to the salon
- Be able to answer questions and handle client objections effectively and confidently
- Understand **buying signals** and when to close the sale

Don'ts:

- Talk all the time; involve the client in the process, and listen to what they say; do not argue, interrogate or interrupt them.
- Work from a standard script that you recite to all clients, it does not help to build individual relationships

- Sell anything that the client does not need or want, they will simply not return to the salon
- Sell if you do not know what you are selling, find out or get someone else to give the client advice
- Get upset and sulk if the client does not take on board your recommendations.

Clients will buy from people that they know and trust

Courtesy of Wella

Hair retail products

Courtesy of Wella

Beauty retail products

The principles of selling using best practice and ethical considerations linked to selling

Ethics are important when selling. Ethics are principles that help to guide the behaviour of an individual or a group of people to identify what is *right* and what is *wrong*. Sometimes what an individual or companies perceive as ethical can be different from country to country or industry to industry. In the hair and beauty sector businesses try to develop long-term relationships with their clients. Stylists and therapists are the representatives of the business, and are responsible for developing and maintaining *client relationships* which are built on *trust*. You can read about 'trust' in Chapter 3 'Salon business systems and processes'. However, relationships with clients cannot be maintained if the stylist or therapist behaves *unethically*. Many businesses will have a policy that will cover ethical issues when selling and what they identify as *good and bad practice*. Similarly, as individuals, we will have our own code of ethics that has been developed and influenced by the people around us, such as our family and friends.

Habia

Nail retail products

ACTIVITY  

Work with a partner. Individually read the list of statements below and decide if you think a statement is either ethical or unethical. Once you have done this, discuss your decisions with your partner and see if you agree with each other.

1 Always put pressure on a client to buy a product
2 Never tell the client the cost of a product until they ask for it
3 Always sell the client the product they want but not necessarily what is best for them
4 Always explain the pros and cons of a service or treatment
5 Never let the client ask too many questions
6 Always answer the client's question even if you don't know the answer
7 Don't tell the client if there are **promotions** available if they don't ask
8 If a product you want to recommend is not available always recommend another one

Sales legislation

It does not matter what retail environment you work in or what is being sold, there is **legislation** to help protect both the customer and the retailer when buying and selling products and services. Listed below are a number of Acts or Regulations that relate to businesses within the hair and beauty sector.

The Trade Descriptions Act (1968)

This Act stops manufacturers, retailers or service industry providers from misleading the customer by using or giving them *false, inaccurate or misleading* information about a product in relation to its *quality, purpose, fitness and price*. The product must also be clearly labelled, so that the customer can see were the product was made and what ingredients it contains.

In May 2008 two new regulations came into force. The Consumer Protection from Unfair Trading Regulations (2008) regulates commercial practices between businesses and customers and the Business Protection from Misleading Marketing Regulations (2008) regulates business to business commercial practices. These regulations work along side, replace or amend parts of The Trade Descriptions Act (1968) and The Consumer Protection Act (1987)

- Consumer Protection from Unfair Trading Regulations (2008)
  - Failure to meet professional standards expected for the skill and care that a provider in their relevant field of expertise could be expected to deliver
  - Giving *misleading* information to customers
  - Using *aggressive* practices such as high pressure selling techniques
- Business Protection from Misleading Marketing Regulations (2008)
  - Prohibits using advertising to mislead traders on issues such as the nature and characteristics of a product, the price, conditions of supply and the rights of the advertiser

The Price Act (1974)

This Act ensures that all products have a price displayed on them for the customer to see.

The Resale Prices Act (1964)

This Act enables the manufacturer of the product to recommend the retail price of the product. However, it is up to the retailer to decide the price; they do not have to use the manufacture's recommended retail price.

The Supply of Goods and Services Act (1982)

This Act relates to the sale of goods and services. In relation to service, the Act states that the service the customer pays for is provided at a reasonable price, with care and attention and in a reasonable timescale. If the service provider breaches the conditions of 'the contract' the customer has a choice to either pay for the service, pay and claim compensation, reduce the payment or not pay at all. However, the service provider may disagree and take legal action to resolve the issue.

In relation to Goods, the Act also states that any goods provided or bought in the course of the service must be of satisfactory quality and *fit for purpose*. If they are not, the customer is entitled to compensation, a replacement or a repair of the goods.

The Consumer Protection Act (1987)

This Act follows European Laws and helps to protect the customer against products that do not reach a certain level of *safety* and cause damage either from the materials used or in the manufacturing process. This will be a product which does not meet the requirements of the Sale of Goods Act (1979). This Act sets out the rules by which an injured person can contact the person responsible for the damage; this is usually the person who is regarded as the *producer* of the product, not the person supplying the product. This Act also made it an offence to mislead the customer concerning the price of goods and services, but this aspect has been moved to new legislation: the Consumer Protection from Unfair Trading Regulations (2008) and the Business Protection from Misleading Marketing Regulations (2008).

Cosmetic Products (Safety) Regulations (1996)

This regulation relates to consumer protection for the use of cosmetic products. It defines a cosmetic product as being any substance or preparation intended to be placed in contact with any part of the external surface of the human body. So in general terms that covers the skin, hair and nails. It also covers the teeth and the mucous membranes or the oral cavity. It lays down the regulations relating to the composition of products, the ingredients used and how they are labelled on the product and also how manufacturers describe and market the product.

EXTEND YOUR LEARNING

Find out more about the different sales legislation. Using the internet carry out research into the different Acts and Legislation. Then write a short report on how you can identify the use of the Regulations within the hair and beauty sector.

The Sale of Goods Act (1979)

This Act states that the person selling goods needs to makes sure that the goods they are selling are of 'satisfactory quality' and must fit the description and the purpose they are intended for.

The difference between promoting and selling products in a retail environment and by professional recommendation

We all know that we can buy hair and beauty products from the high street. The question is why we would buy our products off the shelf with no knowledge of what and why we are buying them. Yes, we want to buy a styling product for our hair, but how do we know which one will suit our hair, and give the result we want.

Let us look at some of the advantages and disadvantages of buying products in both a retail shop or in a hair or beauty salon.

ADVANTAGES OF BUYING PRODUCTS IN A RETAIL SHOP	DISADVANTAGES OF BUYING IN A RETAIL SHOP
Lots of choice	Not knowing which products to buy
Often have cheaper products or special offers on products	People often buy the cheaper products but they may not be the best product to achieve the desired result
	No specialist to ask or give advice

ADVANTAGES OF BUYING IN A PROFESSIONAL SALON	DISADVANTAGES OF BUYING IN A PROFESSIONAL SALON
Salon specialises in a limited range of products	Not always a large stock and products may not always be available
Product range is for both professional and retail use	Can be more expensive that buying on the high street
Professional people to give advice on how and when to use the product for best results	

Courtesy of L'Oréal

Retail display in a salon

Selling by professional recommendation

Professional selling is about putting the clients' needs first. It is about offering a professional service to the client. The advice given will ensure that the client's hair, skin or nails will stay looking good after they have left the salon.

When a client comes in to a salon or spa, they have come for a treatment or service – usually to make them look and feel better, *the feel good factor*. A professional will want to achieve the best possible result they can for their client. This starts with the atmosphere that is created by the salon environment and the individual attention that is given to the client to make them feel 'special'.

A professional stylist, therapist or technician will:

- start with the consultation to find out exactly what the client wants
- analyse and carry out any tests to identify the condition of the hair, skin or nails before making any recommendations for the service or treatment
- discuss the products they will be using and why they have chosen those products
- explain the products they are using and why they are using them during the service or treatment
- show how much of the product is being used and how to apply it
- often give the product to the client to touch, feel and smell.
- answer any questions the client may have and give clear honest advice
- give the client advice on how to maintain the result for as long as possible at home until their next visit
- sometimes advise on additional services to complement the service just carried out or a therapist may have suggested a series of treatments that would be beneficial to the client, such as a six week programme for facial hair removal.

Courtesy of L'Oréal

Selling by professional recommendation

Throughout the appointment period, it is part of the professionals' job to ensure that their client is given the best advice available. It is always up to the client to decide if they want to take on board that advice and purchase recommended products to use at home or to book additional appointments.

However, to be able to sell by professional recommendation you need to first understand the sales process. There are eight main points to learn and remember to become successful:

- You need to have good communication skills and be able to form good client relationships.
- You must enjoy what you are doing and believe in what you do.

- You need to carry out good consultations, ask open and closed questions, find out what products the client is currently using at home and carry out analysis to find out what the client needs and wants.
- You need to understand all the different services or treatments available, how much they are and how long they take to deliver.
- You need to know the different products that are available for sale and their price and understand how each product works and know the features and benefits of the product:
  - Features are the function or characteristic – what the service or treatment is or what a product contains
  - Benefits are the results – what the service or treatment or product can achieve.

  For example: a sun cream is rated SPF 25 (*feature*) this will protect the skin from the sun to help prevent sunburn and the skin drying out and peeling (*benefit*).

  When talking to the client about a product and the results they can achieve, use descriptive words that will help the client form a picture in their mind. This will help the client visualise the end result and the desire to buy.
- You will need to learn how to present and demonstrate how a product works. You will show the client how much product to use, where and how to use it.
- You will let the client to use their **senses** to see, hold, smell and touch the product; this will help the client to get to know and build a relationship with the product.
- You will need to be able to answer any questions and handle any objections the client may have accurately and with confidence. Objections could be based on the client needing more information about the product, service or treatment in which case you will need to give more information. The client may raise objections that clearly indicate that they are not interested in buying anything. In this situation do not become pushy, end the sales process, and carry on the service or treatment in a professional manner so that the client feels comfortable. At the end of the appointment recap on the aftercare advice you have given and if possible give the client product samples to try out at home.
- You also need to know when to *close the sale*. Most people find this the hardest stage to complete. But if you have done your job well, you will have built up a relationship of trust with the client, listened to and understood what the client wants and identified what is needed to create the result. You will have recommended and presented the right products; the 'close' is the natural final step when you ask the client if they would like to buy the product to take the home.

The *close* of a sale usually takes place at the end of the sales process. However, if a client is interested and wants to buy the product they will send out **buying signals**. Buying signals could take place at any time and are the *cue* to the professional to start to close the sale.

Buying signals usually come in the form of questions or comments such as:

- How would I use this product at home?
- How long will it last if I use it every day?
- I like the way it smells.

Or body language such as:

- the client leaning forward
- listening and nodding
- smiling.

Top tip Only recommend a product, service or treatment to a client that they will get benefit from selling by professional recommendation

ACTIVITY

Understanding the different products that are available in the salon for clients to use at home between visits is essential to becoming a professional within the hair and beauty sector. With a partner, chose a number of products that are often available to buy within the hair and beauty sector. Find out as much as possible about each product, for example:

- what the main features and benefits of each product is
- when to use the product
- how much product to use
- how and where to apply the product
- the cost of the product

Think about the questions or objections a client may have about the products and decide on the response you would give. Present your research in a simple report.

Top tip Clients are usually only interested in the benefits a product, service or treatment can give and not the features of the product, service or treatment.

Bring your learning to life

When you are on your work placement or in a salon environment:

- Find out about the different retail products available for the clients to buy.
- How are they displayed?
- Can you write down the main feature and benefit for each retail product?
- When you are observing a professional working with a client, can you identify the different approaches they take with clients when talking about products?

Write a short report on your findings.

The importance of selling by professional recommendation

For every type of business there is competition from other **competitors**, this is no exception for the hair and beauty business. Every business needs to be working at its very best to survive. This means that not only do we have to provide an excellent service to our clients, in surroundings that make the client feel special but we also need to find new ways to provide additional benefits for the client and to raise income for the business. Retailing products is one of the best ways for a salon to do this, as not only does it increase the income to the salon but it also benefits the client.

- The client will receive the best advice and good quality products for them to use at home.
- The client will be the main focus during their visit and giving advice makes clients feel special and of value to the salon. This in itself will create client loyalty and repeat business. In turn this creates a stable profitable business that everyone benefits from.

BUSINESS BENEFITS	STYLIST/ THERAPIST BENEFITS	CLIENT BENEFITS
Increase profits	Increase take home pay	Improve or maintain self image
Increase sales within the business	Receive recognition from the employer	Have trust in the salon/ stylist or therapist
Build and maintain client relationships	Improve client relationship	Receive good advice and guidance on products suitable for them
		Buy products that are not available in general retail outlets

EXTEND YOUR LEARNING    

Identify a hair, beauty or nail salon or a spa facility and design a retail area to complement your chosen site. Research the different professional products and equipment that you feel would retail well:

- Consider the overall design and price of the products
- Use a visual presentation to set the scene for the type of hair or beauty environment you have chosen and explain why and how you have designed the retail area and chosen the products for retail. You can also add into the presentation how much the products and equipment will cost to purchase and at what price you would expect to sell them to clients.

What you have learnt

Basic selling skills

- The selling rules – the 'dos' and 'don'ts when selling to clients

The principles of best practice

- What ethics are and why ethics are important when selling to clients

Sales legislation

- The different types of legislation associated with selling and how the legislation can be used to protect both the client and the salon when buying or selling products or services

The difference between promoting and selling products in a retail environment and by professional recommendation

- The advantages and disadvantages

Selling by professional recommendation

- What is meant by the term 'professional recommendation' and how does it work
- Why it is important for the client, the 'professional' and the business

Assessment activities

Crossword

Across

3 The term used to explain the function or characteristic of a product (7)

5 Another term used for 'selling' (9)

8 Another term used instead of 'special offer' (9)

9 The process used to protect both the customer and the retailer (11)

Down

1 The final step in the selling process (5)

2 The term used to explain what a product can achieve (7)

4 Name one of the 'senses' that a client can use to get to know a product (5)

6 Principles that help to guide the behaviour of a person to identify what is right and what is wrong (6)

7 Type of body language used by a client that can indicate a buying signal (7)

Wordsearch

```
R D T I F O R P M T Q G T M H D B I R K K Y N
W I V D K E G R N S K W Z Q G K C W K I F C D
G U S M C C O M M U N I C A T I O N F D A S D
Z I V I R S I P F R D S O E R U S S E R P V Q
G O V O G F S U P T K Y G A I V J E C B C Y Z
W D E Q I N E J A I W R E L A T I O N S H I P
A D K J W U A B L R V L Y Y Q C G C Y G X V V
I E T K S E L L I N G C L E G I S L A T I O N
P M S Y V N S Q S R I E R A C R E T F A E A A
R O A F I C U D D L E Z L I B V S V S T M P L
O N M C E V P G O X A C H F T E T P C P F H D
F S C K E D I P P S J T O T L E B T O Y S S G
E T L X O C U M J N I I E M S C Q D N X T N E
S R A Z E X I S W R U F R W M N T Y S B C O N
S A W Z P Z Q V T M Y E U H I E L B U Z U I X
I T Q J Y U U K R F N N T N U U N H L U D T C
O E Z R Q G I O F E V E A H W L C D T Y O S Y
N F J D E E T H I C S B E M S F L R A A R E X
A K P F T Q K L H W P R F A Z N I V T T P U R
L V X F P P R I N C I P L E S I E M I M I Q P
Z D F C N Q Y Z E C D E A G P E N H O S E O J
X T N T G W O B U D S U L U L C T S N T M M N
P L Q G G V K A J C J K U S O U J Q Y T G Z P
```

Advice
Aftercare
Benefit
Client
Communication
Consolation
Demonstrate
Ethics
Feature
Influence
Legislation
Policy
Pressure
Principles
Products
Professional
Profit
Questions
Recommendation
Relationship
Sales
Selling
Service
Signals
Skills
Trust

Assessment question: Selling skills

Complete the table below by listing one main feature and two benefits of the products named in the first column.

PRODUCTS	FEATURE	BENEFITS
Hair conditioner		
Sunscreen		
Nail enamel		
Moisturiser		

Answer section

Assessment activities for Chapter 1

Crossword

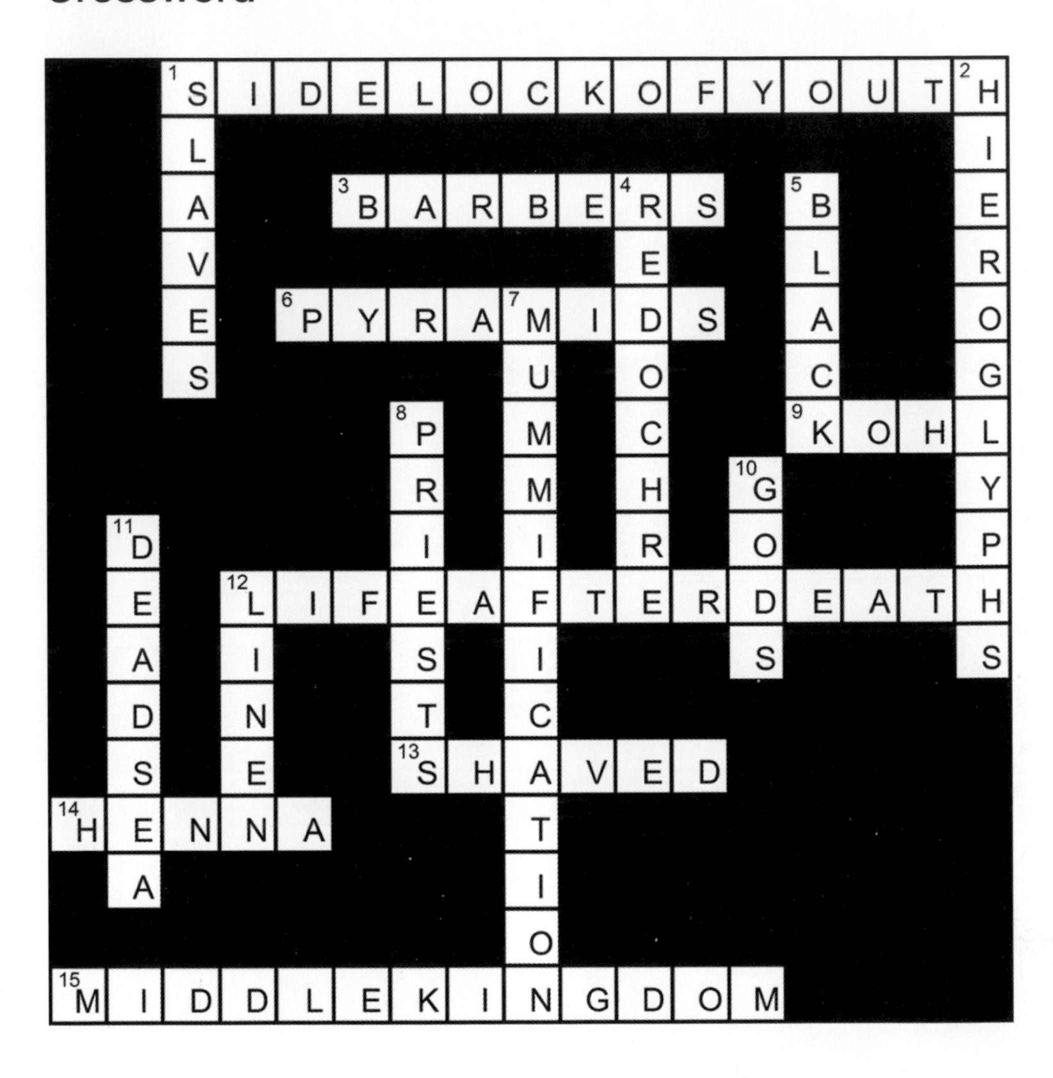

Multiple choice: Culture, subculture and identity

1 Social identity is a group of people with shared
Answer values

2 During the slave trade, many people were taken from
Answer Africa

3 Black identity is a celebration of
Answer being black

4 Teddy boys were a subculture in the
Answer 1950s

5 There is one thing about hair that separates people
Answer length

6 Who were said to be the first teenagers?
Answer Teddy boys

7 Leather jackets were worm by
Answer Rockers

8 Unisex hairstyles were worn by
Answer Mods

9 Mohawks were worn by
Answer Punks

10 Black hair was favoured by
Answer Mods

Assessment activities for Chapter 2

Crossword

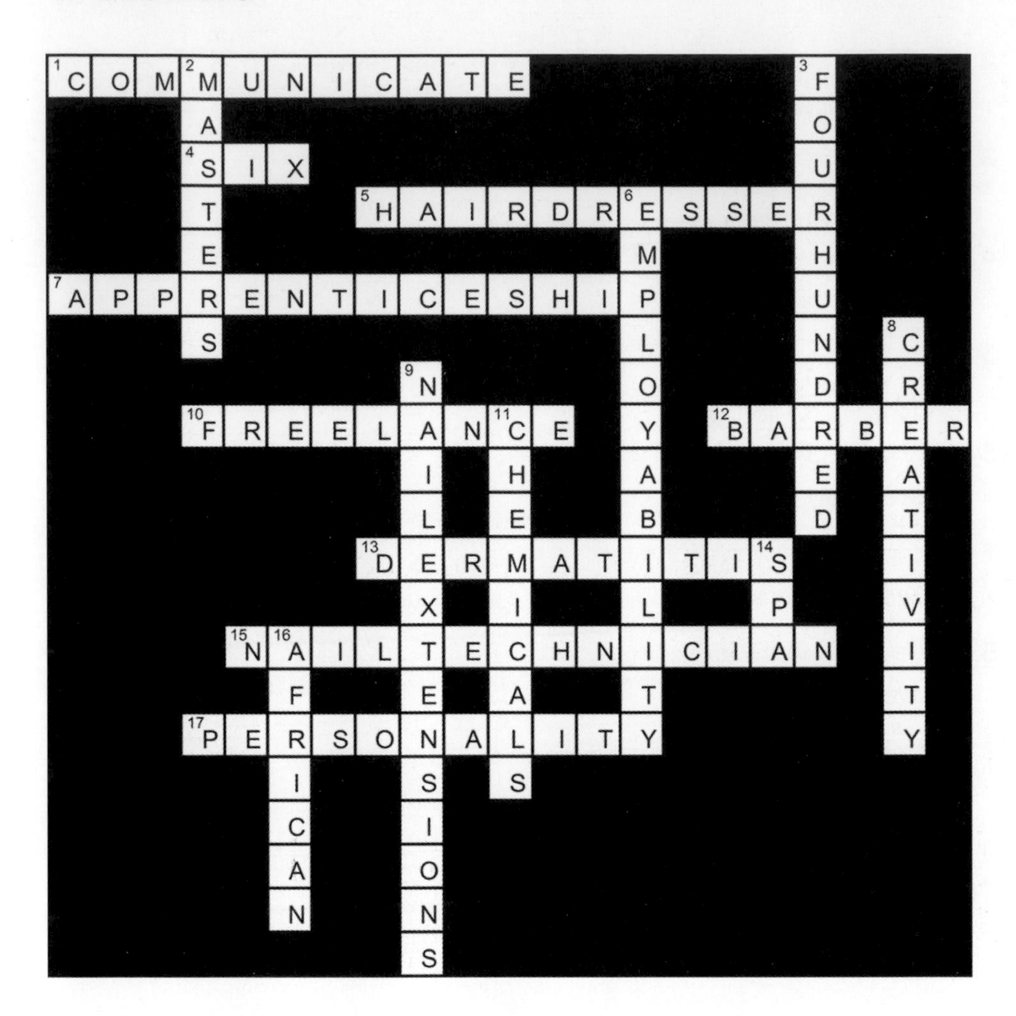

Wordsearch

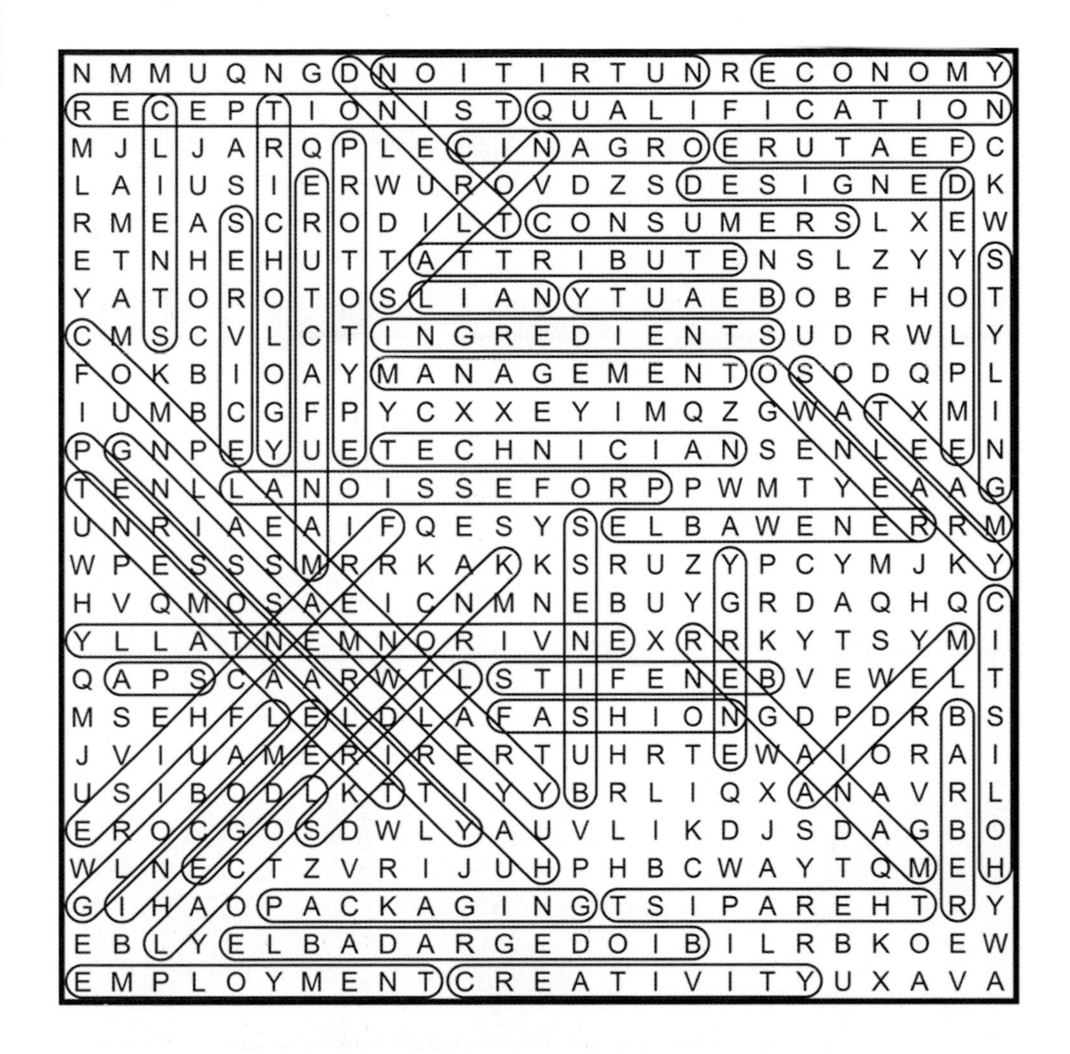

Multiple choice: The world of hair and beauty

1 Top hairdressers will produce one of these each year to predict fashion trends

Answer collection

2 A unisex salon is

Answer a salon for men and women

3 A galvanic treatment is an example of

Answer an electrotherapy

4 Typical progression from a Higher Level Diploma in Hair and Beauty Studies will be to

Answer advanced diploma in hair and beauty studies

5 Team work is important for the hair and beauty sector because

Answer working as a team ensures the business runs efficiently and profitably

6 A conceptual model will be used to

Answer predict what a new product will look like

7 A competence based qualification

Answer ensures you are ready for work

8 Someone who carries out a manicure is most likely to be known as a

Answer nail technician

9 To work at management level in the hair and beauty sector you need to have

Answer foundation degree

10 Once a new product has been designed and developed, it has to be

Answer marketed

Assessment activities for Chapter 3

Crossword

Fill in the blanks

The **reception** is the first area that all visitors and clients to a hair and beauty sector business will see. It is important for the reception area to be welcoming and **comfortable** and to meet the requirements of health and safety and **security**.

The receptionist is the **first** point of contact. Therefore, they must have outstanding **communication** skills to create a **good** first and lasting impression. Receptionists not only have to be well organised people, but they also need computer **literacy** skills as many businesses have a reception **management** system. Receptionists also need **numeracy** skills as they have to **calculate** the costs and take **payment** for treatments and services. The skills of the **receptionist** are as important as the skills carried out by stylists, **therapists** and technicians.

It is important for everyone training in the hair and beauty sector to learn reception skills as not every **business** can justify the **costs** for a full time receptionist. In some businesses all the staff will take some responsibility for working in the reception area.

Multiple choice: Salon business systems and processes

1 The receptionist will require good skills in
Answer communication

2 The reception area must
Answer meet health and safety and security requirements

3 A visitor's book is used for
Answer as a tool for health and safety

4 A good reception area will
Answer look clean, tidy, welcoming and comfortable

5 A computer at the reception area is useful for
Answer operating a reception management system

6 The telephone at the reception area must not be used for
Answer personal calls

7 The magazines at the waiting area of the reception should be
Answer up to date magazines

8 Reading material kept at the waiting area should be
Answer appropriate for all clients

9 Product displays should be

Answer free from dust and dirt

10 The certificates that may be displayed in the salon reception should be

Answer for the qualifications of the staff who work in the salon or spa

Assessment activities for Chapter 4

Crossword

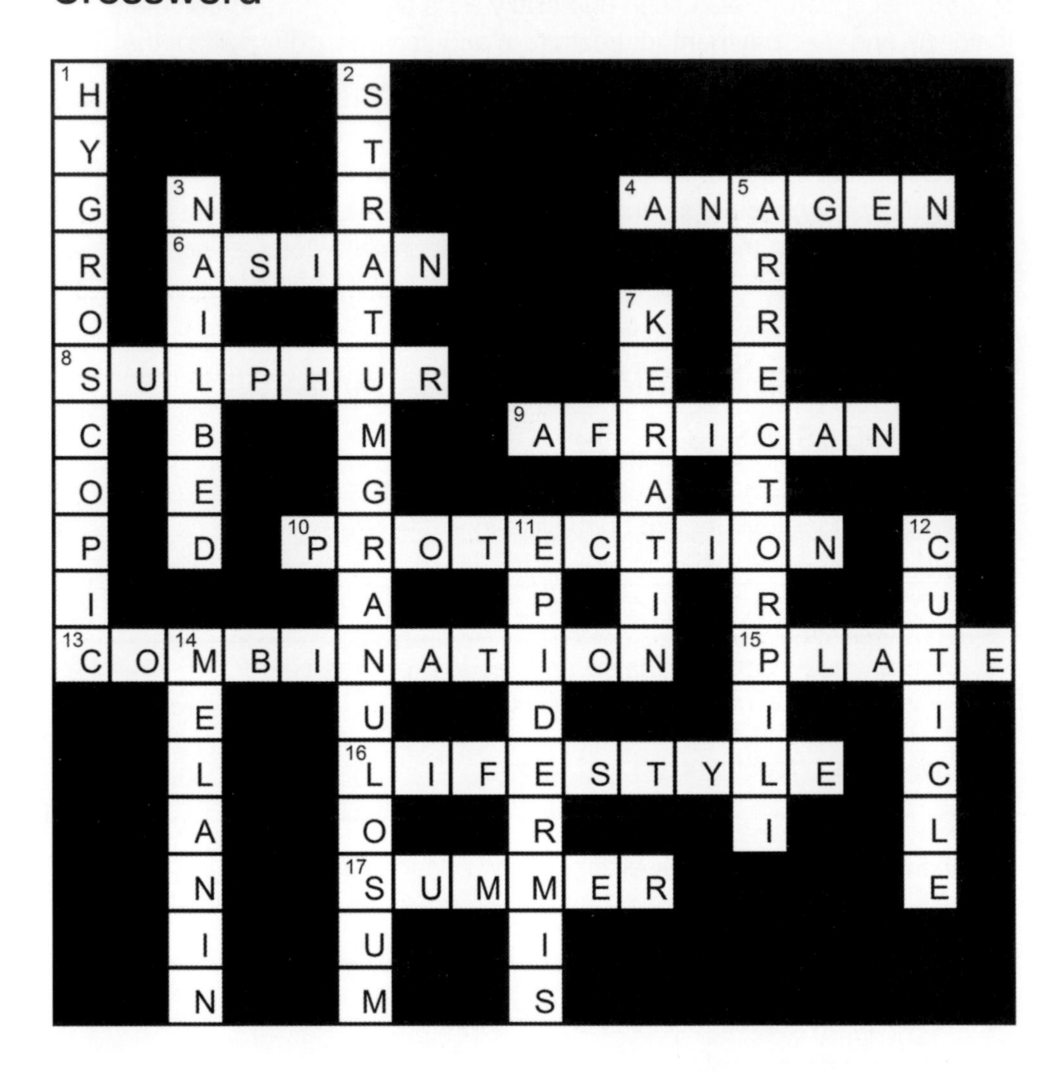

Wordsearch

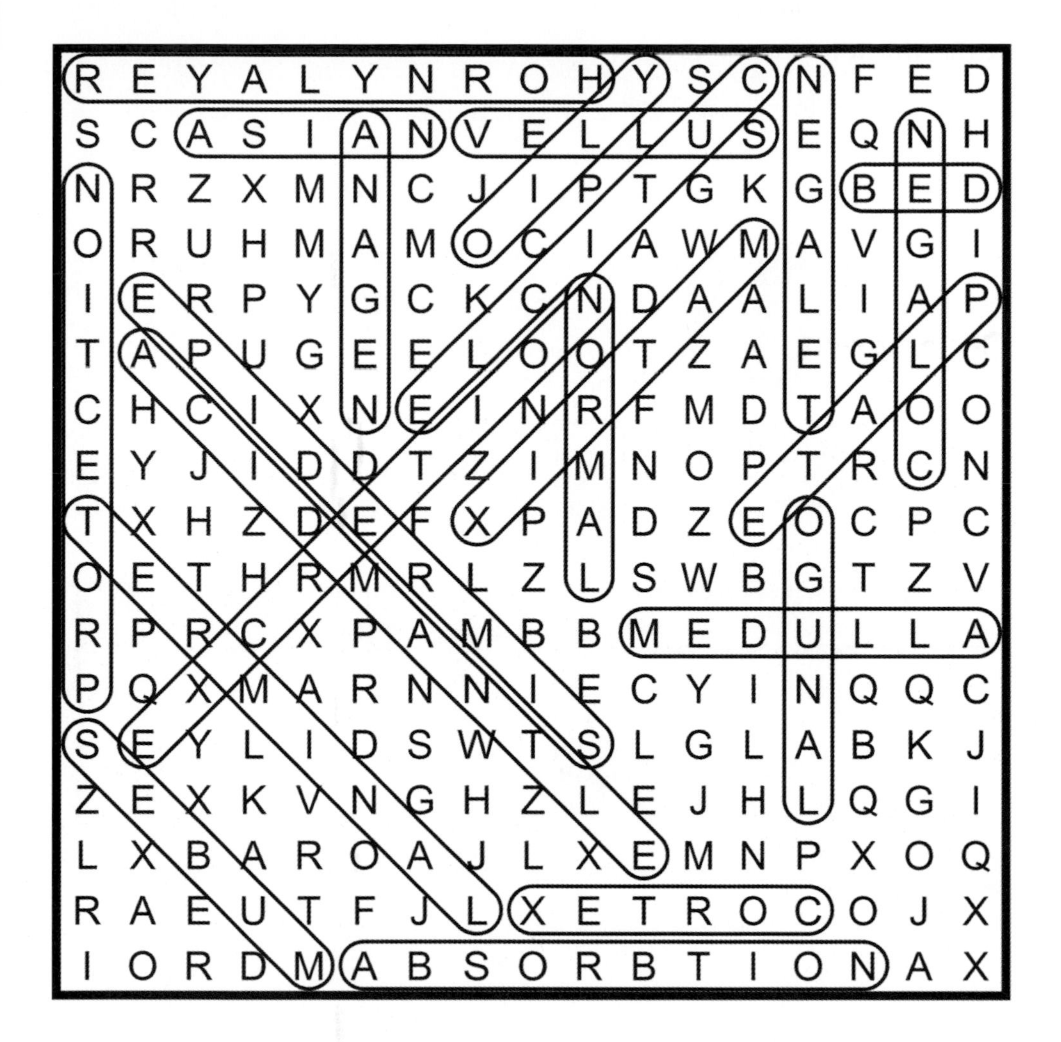
R E Y A L Y N R O H Y S C N F E D
S C A S I A N V E L L U S E Q N H
N R Z X M N C J I P T G K G B E D
O R U H M A M O C I A W M A V G I
I E R P Y G C K C N D A A L I A P
T A P U G E E L O O T Z A E G L C
C H C I X N E I N R F M D T A O O
E Y J I D D T Z I M N O P T R C N
T X H Z D E F X P A D Z E O C P C
O E T H R M R L Z L S W B G T Z V
R P R C X P A M B B M E D U L L A
P Q X M A R N N I E C Y I N Q Q C
S E Y L I D S W T S L G L A B K J
Z E X K V N G H Z L E J H L Q G I
L X B A R O A J L X E M N P X O Q
R A E U T F J L X E T R O C O J X
I O R D M A B S O R B T I O N A X

Assessment questions

Label the following diagram

1 Structure of the skin and hair

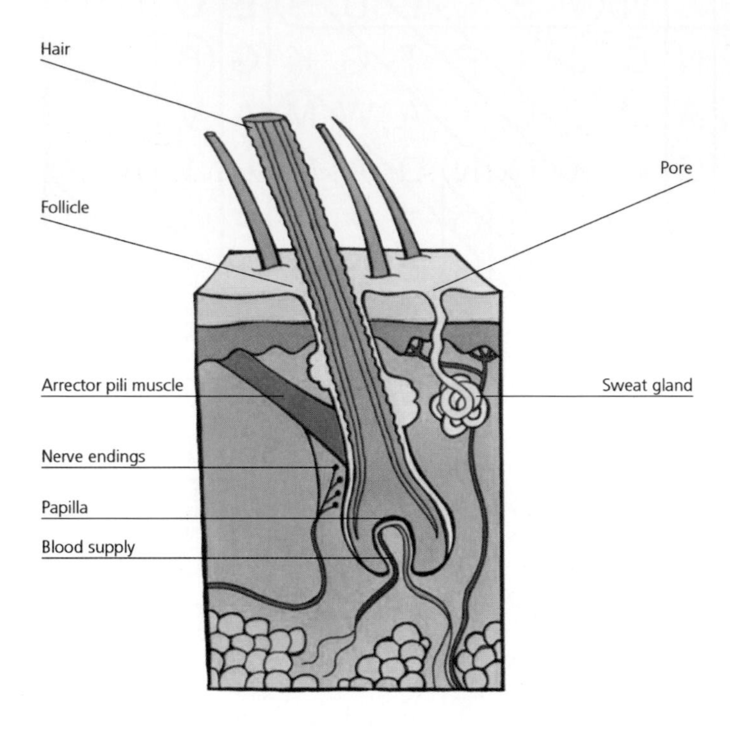

2 Structure of the nail

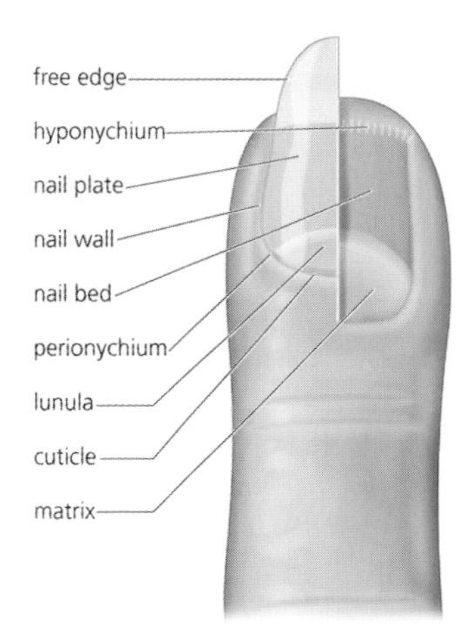

Short questions: Anatomy of the body – the systems of the body

1 Name the six main functions of the skeleton.

Answer 1. Support, 2. Movement, 3. Protection, 4. Blood cell protection, 5. Storage, 6. Endocrine regulation

2 Name the different systems of the body.

Answer 1. Skeleton, 2. Muscular, 3. Nervous, 4. Endocrine, 5. Circulatory, 6. Respiratory, 7. Urinary, 8. Reproductive, 9. Digestive, 10. Immune

3 What does a ligament do?

Answer Connects bones at joints to aid movement between bones

4 Which organ is made up of mainly muscle and pumps blood around the body?

Answer Heart

5 Name the two types of bones found in the human body.

Answer 1. Compact bones, 2. Cancellous bone tissue

6 Bones are made from: 25% water, 30% organic material and 45%

Answer Inorganic material of calcium and phosphorus

7 What do tendons do?

Answer Attach muscle to bone

8 What do muscles do?

Answer Enable different body parts to move

9 Name the three types of muscles.

Answer 1. Skeletal muscles, 2. Smooth muscles, 3. Cardiac muscle

10 If arteries carry blood away from the heart, what carries blood to the heart?

Answer Veins

Assessment activities for Chapter 5

Crossword

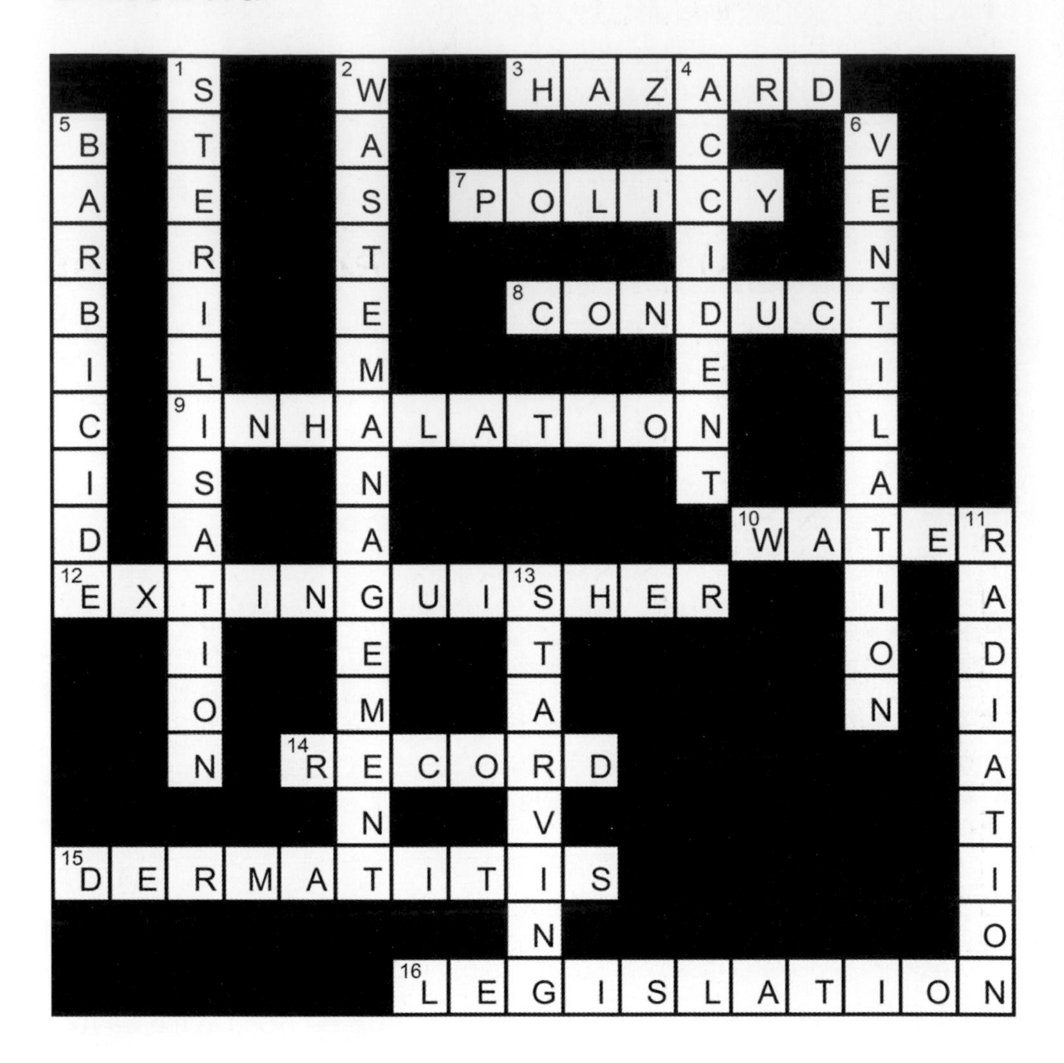

Wordsearch

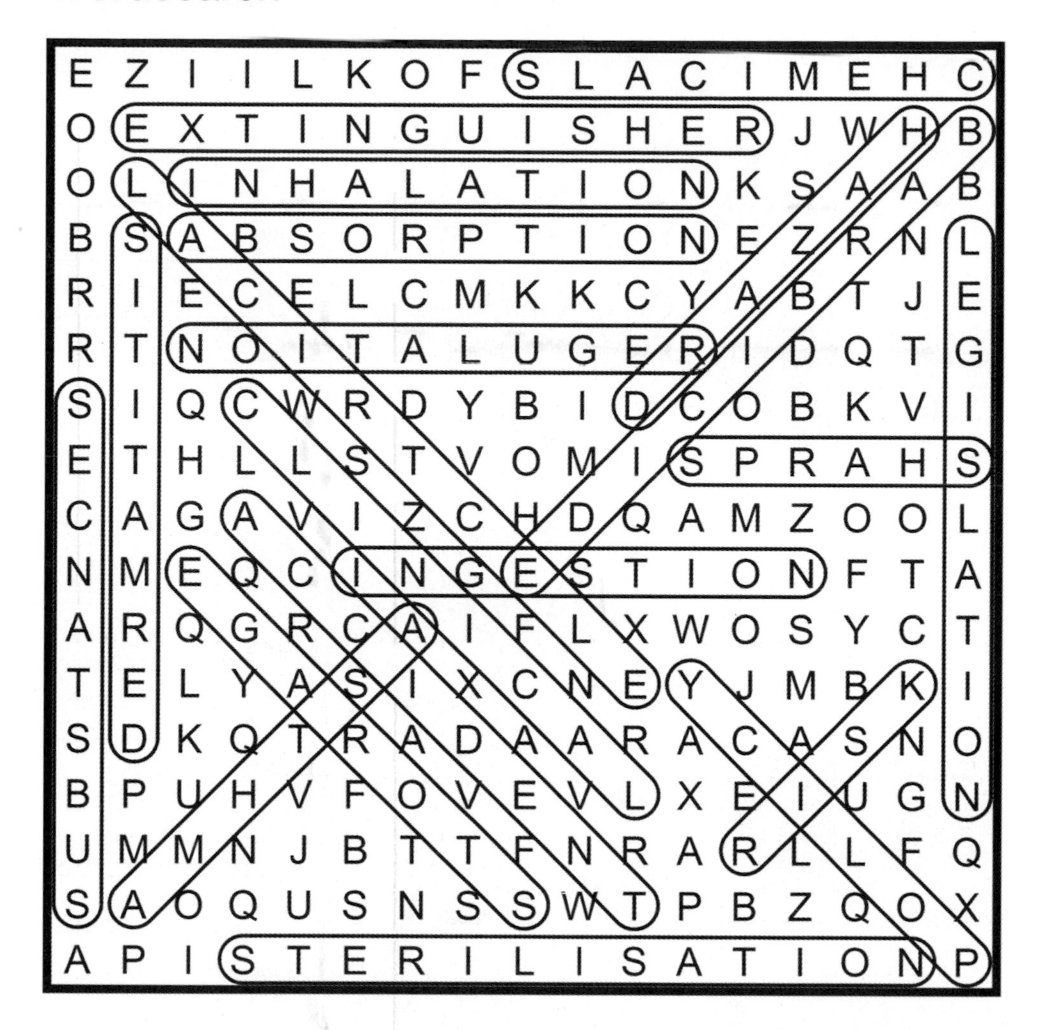
E Z I I L K O F S L A C I M E H C
O E X T I N G U I S H E R J W H B
O L I N H A L A T I O N K S A A B
B S A B S O R P T I O N E Z R N L
R I E C E L C M K K C Y A B T J E
R T N O I T A L U G E R I D Q T G
S I Q C W R D Y B I D C O B K V I
E T H L L S T V O M I S P R A H S
C A G A V I Z C H D Q A M Z O O L
N M E Q C I N G E S T I O N F T A
A R Q G R C A I F L X W O S Y C T
T E L Y A S I X C N E Y J M B K I
S D K Q T R A D A A R A C A S N O
B P U H V F O V E V L X E I U G N
U M M N J B T T F N R A R L L F Q
S A O Q U S N S S W T P B Z Q O X
A P I S T E R I L I S A T I O N P

Assessment question: Balanced diet

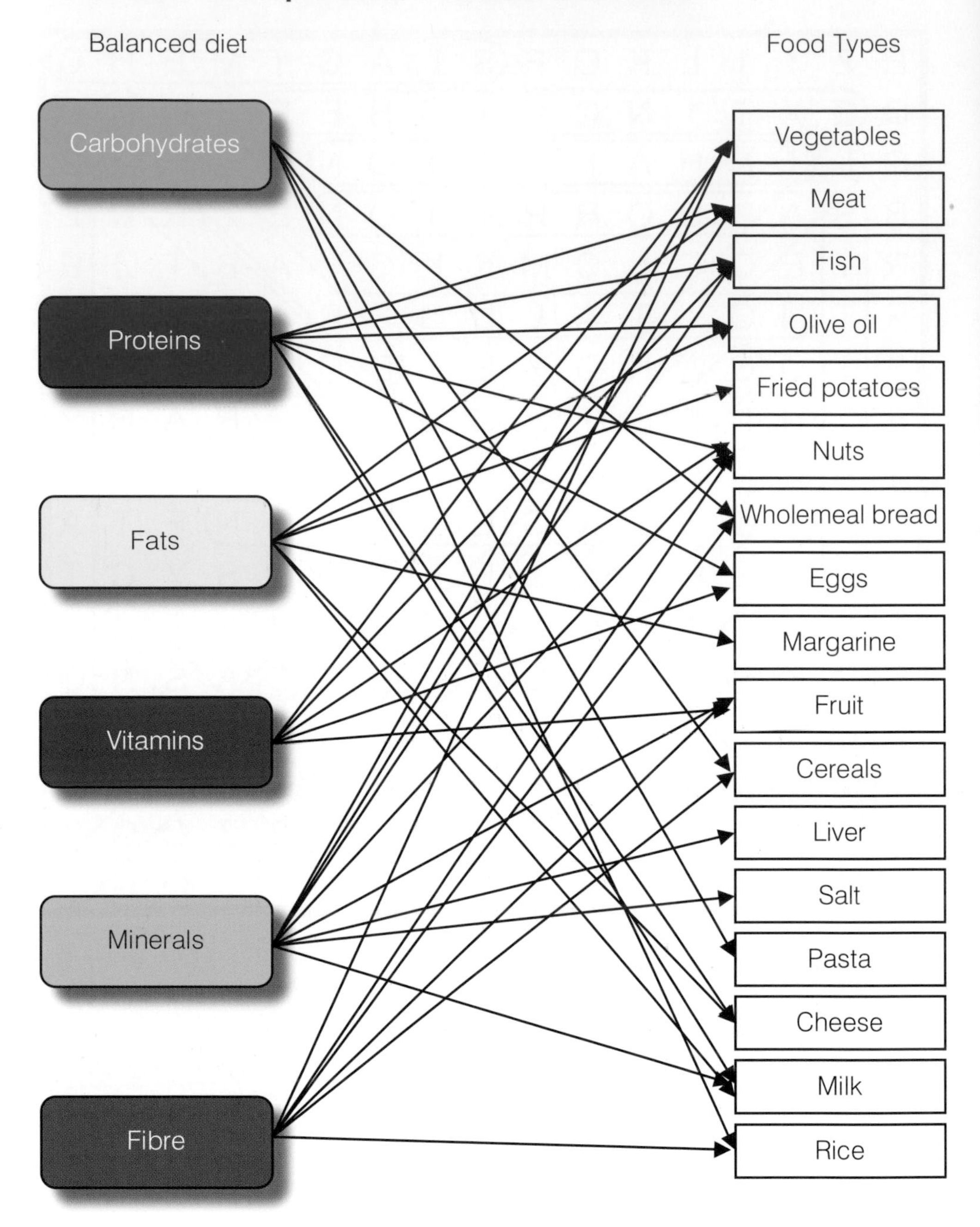

Assessment question: Legislation

Workplace (Health, Safety and Welfare Regulations 1992	Wearing gloves and apron
Health and Safety at Work Act 1974	Making sure there is enough ventilation
Provision and Use of Work Equipment Regulations 1992	Disposal of products
Personal Protective Equipment at Work Regulations 1992	Main Legislation in which nearly all other regulations are made
Control of Substances Hazardous to Health Regulations 2002	Ensuring that equipment is used correctly and in safe working order

Assessment activities for Chapter 6

Crossword

Wordsearch

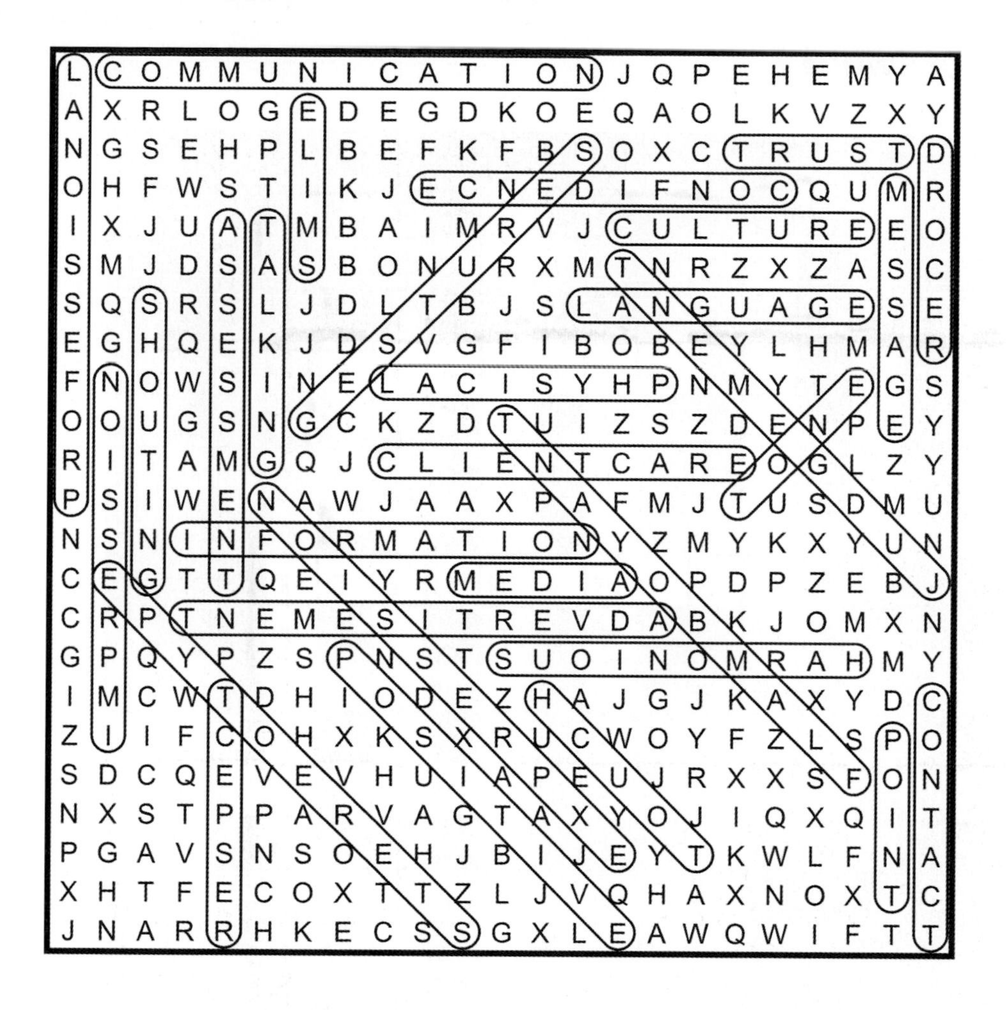
L C O M M U N I C A T I O N J Q P E H E M Y A
A X R L O G E D E G D K O E Q A O L K V Z X Y
N G S E H P L B E F K F B S O X C T R U S T D
O H F W S T I K J E C N E D I F N O C Q U M R
I X J U A T M B A I M R V J C U L T U R E E O
S M J D S A S B O N U R X M T N R Z X Z A S C
S Q S R S L J D L T B J S L A N G U A G E S E
E G H Q E K J D S V G F I B O B E Y L H M A R
F N O W S I N E L A C I S Y H P N M Y T E G S
O O U G S N G C K Z D T U I Z S Z D E N P E Y
R I T A M G Q J C L I E N T C A R E O G L Z Y
P S I W E N A W J A A X P A F M J T U S D M U
N S N I N F O R M A T I O N Y Z M Y K X Y U N
C E G T T Q E I Y R M E D I A O P D P Z E B J
C R P T N E M E S I T R E V D A B K J O M X N
G P Q Y P Z S P N S T S U O I N O M R A H M Y
I M C W T D H I O D E Z H A J G J K A X Y D C
Z I I F C O H X K S X R U C W O Y F Z L S P O
S D C Q E V E V H U I A P E U J R X X S F O N
N X S T P P A R V A G T A X Y O J I Q X Q I T
P G A V S N S O E H J B I J E Y T K W L F N A
X H T F E C O X T T Z L J V Q H A X N O X T C
J N A R R H K E C S S G X L E A W Q W I F T T

Assessment activities for Chapter 7

Crossword

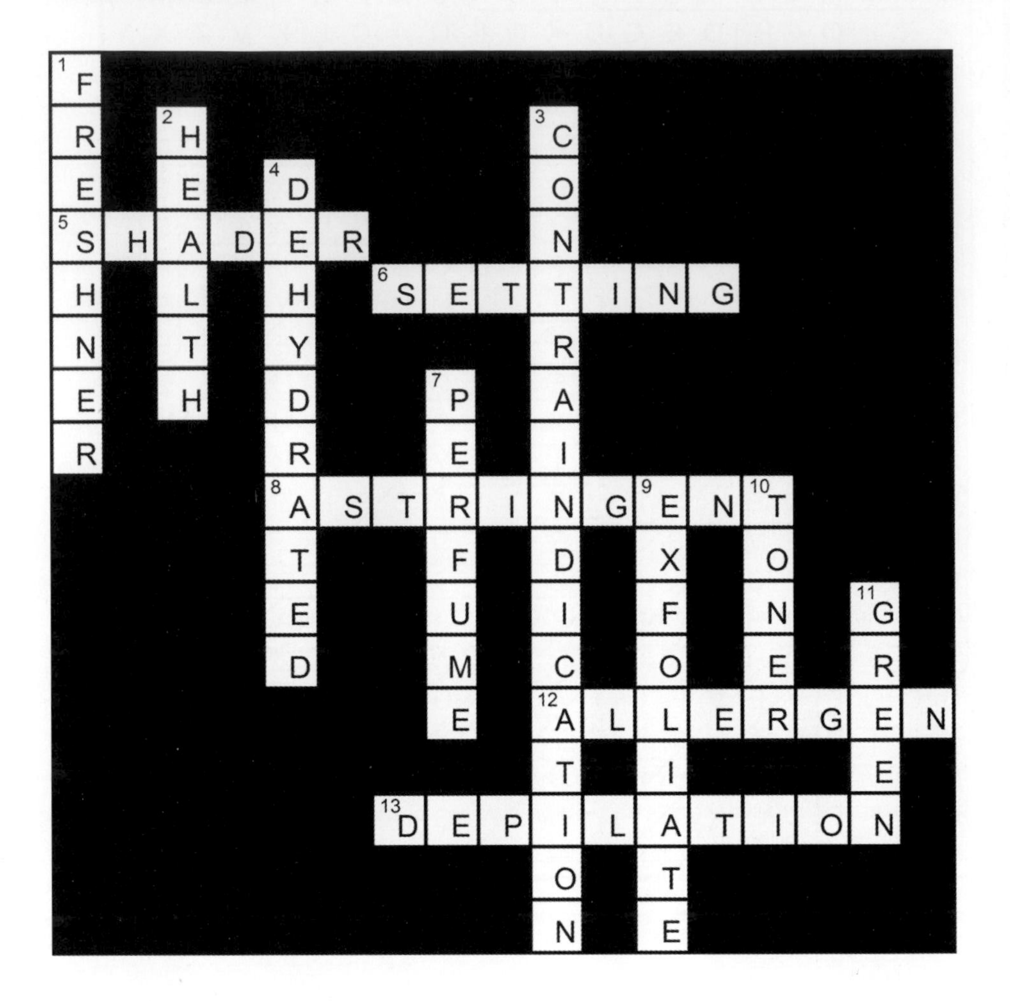

Wordsearch

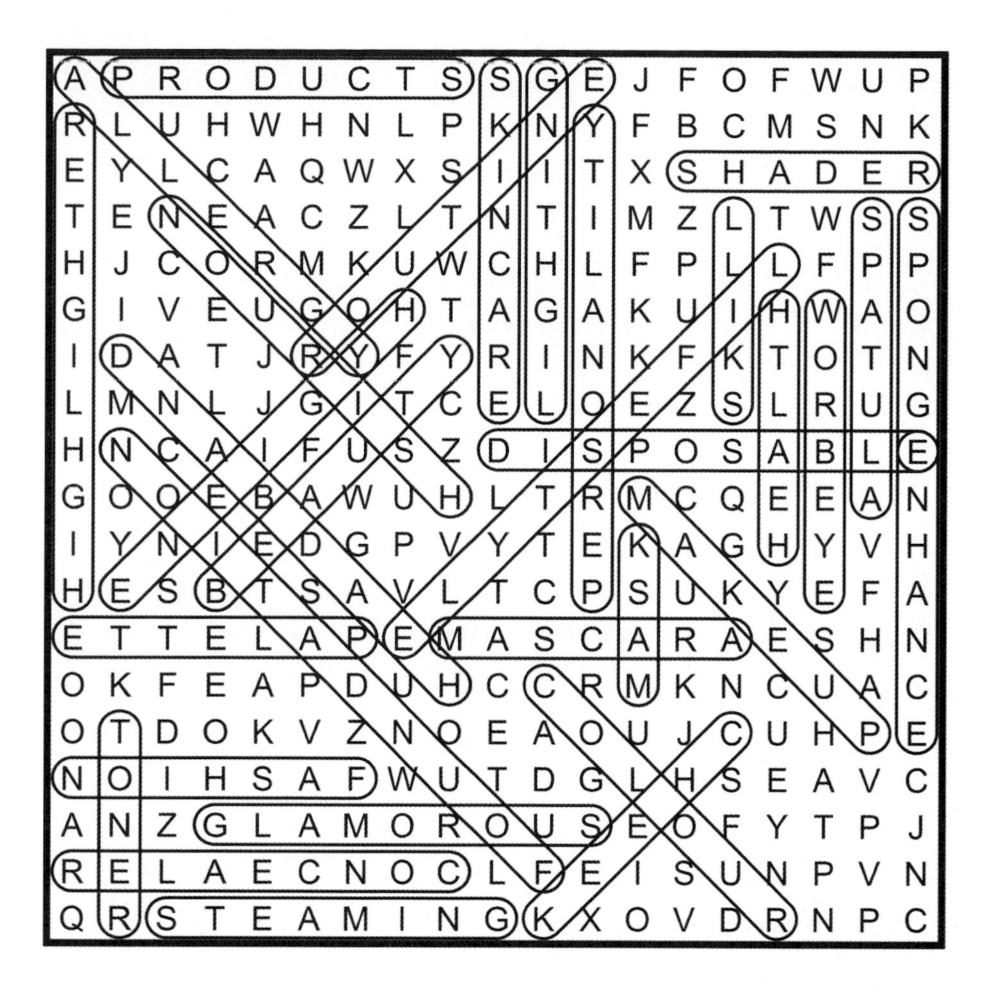

Assessment question: Skin products

PRODUCT TYPE	BEST FOR WHICH TYPE OF SKIN?
Cleansers	
Cleansing milk	Dry skin prone to sensitivity Sensitive skin
Cleansing cream	Very dry skin
Cleansing lotion	Normal to combination skin Oily skin (can contain medicated ingredients – for oily, congested, spotty skin)
Foaming cleanser	Most skin types except very dry or sensitive skin
Cleansing bar	Normal to oily skin, which is not sensitive
Toners/freshners	
Skin bracer/freshner	Dry, delicate skin Sensitive skin Mature skin
Skin tonic	Normal skin
Astringent	Oily skin with no skin sensitivity Mild acne in young skin
Moisturisers	
Moisturising lotion	Normal skin Dehydrated skin Young combination skin Oily skin

Moisturising cream	Mature skin Dry skin

Specialist creams/serums

Night cream	Most skin types, especially dry, dehydrated mature skin.
Neck cream	Most skin types, especially dry, dehydrated mature skin.
Eye cream	All skin types, especially dry, dehydrated skin (often applied at night)
Eye gel	All skin types, especially dry, dehydrated skin and those suffering with slightly puffy eye tissue(often applied in the morning)
Serums/ampoules	A variety of skin types, depending on the active ingredient in the ampoule/serum.

Assessment activities for Chapter 8

Crossword

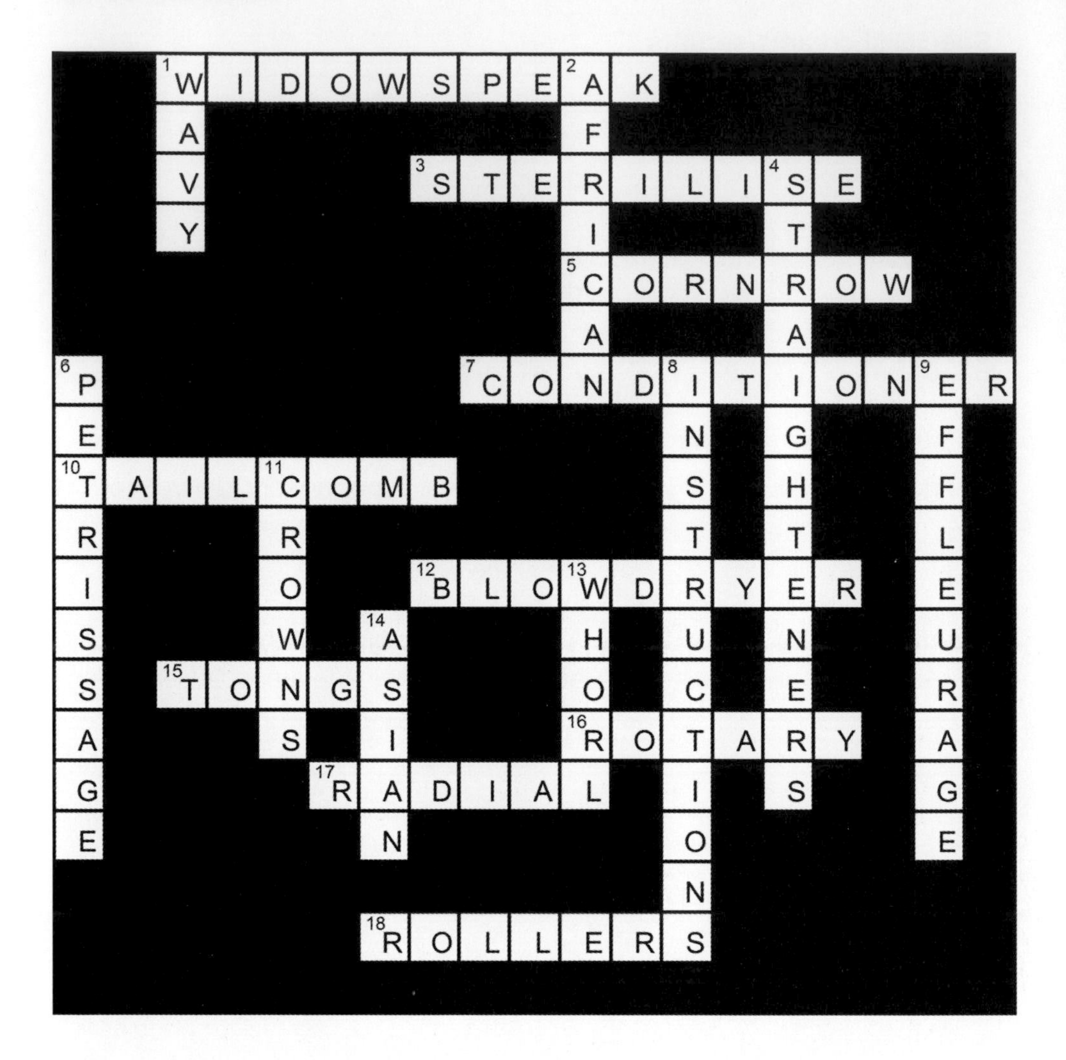

Multiple choice: Hair care and styling

1 The bone that makes the back of the head fat or round is:

- **a** **occipital**
- **b** frontal
- **c** parietal
- **d** mandible

2 A facial shape that has an angular jawline, with length that is much longer than the width is

- **a** oblong
- **b** square
- **c** round
- **d** **rectangular**

3 An ectomorph will have a body that is
- **a** small and slim
- **b** **tall and slim**
- **c** small and round
- **d** tall and round

4 A hair growth pattern known as a whorl can be found
- **a** at the crown
- **b** behind the ears
- **c** **at the nape**
- **d** at the front hairline

5 A hair type can be
- **a** **fine**
- **b** abundant
- **c** long
- **d** curly

6 In relation to temporarily changing the shape of the hair structure when hairstyling, hair with good elasticity will
- **a** **curl well**
- **b** lay flay
- **c** not curl well
- **d** will dry more quickly

7 Shampoos with added oils are good for
- **a** oily hair
- **b** normal hair
- **c** **dry hair**
- **d** coloured hair

8 Effleurage is a
- **a** **smoothing massage movement**
- **b** cleansing massage movement
- **c** stimulating massage movement
- **d** hard massage movement

9 The massage movement used to cleanse the scalp is
- **a** petrissage
- **b** effleurage
- **c** **rotary**
- **d** vibration

10 Coarse is a description of
- **a** **hair texture**
- **b** hair type
- **c** hair density
- **d** hair strength

Short questions: Hairstyling

1 Describe three different facial shapes.

Answer Oval – slightly longer the wide, curved jawline

- Round – the same width and length with curved jawline and hairline
- Square – the same width and length with an angular jawline and hairline
- Rectangular – significantly longer in length than width with an angular jawline and hairline
- Long – significantly longer in length than width with a curved jawline and hairline
- Heart or triangular – the same width and length with a pointed chin
- Pear – slightly longer than wide with a narrow forehead and wider angular or curved jawline
- Diamond – slightly longer than wide with a narrow forehead and pointed chin

2 State the main characteristics of the three different hair types.

Answer Caucasian/European varies from straight to curly

- Asian usually straight
- African Usually very curly, frizzy

3 Describe a mesomorphic body shape.

Answer Athletic build with wide shoulders and a narrow waist

4 Why do you need to consider lifestyle when recommending hairstyles?

Answer To ensure that the hairstyle can be managed and maintained.

5 Where would you find a widows peak?

Answer At the front hairline

6 What is the average rate of growth for hair?

Answer 1.25 cms per month

7 Name two different types of conditioners.

Answer Surface

- Penetrating

8 When would you use a radial brush?

Answer When blow drying hair

9 When would you use a tail comb?

Answer When making sections in hair

10 State three ways to make hair curly or wavy.

Answer Set hair in rollers to make a variety of curl and wave shapes

- Set hair in pin curls to make a variety of curl and wave shapes
- Set hair in Velcro™ rollers to create soft curls and waves
- Set hair in heated rollers to create soft curls and waves
- Curl hair using straighteners to make soft curls
- Curl hair using tongs to make a variety of different types of curl
- Blow dry hair using radial hair brushes to make a variety of soft curls and added volume to hair
- Increase natural curl in hair by using a diffuser attachment with a hand held dryer

Assessment activities for Chapter 9

Crossword

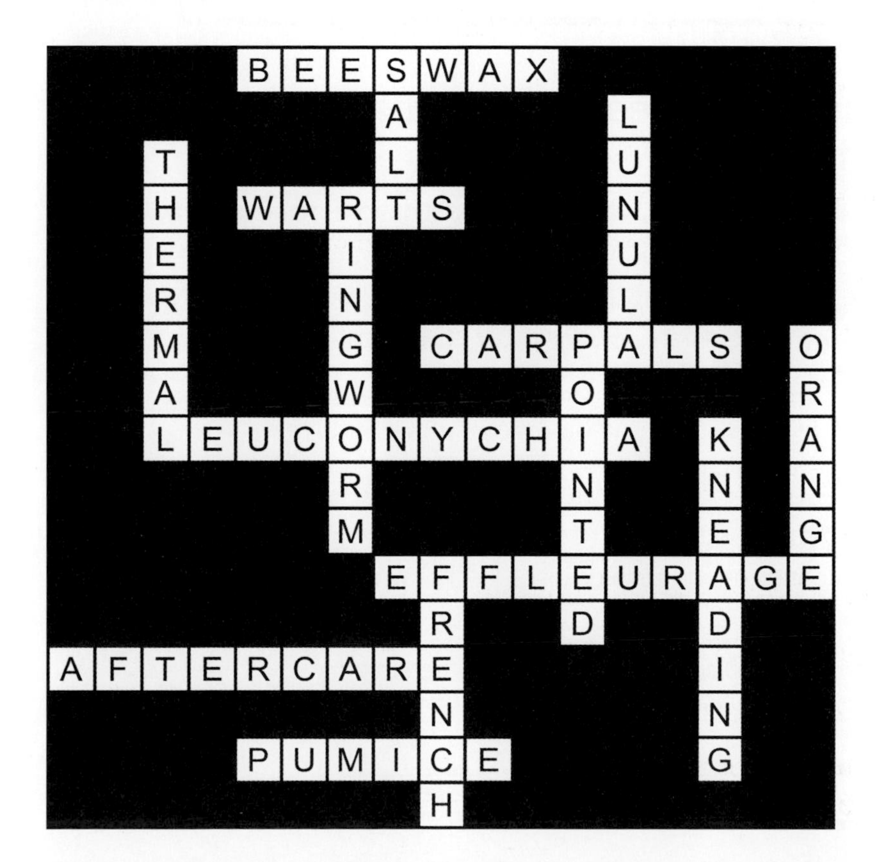

Wordsearch

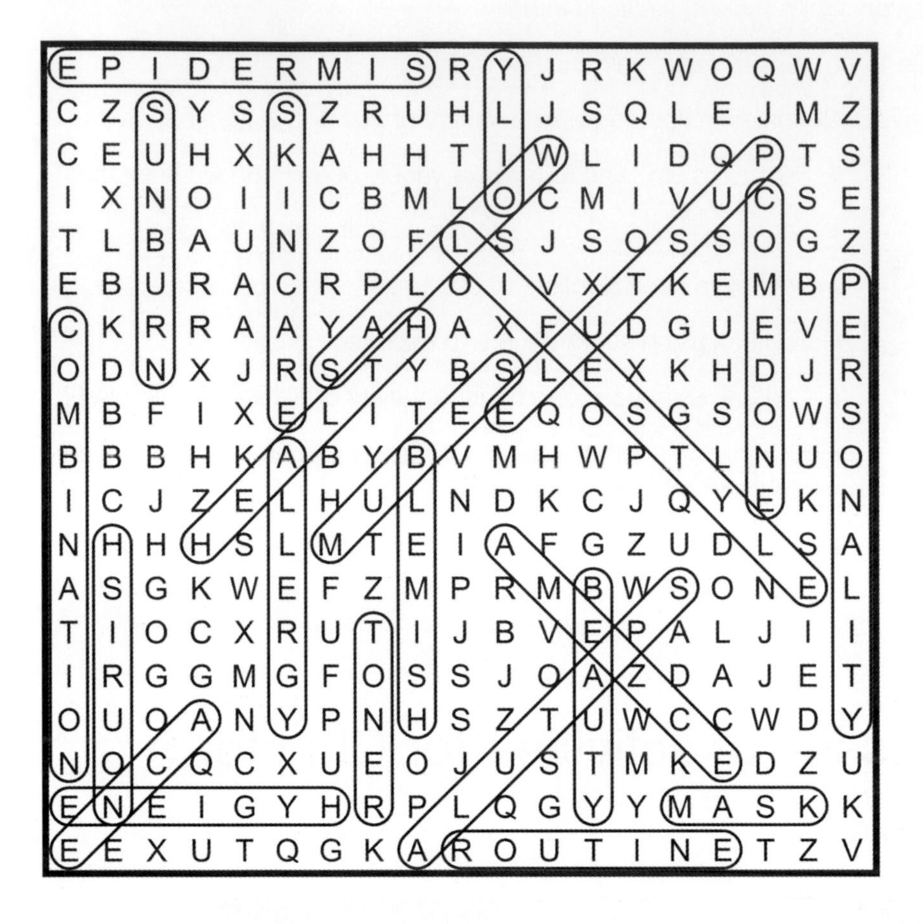

Short questions: Health and Safety for manicure treatments

1 Describe three symptoms of an allergic reaction to a manicure product.

Answer Three from the following:

- Redness of skin
- Swelling
- Itching
- Raised blisters

2 What does 'contra-indication' mean?

Answer A condition, disease or disorder that would prevent the treatment going ahead.

3 List three contra-indications to a manicure treatment.

Answer Three from the following:

- Tinea Unguium
- Paronychia
- Cuts or abrasions

- Infectious skin diseases
- Warts on hands or arms

4 State two methods of sterilising metal manicure tools.

Answer Autoclave and a cold water disinfectant.

5 Why should the manicurist wash their hands before starting the manicure treatment?

Answer Demonstrates to the client that you are hygienic and work professionally.

6 Why should the cuticle knife always be used wet and flat?

Answer To avoid scratching the nail surface, and to avoid cutting the client when working on overgrown cuticles.

7 List three manicure tools that should be thrown away (disposed of) after each manicure.

Answer Emery board, orange stick, spatula.

8 Why is the orange stick always tipped with cotton wool before use in a manicure?

Answer To avoid it being sharp and damaging the nail plate.

Assessment activities for Chapter 10

Crossword

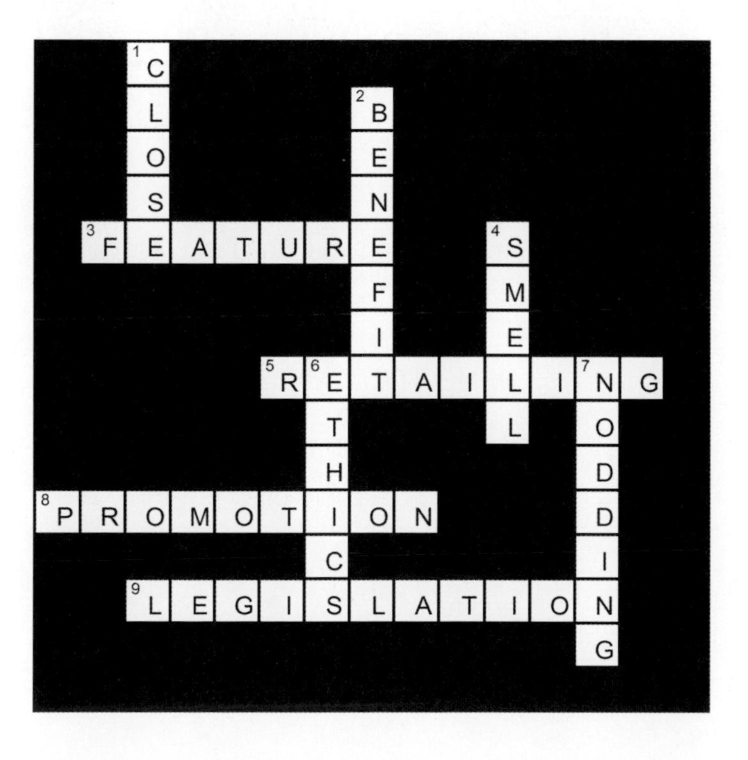

Wordsearch

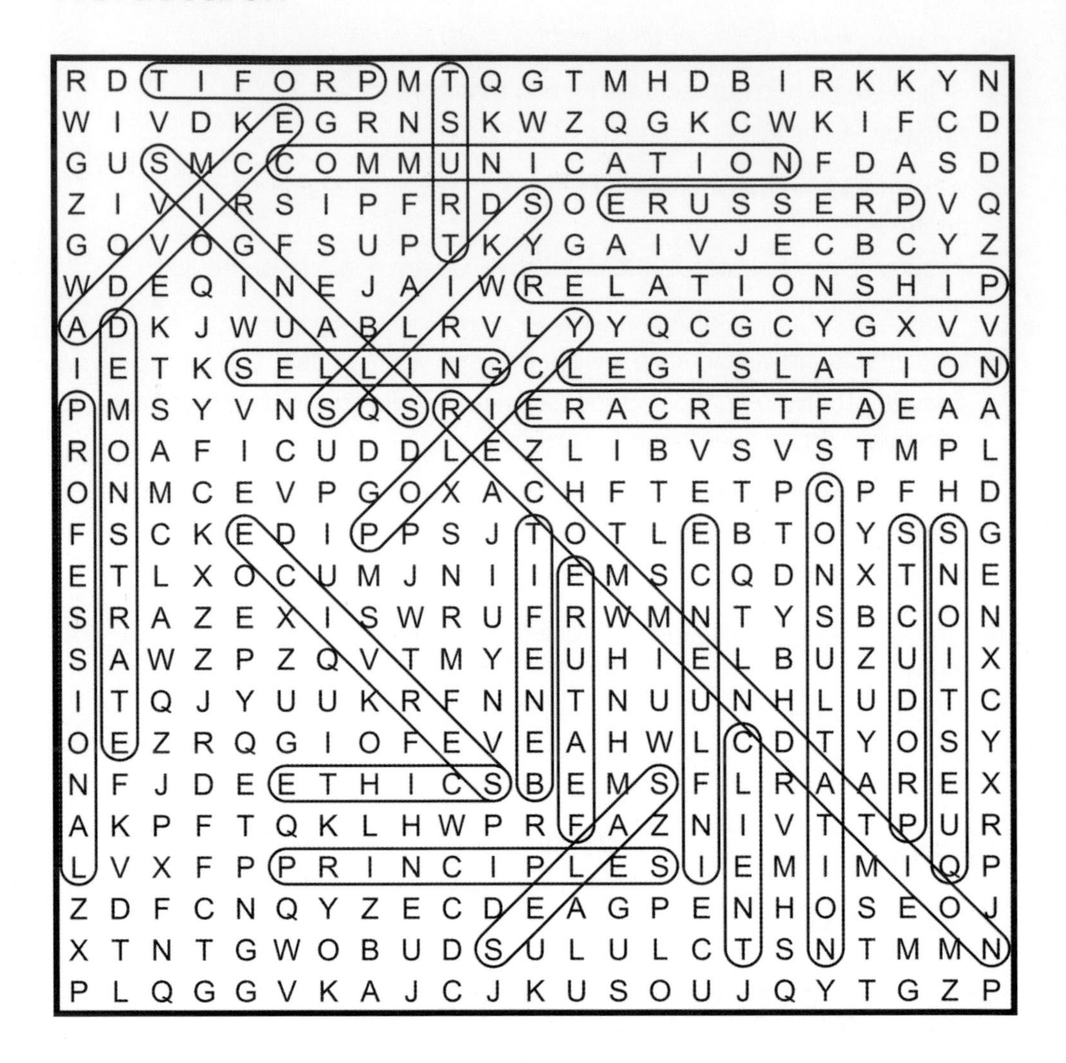

Assessment question: Selling skills

Complete the table below by listing one main feature and two benefits of the products named in the first column.

PRODUCTS	FEATURE	BENEFITS
Hair conditioner	Contains: Oils, waxes or silicones – to lubricate and smooth the hair Mild acid/cationic surfactants – to close the cuticle	Quick and easy to use Coats the hair and improves the look and feel Adds shine and moisture to the hair

	Plastics and proteins – to help hold together damaged areas of the hair	Strengthens the hair Makes it easier to detangle the hair and stops tangles forming
Sunscreen	Contains: Sun Protection Factors (SPF) Oil based Cream based Found in a variety of skin care products	Protects the skin from getting sunburn Moisturises the skin Helps protect against the ageing process from sun damage Waterproof sunscreen will stay on in water
Nail enamel	Contains: Film-forming plastic in a solvent Colour pigments	Easy to apply Decorates the nail plate with colour that is durable and flexible Easy to remove with a nail enamel remover
Moisturiser	Contain: Humectants such as glycerine Plant extracts Oil Water	Maintains the natural moisture and oil balance in the skin Protects the skin from environmental damage Relieves skin sensitivity and tautness Plumps up skin tissue Minimises the appearance of fine lines Use as a protective layer between skin and makeup

Glossary

absorption incorporation of liquid substance into something else for example the skin
acid mantle the protective coating of the skin
afro a hairstyle of African type hair
after-care advice given following a treatment
air brushing technique for decorating nails
alabaster a mineral used to make bottles and containers
alcohol ingredient in skin toner
allergen a substance that causes an allergic reaction on the skin
allergic reaction adverse reaction of the body to products or substances
alopecia areata hair loss appearing as oval or circular patches
alopecia totalis total hair loss from the scalp
alopecia generic term for hair loss
alpha keratin the formation of keratin for hair in its natural position prior to styling
aluminium pigment ingredient in metallic eye shadow
amino acids the basic structural building units of protein
ammonium hydroxide ingredient found in permanent colour
ammonium thioglycollate ingredient found in perm lotion
androgynous a mix of male and female characteristics
antibodies protein in the body produced to fight infection
antiseptic a sanitiser, usually suitable for skin use
apocrine glands glands which become active during puberty
arrector pili muscle muscle found attached to the follicle, which contracts to raise the hair
assimilated the blending of one into another. For example, cultural assimilation where an individual adopts the lifestyle and values of another dominant culture
astringents toner used for oily skin
atoms basic unit of matter
autoclave similar to a pressure cooker, it sterilises equipment such as tweezers
autoclaves method for sterilising tools and equipment
azo dyes ingredient found in temporary colours

bactericidal able to kill bacteria
bactericides substance that kills bacteria
barbicide™ chemical used to disinfect tools and equipment
basement membrane a sheet of cells and fibres that cover the epithelium and the endothelium
bed epithelium thin layer of tissue found on the nail bed that acts as a barrier to infection
beta keratin the formation of keratin for hair in its position after styling
black identity the promotion of West African culture in preference European culture
blood vessels part of the circulatory system that transports blood around the body
body language method of communication using the body and facial expressions
body mass index (BMI) measure of body fat based on height and weight
body odour (BO) unpleasant smell of stale sweat, dirt and bacteria
bone marrow found in the inner cavity of bones. Red bone marrow produces new blood cells and yellow bone marrow is used as a storage area for fat cells
bones rigid organ that forms the skeleton
bulb enlarges base of the hair root
buying signals clues that a sale may take place

calcium chemical element found in bone
calluses areas of skin that have thickened, usually on the foot, giving the appearance of thick yellowish hardened skin
capillaries the smallest of blood vessels
capillary action the flow of liquid through porous media
capital t the T shaped zone of the face covering the forehead, nose and chin
carbohydrates food group
carbon mineral used in comb production
carbon and manganese minerals used as pigments
cartilage tissue of the skeletal system
cationic polymers ingredient of shampoo
cell smallest unit of an organism that is classified as living, and is often called the building block of life
census method for acquiring information about the population of the country
cerussite mineral containing lead
chain a group of salons all having the same name and identity
chemotherapy the treatment of disease by chemicals
cheque guarantee card card issued by the bank to ensure that a cheque will be accepted for payment
cicatricial alopecia hair loss caused by damage to the dermis through scarring

circuit a network that has a closed loop, giving a return path for the current
clinical waste waste that contains human tissue, blood or body fluid
closed questions questioning technique used to gain a limited response
coal tar ingredient in shampoo used to treat dandruff
code of practice document that outlines how a safe and secure working environment can be maintained
collagen main protein of connective tissue
colour circle formation of colours to identify those that complement and those that neutralise each other
colour spectrum the range of colours found in natural light
comedone a blocked pore – a blackhead
commission method for paid wage based on the income generated by the stylist, therapist or technician for the salon
competence based a qualification designed to ensure job readiness
competitor a rival
conduction when heat is passed through material such as wood or metal
conductors substance that allows the passage of an electrical current
consultation examination of and communication with a client prior to treatments and services
contact dermatitis skin condition caused by allergy to products
continuing professional development (CPD) activities which ensure skills and knowledge are up to date
contra-action action taken to correct an unwanted reaction to a treatment
contra-indication an existing condition that will prevent certain treatments and services being carried out
convection occurs when liquid or gas is heated
cornrows scalp plaits formed in rows following the shape of the head
cortex the main section of hair structure
cortical cells cells of the cortex
cosmetologists term used in America to describe a job role for hair and beauty
cowlick hair growth pattern found at the front hairline
cranium the bones of the head
cross-infection transfer of infection, from one area of the body to another, or to another person
crown circular pattern of hair growth
curl development test test carried out during a permanent wave service
cuticle outside layer of the hair or skin growing around the base of the nail

dandruff excess shedding of dead skin cells of the scalp
debit card card issued by the bank to allow the transaction of payments or the withdrawal of money from the holder's account
depilation temporary removal of excess hair e.g. by waxing
depth term used to describe the how light or how dark hair is
dermis the inner layer of the skin, just under the epidermis which contains all the skin appendages
design brief document and drawings outlining plans for future actions
designated person a person with specific responsibilities such as health and safety
desquamation skin cells being shed from the surface of the skin
detergent material to assist with cleaning
disinfected removal of germs such as bacteria
disposable income the amount of money left over for spending once essential living costs have been removed
disulphide bridges strong cross linkages found in hair
dreadlocks hairstyle worn by those of the Rastafarian faith
dyslexia condition where the individual has difficulty with written language

eccrine glands sweat producing glands
ectomorph tall, slim body shape
effleurage smooth, stoking, soothing massage technique
elasticity test test to identify the condition of the cortex
electrons negatively charged particle
employability skills the skills that employers value above the technical skills required to work in a particular industry
enamel/polish secure a range of items that have a flat back, that can be 'secured' in wet nail enamel e.g. jewels, studs, flowers
endomorph rounded body shape
epidermis the outer layer of the skin
epilation permanent removal of excess hair e.g. by electrolysis
eponychium the living skin at the base of the nail plate
ethics principles that help to guide the behaviour of an individual or a group of people to identify what is right and what is wrong
eumelanin black and brown pigments of hair colour
exfoliate remove dead skin cells

fades very closely cropped hair, blended into longer lengths
faradic current used to stimulate muscles to improve body tone through muscular contractions
fats food group
fibre used to help digestion
fibroblasts cells found in collagen
fibula long bone of the lower leg
franchise business organisation exchanging brand and business acumen for a fee
franchisee the person who buys the franchise

frankincense aromatic resin obtained from trees
free edge area of nail that extends past the nail bed
freehand technique used to decorate nails without the use of templates
freelance self-employed stylist, therapist or technician who visits clients to provide treatments and services
French manicure nails are painted to resemble a natural nail, with the tips white and the rest of the nail pink, peach or beige
friction short, fast rubbing action
frontal bone of the cranium
fungicidal able to kill fungus
fungicides substance that kills fungus

galvanic electrical treatment applied to the face, neck and body
general waste waste from hair and beauty salons such as hair, papers, tissues, empty bottles
generic inheritance genes inherited from parents and ancestors
global worldwide
granite mineral found in water
gross price the total price including VAT

hair follicle tube-like indentation in which the hair sits
hangnail a break in the nail wall that becomes very sharp and sore
hard water water containing dissolved minerals
hazard something with the potential to cause harm
henna a dye extracted from the leaves of a plant, used to tint hair and in mehndi designs for the hands and feet
henna from the plant group Lawsonia. Dried leaves used to colour hair in shades of red
hieroglyphs symbols used by scribes in Ancient Egypt to depict words and numbers
high frequency electrical treatment applied to the face, neck and body
hormones chemicals released by cells that affect other parts of the body
hot combs heated combs used to temporarily straighten African type hair
humectants ingredient in skin toner
hydrogen bonds weak bond found in hair structure
hydrogen peroxide weak acid with oxidising properties used in chemical hairdressing services
hydrophilic water loving molecule
hygiene standard of cleanliness required in the salon to avoid the spread of infection
hygroscopic able to absorb moisture
hypodermis basement membrane found at the base of the dermis
hyponychium thickened layer of skin found under the free edge of the nail

image external form or appearance
incineration converting waste to heat, steam, gas and ash
incompatibility test test to identify the presence of metallic salts
individual learning plan actions to support and assist a learner to complete a learning programme
ingestion taking into the body by swallowing
inhalation taking into the body by breathing
insulators substance which does not allow the passage of an electrical current
international colour chart (ICC) chart depicting the range of colours of natural and artificially coloured hair
ion exchange the process to remove the minerals, calcium and magnesium, and replace them with another, usually sodium

keratin the protein in skin, nails and hair, produced by keratinocytes
keratinisation The hardening of the protein of the hair and skin
keratinocyte cell which produces the protein keratin
kohl eye makeup used today and in ancient times

landfill burying of waste to dispose of it
langerhan cells cells found in the stratum spinosum layer of the epidermis which absorbs and removes foreign bodies that enter the skin
lanolin ingredient found in conditioner
laser hair removal a method for the permanent removal of unwanted hair
laurionite mineral used as an ingredient in makeup in ancient times
learner centred learning programme which is tailored to the individual needs of the learner
legislation laws and regulations
lethargic tired, lacking in energy
liberty spikes punk hairstyle inspired by the Statue of Liberty
ligament fibrous tissue that connects one bone to another bone
lithium hydroxide ingredient of relaxer
local authority local government
locks interlocked coils of African type hair
lulur Javanese body treatment, often taken by brides in the days leading up to their wedding
lunula visible part of the nail matrix
lymphatic system the system that closely connects to the blood system and helps collect waste. Its main function is defence, helping to prevent infection

macrofibrils bundles of cells within the cortex
magnesium mineral found in hard water
malachite green pigmented mineral
mandiblc jaw bone
manganese and carbon minerals used as pigments
marketing plan actions used to meet the marketing objectives for the business
medulla space found within the central core of the hair
mehndi the application of henna to the hands, feet and nails, creating intricate designs
melanin the natural colour pigment of hair
melanocyte cells cells which produce melanin
mesdemet makeup also known as kohl
mesomorph wide shouldered and narrow waisted body shape
metacarpals bones of the hand
metatarsal bones of the foot
micro-businesses businesses employing less than 50 people
microcurrent electrical current used for face and body treatments
microfibrils small bundles of cells found in macrofibrils
microns a micron is one millionth of a metre
micro-organisms viruses, bacteria and fungus are all types of micro-organism. Micro-organisms that cause diseases are often called germs
migrate leave one place and settle in another
mineral salts food group
mohawk punk inspired hairstyle
multi-task completing more than one task at the same time
myrrh aromatic gum resin
mytosis cell division

nail art the decorating of the nails on the hands and feet
nail enamel a coloured or clear product used to enhance the nail, also adding protection
nail enamel remover substance used to remove nail enamel
nail technician a person who carries out treatments and services on the nails of the hands and feet
nape whorls hair growth pattern found at the nape of the neck
national occupational standards (NOS) the standards which describe tasks completed for a job role
national vocational qualification (NVQ) a nationally recognised qualification used to ensure job readiness
nerves fibrous connection used to carry impulses around the body
net price price excluding VAT
neurons sensor that sends messages to the central nervous system
neutralising the process used to fix the position of bonds changed during the perming process
New Kingdom period of time in Ancient Egypt judged to be from 1550 to 1069 BC
nito dyes ingredient found in semi-permanent colour
non-medical oedema a swelling (oedema) in an area that isn't caused by a medical condition
non-verbal communication method of communication which does not include talking
norms sociological term to describe the expected behaviour in society
nucleus central part of a cell

occipital bone of the cranium
occupational asthma caused by chemical products or fine particles of dust from skin and nails
ochre pigment used to colour makeup
Old Kingdom period of time in Ancient Egypt judged to be from 3100 to 2125 BC
open questions questioning technique used to gain an extended response
ossification hardening process of bones
osteoclasts cells used to break down old bone cells to make new bone cells
osteocytes mature bone cells
overheads routine costs for operating a business

papilla the point from which all new cells for the hair are developed
papillary layer outermost layer of the dermis that extends into the epidermis
papule a raised red lump
para dyes ingredient found in quasi and permanent colour
para-phenylenediamines (PPD) chemical used in permanent colours
parasites organism that relies on a host for food and nourishment
parietal bone of the cranium
patterns shapes and lines cut into African type hair
pearlescent pigments ingredient found in eye shadow and hair products to give a soft shimmer
peptides chain of amino acid
permanent colour artificial hair colour that is not washed from the hair and has to grow out
permed chemically produced, permanent curls and waves
personal protective equipment (PPE) equipment used to protect self from harmful chemicals
personal space an invisible area around a person that they consider to be their territory
petrissage circular, relaxing massage movement
phalanges bones of the fingers and toes
pheomelanin red and yellow pigment of hair colour
pheromones chemical signal that triggers a natural response in another member of the same species
phosgenite lead compound used in makeup of ancient times

physical communication method of communication involving physical contact
pigment type of material which affects the colour of light reflection and absorption
pigmentation the amount and distribution of melanin (pigment) in the skin. As we age it can become uneven
plaits interwoven strands of hair
polish secures nail accessories that stick to the nail polish and then are sealed in place with sealer/top coat
polypeptides chains of amino acid
pore opening at the skin for the sweat duct
porosity test test to determine the condition of the cuticle
porosity ability to absorb liquids
portfolios a collection of evidence, articles or images
posture position of the body
potassium ingredient of relaxer
preservatives ingredient to maintain the condition of a product
pressure test test to confirm the pressure used on clients before treatments such as massage
primary colours red, yellow and blue
prisms used to break up light to show the range of colours of the spectrum
professional recommendation providing advice and guidance on the purchase of products
promotions methods of marketing a service or product, perhaps by reducing the price for a given period of time, or offering a special price to a particular group of people, e.g. pensioners, students, etc.
proteins organic compounds made of amino acids and a food group
protein fibres found in skin structure
protofibrils small bundles of cells found in microfibrils
protons positively charged particles
prototype a trial model
psoriasis excessive growth and shedding of the skin
public liability insurance insurance for accidental damage or injury to clients
pull test test carried out prior to insertion of hair extensions
purified cleansed
pustule an infected spot, usually with a raised yellow (pus) centre

quasi/quasi-permanent colour artificial hair colour which does not wash from hair, but has tones which gradually fade
quiff hairstyle in which the hair at the front of the head is lifted, raised and folded

radiation heat is transmitted without contact
realistic learning environment (RLE) working environment based on a salon where hair and beauty skills are taught
realistic working environment (RWE) working environment based on a commercial salon where hair and beauty skills are taught
reception management system computer based systems used to manage the procedures of the reception
receptors nerve ending designed to recognise different sensations
record card the card that records all the client's personal details. It must be filled in prior to the first treatment and updated regularly
recycling reprocessing waste into new products
relaxing process of reducing and removing natural curl in hair, leaving it permanently straight
repetitive strain injury (RSI) injury caused by continuous similar movement of the body
research and development (R&D) investigation to gather knowledge
restructurants ingredient of conditioners designed to repair damaged hair
reticular layer layer of the dermis
risk the likelihood of someone being harmed by a hazard
risk assessment to identify potential harmful risks during an activity
root section of hair found at the base of the follicle
rotary round, revolving massage technique

salt linkages weak bond found in hair structure
sebaceous glands glands of the hair that produce the natural oil, sebum
sebum natural oil of the hair and skin
secondary colours orange, purple and green
self-employed not employed by an employer
semi-permanent colour artificial hair colour that washes from the hair in approximately six shampoos
senses taste, sight, sound, smell and touch
sensory nerve endings which register touch, pressure, pain and temperature
set hair is wrapped onto rollers or other styling equipment to create curl or smooth and straighten hair
shaft section of hair that is above the surface of the skin
shampoo product used to cleanse the hair and scalp
sharp and blunt test test used to check the nerve response to the types of current used in some electrotherapy treatments
sharps syringes, blades and needles
side lock of youth hairstyle of children in Ancient Egypt
silicones ingredient of shampoo
skeleton body framework of bones
skin allergy an allergic reaction by the skin, that may include redness, swelling and irritation
skin analysis detailed assessment of the skin condition and the overall skin type

skin appendages appendages associated with the skin that serve a particular function
skin test test to identify allergies to colour products
skin toners product used to remove skin cleaners and shrink the pores
skull bones of the head
small and medium sized enterprises (SMEs) businesses employing less than 50 people
social identity group of people with shared values
sociological the study of society
sodium sulphite ingredient of hair colour
sodium found in hairdressing products
soft water contains fewer dissolved minerals that hard water
squoval a nail shape that is primarily square, but the corners have been shaped to soften the final result
stance position of the body
standard industrial classification (SIC) method of categorising job roles
static electricity build up of an electrical charge on the surface of objects
stenciling method used for nail art
sterilisation of tools/equipment to totally destroy any micro-organisms on the equipment
sterilised complete eradication of all living organisms
steroids medication that can lead to excessive hair growth
stock taking method for calculating the amount of stock held by the business
story board a display board that tells the 'story' of the project or activity, made as visual as possible with magazine cuttings, captions etc.
strand test test used to identify hair colour development
subcultures a group of people with common shared interests and values
sudoriferous sweat gland
sulphur bonds bonds found in the cortex of hair
surface tension surface of a liquid such as water
surfactants ingredient of shampoo
sweat glands glands which regulate body temperature by excreting sweat through small openings in the skin. The sweat evaporates and cools the body

tactile test test to check reaction to temperature for beauty therapy treatments such as electrotherapy
tarsal bones of the foot
temporary colour artificial hair colour that washes from the hair in one shampoo
tendons collagen fibres that attach muscle to bone
tertiary colour result of mixing a primary and secondary colour together
tibia long bone of the leg
tone the colour of hair that is seen for example, warm, gold, red, ash
tourmaline mineral used in comb production
toxicity the degree to which a substance is able to damage an exposed organism
traction alopecia hair loss caused by excessive tension to the hair root
translucent allowing light to pass through without being transparent
treatment liability insurance insurance for damage to clients caused by the treatments and services
treatment plan a plan that details the main priorities of the treatment, to suit the clients needs

udju green makeup used in Ancient Egypt
ultra-violet cabinet a machine that uses ultra-violet rays to disinfect small objects
ultra-violet (UV) light box sterilisation method for tools and equipment
unisex hair salon for both men and women

vacuum suction mechanical treatment applied to the face or body
vapours moisture or other substance suspended in air
verbal communication method of communication involving speaking and listening
visitors' book book kept at reception signed by visitors to the building
visuals aids images used to support descriptions
vitamin D derived from sunlight
vitamins food group
vocationally related qualifications (VRQs) preparation for work qualifications based on the National Occupational standards

waste management collection, transport, processing, recycling or disposal of waste material
widows peak hair growth pattern found at the front hairline
wrapped styling method used to smooth and straight African type hair

zinc pyrithione ingredient in shampoo used to treat dandruff

Index